Quantitative Analysis for Management
Volume 1
Third Edition

A Pearson Custom Publication

Quantitative Analysis for Management
Volume 1
Third Edition

Compiled from:

Statistics for Economics, Accounting and Business Studies
Fourth Edition
Michael Barrow

Quantitative Methods for Business and Economics
Second Edition
Glyn Burton, George Carrol and Stuart Wall

Statistics for Business and Economics
Sixth Edition
Paul Newbold, William L. Carlson and Betty Thorne

PEARSON
Custom
Publishing

Pearson Education Limited
Edinburgh Gate
Harlow
Essex CM20 2JE

And associated companies throughout the world

Visit us on the World Wide Web at:
www.pearsoned.co.uk

First published 2006

This Custom Book Edition © 2009 Published by Pearson Education Limited

Compiled from:

Statistics for Economics, Accounting and Business Studies
Fourth Edition
Michael Barrow
ISBN 978 0 273 68308 7
Copyright © Pearson Education Limited 1988, 2006

Quantitative Methods for Business and Economics
Second Edition
Glyn Burton, George Carrol and Stuart Wall
ISBN978 0 273 65570 1
Copyright © Pearson Education Limited 1999, 2002

Statistics for Business and Economics
Sixth Edition
Paul Newbold, William L. Carlson and Betty Thorne
ISBN 978 0 13 188090 0
Copyright © 2007, 2003, 1995 by Pearson Education, Inc., Upper Saddle River,
New Jersey, 07458.

ISBN 978 1 84776 207 8

Printed and bound in Great Britain by Henry Ling Limited at the Dorset Press,
Dorchester, DT1 1HD.

Contents

Introduction

These two volumes have been compiled from selected chapters of texts in the Pearson range of academic books. This has been done so that you get all the necessary background reading for the Quantitative Analysis for Management modules (QAMI and QAMII) without having to consult, or buy, a variety of different texts. As such, these two volumes are unique and have been designed specifically for the QAMI and QAMII modules at Warwick Business School.

These two volumes are arranged such that the first volume corresponds to the QAMI module and the second volume to the QAMII module.

QAMI and QAMII are applied modules rather than theoretical ones and emphasis is placed on learning to use the material covered in both of the modules. Therefore you will find that you are supplied here with many worked examples. Similarly you will be asked to undertake examples on your own in order to practise the applications and you will be required to discuss your results in tutorials.

The Contents pages of each of these two volumes provide a list of topics where each topic represents a chapter from a source text. The Contents pages also indicate the exact source text of each topic. Note that when you consult a particular topic you will sometimes see that the front page lists the various sections of that topic. These sections are numbered using the original chapter numbers from the source text (and not the topic number here). This is also true with respect to the numbering of figures and diagrams within that topic. This should not cause any confusion since when reading material from a particular topic it is still numbered consistently within that topic.

Topic 1

Why Study Statistics?

Chapter 1

Why Study Statistics?

Introduction

In our information age, the world abounds with data. Newspaper articles and television news reports include statements such as "The Dow-Jones average fell 6 points today" or "The Consumer Price Index rose by .8% last month" or "The latest survey indicates that the president's approval rating now stands at 63%" or "Ninety-eight percent of patients in a clinical study did not experience any significant side effects to a new breast cancer drug." It is becoming the case that in order to obtain an intelligent appreciation of current developments, we need to absorb and interpret substantial amounts of data. Government, business, and scientific researchers spend billions of dollars collecting data. The federal government has contributed to this development, both through its own collection efforts and through requirements for corporations to release information. The private sector, too, has played its part. The well-publicized Gallup surveys of voters' attitudes and Nielsen ratings of the week's television shows are merely the tip of a vast iceberg of market research studies. The amount of data collected has grown at a phenomenal rate over the past few years.

We must make sense of all the data. The computer age has given to us both the power to rapidly process, summarize, and analyze data and the encouragement to produce and store more data. Computers bring data, such as stock quotes, to our fingertips. We must properly analyze and interpret all of this data.

1.1 DECISION MAKING IN AN UNCERTAIN ENVIRONMENT

Decisions are often based on incomplete information. For example, upon admission to a university, first-year students are expected to select a major. Yet many of these students may not have a clear career goal in mind. Or cancer patients may be asked to participate in a clinical study to test a new experimental drug (Reference 1) when information about the side effects, survival rates, and recurrence rates are not yet available for this new medication. Similarly, business decisions are made regularly in an environment where decision makers cannot be certain of the future behavior of those factors that will eventually affect the outcome resulting from various options under consideration.

In submitting a bid for a contract, a manufacturer will not be completely certain of the total future costs involved and will not have knowledge about bids to be submitted by competitors. In spite of this uncertainty, the manufacturer must make a bid. An investor does not know with certainty whether financial markets will be buoyant, steady, or depressed. Nevertheless, the investor must decide how to balance a portfolio among stocks, bonds, and money market instruments while future market movements are unknown.

Consider the following statements:

* "The price of IBM stock will be higher in six months than it is now."
* "If the federal budget deficit is as high as predicted, interest rates will remain high for the rest of the year."
* "The annual income of a college graduate will be greater than the annual income of an individual without a college education."

Each of these statements contains language suggesting a spurious amount of certainty. At the time the assertions were made, it would have been impossible to be *sure* of their truth. Although an analyst may believe that developments over the next few months will be such that the price of IBM stock is anticipated to rise over the period, he or she will not be certain of this. Thus, the statements should be modified, as indicated by the following examples:

* "The price of IBM stock is *likely* to be higher in six months than it is now."
* "If the federal budget deficit is as high as predicted, it is *probable* that interest rates will remain high for the rest of the year."
* "The annual income of a college graduate *probably* will be greater than the annual income of an individual without a college education."

Careful wording is very important. To replace unwarrantedly precise statements with unnecessarily vague statements is inadequate. After all, what is meant by "is likely to be" or "it is probable that"? Close attention must be given to expressing the ideas that are meant, especially when dealing with probability or uncertainty.

EXERCISES

Basic Exercises

1.1 Modify the following statements to reflect possible uncertainty:
   a. The best opportunities for improvement in market share for this product lie in an advertising campaign aimed at the 18- to 25-year-old age group.
   b. If a bid is submitted at this level, it will be lower than the competitor's bids and the contract will be secured.

c. The cost of gasoline in the United States will be higher in 2 months.

1.2 Give an example of a marketing decision that must be made under conditions of uncertainty.

1.3 Give an example of a financial decision that must be made under conditions of uncertainty.

1.2 SAMPLING

Before bringing a new product to market, a manufacturer wants to arrive at some assessment of the likely level of demand and may undertake a market research survey. The manufacturer is, in fact, interested in *all* potential buyers (the population). However, populations are often so large that they are unwieldy to analyze; collecting complete information for a population could be impossible or prohibitively expensive. Even in circumstances where sufficient resources seem to be available, time constraints make the examination of a subset (sample) necessary.

> ### Population and Sample
> A **population** is the complete set of all items that interest an investigator. Population size, N, can be very large or even infinite. A **sample** is an observed subset of population values with sample size given by n.

Examples of populations include:

- All registered voters in the United States
- All students in your university
- All families living in West Palm Beach, Florida
- All stocks traded on the New York Stock Exchange
- All medical insurance claims received by a company in a given year
- All accounts receivable for a corporation

Our eventual aim is to make statements based on sample data that have some validity about the population at large. We need a sample, then, that is representative of the population. How can we achieve that? One important principle that we must follow in the sample selection process is randomness.

> ### Random Sampling
> **Simple random sampling** is a procedure used to select a sample of n objects from a population in such a way that each member of the population is chosen strictly by chance, each member of the population is equally likely to be chosen, and every possible sample of a given size, n, has the same chance of selection. This method is so common that the adjective *simple* is generally dropped, and the resulting sample is called a **random sample**.

Sampling is widely used in all areas of business, as well as in other disciplines. Sample output is selected to determine if a production process is operating correctly. An audit of accounts receivable will generally be based on a sample. During presidential election years, estimates of voter preference are obtained from samples of registered voters, or perhaps an exit poll of voters may be used to attempt to predict which candidate will obtain a state's electoral votes. However, taking a sample is merely a means to an end. We need to study statistics *not to make statements about the sample but, rather, to draw conclusions about the wider population*. Statistics is the study of how to make decisions about a population when our information has been obtained from a sample. Some uncertainty will always remain.

Suppose that we want to know the average age of registered voters in the United States. Clearly, the population size is so large that we might take only a random sample, perhaps 500 registered voters, and calculate their average age. Because this average is based on sample data, it is called a *statistic*. If we were able to calculate the average age of the entire population, then the resulting average would be called a *parameter*. Throughout this book we will study ways to make decisions about a parameter, based on a statistic. We must realize that some element of uncertainty will always remain, as the exact value of the parameter is not known.

> **Parameter and Statistic**
> A **parameter** is a specific characteristic of a population. A **statistic** is a specific characteristic of a sample.

EXERCISES

Basic Exercises

1.4 Give an example of a parameter for each of the following populations:

  a. Incomes of all families living in West Palm Beach, Florida
  b. Annual returns of all stocks traded on the New York Stock Exchange
  c. Costs of all medical insurance claims received by a company in a given year
  d. Values of all accounts receivable for a corporation

1.5 Your college surveyed its students to determine average weekly time spent surfing the Internet. From a random sample of 174 students the average time was computed to be 6.1 hours.

  a. What is the population?
  b. What is the sample?
  c. What is the statistic?
  d. Is the value 6.1 hours a parameter or a statistic?

1.6 One airline claims that less than 1% of its scheduled flights out of Orlando International Airport depart late. From a random sample of 200 flights, 1.5% were found to depart later than the scheduled time.

  a. What is the population?
  b. What is the sample?
  c. What is the statistic?
  d. Is 1.5% a parameter or a statistic?

1.3 DESCRIPTIVE AND INFERENTIAL STATISTICS

To think statistically will involve steps from problem definition to decision making. After we identify and define a problem, we collect data produced by various processes according to a design and analyze that data using one or more statistical procedures.

From this analysis, we obtain information. Information is in turn converted into knowledge, using understanding based on specific experience, theory, literature, and additional statistical procedures. Both descriptive and inferential statistics are used to change data into knowledge that leads to better decision making.

> ## Descriptive and Inferential Statistics
> **Descriptive statistics** include graphical and numerical procedures that are used to summarize and process data and to transform data into information. **Inferential statistics** provide the bases for predictions, forecasts, and estimates that are used to transform information into knowledge.

Describing Data

We see a picture of the daily production pattern in a cereal manufacturing plant in Example 1.1.

Example 1.1 Cereal Production (Descriptive Statistics)

A production manager of Wheat Cereals formed a team of employees to study the cereal manufacturing process. During the first phase of the study a random selection of packages were weighed, and the density of the cereal product was measured. Next, the manager wanted to study data related to patterns in daily output. Production rates (in 1,000s) for a 10-day period were obtained. Show these results graphically and comment on your findings:

Day	1	2	3	4	5	6	7	8	9	10
Packages (1,000s)	84	81	85	82	85	84	109	110	60	63

Solution   From Figure 1.1 the production manager can identify days of low production, as well as days of increased production.

There did not seem to be much difference in the number of packages produced on each of the first six days. There were variations from day to day, but all six points had numerical values that were very close. However, on days 7 and 8 the production level appeared to be higher. In contrast, on days 9 and 10 the production level appeared to be lower. Based on these observations, the team attempted to identify the conditions that resulted in higher and lower productivity. For example, perhaps on days 9 and 10 key workers were absent, or maybe there had been a change in the method of production, or perhaps there had been a change in raw materials. Similar efforts would lead to identification of the conditions that contributed to increased productivity on days 7 and 8.

Making Inferences

Inferential statistics is a process, not just a numerical result. This process might include estimation, hypothesis testing, analysis of relationships, or forecasting. First, we may want to *estimate a parameter*. Suppose Florin's Flower Mart wants to develop

Figure 1.1
Daily Cereal
Production at
Wheat Cereals

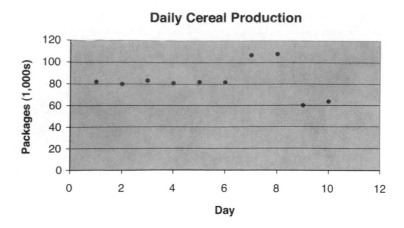

a new marketing strategy. Information about the spending habits of the store's customers might be helpful. Florin may want to:

* Estimate the *average* age of the store's customers
* Estimate the difference in the average amount customers charge to a Visa credit card and the average amount customers charge to American Express
* Estimate the proportion of customers that are dissatisifed with the store's delivery system

Second, we may want to *test a hypothesis* about a parameter. For example, Florin may want to:

* Test if customers have a different preference for color of roses this year than they had last year
* Test if fewer than 25% of the store's shoppers are tourists
* Test if weekend sales are higher than weekday sales
* Test if the *average* amount customers spent on their last purchase exceeded $40

Answers to these types of questions may help Florin develop an advertising campaign that results in reduced costs, increased profits, and increased customer satisfaction.

Third, we may want to *analyze relationships* between two or more variables. The chief financial officer (CFO) of General Motors is interested in making strategic decisions that affect the entire corporation. In those cases the CFO may utilize macroeconomic data series available from sources such as the Department of Commerce's Bureau of Economic Analysis to analyze relationships among such variables as gross domestic product, interest rate, per capita income, total investment, and money supply, which indicate the overall state of the national economy. The CFO may ask these questions:

* Does the rate of growth of the money supply influence the inflation rate?
* If General Motors increases the price of midsize cars by 5%, what will be the effect on the sales of these cars?
* Does minimum wage legislation affect the level of unemployment?

How does one begin to answer the question about the effect on the demand for automobiles of a 5% increase in prices? Simple economic theory tells us that, all other things being equal, an increase in price will be associated with a reduction in the quantity demanded. However, such theory is purely qualitative. It does not tell us *by how much* the quantity demanded will fall. To proceed further, information on how demand has responded to price changes in the past must be collected and assessed. By studying inferential statistics we will learn how to collect information and to analyze relationships.

Fourth, we may need to **forecast**, or make reliable predictions. Investment decisions must be made well ahead of the time at which a new product can be brought to market, and forecasts of likely market conditions some years into the future are obviously desirable. For established products short-term sales forecasts are important in the setting of inventory levels and production schedules. Predictions of future interest rates are important to a company deciding whether to issue new debt. In formulating a coherent economic policy, the government requires forecasts of the likely outcomes for variables such as gross domestic product. Forecasts of future values are shaped by regularities discovered in the past behavior of these variables. Thus, data are collected on the past behavior of the variable to be predicted and on the behavior of other related variables. We will use inferential statistics to analyze this information and may then suggest likely future trends.

EXERCISES

Basic Exercises

1.7 Suppose that you own a grocery store.
   a. Give an example of a question that could be answered using descriptive statistics.
   b. Give an example of a question where estimating a parameter would be helpful.
   c. Give an example of a question concerning a possible relationship between two variables of interest to your grocery business.
   d. Give an example of a forecasting question.

1.8 Determine if descriptive statistics or inferential statistics should be used to obtain the following information:
   a. A graph that shows the number of defective bottles produced during the day shift over one week's time
   b. An estimate of the percentage of employees who arrive to work late
   c. An indication of the relationship between years of employee experience and pay scale

SUMMARY

Decisions must be made in times of uncertainty. All areas of business, as well as other disciplines, use statistics to make such decisions. Accountants may need to select samples for auditing purposes. Financial investors use statistics to understand the market's fluctuations and to choose between various portfolio investments. Managers who want to know if customers are satisfied with their company's products or services may use surveys to find out. Perhaps a marketing executive wants information concerning customers' taste preferences, their shopping habits, or the demographics of Internet shoppers. For each of these situations, we must carefully define the problem, determine what data are needed, collect the data, summarize the data, and then make inferences and decisions based on the data obtained. Statistical thinking is essential from initial problem definition to final decision, which may lead to reduced costs, increased profits, improved processes, and increased customer satisfaction.

KEY WORDS

- descriptive statistics
- inferential statistics
- parameter
- population
- random sample
- sample
- simple random sampling
- statistic

CHAPTER EXERCISE AND APPLICATION

1.9 ● A random sample of 100 university students was asked a series of questions to obtain demographic data on their status as an American or an international student, major, gender, age, year in school, and current grade point average (GPA). Other questions asked for their levels of satisfaction with campus parking, campus housing, and campus dining. Responses to these satisfaction questions were measured on a scale from 1 to 5 with 5 being the highest level of satisfaction. Finally, these students were asked if they planned to attend graduate school within 5 years of their college graduation (0: no; 1: yes). These data are contained in the data file **Finstad and Lie Study**.

a. Give an example of how to apply descriptive statistics to this data.
b. Give an example of an estimation question that could be answered by inferential statistics.
c. Give an example of a possible relationship between two variables.

REFERENCE

1. The North American Fareston versus Tamoxifen Adjuvant Trial for Breast Cancer. *www.naftatrial.com*.

Topic 2

Describing Data: Graphical

Chapter 2

Describing Data: Graphical

Introduction

Once we carefully define a problem, we will need to collect data. Often the number of observations collected is so large that the actual findings of the study are unclear. Our goal in this chapter is to summarize data in such a way that a clear and accurate picture emerges. We want to reduce a mass of data as far as possible, while guarding against the possibility of obscuring important features through too extreme a reduction. Unfortunately, there is no single "right way" to describe data. Rather, the appropriate line of attack is typically problem-specific, depending on two factors, the type of data and the purpose of the study.

It has been said that a picture is worth a thousand words. Likewise, a graph is worth a thousand numbers. In this chapter we introduce tables and graphs that help us gain a better understanding of data and that provide visual support for improved decision making. Reports are enhanced by the inclusion of appropriate tables and graphs, such as frequency distributions, bar charts, pie charts, Pareto diagrams, line charts, histograms, stem-and-leaf displays, or ogives. Visualization of data is important. We should always ask, What does the graph suggest about the data? What is it that we see?

Communication is often the key to success, and data communication is no exception. Proper analysis and interpretation of data are essential in order to communicate outcomes in a meaningful manner. Charts and graphs can improve our data communication with clients, customers, boards of directors, or other constituents. In later chapters we will develop numerical procedures to describe data.

2.1 CLASSIFICATION OF VARIABLES

Variables can be classified in several ways. One method of classification refers to the type and amount of information contained in the data. Data are either categorical or numerical. Another method is to classify data by levels of measurement, giving either qualitative or quantitative variables.

Categorical or Numerical

Categorical variables produce responses that belong to groups or categories. For example, responses to yes/no questions are categorical. "Do you own a mobile phone?" and "Did you ever visit Oslo, Norway?" are limited to yes or no answers. A health care insurance company may classify incorrect claims according to the type of errors, such as procedure and diagnostic errors, patient information errors, and contract errors. Other examples of categorical variables include questions on gender, marital status, and your major in college. Sometimes categorical variables include a range of choices, such as "strongly disagree" to "strongly agree." For example, consider a faculty evaluation where students are to respond to statements such as "The instructor in this course was an effective teacher" (1: strongly disagree; 2: slightly disagree; 3: neither agree nor disagree; 4: slightly agree; 5: strongly agree).

Numerical variables include both discrete and continuous variables. A **discrete numerical variable** may (but does not necessarily) have a finite number of values. However, the most common type of discrete numerical variable that we will encounter produces a response that comes from a counting process. Examples of discrete numerical variables include the number of students enrolled in a class, the number of university credits earned by a student at the end of a particular semester, the number of Microsoft stocks in an investor's portfolio, and the number of insurance claims filed following a particular hurricane in Florida.

A **continuous numerical variable** may take on any value within a given range of real numbers and usually arises from a measurement (not a counting) process. Examples of continuous numerical variables include height, weight, time, distance, and temperature. Someone might say that he is 6 feet (or 72 inches) tall, but his height could actually be 72.1 inches, 71.8 inches, or some other similar number, depending on the accuracy of the instrument used to measure height. Other examples of continuous numerical variables include the weight of cereal boxes, the time to run a race, and the distance between two cities. In each case the value could deviate within a certain amount, depending on the precision of the measurement instrument used. We tend to truncate continuous variables in daily conversation and treat them as though they were the same as discrete variables without even giving it a second thought. However, the difference is very important in statistics because it is one of the determinants of what statistical procedures are most appropriate in different contexts.

Measurement Levels

We can also describe data as either **qualitative** or **quantitative**. With qualitative data there is no measurable meaning to the "difference" in numbers. For example, one basketball player is assigned the number "20" and another player has the number "10." We cannot conclude that the first player is twice as good as the second player. However, with quantitative data there is a measurable meaning to the difference in numbers. When one student scores 90 on an exam and another student scores 45, the difference is measurable and meaningful.

We will see that qualitative data include nominal and ordinal levels of measurement. Quantitative data include interval and ratio levels of measurement.

Nominal and ordinal levels of measurement refer to data obtained from categorical questions. Responses to questions on gender, country of citizenship, political affiliation, and ownership of a mobile phone are **nominal**. Nominal data are considered the lowest or weakest type of data, since numerical identification is chosen strictly for convenience.

The values of nominal variables are words that describe the categories or classes of responses. The values of the gender variable are male and female; the values of "Did you ever visit Oslo, Norway?" are "yes" and "no." We arbitrarily assign a code or number to each response. However, this number has no meaning other than for categorizing. For example, we could code gender responses or yes/no responses as

| 1 = Male | 1 = Yes |
| 2 = Female | 2 = No |

Ordinal data indicate the rank ordering of items, and similar to nominal data the values are words that describe responses. Some examples of ordinal data and possible codes are:

1. Product quality rating (1: poor; 2: average; 3: good)
2. Satisfaction rating with university food service (1: very dissatisfied; 2: moderately dissatisfied; 3: no opinion; 4: moderately satisfied; 5: very satisfied)
3. Consumer preference among three different types of soft drink (1: most preferred; 2: second choice; 3: third choice)

In these examples the responses are ordinal, or put into a rank order, but there is no measurable meaning to the "difference" between responses. That is, the difference between your first and second choices may not be the same as the difference between your second and third choices.

Interval and ratio levels of measurement refer to data on an ordered scale where meaning is given to the *difference* between measurements. An interval scale indicates rank and distance from an arbitrary zero measured in unit intervals. That is, data are provided relative to an arbitrarily determined benchmark. Temperature is a classic example of this level of measurement, with arbitrarily determined benchmarks generally based on either Fahrenheit or Celsius degrees. Suppose that it is 80 degrees Fahrenheit in Orlando, Florida, and only 20 degrees Fahrenheit in St. Paul, Minnesota. We can conclude that the difference in temperature is 60 degrees, but we cannot say that it is four times as warm in Orlando as it is in St. Paul. Suppose that, when Fahrenheit temperature was established, freezing was set at 500 degrees. Then in our Orlando/St. Paul temperature example it would have been 548 degrees in Orlando and 488 degrees in St. Paul (still a difference of 60 degrees). The year is another example of an interval level of measurement, with benchmarks based on the Gregorian or Islamic calendar.

Ratio scale data do indicate both rank and distance from a natural zero, with ratios of two measures having meaning. A person who weighs 200 pounds is twice the weight of a person who weighs 100 pounds; a person who is 40 years old is twice the age of someone who is 20 years old.

After collecting data, we first need to classify responses as categorical or numerical or by measurement scale. Next, we assign an arbitrary number to each response. Some graphs are used generally for categorical variables, and others are appropriate for numerical variables.

Note that data files usually contain "missing values." For example, respondents to a questionnaire may choose not to answer certain questions about gender, age, income, or some other sensitive topic. Missing values require a special code in the data entry stage. Unless missing values are properly handled, it is possible to obtain erroneous output. Statistical software packages handle missing values in different ways.

EXERCISES

Basic Exercises

2.1 State whether each of the following variables is categorical or numerical. If categorical, give the level of measurement. If numerical, is it discrete or continuous?

　a. Number of e-mail messages sent daily by a financial planner

　b. Actual cost of a student's textbooks for a given semester

　c. Your monthly electricity bill

　d. Faculty ranks (professor, associate professor, assistant professor, instructor)

2.2 The public relations office of a professional basketball team wants information about fans that attend postseason tournament games. A questionnaire is given to each fan upon entrance to the postseason game. Is the answer to each of the following questions categorical or numerical? If categorical, give the level of measurement. If numerical, is it discrete or continuous?

　a. Are you a season-ticket holder?

　b. Do you live in Orange County?

　c. What was the actual cost of your ticket to this postseason game?

2.3 A questionnaire was distributed to students at a liberal arts college to find out the level of student satisfaction with various activities and services. For exam-

ple, concerning the "method of registration for classes for the next semester," students were asked to check one of the following boxes:

☐ very satisfied
☐ moderately satisfied
☐ neutral
☐ moderately dissatisfied
☐ very dissatisfied

Is a student's response to this question numerical or categorical? If numerical, is it discrete or continuous? If categorical, give the level of measurement.

2.4 Faculty at one university were asked a series of questions in a recent survey. State the type of data for each question.

　a. Indicate your level of satisfaction with your teaching load (very satisfied; moderately satisfied; neutral; moderately dissatisfied; very dissatisfied).

　b. How many articles did you have published in refereed journals during the last year?

　c. Did you attend the last university faculty meeting?

　d. Do you think that the teaching evaluation process needs to be revised?

2.5 A sample of customers in a specialty ice cream store was asked a series of questions. Identify the type of data for each question.

　a. What is your favorite flavor of ice cream?

　b. How many times a month do you eat ice cream?

c. Do you have children under the age of 10 living in your home?

d. Have you tried our latest specialty ice cream flavor?

2.6 Residents in one housing development were asked a series of questions by their homeowners' association. Identify the type of data for each question.

a. Did you play golf during the last month on the development's new golf course?

b. How many times have you eaten at the country club restaurant during the last three months?

c. Do you own a camper?

d. Rate the new security system for the development (very good, good, poor, very poor).

Application Exercises

2.7 A survey of students at one college was conducted to provide information to address various concerns

about the college's library. The data are stored in the data file **Library**.

a. Give an example of a categorical variable with ordinal responses.

b. Give an example of a categorical variable with nominal responses.

c. Give an example of a numerical variable with discrete responses.

2.8 A group of business students conducted a survey on their campus to determine student demand for a particular product, a protein supplement for Smoothies. They randomly sampled 113 students and obtained data that could be helpful in developing their marketing strategy. The responses to this survey are contained in the data file **Smoothies**.

a. Give an example of a categorical variable with ordinal responses.

b. Give an example of a categorical variable with nominal responses.

2.2 GRAPHS TO DESCRIBE CATEGORICAL VARIABLES

We can describe categorical variables using frequency distribution tables and graphs such as bar charts, pie charts, and Pareto diagrams. These graphs are commonly used by managers and marketing researchers to describe data collected from surveys and questionnaires.

Frequency Distribution

A **frequency distribution** is a table used to organize data. The left column (called classes or groups) includes all possible responses on a variable being studied. The right column is a list of the frequencies, or number of observations, for each class.

Tables

The classes that we use to construct frequency distribution tables of a categorical variable are simply the possible responses to the categorical variable.

Example 2.1   Central Florida's Top Company Employers in 2003 (Bar and Pie Charts)

What companies were the top employers in central Florida in 2003?

Solution   The *Orlando Sentinel* annually lists the top employers in central Florida (Reference 7). Table 2.1 is a frequency distribution of the five companies with the largest number of employees in this area.

Table 2.1   Central Florida's 2003 Top Employers

COMPANY	NUMBER OF EMPLOYEES
Disney World	51,600
Florida Hospital	19,283
Publix Supermarkets Inc.	15,325
Wal-Mart Stores Inc.	14,995
Universal Orlando	12,000

Bar Charts and Pie Charts

Bar charts and pie charts are commonly used to describe categorical data. If our intent is to draw attention to the *frequency* of each category, then we will most likely draw a **bar chart**. If our intent is to emphasize the proportion of each category, then a **pie chart** is a likely choice. In a bar chart the height of a rectangle represents this frequency. There is no need for the bars to touch. Figure 2.1 is a bar chart of the categorical data on top central Florida employers contained in Table 2.1.

An interesting and useful extension to the simple bar chart can be used when components of individual categories are also of interest. For example, Table 2.2 shows the number of students enrolled in three business majors for two different years at one small private university.

This information can be shown in a bar chart by breaking down the total number of students for each year so that the three components are distinguished by differences in shading, as shown in Figure 2.2A. This kind of chart is called a *component* or

Figure 2.1
Top Five
Employers in
Central Florida,
2003

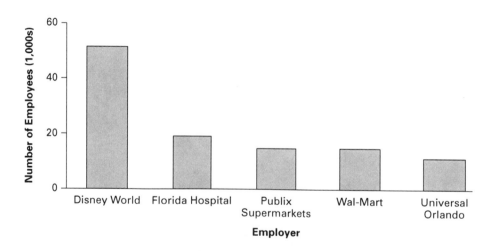

Table 2.2   Student Enrollment in Three Business Majors, 2000 and 2005

MAJOR	2000	2005
Finance	160	250
Marketing	140	200
Accounting	100	150

Figure 2.2A
Finance, Marketing, and Accounting Majors, 2000, 2005 (Component Bar Chart)

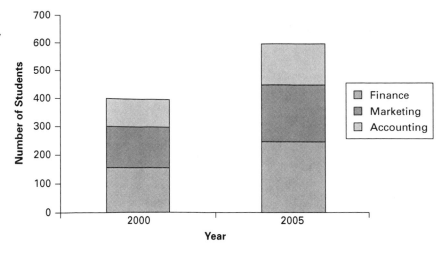

Figure 2.2B
Finance, Marketing, and Accounting Majors, 2000, 2005 (Cluster Bar Chart)

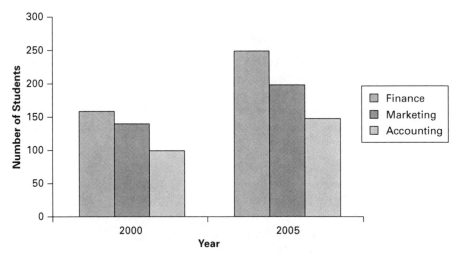

stacked bar chart. Figure 2.2B shows the same data in a bar chart that is called a *cluster* or *side-by-side* bar chart. Both graphs allow us to make visual comparisons of totals and individual components. In this example, it appears that the increase in enrollment between 2000 and 2005 was fairly uniform over the three majors.

If we want to draw attention to the *proportion* of frequencies in each category, then we will probably use a pie chart to depict the division of a whole into its constituent parts. The circle (or "pie") represents the total, and the segments (or "pieces of the pie") cut from its center depict shares of that total. The pie chart is constructed so that the area of each segment is proportional to the corresponding frequency.

Example 2.2   Travel Expenditures

A university administrator requested a breakdown of travel expenses for faculty to attend various professional meetings. It was found that 31% of the travel expenses were spent for transportation costs, 25% for lodging, 12% for food, 20% for conference registration fees; the remainder was spent for miscellaneous costs. Graph this data.

Solution   Figure 2.3 is a pie chart of the travel expenses.

Figure 2.3   Travel Expenditures (Pie Chart)

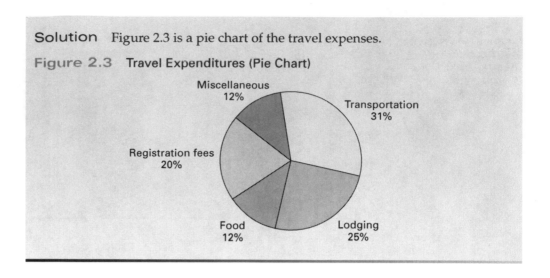

Pareto Diagrams

Managers who need to identify major causes of problems and attempt to correct them quickly with a minimum cost will frequently use a special bar chart known as a *Pareto diagram*. The Italian economist Vilfredo Pareto (1848–1923) noted that in most cases a small number of factors are responsible for most of the problems. We arrange the bars in a Pareto diagram from left to right to emphasize the most frequent causes of defects.

Pareto Diagram
A **Pareto diagram** is a bar chart that displays the frequency of defect causes. The bar at the left indicates the most frequent cause and bars to the right indicate causes with decreasing frequencies. A Pareto diagram is used to separate the "vital few" from the "trivial many."

Pareto's result is applied to a wide variety of behavior over many systems. It is sometimes referred to as the "80–20 Rule." A cereal manufacturer may find that most of the packaging errors are due to only a few causes. A student might think that 80% of the work on a group project was done by only 20% of the team members. The use of a Pareto diagram can also improve communication with employees or management and within production teams. Example 2.3 illustrates the Pareto principle applied to a problem in a health insurance company.

Example 2.3   Insurance Claims Processing Errors (Pareto Diagram)

Analysis and payment of health care insurance claims is a complex process that can result in a number of incorrectly processed claims. These errors lead to an increase in staff time to obtain the correct information and possibly errors in

Insurance

actual payment. The payee usually detects errors resulting in underpayment. The recipient may often overlook overpayments. These errors can increase costs substantially in addition to having negative effects on customer relationships. Considerable effort is devoted to analyzing the reporting and claims-processing activity so that procedures for minimizing errors can be developed. A major health insurance company set a goal to reduce errors by 50%. Show how we would use Pareto analysis to help the company determine the significant factors contributing to process errors. The data are stored in the data file **Insurance**.

Solution   The health insurance company conducted an intensive investigation of the entire claims submission and payment process. A team of key company personnel was selected from the claims processing, provider relations and marketing, internal auditing, data processing, and medical review departments. Based on their experience and a review of the process, the team members finally agreed on a list of possible errors. Three of these (procedure and diagnosis codes, provider information, and patient information) are related to the submission process and must be checked by reviewing patient medical records in clinics and hospitals. Three possible errors (pricing schedules, contract applications, and provider adjustments) are related to the processing of claims for payment within the insurance company office. Program and system errors are included in the category "Others."

A complete audit of a random sample of 1,000 claims began with checking each claim against medical records in clinics and hospitals and then proceeded through the final payment stage. Claims with errors were separated, and the total number of errors of each type was recorded. If a claim had multiple errors, then each error was recorded. In this process many decisions were made concerning error definition. If a child was coded for a procedure typically used for adults and the computer processing system did not detect this, then this error was recorded as error 7 (Program and System Errors) and also as error 3 (Patient Information). If treatment for a sprain was coded as a fracture, this was recorded as error 1 (Procedure and Diagnosis Codes). Table 2.3 is a frequency distribution of the categories and the number of errors in each category.

Next, the team constructed the Pareto diagram in Figure 2.4.

Table 2.3   Errors in Health Care Claims Processing

Category	Error Type	Frequency
1	Procedure and diagnosis codes	40
2	Provider information	9
3	Patient information	6
4	Pricing schedules	17
5	Contract applications	37
6	Provider adjustments	7
7	Others	4

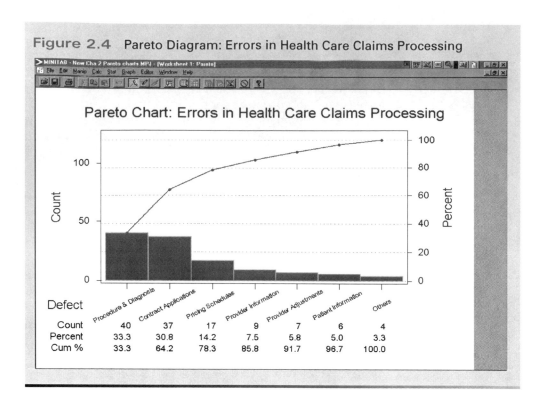

Figure 2.4   Pareto Diagram: Errors in Health Care Claims Processing

We can see in Figure 2.4 that, as the defect percentages for the types of error are added (from left to right), the increase in the cumulative frequency line indicates the relative improvement that would result from correcting each of the most frequent problems. From the Pareto diagram the analysts saw that error 1 (Procedure and Diagnosis Codes) and error 5 (Contract Applications) were the major causes of error. The combination of errors 1, 5, and 4 (Pricing Schedules) resulted in nearly 80 percent of the errors. By examining the Pareto diagram in Figure 2.4, the analysts can quickly determine which causes should receive most of the problem correction effort. Pareto analysis separated the "vital few" causes from the "trivial many."

Armed with this information, the team made a number of recommendations to reduce errors and bring the process under control.

1. Special training sessions would be held for hospital and clinic claims' processors.
2. Surprise random audits would check for coding errors.
3. Monetary penalties would be assessed for organizations with excessive errors.
4. Two people would each prepare the complete set of contract application tables separately. Next, all of the table entries would be compared using a computer program, and any differences would be resolved.
5. A master set of model claims would be prepared and used to test for correct contract applications.

The Pareto diagram and recommendations helped to reduce errors. Overpayments on claims, as well as the staff work required to correct the errors, were reduced.

EXERCISES

Basic Exercises

2.9 The travel expenses for one company are

Item	Percent
Airlines	41
Lodging	25
Meals	12
Car rentals	18
Other	4

a. Construct a pie chart.
b. Construct a bar chart.

2.10 A company has determined that there are seven possible defects for one of its product lines. Construct a Pareto diagram for the following defect frequencies:

Defect Code	Frequency
A	10
B	70
C	15
D	90
E	8
F	4
G	3

2.11 Employees were asked to indicate their level of satisfaction with their current medical insurance. Responses from a random sample of employees follow:

Very satisfied	29
Moderately satisfied	55
No opinion	5
Moderately dissatisfied	20
Very dissatisfied	9

a. Draw a bar chart.
b. Draw a pie chart.

2.12 The supervisor of a plant obtained a random sample of employee ages and times to complete a task (in seconds). Graph the data with a component bar chart.

Age/Time	Less Than 40 Seconds	40 to Less Than 60 Seconds	At Least 1 Minute
Under 21	10	13	25
21 < 35	16	20	12
35 < 50	18	22	8
50 or older	10	27	19

Application Exercises

2.13 Suppose that an estimate of U.S. federal spending showed that 46% was for entitlements, 18% was for defense, 15% was for grants to states and localities, 14% was for interest on debt, 6% was for other federal operations, and 1% was for deposit insurance. Construct a pie chart to show this information.

2.14 The following table gives a partial list of the number of endangered wildlife species both inside and outside the United States as of April 2004 (Reference 4):

Item	Endangered Wildlife Species in United States	Endangered Wildlife Species in Foreign Countries
Mammals	69	251
Birds	77	175
Reptiles	14	64
Amphibians	12	8
Fishes	71	11

SOURCE: U.S. Fish and Wildlife Service

a. Construct a bar chart of the number of endangered wildlife species in the United States.
b. Construct a bar chart of the number of endangered wildlife species outside the United States.
c. Construct a bar chart to compare the number of endangered species in the United States to the number of endangered species outside the United States.

2.15 Jon Payne, tennis coach, kept a record of the most serious type of errors made by each of his players during a 1-week training camp. The data are stored in the data file **Tennis**.

a. Construct a Pareto diagram of total errors committed by all players.
b. Construct a Pareto diagram of total errors committed by male players.
c. Construct a Pareto diagram of total errors committed by female players.
d. Construct a component bar chart showing type of error and gender of the player.

2.16 On what type of Internet activity do you spend the most time? The responses from a random sample of 700 Internet users were banking on-line, 40; buying a product, 60; getting news, 150; sending or reading e-mail, 200; buying or making a reservation for travel, 75; checking sports scores or information, 50; and searching for an answer to a question, 125. Describe the data graphically.

2.17 A group of business students at one university decided to develop their entrepreneurship skills by starting a business to sell Smoothies on campus.

They randomly sampled 113 students to obtain data that would be helpful in developing their marketing strategy. One question on the survey asked students to identify their own level of health consciousness. The responses to this survey are contained in the data file **Smoothies**.

a. Draw a bar chart.
b. Draw a pie chart.

2.18 ● From the data file **Smoothies**, construct component bar charts of the responses for the following variables:

a. Gender and level of health consciousness
b. Desire for protein supplement and level of health consciousness

2.19 Data on U.S. Exports and Imports and on the merchandise trade balance by country are found in the *Statistical Abstract of the United States* (Reference 6).

a. Graph the top 10 purchasers of U.S. exports for the most recent year available.
b. Graph the top 10 suppliers of U.S. imports for the most recent year available.

2.3 GRAPHS TO DESCRIBE TIME-SERIES DATA

Suppose that we take a random sample of 100 boxes of a new variety of cereal. If we collect our sample at one point in time and weigh each box, then the measurements obtained are known as *cross-sectional* data. However, we could collect and measure a random sample of 5 boxes every 15 minutes or 10 boxes every 20 minutes. Data measured at successive points in time are called *time-series* data. We will study this type of data in more depth in Chapter 19. But for now we will look at a graph of time-series data called a *line chart* or *time-series plot*.

> ### Line Chart (Time-Series Plot)
> A **line chart**, also called a **time-series plot**, is a series of data plotted at various time intervals. Measuring time along the horizontal axis and the numerical quantity of interest along the vertical axis yields a point on the graph for each observation. Joining points adjacent in time by straight lines produces a time-series plot.

The technology of the twenty-first century provides quick access to data that can assist decision making, and much of this data is time-series data. E-commerce is important to all of us. On-line shoppers can purchase just about anything: airline tickets, automobiles, electronics, books, flowers, stocks, and so on. The nation's retailers report to the government how much of their business is done on-line, and this information is used in monthly government reports on the status of the economy. These data are collected at successive time intervals.

Numerous firms analyze and sell Internet surveys and statistical data. To develop marketing plans, many companies need demographics concerning on-line shoppers, as well as off-line shoppers. Often the observations are measured at successive time intervals (annually, monthly, weekly, hourly, and so on). Colleges and universities study admission enrollment figures over time to better understand the trends in enrollment. Physicians monitor weekly (or monthly) blood counts for cancer patients. We use a time-series plot to describe graphically all of these examples.

University Enrollments, 1995–2005

Example 2.4 Trends in University Enrollment (Time-Series Plot)

The president of a small private four-year university requested data on the number of first-year students and the number of transfer students who entered the university from 1995 to 2005. The data are stored in the data file **University Enrollments, 1995–2005**.

Solution From Figure 2.5 we can see that first-year enrollments have increased since 2000 and that a peak for transfer students in 2002 has been followed by a steady decrease. The admissions staff should determine factors leading to both enrollment trends.

Figure 2.5 New Student Enrollment, 1995–2005

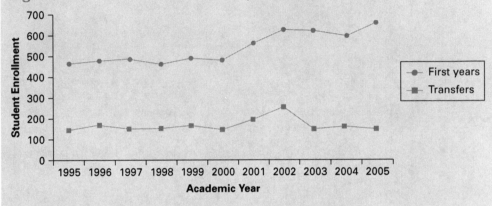

Quarterly Sales 2001–2006

Example 2.5 Quarterly Sales of a Corporation Over Six Years (Time-Series Plot)

Quarterly sales for a corporation over a 6-year period are given in Table 2.4 and stored in the data file **Quarterly Sales 2001–2006**. Describe the data graphically.

Solution Figure 2.6 is a time-series plot of all 24 time intervals. We notice in Figure 2.6 that first-quarter sales are consistently followed by a drop in

Table 2.4 Quarterly Sales, 2001–2006 (1,000s)

	QUARTER			
YEAR	1	2	3	4
2001	271	199	240	255
2002	341	246	245	275
2003	351	283	353	292
2004	401	282	306	291
2005	370	242	281	274
2006	356	245	304	279

second-quarter sales. Perhaps the season of the year is a factor. In Chapter 19 we will develop methods to adjust time-series data for seasonality, trends, cyclical behavior, or some other irregular component.

Figure 2.6 Quarterly Sales, 2001–2006 (Time-Series Plot)

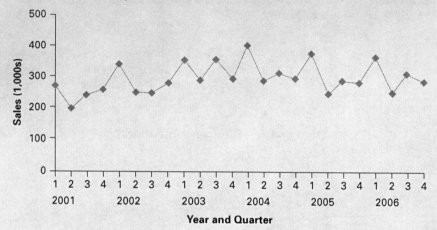

If we are interested only in a comparison of first- and second-quarter sales, then a time-series plot such as that in Figure 2.7 might be of interest.

Figure 2.7 First- and Second-Quarter Sales, 2001–2006 (Time-Series Plot)

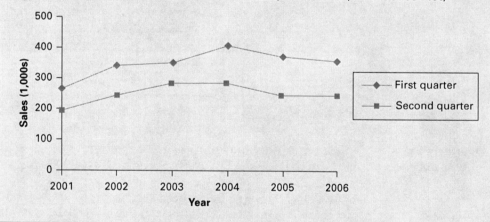

EXERCISES

Basic Exercises

2.20 Construct a time-series plot for the following data on weekend or night mobile phone usage (in minutes):

Month	Weekend or Night
January	575
February	603
March	469
April	500
May	586
June	540

2.21 What percent of undergraduate alumni made donations to their alma mater? The Institutional Research Office at one university reported the following percentages for the period from 2001 to 2005. Draw a time-series plot of the data. What action could the school take?

Year	Percent
2001	26.72
2002	27.48
2003	24.89
2004	25.83
2005	30.22

Application Exercises

2.22 ● Degrees awarded from 1998 to 2005 by degree type at a private four-year university are stored in the data file **Degrees 1998–2005**.

   a. Graph the data with a time-series plot.

   b. What possible conclusions or actions might the university consider?

2.23 Information about the gross domestic product in the area of manufacturing can be found in the *Statistical Abstract of the United States* (Section 21: Manufactures) (Reference 5). The U.S. Census Bureau, the *Annual Survey of Manufacturers*, and the *Current Industrials Report* are the major sources for this information.

   a. Use a time-series plot to graph the gross domestic product in manufacturing in current dollars by industry for durable goods (such as wood products, furniture and related products, motor vehicles, and equipment) from 1998 to 2003.

   b. Use a time-series plot to graph the gross domestic product in manufacturing in chained dollars (2000) by industry for nondurable goods (such as food, apparel, and leather products) from 1998 to 2003.

2.24 ● The data file **Exchange Rate** shows an index of the value of the U.S. dollar against trading partners' currencies over 12 consecutive months. Graph the data with a time-series plot.

2.25 ● The inventory-sales ratio for manufacturing and trade in the United States over a period of 12 years is stored in the data file **Inventory Sales**. Plot the data with a time-series plot.

2.26 Select annual returns on a stock market index over 14 years from the Internet. Graph the data with a time-series plot.

2.27 ● The data file **Gold Price** shows the year-end price of gold (in dollars) over 14 consecutive years. Graph the data with a time-series plot.

2.28 ● The data file **Housing Starts** shows private housing units started per thousand persons in the U.S. population over a period of 24 years. Describe the data with a graph.

2.29 ● Earnings per share of a corporation over a period of 28 years are stored in the data file **Earnings per Share**. Graph the series and comment on the plot.

2.4 GRAPHS TO DESCRIBE NUMERICAL VARIABLES

In this section we briefly present histograms, ogives, and stem-and-leaf displays that summarize and describe numerical data. First, we consider a frequency distribution for numerical data.

Frequency Distributions

Similar to a frequency distribution for categorical data (Section 2.2), a frequency distribution for numerical data is a table that summarizes data by listing the classes in the left column and the number of observations in each class in the right column. However, the classes or intervals for a frequency distribution of numerical data are not as easily identifiable.

To determine the intervals of a frequency distribution for numerical data requires answers to certain questions: How many intervals should be used? How wide should each interval be? There are some general rules (such as Equation 2.1 and Equation 2.2) for preparing frequency distributions that make it easier for us to answer these type of questions, to summarize data, and to communicate results.

Construction of a Frequency Distribution

Rule 1: Determine *k*, the number of intervals (classes).
Rule 2: Intervals (classes) should be the same width, *w*; the width is determined by the following:

$$w = \text{Interval Width} = \frac{(\text{Largest Number} - \text{Smallest Number})}{\text{Number of Intervals}} \qquad (2.1)$$

Both *k* and *w* should be rounded upward, possibly to the next largest integer.
Rule 3: Intervals (classes) must be inclusive and nonoverlapping.

Rule 1. Number of Intervals

The number of intervals (classes) used in a frequency distribution is decided in a somewhat arbitrary manner.

Quick Guide to Approximate Number of Intervals for a Frequency Distribution

Sample Size	Number of Intervals	
Fewer than 50	5–7	
50 to 100	7–8	
101 to 500	8–10	(2.2)
501 to 1,000	10–11	
1,001 to 5,000	11–14	
More than 5,000	14–20	

Practice and experience provide the best guidelines. Larger data sets require more intervals; smaller data sets require fewer intervals. If we select too few classes, the patterns and various characteristics of the data may be hidden. If we select too many classes, we will discover that some of our intervals may contain no observations or have a very small frequency.

Rule 2. Interval Width

After choosing the number of intervals, the next step is to choose the interval width:

$$w = \text{Interval Width} = \frac{(\text{Largest Number} - \text{Smallest Number})}{\text{Number of Intervals}}$$

The interval width is often rounded to a convenient whole number to provide for easy interpretation.

Rule 3. Inclusive and Nonoverlapping Intervals

Intervals must be inclusive and nonoverlapping. Each observation must belong to one and to only one interval. Consider a frequency distribution for the ages (rounded to the nearest year) of a particular group of people. If the frequency distribution contains the intervals "age 20 to age 30" and "age 30 to age 40," to which of these two classes would a person age 30 belong?

The *boundaries*, or endpoints, of each class must be clearly defined. To avoid overlapping, age intervals could be defined as "age 20 *but less than* age 30," followed by "age 30 *but less than* age 40" and so on. Another possibility is to define the age intervals as "20–29," "30–39," and so forth. Since age is an integer, no overlapping occurs. Boundary selection is subjective. Simply be sure to define interval boundaries that promote a clear understanding and interpretation of the data.

We must not overemphasize the rules to determine the number of intervals and the interval widths or underemphasize selecting class numbers that will show the most clear data patterns.

Two special frequency distributions are the *cumulative frequency distribution* and the *relative cumulative frequency distribution*.

Relative, Cumulative, and Relative Cumulative Frequency Distributions

A **relative frequency distribution** is obtained by dividing each frequency by the number of observations and multiplying the resulting proportion by 100%. A **cumulative frequency distribution** contains the total number of observations whose values are less than the upper limit for each interval. We construct a cumulative frequency distribution by adding the frequencies of all frequency distribution intervals up to and including the present interval. In a **relative cumulative frequency distribution**, cumulative frequencies can be expressed as cumulative proportions or percents.

Example 2.6   Mobile Phone Usage (Statistical Thinking)

Mobile Usage

Jennie Bishop, marketing director for a leading mobile phone company, obtained records of minutes used by a random sample of 110 subscribers to the company's low-end user plan (250 peak minutes per month). Table 2.5 is a list of minutes used by each subscriber in the sample during one particular month. The data are stored in the data file **Mobile Usage**. What do the data indicate?

Table 2.5   Mobile Phone Usage (Peak Minutes)

271	236	294	252	254	263	266	222	262	278	288
262	237	247	282	224	263	267	254	271	278	263
262	288	247	252	264	263	247	225	281	279	238
252	242	248	263	255	294	268	255	272	271	291
263	242	288	252	226	263	269	227	273	281	267
263	244	249	252	256	263	252	261	245	252	294
288	245	251	269	256	264	252	232	275	284	252
263	274	252	252	256	254	269	234	285	275	263
263	246	294	252	231	265	269	235	275	288	294
263	247	252	269	261	266	269	236	276	248	298

Solution   Table 2.5 by itself offers little guidance to help the marketing director develop a marketing strategy. We can find some information in Table 2.5: The smallest amount of peak minutes used was 222 minutes, and the maximum time used was 298 minutes. However, we will need more information than this before submitting any report to senior-level executives. To better understand what the data in Table 2.5 indicate, we first develop a frequency distribution.

From the Quick Guide we develop a frequency distribution with eight classes for the data in Table 2.5. From Equation 2.1, the width of each class is

$$w = \frac{299 - 222}{8} = 10 \text{ (rounded up)}$$

Since the smallest value is 222, one choice for the first interval is "220 but less than 230." Subsequent intervals of equal width are added to the frequency distribution, as well as the number of minutes that belong to each class. Table 2.6 is a frequency distribution for the mobile phone data in Table 2.5.

Table 2.6   Frequency and Relative Frequency Distributions for Mobile Phone Usage

MOBILE PHONE USAGE (IN MINUTES)	FREQUENCY	PERCENT
220 less than 230	5	4.5
230 less than 240	8	7.3
240 less than 250	13	11.8
250 less than 260	22	20.0
260 less than 270	32	29.1
270 less than 280	13	11.8
280 less than 290	10	9.1
290 less than 300	7	6.4

The manager may want to know mobile usage below (or above) a certain amount of time. Table 2.7 is a cumulative frequency distribution and a cumulative percent distribution.

The frequency distributions in Table 2.6 and Table 2.7 are an improvement over the original list of data in Table 2.5. We have at least summarized 110 observations into 8 categories and are able to tell Jennie that less than one-fourth (23.6%) of the subscribers sampled used their mobile phones within the guidelines of their plans during the month of the study. The marketing manager might suggest that an advertising campaign be initiated to promote a plan with an increase in peak minutes.

Table 2.7   Cumulative Frequency and Relative Cumulative Frequency Distributions for Mobile Phone Usage

MOBILE PHONE USAGE (IN MINUTES)	CUMULATIVE FREQUENCY	CUMULATIVE PERCENT
Less than 230	5	4.5
Less than 240	13	11.8
Less than 250	26	23.6
Less than 260	48	43.6
Less than 270	80	72.7
Less than 280	93	84.5
Less than 290	103	93.6
Less than 300	110	100.0

Histograms and Ogives

Once we develop frequency distributions, we are ready to graph this information. We will briefly discuss *histograms* and *ogives*.

> ### Histogram
> A **histogram** is a graph that consists of vertical bars constructed on a horizontal line that is marked off with intervals for the variable being displayed. The intervals correspond to those in a frequency distribution table. The height of each bar is proportional to the number of observations in that interval. The number of observations can be displayed above the bars.

> ### Ogive
> An **ogive**, sometimes called a *cumulative line graph*, is a line that connects points that are the cumulative percent of observations below the upper limit of each interval in a cumulative frequency distribution.

Figure 2.8 is a histogram of the mobile usage frequencies in Table 2.6. Figure 2.9 is an ogive that describes the cumulative relative frequencies in Table 2.7.

The shape of a histogram reveals whether the data are evenly spread from the middle of the graph. That is, for some histograms we will see that the middle or

Figure 2.8
Mobile Phone Usage
(Histogram)

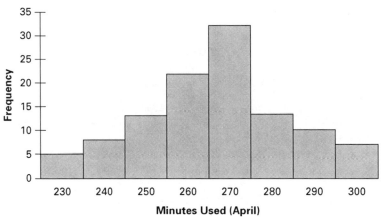

Figure 2.9
Mobile Phone Usage
(Ogive)

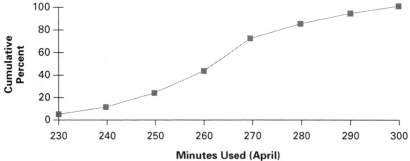

center of the graph divides the graph into two "mirror images," so that the portion on one side of the middle is nearly identical to the portion on the other side. Histograms that have this shape are *symmetric*; those without this shape are asymmetric or *skewed*.

Symmetry
The shape of a histogram is said to be **symmetric** if the observations are balanced, or approximately evenly distributed, about the middle of the histogram.

Skewness
A distribution is **skewed**, or asymmetric, if the observations are not symmetrically distributed on either side of the middle. A *positively skewed* distribution has a tail that extends to the right, in the direction of positive values. A *negatively skewed* distribution has a tail that extends to the left, in the direction of negative values.

Figure 2.10A depicts a histogram that is symmetric. By contrast, the histogram of Figure 2.10B has a long tail to the right, with a far more abrupt cutoff to the left. This

Figure 2.10A Symmetric Distribution

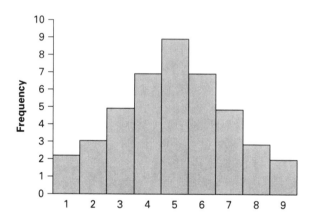

Figure 2.10B   Positively Skewed Distribution

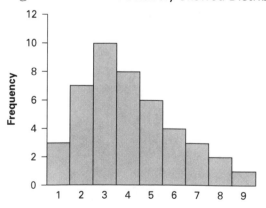

Figure 2.10C   Negatively Skewed Distribution

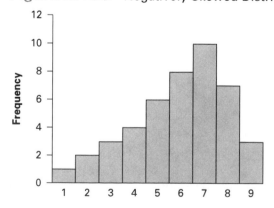

distribution is *skewed to the right*, or *positively skewed*. The distribution in Figure 2.10C is negatively skewed, with the lowest observations extending over a wide range to the left. In Chapter 3 we will learn more about factors that contribute to skewness and how to measure skewness numerically.

Although histograms may provide us with insight as to the shape of the distribution, it is important to remember that histograms may not be "mathematically correct," since they often cannot be scaled on the vertical axis. In Section 2.6 we provide some warnings about histograms that distort the truth.

Stem-and-Leaf Displays

Exploratory data analysis (EDA) consists of procedures used to describe data in simple arithmetic terms with easy-to-draw pencil-and-paper pictures (Reference 11). One such procedure is the *stem-and-leaf display*. Before computers, this procedure was a quick way to identify possible patterns in small data sets. We include here only a brief discussion of this procedure.

> ### Stem-and-Leaf Display
> A **stem-and-leaf display** is an EDA graph that is an alternative to the histogram. Data are grouped according to their leading digits (called the stem), while listing the final digits (called leaves) separately for each member of a class. The leaves are displayed individually in ascending order after each of the stems.

The number of digits in each class indicates the class frequency. The individual digits indicate the pattern of values within each class. Except for extreme *outliers* (data values that are much larger or smaller than other values in the data set), all stems are included even if there are no observations in the corresponding subset. The number of digits in the stem varies according to the data set.

Accounting GPAs

> ### Example 2.7 Grade Point Averages (Stem-and-Leaf Display)
> Grade point averages (GPAs) of a random sample of recently graduating accounting majors were obtained. What information does the stem-and-leaf display in Figure 2.11 provide? The data are stored in the data file **Accounting GPAs**.
>
> **Solution** Each student's GPA was recorded to the nearest hundredth. Figure 2.11 is the output obtained using Minitab (there may be variations in the stem-and-leaf display obtained with other software). We can make several observations from Figure 2.11. For example, we see that a GPA of 3.25 is recorded as a stem of "32" and a leaf of "5." The lowest GPA is 2.12 and the highest GPA is 3.87. The leftmost column of the Minitab output contains cumulative frequencies, separated by a number in parentheses. In Figure 2.11 the number 10 (in parentheses) tells us that the data are centered at GPAs from 3.00 to 3.09. The number 40 in the leftmost column indicates that 40 students had a GPA under 2.90. The number 27 in the leftmost column tells us that 27 students had a GPA of at least 3.40.

Figure 2.11 Stem-and-Leaf Display for Grade Point Averages

Cumulative Frequency	Stem	Leaf
1	21	2
3	22	2 9
7	23	3 4 5 9
13	24	0 1 3 4 7 9
19	25	1 2 3 5 5 7
24	26	1 1 1 2 6
30	27	1 2 3 5 6 8
40	28	0 2 3 4 4 4 5 6 9 9
51	29	0 1 2 2 4 4 4 5 7 7 7
(10)	30	1 1 1 2 6 7 8 8 8 9
51	31	0 1 1 1 2 4 5 6 8
42	32	1 1 4 5 6 8 9
35	33	1 2 3 5 7 8 8 9
27	34	0 0 1 1 1 3 3 3 4 6
17	35	1 6 7 7
13	36	0 1 2 5 5 6 6 8 8
4	37	2 3
2	38	0 7

EXERCISES

Basic Exercises

2.30 Use the Quick Guide to find an approximate number of classes for a frequency distribution if the sample size is:

a. $n = 47$
b. $n = 80$
c. $n = 150$
d. $n = 400$
e. $n = 650$

2.31 Determine an appropriate interval width for a random sample of 110 observations that fall between and include:

a. 20 to 85
b. 30 to190
c. 40 to 230
d. 140 to 500

2.32 Consider the following data:

17	62	15	65
28	51	24	65
39	41	35	15
39	32	36	37
40	21	44	37
59	13	44	56
12	54	64	59

a. Construct a frequency distribution.
b. Draw a histogram.
c. Draw an ogive.
d. Draw a stem-and-leaf display.

2.33 Construct a stem-and-leaf display for the hours that 20 students spent studying for a marketing test.

3.5	2.8	4.5	6.2	4.8	2.3	2.6	3.9	4.4	5.5
5.2	6.7	3.0	2.4	5.0	3.6	2.9	1.0	2.8	3.6

2.34 Consider the following frequency distribution:

Class	Frequency
0 < 10	8
10 < 20	10
20 < 30	13
30 < 40	12
40 < 50	6

a. Construct a relative frequency distribution.
b. Construct a cumulative frequency distribution.
c. Construct a cumulative relative frequency distribution.

Application Exercises

2.35 The following table shows the age distribution of Internet visitors to travel agency Web sites during December 2003 (Reference 12):

Age	Percent
18–24	11.30
25–34	19.11
35–44	23.64
45–54	23.48
55+	22.48

a. Construct a relative cumulative frequency distribution.
b. What percent of the Internet visitors were under 45 years of age?
c. What percent of the Internet visitors were at least 35 years of age?

2.36 The demand for bottled water increases during the hurricane season in Florida. The operations manager at a plant that bottles drinking water wants to be sure that the filling process for 1-gallon bottles is operating properly. Currently, the company is testing the volumes of 1-gallon bottles. A random sample of 75 bottles is tested. Study the filling process for this product and submit a report of your findings to the operations manager. Construct a frequency distribution, cumulative frequency distribution, histogram, ogive, and stem-and-leaf display. Incorporate these graphs into a well-written summary. How could we apply statistical thinking in this situation? The data are stored in the data file **Water**.

2.37 The test scores of 40 students are stored in the data file **Scores**.

a. Construct a frequency distribution of the data.
b. Construct a cumulative frequency distribution of the data.
c. Based on your answer to part (a), construct an appropriate histogram of the data.
d. Construct a stem-and-leaf display of the data.

2.38 Percentage returns for the 25 largest U.S. common stock mutual funds for a particular day are stored in the data file **Returns**.

a. Construct a histogram to describe the data.
b. Draw a stem-and-leaf display to describe the data.
c. Construct an ogive to describe the data.

2.39 Ann Thorne, the operations manager at a suntan lotion manufacturing plant, wants to be sure that the filling process for 8 oz (237 mL) bottles of SunProtector is operating properly. Suppose that a random sample of 100 bottles of this lotion is selected, the contents are measured, and the volumes (in mL) are stored in the data file **Sun**. Describe the data graphically.

2.5 TABLES AND GRAPHS TO DESCRIBE RELATIONSHIPS BETWEEN VARIABLES

In the preceding sections we developed graphs to describe a single variable. These "pictures" helped us to better analyze information contained in a large data set. In this section we extend graphical measures to describe relationships between two variables. First, we present a *scatter plot* to study possible relationships between two quantitative variables. Next, we look at two-way *cross tables* to consider possible relationships between qualitative variables.

Business and economic analyses are often concerned about relationships between variables. Do higher SAT mathematics scores predict higher college GPAs? What is the change in quantity sold as the result of a change in price? How are total sales influenced by total disposable income in a geographic region? Does advertising increase sales? What is the change in infant mortality in developing countries as per capita income increases?

In these examples we notice that one variable may depend to a certain extent on the other variable. For example, a student's GPA may depend on his or her SAT math score. We then call GPA the *dependent variable* and label it Y. We call SAT math score the *independent variable* and label it X. Similarly, we would label the quantity sold as Y and the price of a commodity as X.

To answer these questions, we gather and analyze random samples of data collected from relevant populations. Our analysis begins with constructing a graph called a scatter plot (or scatter diagram).

Scatter Plots

A picture often provides insight as to the relationship that may exist between two variables.

Scatter Plot

We can prepare a **scatter plot** by locating one point for each pair of two variables that represent an observation in the data set. The scatter plot provides a picture of the data, including the following:

1. The range of each variable
2. The pattern of values over the range
3. A suggestion as to a possible relationship between the two variables
4. An indication of outliers (extreme points)

We could prepare scatter plots by plotting individual points on graph paper. However, all modern statistical packages contain routines for preparing scatter plots directly from an electronic data file. Preparation of such a plot—as shown in Example 2.8—is a common task in any initial data analysis that occurs at the beginning of an economic or business study. In Example 2.8 we illustrate a scatter plot of two quantitative variables.

Example 2.8   Entrance Scores and College GPA (Scatter Plots)

Are SAT mathematics scores a good indicator of college success? All of us have taken one or more academic aptitude tests as part of a college admission procedure. The admissions staff at your college used the results of these tests to determine your admission status. Table 2.8 gives the SAT math scores from a test given before admission to college and the GPAs at college graduation for a random sample of 11 students at one small private university in the Midwest. Draw a scatter plot and determine what information it provides.

Solution   Using Excel, we obtain Figure 2.12, a scatter plot of the dependent variable, college GPA, and the independent variable, SAT math score.

We can make several observations from examining the scatter plot in Figure 2.12. GPAs range from around 2.5 to 4, and SAT math scores range from 450 to 700. An interesting pattern is the positive upward trend—GPA scores tend to increase directly with increases in SAT math scores. Note also that the relationship does not provide an exact prediction. Some students with low SAT math scores have higher GPA scores than do students with higher SAT math scores. We see that the basic pattern indicates that higher entrance scores predict higher grade point averages, but the results are not perfect.

Table 2.8   SAT Math Versus GPA

SAT MATH	GPA
450	3.25
480	2.60
500	2.88
520	2.85
560	3.30
580	3.10
590	3.35
600	3.20
620	3.50
650	3.59
700	3.95

Figure 2.12   GPA Versus SAT Math Score for Graduating Seniors

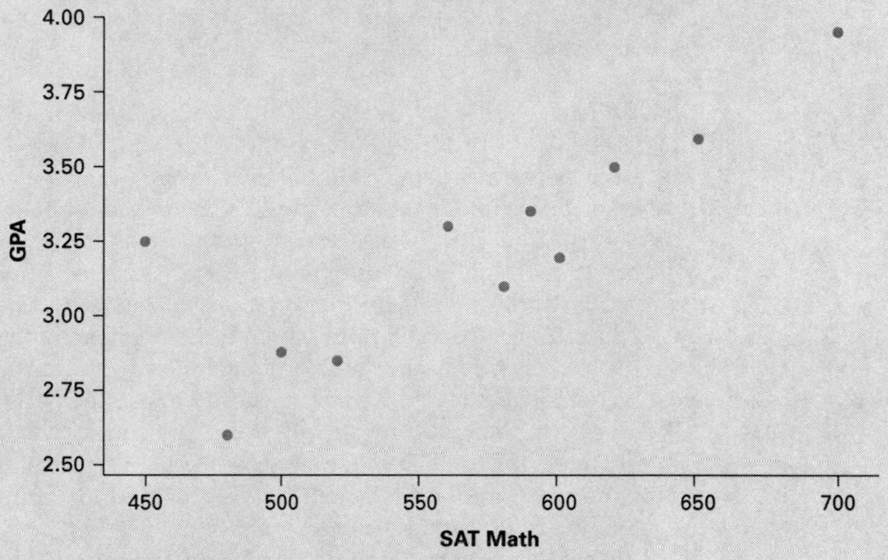

Cross Tables

There are situations in which we need to describe relationships between categorical or ordinal variables. Market research organizations describe attitudes toward products, measured on an ordinal scale, as a function of educational levels, social status measures, geographic areas, and other ordinal or categorical variables. Personnel departments study employee evaluation levels versus job classifications, educational levels, and other employee variables. Production analysts study relationships between departments or production lines and performance measures to determine reasons for product change, reasons for interruption of production, and quality of output. These situations are usually described by cross tables and pictured by bar charts.

Cross Tables

A **cross table,** sometimes called a contingency table, lists the number of observations for every combination of values for two categorical or ordinal variables. The combination of all possible intervals for the two variables defines the cells in a table. A cross table with *r* rows and *c* columns is referred to as an *r* × *c* cross table.

Example 2.9 Product Demand by Residential Area (Cross Table)

A building products retailer has been working on a plan for new store locations as part of a regional expansion. In one city proposed for expansion there are three possible locations: north, east, and west. From past experience the retailer knows that the three major profit centers in her stores are tools, lumber, and paint. In selecting a location, the demand patterns in the different parts of the city are important. Thus, she has requested help from the market research department to obtain and analyze relevant data. This retailer believes that she has a comparative advantage in selling tools.

Solution Table 2.9 is a 3x4 contingency table for the variables "residential location" and "product purchased." This table has been prepared by market research personnel using data obtained from a random sample of households in three major residential areas of the city. Each residential area had a separate phone number prefix, and the last four digits were chosen using a computer random number generator. If the number was not a residence, another phone number was generated randomly. If the phone number was not answered, the number was called again up to a maximum of five times to ensure a high participation rate.

In each residential area 250 households were contacted by telephone and asked to indicate which of three categories of products they had purchased during their last trip to a building supply store. The survey was conducted to determine the demand for tools, lumber, and paint. The three residential areas contain the same number of households, and, thus, the random sample of 750 represents the population of households in the entire city.

Every cell in Table 2.9 shows the number of sampled households in each of the residential areas that had purchased tools, lumber, or paint in the past month. If they had purchased from more than one category, they indicated the category with the largest sales value. For example, 100 sampled households in the east area had purchased tools, and 75 sampled households in the west area had purchased

Table 2.9 Cross Table of Household Demand for Products by Residential Area

AREA	TOOLS	LUMBER	PAINT	NONE	TOTAL
East	100	50	50	50	250
North	50	95	45	60	250
West	65	70	75	40	250
TOTAL	215	215	170	150	750

paint. At the right side of each row we see the total number of sampled households (250) in that row. Similarly, the number of sampled households that had purchased from each product category is displayed at the bottom of each column. The displays at the right-hand side of the rows and the bottom of the columns are referred to as marginal distributions. These numbers are the frequency distributions for each of the two variables presented in the cross table.

Table 2.9 provides a summary of the purchase patterns for households in the three neighborhoods. Figure 2.13 is a cluster bar chart of Table 2.9. If geographic region and products purchased were unrelated, we would expect similarities in the bar charts.

However, we see that the bar charts do differ, suggesting a relationship between these two variables. Based on this research the marketing staff now know that people in the east area are more frequent purchasers of tools, whereas households in the north purchase more lumber. Demand for paint is highest in the west. Based on these patterns the retailer decides to locate in the east because of the greater potential for tool sales.

Figure 2.13   Household Demand for Products by Residential Area

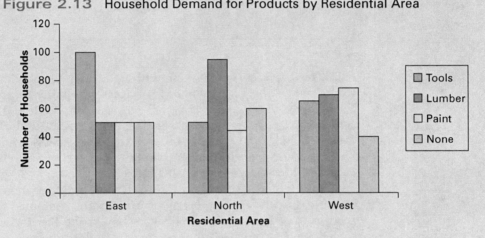

Example 2.10   Sources of Drinking Drivers (Cross Table)

A research team was assigned the task of determining the alcohol consumption sources of motor vehicle drivers with various blood alcohol levels.

Solution   A random sample of drivers was obtained, and the resulting data were used to prepare Table 2.10. This table displays the relationship between blood alcohol concentration and the location of the first drinking episode for night drivers who had been drinking. The data for this table were obtained from a random sample of drivers in Washtenaw County, Michigan, during the hours of 7 P.M. to 3 A.M. The columns indicate the blood alcohol concentration (BAC) of the driver, obtained from a breath test. Common interpretations of these concentrations are $\leq 0.02\%$, essentially no blood alcohol and no driving impairment;

Table 2.10   Cross Table of Driver BAC by Location of First Drinking Episode

	BAC				
LOCATION	≤ 0.02%	0.03%–0.04%	0.05%–0.09%	≥ 0.10%	TOTAL
Bar					
Number	22	25	17	14	78
Percent	28.2	32.1	21.8	17.9	100.0
Restaurant					
Number	11	3	9	1	24
Percent	45.8	12.5	37.5	4.2	100.0
Own home					
Number	45	16	11	10	82
Percent	54.9	19.5	13.4	12.2	100.0
Another home					
Number	42	10	6	0	58
Percent	72.5	17.2	10.3	0	100.0
Total					
Number	120	54	43	25	242
Percent	49.6	22.3	17.8	10.3	100.0

0.03% to 0.04%, social drinking with no impairment for most drivers; 0.05% to 0.09%, almost all drivers will have noticeable impairment and could be convicted by a court; ≥0.10%, all drivers are seriously impaired and represent a threat to other vehicles and pedestrians. Table 2.10 also includes the percentage of drivers in each intoxication category for each row. This makes it possible to compare the various sources of drinking drivers easily, even though the number of drivers from each drinking source is different.

From Table 2.10 it was possible to obtain some important indications concerning drinking and driving behavior. The sample contained only drivers who had consumed at least one alcoholic beverage during the day. From the bottom row, which summarizes the entire set, over 70% did not have BACs that would seriously reduce their driving ability (e.g., ≤0.02% and 0.03% to 0.04%). The most likely source of seriously impaired drivers was bars. For the 78 people who drank first in a bar, 17.9% had BACs at or above 0.10%. For the 82 drivers who began drinking at home, 12.2% were at the highest BAC level. However, in this group of home drinkers almost 75% were in the lowest two BAC categories and thus not seriously impaired. Those people who had their first drink in another home were least likely to have high BAC levels. One important outcome of this analysis is that efforts to reduce the number of seriously impaired drivers should consider bars as a major source (Reference 2).

Graphs have a stronger visual impact than cross tables. The component bar chart in Figure 2.14 is certainly a stronger visual presentation of the blood alcohol content than the cross table in Table 2.10.

Statistical computer programs can prepare most of these tables. In Chapter 16 more powerful statistical procedures for analyzing cross tables will be presented.

Figure 2.14
Driver BAC by
Location of First
Drinking Episode

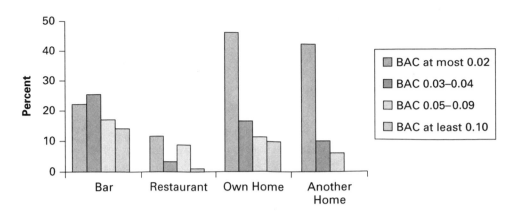

EXERCISES

Basic Exercises

2.40 Prepare a scatter plot of the following data:

(5, 53) (21, 65) (14, 48) (11, 66) (9, 46) (4, 56)

(7, 53) (21, 57) (17, 49) (14, 66) (9, 54) (7, 56)

(9, 53) (21, 52) (13, 49) (14, 56) (9, 59) (4, 56)

2.41 Refer to Example 2.9. Suppose that the market survey data had resulted in the following table instead of the data in Table 2.9. Explain the conclusions from this survey in terms of the product strategy.

Revised Cross Table of Household Demand for Products by Residential Area

Area	Tools	Lumber	Paint	None	Total
East	100	40	60	50	250
North	70	45	95	40	250
West	75	70	65	40	250
Total	245	155	220	130	750

2.42 Three subcontractors, A, B, and C, supplied 58, 70, and 72 parts, respectively, to a plant during the last week. Of the parts supplied by subcontractor A, only 4 were defective. From the parts supplied by subcontractor B, 60 were good parts; from those supplied by subcontractor C, only 6 were defective.

a. Set up a cross table for the data.
b. Draw a bar chart.

Applications Exercises

2.43 Bishop's supermarket records the actual price for consumer food products and the weekly quantities sold. Use the data file **Bishop** to obtain the scatter plot for the actual price of a gallon of orange juice and the weekly quantities sold at that price. Does the scatter plot follow the pattern from economic theory?

2.44 Acme Delivery offers three different shipping rates for packages under 5 pounds delivered from Maine to the West Coast: regular, $3; fast, $5; and lightning,

$10. To test the quality of these services, a major mail-order retailer shipped 15 packages at randomly selected times from Maine to Tacoma, Washington. The packages were shipped in groups of three by the three services at the same time to reduce variation resulting from the shipping day. The following data show the shipping cost, x, and the number of days, y, in (x, y) pairs:

(3, 7) (5, 5) (10, 2) (3, 9) (5, 6) (10, 5) (3, 6) (5, 6) (10, 1)

(3, 10) (5, 7) (10, 4) (3, 5) (5, 6) (10, 4)

Prepare a scatter plot of the points and comment on the relationship between shipping cost and observed delivery time.

2.45 Sales revenue totals (in dollars) by day of the week are contained in the **Stordata** data file. Prepare a cross table that contains the days of the week as rows and the four sales quartile intervals as columns.

a. Compute the row percentages.
b. What are the major differences in sales level by day of the week as indicated by the row percentages?
c. Describe the expected sales volume patterns over the week based on this table.

2.46 Many small cities make significant efforts to attract commercial operations such as shopping centers and large retail stores. One of the arguments is that these facilities will contribute to the property that can be taxed and thus provide additional funds for local government needs. The data stored in the data file **Citydat** come from a study of municipal revenue generation capability. Prepare a scatter plot of "taxbase"—the assessed value of all city property in millions of dollars—versus "comper"—the percent of assessed property value that is commercial property. What information does this scatter plot provide about the assessable tax base and percent of commercial property in the city?

2.6 DATA PRESENTATION ERRORS

Poorly designed graphs can easily distort the truth. We have considered several graphs that summarize and present data. Used sensibly and carefully, these can be excellent tools for extracting the essential information from what would otherwise be a mere mass of numbers. Unfortunately, it is not invariably the case that an attempt at data summarization is carried out either sensibly or carefully. In such circumstances one can easily be misled by the manner in which the summary is presented. We must draw from data as clear and accurate a picture as possible. Improper graphs can produce a distorted picture, yielding a false impression. It is possible to convey the wrong message without being deliberately dishonest.

In this section we present some examples of misleading graphs, the intent being not to encourage their use but to caution against their dangers. Example 2.11 shows that distortions in histograms can lead to incorrect conclusions. Example 2.12 illustrates that different choices for the vertical axis in time-series plots can lead to different conclusions. There are many other possibilities for misleading graphs, and for further study we recommend Edward Tufte (Reference 10) and Howard Wainer (Reference 13), who are leaders in the area of data presentation. They have studied the proper design of graphs, as well as the causes and dangers of making inferences from graphs that are poorly drawn.

Misleading Histograms

We know that the width of all intervals should be the same. Suppose a data set contains many observations that fall into a relatively narrow part of the range, while others are widely dispersed. We might be tempted to construct a frequency distribution with narrow intervals where the bulk of the observations lie and broader ones elsewhere. Even if we remember that it is the *areas*, rather than the heights, of the rectangles of the histogram that must be proportional to the frequencies, it is still never a desirable option to construct such a histogram with different widths, as it may easily deceive or distort the findings. We include this section simply to point out potential errors that we might find in histograms. In Example 2.11 we illustrate the construction of a histogram when interval widths are not all the same.

Example 2.11   Grocery Receipts (Unequal Interval Widths)

The dollar amounts of a random sample of 692 grocery receipts are contained in Table 2.11.

One possible error in contructing a histogram is to make the *heights* of the rectangles, and not the *areas* of the rectangles, proportional to the frequencies. We see this misleading histogram in Figure 2.15. Inspection of this incorrect histogram gives us the mistaken impression of a very large proportion of observations in the highest class. *Under no circumstance should we ever construct a histogram with this error. We illustrate this mistake only as a warning against deceptive graphs.*

With continuous upgrades in software packages has come an increase in the use and misuse of computer-generated graphs. Figure 2.16 illustrates a computer-generated histogram with equal interval widths, even though three of the classes vary in width. Again, *under no circumstance should we ever construct a histogram with this error. We illustrate this mistake only as a warning against deceptive graphs.*

Table 2.11   Grocery Receipts (Dollar Amounts)

DOLLAR AMOUNT	NUMBER OF RECEIPTS	PROPORTIONS
$ 0 < $10	84	84/692
$10 < $20	113	113/692
$20 < $30	112	112/692
$30 < $40	85	85/692
$40 < $50	77	77/692
$50 < $60	58	58/692
$60 < $80	75	75/692
$80 < $100	48	48/692
$100 < $200	40	40/692

To construct a histogram, we should observe that the quantities in Table 2.11 are interpreted in the usual way. Thus, of all these receipts, 113/692, or 16.3%, were in the range from $10 to under $20. We need to draw a histogram with the *areas* of the rectangles drawn over the intervals proportional to their frequencies. Since each of the first six intervals has a width of 10, we can draw rectangles of heights 84, 113, 112, 85, 77, and 58 over these intervals. The next two intervals have a width of 20, that is, twice the width of each of the first six. Thus, in order for their areas to be proportional to the frequencies, the rectangles drawn over these intervals should have heights that are one-half of the corresponding frequencies, that is 37.5 and 24.

Finally, the last interval has a width of 100, ten times the width of each of the first six. It follows that the height of the rectangle drawn over this last interval

Figure 2.15   Misleading Histogram of Grocery Receipts (Error: Heights Proportional to Frequencies)

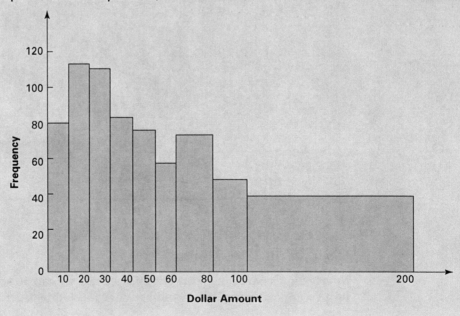

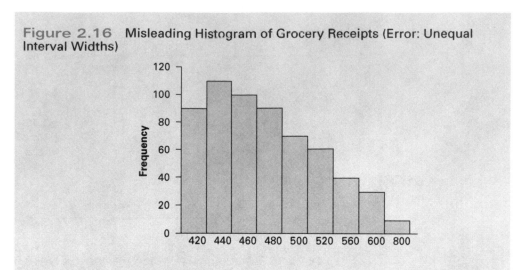

Figure 2.16   Misleading Histogram of Grocery Receipts (Error: Unequal Interval Widths)

should be one-tenth of the frequency. That is, the height of the last rectangle should be 4. The reason that we make the areas of these rectangles proportional to the frequencies is that visually we associate area with size. We see in Figure 2.17 a histogram that avoids the errors illustrated in Figure 2.15 and Figure 2.16.

Figure 2.17   Grocery Receipts (Histogram)

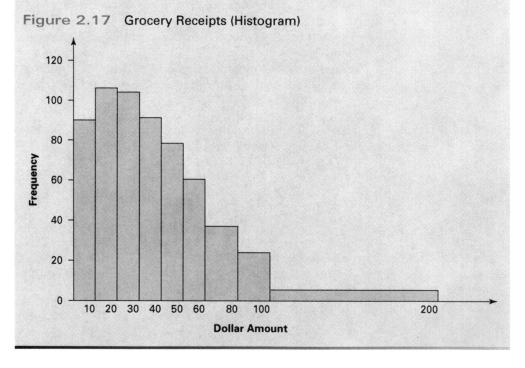

Misleading Time-Series Plots

By selecting a particular scale of measurement, we can, in a time-series plot, create an impression either of relative stability or of substantial fluctuation over time.

**SAT Math
1986–2006**

Example 2.12   SAT Math Scores 1986–2006
(Choice of Scale for Time-Series Plot)

The average SAT mathematics scores for the incoming first-year students at one university from 1986 to 2006 are contained in the data file **SAT Math 1986–2006**. Graph this data with a time-series plot.

Solution   We show here two possible time-series plots for the SAT math scores contained in the data file **SAT Math**. Figure 2.18 suggests quite wide fluctuations in average scores. Precisely the same information is graphed in Figure 2.19, but now with a much coarser scale on the vertical axis. The resulting picture in Figure 2.19 is much flatter, suggesting considerably less variability in average scores over time.

Figure 2.18   SAT Math Scores: First-Year Students, 1986–2006

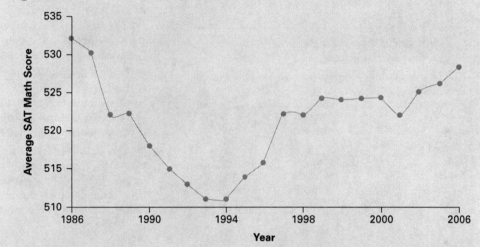

Figure 2.19   Revised Time Plot for SAT Math Scores: First-Year Students, 1986–2006

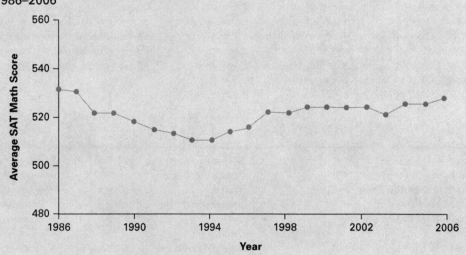

There is no "correct" choice of scale for any particular time series plot. Rather, the conclusion from Example 2.12 is that looking at the shape of the plot alone is inadequate for obtaining a clear picture of the data. It is also necessary to keep in mind the scale on which the meaurements are made.

EXERCISES

Basic Exercises

2.47 A supervisor of a plant kept records of the time (in seconds) that employees needed to complete a particular task. The data are summarized as follows:

Time	30 < 40	40 < 50	50 < 60	60 < 80	80 < 100	100 < 150
Number	10	15	20	30	24	20

a. Graph the data with a histogram.
b. Discuss possible errors.

2.48 The following table lists the number of daily visitors to a new business Web site during 2006.

Month	Number	Month	Number
Jan-06	5,400	Jul-06	5,600
Feb-06	5,372	Aug-06	5,520
Mar-06	5,265	Sept-06	5,280
Apr-06	5,250	Oct-06	5,400
May-06	5,289	Nov-06	5,448
Jun-06	5,350	Dec-06	5,500

a. Graph the data with a time-series plot using a vertical scale from 5,000 to 5,700.
b. Graph the data with a time-series plot using a vertical scale from 4,000 to 7,000.
c. Comment on the difference between these two time-series plots.

Application Exercises

2.49 The data file **Exchange Rate** shows an index of the value of the U.S. dollar against trading partners' currencies over 12 consecutive months.

a. Draw a time-series plot of this data using a vertical axis that ranges from 92 to 106.
b. Draw a time-series plot of this data using a vertical axis that ranges from 75 to 120.
c. Comment on these two time-series plots.

2.50 The data file **Inventory Sales** shows the inventory-sales ratio for manufacturing and trade in the United States over a period of 12 years. Draw two time-series plots for this series with different vertical ranges. Comment on your findings.

SUMMARY

In this chapter we have shown how to describe data using graphs. First, we studied graphs such as the histogram to summarize a numerical variable. Next, we used bar charts, pie charts, and Pareto diagrams to describe a categorical variable. Then, we considered describing the relationships between (1) two quantitative variables, (2) a quantitative variable and an ordinal variable, and (3) two categorical variables. We have shown that scatter plots can provide valuable information at the beginning of a study as to a possible pattern of the data points.

KEY WORDS

- bar chart
- categorical variable
- continuous numerical variable
- cross table
- cumulative frequency distribution
- discrete numerical variable
- frequency distribution
- histogram
- line chart
- measurement levels
- nominal
- numerical variable
- ogive
- ordinal
- Pareto diagram
- pie chart
- qualitative
- quantitative
- relative frequency distribution
- relative cumulative frequency distribution
- scatter plot
- skewness
- stem-and-leaf display
- symmetry
- time-series plot

CHAPTER EXERCISES AND APPLICATIONS

2.51 Describe graphically the time (in hours) that 20 students studied for a statistics test.

6.5	5.8	4.5	6.2	4.8	7.3	4.6	3.9	4.4	5.5
5.2	6.7	3.0	2.4	5.0	3.6	2.9	4.0	2.8	3.6

2.52 A sample of 20 financial analysts was asked to provide forecasts of earnings per share of a corporation for next year. The results are summarized in the following table:

FORECAST ($ per share)	9.95 <10.45	10.45 <10.95	10.95 <11.45	11.45 <11.95	11.95 <12.45
NUMBER OF ANALYSTS	2	8	6	3	1

    a. Draw the histogram.
    b. Find the relative frequencies.
    c. Find the cumulative frequencies.
    d. Find and interpret the relative cumulative frequencies.

2.53 In one region it was found that 28% of people with incomes less than $50,000 use the Internet; 48% of those with incomes between $50,000 to $74,999 use the Internet; and 70% of those with incomes of at least $75,000 use the Internet. Use a pie chart or a bar chart to plot this data.

2.54 Dr. James Mallet, professor and director of the Roland George Investment Institute at Stetson University, reported in *USA Today* (Reference 3) that the trend for student-managed funds is increasing. Use a time-series plot to describe the quarterly returns of one university MBA Investment Fund versus those of the S&P 500:

	Nov. 1998	Feb. 1999	May 1999	Aug. 1999	Nov. 1999
MBA Investment Fund	16.1%	12.5%	2.5%	3.6%	7.0%
S&P 500	21.6%	6.4%	5.1%	1.4%	5.2%

2.55 Are Americans familiar with the new tax laws? One survey (Reference 1) found the following percentages of respondents who were familiar with tax law changes: 70% were familiar with the child tax credit, 52% with the marriage penalty, 51% with capital gains, 44% with dividends, and 41% with marginal tax rates; 25% were unaware of any changes. Describe the data graphically.

2.56 A team of undergraduate business students was asked to recommend improvement to the data entry process at the county appraiser's office. The team identified several types of errors, such as posting an incorrect name or entering an incorrect parcel number. The deed abstractors were asked to keep a record of the errors in data entry that were sent to them. The following table is a frequency distribution of errors:

Defect	Total
Posting error in name	23
Posting error in parcel	21
Property sold after tax bills were mailed	5
Inappropriate call transfer (not part of deeds/mapping)	18
Posting error in legal description/ incomplete legal description	4
Deeds received after tax bills printed	6
Correspondence errors	2
Miscellaneous errors	1

    a. Construct a Pareto diagram of these defects in data entry.
    b. What recommendations would you suggest to the county appraiser?

2.57 What are the top overall Internet sites (measured by the total number of users who actually visit the site during a given month)? The following table indicates the top six sites during December 2003 (Reference 9). Graphically display the data.

Site	Unique Visitors (1,000s)
Yahoo! sites	111,271
Time Warner Network	110,471
MSN-Microsoft sites	110,021
eBay	69,169
Google sites	61,501

2.58 From the Nielsen/Net Ratings, January 2004 (Reference 8), the following table shows the weekly traffic increase for the top five health, fitness, and nutrition Internet sites. Graph and discuss factors that may have contributed to this growth.

Site	Unique Visitors 1/4/2004	Unique Visitors 12/28/2003
eDiets	1,036,000	472,000
Weight Watchers	876,000	445,000
WebMD	853,000	524,000
AOL Health	713,000	448,000
Yahoo! Health	590,000	396,000

2.59 What is the relationship between the price of paint and the demand for this paint? A random sample of (price, quantity) data for seven days of operation was obtained. Prepare a plot and describe the relationship between quantity and price, with emphasis on any unusual observations.

(10, 100) (8, 120) (5, 200) (4, 200) (10, 90) (7, 110) (6, 150)

2.60 A consumer goods company has been studying the effect of advertising on total profits. As part of this study, data on advertising expenditures (1000s) and total sales (1000s) were collected for a five-month period and are as follows:

(10, 100)   (15, 200)   (7, 80)   (12, 120)   (14, 150)

The first number is advertising expenditures and the second is total sales. Plot the data.

2.61 The president of Floor Coverings Unlimited wants information concerning the relationship between retail experience (years) and weekly sales (in hundreds of dollars). He obtained the following random sample of experience and weekly sales:

(2, 5) (4, 10) (3, 8) (6, 18) (3, 6) (5, 15) (6, 20) (2, 4)

The first number for each observation is years of experience and the second is weekly sales. Plot the data.

2.62 A random sample of 12 college baseball players participated in a special weight-training program in an attempt to improve their batting averages. The program lasted for 20 weeks immediately prior to the start of the baseball season. The average number of hours per week and the change in their batting averages from the preceding season are as follows:

(8.0, 10)   (20.0, 100)   (5.4, –10)   (12.4, 79)   (9.2, 50)
(15.0, 89)   (6.0, 34)   (8.0, 30)   (18.0, 68)   (25.0, 110)
(10.0, 34)   (5.0, 10)

Plot the data. Does it appear that the weight-training program was successful?

2.63 Four types of checking accounts are offered by one bank. Suppose that recently a random sample of 300 bank customers was surveyed and asked several questions. It was found that 60% of the respondents preferred Easy Checking, 12% Intelligent Checking, 18% Super Checking, and the remainder Ultimate Checking. Of those who selected Easy Checking, 100 were females; one-third of the respondents who selected Intelligent Checking were males; half of the respondents who selected Super Checking were males; 80% of respondents who selected Ultimate Checking were males.

a. Describe the data with a cross table.
b. Describe the data graphically.

2.64 How did people first learn about a new product? A random sample of 200 shoppers at a particular store was asked their age and whether they heard about the product from a friend or through a local newspaper advertisement. The results indicated that 50 respondents were under 21 years of age, 90 people were in the age group between 21 and 35, and 60 respondents were older than 35 years of age. Of those under 21 years old, 30 heard about the product from a friend, and the remainder learned about the product through an advertisement in the local paper. One-third of the people in the age category from 21 to 35 first learned about the product from the same newspaper advertisement; the remainder of this age group learned about the product from a friend. A friend first told 30 percent of the people in the over-35 age category about the product; the remainder learned about it from the local newspaper advertisement.

a. Describe the data with a cross table.
b. Describe the data graphically.

2.65 A random sample of customers was asked to select their favorite soft drink from a list of five brands. The results showed that 30 preferred brand A, 50 preferred brand B, 46 preferred brand C, 100 preferred brand D, and 14 preferred brand E.

a. Construct a pie chart.
b. Construct a bar chart.

2.66 From the data file **Smoothies**, construct cross tables of these variables:

a. Gender and level of health consciousness
b. Desire for protein supplement and level of health consciousness

2.67 Construct a time-series plot of population growth for the state of New York from 1997 to the present. (*Hint*: check www.census.gov or www.bea.doc.gov.)

2.68 From the data file **Florin** construct the following:

a. A cross table of the variables "method of payment" and "day of purchase."
b. A pie chart of "Rose" color preference.

2.69 A supermarket developer has conducted a large study to determine alcohol preferences based on the type of vehicle typically driven to a shopping center. A random sample of 100 car drivers and a second random sample of 100 pickup truck drivers were interviewed and asked to indicate their preference for beer or wine. The results indicated that 68% of car drivers preferred wine, while 71% of pickup truck drivers preferred beer. Construct a cross table and bar chart of this information.

REFERENCES

1. Block, Sandra. Source: H&R Block November 2003 survey. Reprinted in "The Trouble with Taxes: They're Too Hard, They Don't Make Sense, and There's No Easy Fix." *USA Today*, April 9, 2004, p. B1.

2. Carlson, William L. "Alcohol Usage of the Nighttime Driver." *Journal of Safety Research* 4 (March 1972), p. 12.

3. Fogarty, Thomas A. "Student-Run Funds Teach Real Skills with Real Cash." *USA Today*, December 13, 1999, p. 12B.

4. "No. 373. Threatened and Endangered Wildlife and Plant Species Number: 2004." Source: U.S. Fish and Wildlife Service, *Endangered Species Bulletin*. Reprinted in *Statistical Abstract of the United States*, Section 6: Geography and Environment, p. 227. See http://www.census.gov/prod/2004pubs/04statab/geo.pdf. Information for the current year is available at http://www.census.gov/statab/www/.

5. "No. 972. Gross Domestic Product in Manufacturing in Current and Real (2000) Dollars by Industry: 1998–2003." Source: U.S. Bureau of Economic Analysis, *Survey of Current Business*, July 2004. Reprinted in *Statistical Abstract of the United States*, Section 21: Manufacturers, p. 628. See http://www.census.gov/prod/2004pubs/04statab/manufact.pdf. Information for the current year is available at http://www.census.gov/statab/www/.

6. "No. 1298. U.S. Exports, Imports, and Merchandise Trade Balance by Country: 1999–2003." Source: U.S. Census Bureau. Reprinted in *Statistical Abstract of the United States*, Section 28: Foreign Commerce and Aid, pp. 814–17. See http://www.census.gov/prod/2004pubs/04statab/foreign.pdf. Information for the current year is available at http://www.census.gov/statab/www/.

7. "Top Employers by Industry: Top-Ranked Companies Among the 100 Biggest Employers in Central Florida." Source: Respective companies; *Sentinel* research. *Orlando Sentinel*, December 8, 2003. See http://www.orlandosentinel.com/business.

8. "Top Health, Fitness & Nutrition Sites, Week Ending January 4 (U.S., Home)." Source: Nieslen/NetRatings, January 2004. Reprinted by Janis Mara in "Users Shrink, Sites Expand." ClickZ Stats, January 19, 2004. See *www.clickz.com/stats/markets/healthcare/article.php/10101_3298631*.

9. "Top Properties of December 2003 U.S., Home, Work and University." Source: conScore Media Metrix. Reprinted in "U.S. Web Usage and Traffic, December 2003." ClickZ Stats, January 27, 2004. See *www.clickz.com/stats/big_picture/traffic_patterns/article.php/5931_3301321*.

10. Tufte, E. R. *The Visual Display of Quantitative Information* (Cheshire, CT: Graphics Press, 1983).

11. Tukey, J. *Exploratory Data Analysis* (Reading, MA: Addison-Wesley, 1977).

12. "Visitors to Travel Agency Sites by Age, U.S. December 2003." Source: Hitwise. Reprinted by Robyn Greenspan in "Internet High on Travel Destinations." ClickZ Stats, January 28, 2004. See *www.clickz.com/stats/markets/travel/article.php/6071_3304691*.

13. Wainer, H. *Visual Revelations: Graphical Tales of Fate and Deception from Napoleon Bonaparte to Ross Perot* (New York: Copernicus/Springer-Verlag, 1997).

Topic 3

Describing Data: Numerical

Chapter 3

Describing Data: Numerical

Introduction

In Chapter 2 we described data graphically. In this chapter we describe data numerically with measures of central tendency, measures of variability, measures for grouped data, and measures of the direction and strength of relationships between two variables.

3.1 MEASURES OF CENTRAL TENDENCY

We are often able to determine if data tend to center or cluster around some value by constructing a histogram. Measures of central tendency provide numerical information about a "typical" observation in the data. In this section we discuss the mean, median, mode, and symmetry of data (for the geometric mean, see the Appendix of this chapter).

Mean, Median, Mode

In Chapter 1 we introduced the terms *parameter* and *statistic*. A parameter refers to a specific population characteristic; a statistic refers to a specific sample characteristic. Measures of central tendency are usually computed from sample data, rather than from population data. One measure of central tendency that quickly comes to mind is the *mean*.

Arithmetic Mean

The **arithmetic mean** (or simply *mean*) of a set of data is the sum of the data values divided by the number of observations. If the data set is the entire population of data, then the *population mean*, μ, is a *parameter* given by

$$\mu = \frac{\sum_{i=1}^{N} x_i}{N} = \frac{x_1 + x_2 + \cdots + x_N}{N} \tag{3.1}$$

where N = population size and Σ means "the sum of."

If the data set is from a sample, then the *sample mean*, $\bar{x}$, is a *statistic* given by

$$\bar{x} = \frac{\sum_{i=1}^{n} x_i}{n} = \frac{x_1 + x_2 + \cdots + x_n}{n} \tag{3.2}$$

where n = sample size and Σ means "the sum of."

To locate the *median*, we must arrange the data in either increasing or decreasing order.

Median

The **median** is the middle observation of a set of observations that are arranged in increasing (or decreasing) order. If the sample size, n, is an odd number, the median is the middle observation. If the sample size, n, is an even number, the median is the average of the two middle observations. The median will be located in the

$$0.50\,(n + 1)\text{th ordered position} \tag{3.3}$$

Mode

The **mode**, if one exists, is the most frequently occurring value.

Example 3.1 Times Needed to Walk a 5K Race (Measures of Central Tendency)

The Komen Race for the Cure® Series is the largest 5K run/fitness walk in the world. The Susan G. Komen Breast Cancer Foundation raises funds for and awareness of the fight to eradicate breast cancer; supports education, screening, and treatment projects in communities around the world; celebrates breast cancer survivorship, and honors those who have lost their battle with the disease (Reference 3). Find the measures of central tendency for a sample of five times (in minutes) participants needed to walk a recent Race for the Cure®:

$$45 \quad 53 \quad 45 \quad 50 \quad 48$$

Solution The sample mean time is

$$\bar{x} = \frac{\sum\limits_{i=1}^{n} x_i}{n} = \frac{45 + 53 + 45 + 50 + 48}{5} = 48.2$$

When we arrange the data in increasing order:

45   45   48   50   53

the median is 48; two numbers are less than 48 minutes and two numbers are greater than 48 minutes. Since the mean and the median are very close, it makes little difference which value we use to describe the center of the data. The mode is 45 minutes, since it occurs twice and all the other times occur only once. However, the mode in this case is the smallest value and is not the best indicator of central tendency. If the sample included a sixth participant's time of 53 minutes:

45   45   48   50   53   53

the median would be located in the $0.5(n + 1)$th position, or the 3.5th ordered observation, which would be 49 minutes. We see now that the data are bimodal, with modes 45 and 53.

The decision as to whether the mean, median, or mode is the appropriate measure to describe the central tendency of data is context-specific. One factor that influences our choice is the type of data, categorical or numerical, as discussed in Chapter 2. The mean is generally the preferred measure to describe numerical data, but not categorical data. If one person strongly agrees (coded 5) with a particular statement and another person strongly disagrees (coded 1), is the mean "no opinion"? Or suppose that a committee consists of two males (each coded as 1) and three females (each coded as 2). The arithmetic mean $[(1 + 1 + 2 + 2 + 2)/5 = 1.6]$ is meaningless. But the mode of 2 indicates more females than males are on this committee. Clearly, categorical data are best described by the mode or the median. Perhaps the most obvious use of the median and mode is by manufacturers who produce goods, such as clothing, in various sizes. The size of items sold most often, the mode, is then the one in heaviest demand. Knowing that the mean shirt size of European men is 41.13 or that the average shoe size of American women is 8.24 is useless, but knowing that the modal shirt size is 40 or the modal shoe size is 7 is valuable for inventory decisions. However, the mode may not represent the true center of numerical data. For this reason, the mode is used less frequently than either the mean or the median in business applications.

Example 3.2 Percentage Change in Earnings per Share (Measures of Central Tendency)

A random sample of eight U.S. corporations showed the following percentage changes in earnings per share in the current year compared with the previous year:

0%   0%   8.1%   13.6%   19.4%   20.7%   10.0%   14.2%

Solution   The mean percentage change in earnings per share for this sample is

$$\bar{x} = \frac{\sum\limits_{i=1}^{n} x_i}{n} = \frac{0 + 0 + 8.1 + 13.6 + \cdots + 14.2}{8} = 10.75 \qquad \text{or } 10.75\%$$

and the median percentage change in earnings per share is 11.8%. The mode is 0%, since it occurs twice and the other percentages occur only once. But this modal percentage rate does not represent the center of this sample data.

Another factor to consider is the presence of outliers. Whenever there are outliers in the data, we need to look for possible causes. First, check to see if an error in data entry occurred. The mean will be greater if large outliers are present, and it will be less when the data contain small outliers. The median is the preferred measure to describe the distribution of incomes in a city, state, or country. Since incomes usually contain a small proportion of very high values, the mean income will be higher. The median income, however, is the level of income or wealth exceeded by half the households in the population. Even though outliers influence the mean, we will see in Chapter 8 that certain properties of the mean make it more attractive than the median in many situations.

In spite of its advantage in discounting extreme observations, the median is used less frequently than the mean. The reason is that the theoretical development of inferential procedures based on the mean, and measures related to it, is considerably more straightforward than the development of procedures based on the median.

Shape of the Distribution

In Figure 2.10 of Chapter 2 we presented histograms that were **symmetric**, positively **skewed**, and negatively skewed. The mean and the median of a symmetric distribution are equal, since observations are balanced, or evenly distributed about the center. The mean of a positively skewed distribution will be greater than its median. The mean of a negatively skewed distribution will be less than its median.

Distributions of incomes or wealth of households in a city, state, or country tend to contain a relatively small proportion of high values. A large proportion of the population has relatively modest incomes, but the incomes of, say, the highest 10% of all earners extend over a considerable range. As a result, the mean of such distributions is typically quite a bit higher than the median. The mean, which is inflated by the very wealthy, gives too optimistic a view of the economic well-being of the community. The median is then preferred to the mean.

One possible source for skewness is the presence of outliers. Unusually large observations tend to increase the mean, possibly resulting in positive skewness. Similarly, if there are any unusually small observations in the data, the value of the mean will decrease, possibly leading to negative skewness. Sometimes skewness is simply inherent in the distribution. If skewness is zero or close to zero, the distribution is symmetric or approximately symmetric. A negative value of skewness tells us that the distribution is skewed to the left. Similarly, a positive value of skewness tells us that the distribution is skewed to the right.

Manual computation of skewness involves descriptive measures introduced later in this chapter. In Example 3.3 we will make use of technology, leaving further discussion of skewness to the Appendix of this chapter.

Example 3.3   Annual Salary (Skewness)

Annual salaries for a sample of five employees are

| $39,000 | $37,500 | $35,200 | $40,400 | $100,000 |

Describe the central tendency and symmetry of the data.

Solution   First, we check for data accuracy. Finding no error (the outlier of $100,000 is a correct salary), we calculate the mean annual salary as $50,420, a value that does not seem to represent a "typical" salary. The median salary of $39,000 is the preferred measure of central tendency. These data have no mode. Since the mean is much larger than the median, we expect the data to be positively skewed, which is confirmed in Figure 3.1, with skewness approximately equal to 2.21.

Figure 3.1
Skewness of Annual Salaries (Excel Output)

Annual Salaries	
Mean	**50420**
Standard Error	12424.91
Median	**39000**
Mode	#N/A
Standard Deviation	27782.94
Sample Variance	7.72E+08
Kurtosis	4.905059
Skewness	**2.209069**

We want to be careful to repeat that the choice of the measure of central tendency is context- or problem-specific. We do *not* intend to imply that the median should *always* be preferred to the mean when the population or sample is skewed. There are times when the mean would still be the preferred measure even if the distribution were skewed. Consider an insurance company that most likely faces a right-skewed distribution of claims. If the company wants to know the most typical claim size, the median is preferred. But suppose the company wants to know how much money needs to be budgeted to cover claims. Then the mean is preferred.

EXERCISES

Basic Exercises

3.1   A random sample of 5 weeks showed that a cruise agency received the following number of weekly specials to the Caribbean:

    20   73   75   80   82

   a. Compute the mean, median, and mode.
   b. Which measure of central tendency best describes the data?

3.2   A department store manager is interested in the number of complaints received by the customer service department about the quality of electrical products sold by the store. Records over a 5-week period show the following number of complaints for each week:

    13   15   8   16   8

   a. Compute the mean number of weekly complaints.
   b. Calculate the median number of weekly complaints.
   c. Find the mode.

3.3   Ten economists were asked to predict the percentage growth in the Consumer Price Index over the next year. Their forecasts were

3.6	3.1	3.9	3.7	3.5
3.7	3.4	3.0	3.7	3.4

a. Compute the sample mean.
b. Compute the sample median.
c. What is the mode?

3.4 A department store chain randomly sampled 10 stores in a state. After a review of sales records, it was found that, compared with the same period last year, the following percentage increases in dollar sales had been achieved over the Christmas period this year:

10.2	3.1	5.9	7.0	3.7
2.9	6.8	7.3	8.2	4.3

a. Calculate the mean percentage increase in dollar sales.
b. Calculate the median.
c. Comment on symmetry.

3.5 A sample of 12 senior executives found the following results for percentage of total compensation derived from bonus payments:

15.8	17.3	28.4	18.2	15.0	24.7
13.1	10.2	29.3	34.7	16.9	25.3

a. Compute the sample median.
b. Compute the sample mean.

3.6 The demand for bottled water increases during the hurricane season in Florida. A random sample of 7 hours showed that the following numbers of 1-gallon bottles were sold in one store:

40	55	62	43	50	60	65

a. Describe the central tendency of the data.
b. Comment on symmetry or skewness.

3.7 A manufacturer of portable radios obtained a sample of 50 radios from a week's output. The radios were thoroughly checked, and the number of defects was recorded as follows:

Number of defects	0	1	2	3
Number of radios	12	15	17	6

Find the measures of central tendency.

3.8 The ages of a sample of 12 students enrolled in an on-line macroeconomics course are

21	22	27	36	18	19
22	23	22	28	36	33

a. What is the mean age for this sample?
b. Find the median age.
c. What is the modal age?

Application Exercises

3.9 ⊚ The assessment rates (in percentages) assigned to a random sample of 40 commercially zoned parcels of land in the year 2005 are contained in the data file **Rates**.

a. Compute the mean, median, and modal percentage assessment rates.
b. Describe the symmetry or skewness of the data.

3.10 ⊚ A sample of 33 accounting students recorded the number of hours spent studying the course material during the week before the final exam. The data are stored in the data file **Study**.

a. Compute the sample mean.
b. Compute the sample median.
c. Comment on symmetry or skewness.

3.11 ⊚ The data file **Sun** contains the volumes for a random sample of 100 bottles (237 mL) of a new suntan lotion.

a. Find and interpret the mean volume.
b. Determine the median volume.
c. Are the data symmetric or skewed? Explain.

3.2 MEASURES OF VARIABILITY

The mean alone does not provide a complete or sufficient description of data. In this section we present descriptive numbers that measure the variability or spread of the observations from the mean. In particular, we include the range, interquartile range, variance, standard deviation, and coefficient of variation. We will also describe data numerically by the five-number summary, with a brief discussion of basic rules to help us determine the percentage of observations within varying distances of the mean.

No two things are exactly alike. This is one of the basic principles of statistical quality control. Variation exists in all areas. In sports, the star basketball player might score five 3-pointers in one game and none in the next, or he may play 40 minutes in one game and only 24 minutes in the next. Variation is obvious in the music industry; the weather varies greatly from day to day, and even from hour to hour; grades on a test differ for students taking the same course with the same instructor; a person's blood pressure, pulse, cholesterol level, and caloric intake will vary daily.

While two data sets could have the same mean, the individual observations in one set could vary more from the mean than do the observations in the second set. Consider the following two sets of sample data:

Sample A	1	2	1	36
Sample B	8	9	10	13

Although the mean is 10 for both samples, clearly, the data in sample A are further from 10 than are the data in sample B. We need descriptive numbers to measure this spread.

Range and Interquartile Range

Range
Range is the difference between the largest and smallest observations.

The greater the spread of the data from the center of the distribution, the larger the range will be. Since the range takes into account only the largest and smallest observations, it is susceptible to considerable distortion if there is an unusual extreme observation. Although the range measures the *total* spread of the data, the range may be an unsatisfactory measure of variability (spread) because outliers, either very high or very low observations, influence it. One way to avoid this difficulty is to arrange the data in ascending or descending order, discard a few of the highest and a few of the lowest numbers, and find the range of those remaining. The *interquartile range* measures the spread of the middle 50% of the data.

Interquartile Range
The **Interquartile range (*IQR*)** measures the spread in the *middle 50%* of the data; it is the difference between the observation at Q_3, the **third quartile** (or 75th **percentile**), and the observation at Q_1, the **first quartile** (or 25th *percentile*). Thus,

$$IQR = Q_3 - Q_1 \tag{3.4}$$

where Q_3 is located in the $0.75(n + 1)$th position when the data are in increasing order and Q_1 is located in the $0.25(n + 1)$th position when the data are in increasing order.

From Equation 3.3 we have already seen that the median is the 50th percentile, or the second quartile (Q_2), and is located in the $0.50(n + 1)$th ordered position.

Five-Number Summary
The **five-number summary** refers to the five descriptive measures: minimum, first quartile, median, third quartile, and maximum. Clearly,

$$\text{Minimum} < Q_1 < \text{Median} < Q_3 < \text{Maximum}$$

Example 3.4 Waiting Times at Gilotti's Grocery (Five-Number Summary)

Gilotti's Grocery advertises that customers wait less than 1 minute to pay if they go through the Speedy Transaction Aisles. Figure 3.2 is a stem-and-leaf display for a sample of 25 waiting times (in seconds). Compute the five-number summary.

Figure 3.2	Stem-and-leaf										
Waiting Times at	Minutes N = 25										
Gilotti's Grocery	Leaf Unit = 1.0										
	9	1 1 2 4 6 7 8 8 9 9									
	(9)	2 1 2 2 2 4 6 8 9 9									
	7	3 0 1 2 3 4									
	2	4 0 2									

Solution From the stem-and-leaf display we see that the minimum time is 11 seconds and the maximum time is 42 seconds. The first quartile, Q_1, is located in the 0.25(25 + 1)th ordered position = 6.5th ordered position. The value is 18 seconds. The third quartile, Q_3, is located in the .75(25 + 1)th ordered position = 19.5th ordered position. The value is 30.5 seconds. The median time is 22 seconds. The range is calculated as 42 – 11 = 31 seconds; interquartile range = 30.5 – 18 = 12.5 seconds; that is, the *middle 50%* of the data have a spread of only 12.5 seconds.

Variance and Standard Deviation

Although range and interquartile range measure the spread of data, both measures take into account only two of the data values. We need a measure that considers each of the data values. Such a measure would *average* the total (Σ) distance between each observation and the mean. This distance would be negative for values smaller than the mean (and distance is not negative). If each of these differences is squared, $(x_i - \bar{x})^2$, then each observation (both above and below the mean) contributes to the sum of the squared terms. The average of the sum of squared terms is called the *variance*.

Variance

With respect to **variance**, the *population variance*, σ^2, is the sum of the squared differences between each observation and the population mean divided by the population size, N:

$$\sigma^2 = \frac{\sum_{i=1}^{N}(x_i - \mu)^2}{N} \tag{3.5}$$

The *sample variance*, s^2, is the sum of the squared differences between each observation and the sample mean divided by the sample size, n, minus 1.

$$s^2 = \frac{\sum_{i=1}^{n}(x_i - \bar{x})^2}{n-1} \tag{3.6}$$

Notice that, for sample data, variance in Equation 3.6 is found by dividing the numerator by $(n-1)$ and not n. Since our goal is to find an average of squared deviations about the mean, one would expect division by n. So why is sample variance found by division of $(n-1)$? If we were to take a very large number of samples, each of size n, from the population and compute the sample variance, as given in Equation 3.6 for each of these samples, then the average of all of these sample variances would be the population variance, σ^2. In Chapter 8 we will see that this property indicates that the sample variance is an "unbiased estimator" of the population variance, σ^2. For now, we rely on mathematical statisticians who have shown that, if the population variance is unknown, a sample variance is a better estimator of the population variance if the denominator in the sample variance is $(n-1)$, rather than n.

To compute the variance requires squaring the distances, which then changes the unit of measurement to square units. The *standard deviation*, which is the square root of variance, restores the data to their original measurement unit. If the original measurements were in feet, the variance would be in feet squared, but the standard deviation would be in feet. The standard deviation measures the *average* spread around the mean.

Standard Deviation

With respect to **standard deviation**, the population *standard deviation*, σ, is the (positive) square root of the population variance and is defined as

$$\sigma = \sqrt{\sigma^2} = \sqrt{\frac{\sum_{i=1}^{N}(x_i - \mu)^2}{N}} \tag{3.7}$$

The *sample standard deviation, s*, is

$$s = \sqrt{s^2} = \sqrt{\frac{\sum_{i=1}^{n}(x_i - \bar{x})^2}{n-1}} \tag{3.8}$$

Example 3.5   Test Grades in an Introductory Marketing Class (Measures of Variability)

A professor teaches two large sections of introductory marketing and randomly selects a sample of test scores from both sections. Find the range and standard deviation for each sample:

Section 1	50	60	70	80	90
Section 2	72	68	70	74	66

Solution   Although the average grade for both sections is 70, we notice that the grades in section 2 are closer to the mean, 70, than are the grades in section 1. And just as we would expect, the range of section 1, 40, is larger than the range of section 2, which is 8.

Similarly, we would expect the standard deviation for section 1 to be greater than the standard deviation for section 2.

$$s_1 = \sqrt{s_1^2} = \sqrt{\frac{(50-70)^2 + (60-70)^2 + (70-70)^2 + (80-70)^2 + (90-70)^2}{4}}$$

$$= \sqrt{250} = 15.8$$

$$s_2 = \sqrt{s_2^2} = \sqrt{\frac{(72-70)^2 + (68-70)^2 + (70-70)^2 + (74-70)^2 + (66-70)^2}{4}}$$

$$= \sqrt{10} = 3.16$$

Example 3.6 illustrates one application of standard deviation in the area of finance.

Example 3.6   Risk of a Single Asset (Standard Deviation)

Wes and Jennie Moore, owners of Moore's Foto Shop in western Pennsylvania, are considering two investment alternatives, asset A and asset B. They are not sure which of these two single assets is better, and they ask Sheila Newton, a financial planner, for some assistance.

Solution   Sheila knows that the standard deviation, s, is the most common single indicator of the risk or variability of a single asset. In financial situations the fluctuation around a stock's actual rate of return and its expected rate of return is called the *risk* of the stock. The standard deviation measures the variation of returns around an asset's mean. Sheila obtains the rates of return on each asset for the last five years and calculates the means and standard deviations of each asset. The results are shown in Table 3.1. Notice that each asset has the same average rate of return of 12.2%. However, once Sheila obtains the standard deviations, it becomes apparent that asset B is a more risky investment.

Table 3.1   Rates of Return: Assets A and B

	RATES OF RETURN	
YEAR	ASSET A	ASSET B
5 years ago	11.3%	9.4%
4 years ago	12.5	17.1
3 years ago	13.0	13.3
2 years ago	12.0	10.0
1 year ago	12.2	11.2
Total	61.0	61.0
Average rate of return	12.2%	12.2%
Standard deviation	**0.63**	**3.12**

Chebychev's Theorem and the Empirical Rule

A Russian mathematician, Pafnuty Lvovich Chebychev (1821–1894), established data intervals for any data set, *regardless* of the shape of the distribution.

Chebychev's Theorem

For any population with mean μ, standard deviation σ, and $k > 1$, the percent of observations that lie within the interval $[\mu \pm k\sigma]$ is

$$at\ least\ 100\left[1 - \left(1/k^2\right)\right]\% \qquad (3.9)$$

where k is the number of standard deviations.

To see how Chebychev's theorem works in practice, we construct Table 3.2 for selected values of k. Suppose that the mean grade on an exam is 72, with a standard deviation of 4. According to Chebychev's theorem, at least 75% of the scores are in the interval between 64 and 80, and at least 88.9% of the scores are in the interval between 60 and 84. Or suppose that the mean salary for a sample of workers is $33,500 and the standard deviation is $1,554. By Chebychev's theorem at least 55.6% of the salaries must fall within (1.5) ($1,554) = $2,331 around the mean—that is, within the range $31,169 to $35,831. Similarly, at least 75% of the salaries in this population must fall within $3,108 around the mean—that is, within the range $30,392 to $36,608.

The advantage of Chebychev's theorem is that its applicability extends to any population. However, it is within this guarantee that its major drawback lies. For many populations the percentage of values falling in any specified range is much higher than the *minimum* assured by Chebychev's theorem. In the real world many large populations provide mounded data that is at least approximately symmetric, with many of the data points clustered around the mean. We will discuss in Chapter 6 a more exact formula, but for now we will only introduce a rule that applies to many mounded distributions.

Empirical Rule (68%, 95%, or Almost All)

For many large populations the **empirical rule** provides an estimate of the approximate percentage of observations that are contained within one, two, or three standard deviations of the mean:

- Approximately **68%** of the observations are in the interval $\mu \pm 1\sigma$.
- Approximately **95%** of the observations are in the interval $\mu \pm 2\sigma$.
- Almost all of the observations are in the interval $\mu \pm 3\sigma$.

Suppose that we have a large population of salaries with a mean of $33,500 and a standard deviation of $1,554. Then by the empirical rule we estimate that roughly 68% of the salaries are between $31,946 and $35,054 and that approximately 95% fall within the range $30,392 to $36,608. There is only a relatively small chance that an observation will differ from the mean by more than $\pm 2\sigma$; any observation that differs from the mean by more than $\pm 3\sigma$ is an outlier.

Table 3.2   Chebychev's Theorem for Selected Values of k

Selected Values of k	1.5	2	2.5	3
$[1 - (1/k^2)]\%$	55.6%	75%	84%	88.9%

Example 3.7 Shipping Times (Chebychev's Theorem and the Empirical Rule)

A group of 13 students is studying in Istanbul, Turkey, for five weeks. As part of their study of the local economy, they each purchased an Oriental rug and arranged for its shipment back to the United States. The shipping time, in days, for each rug was

31	31	42	39	42	43	34
30	28	36	37	35	40	

Estimate the percentage of days that are within two standard deviations of the mean. Is it likely to take 2 months for a delivery?

Solution   The mean is 36 days, and the standard deviation is approximately 5 days. By Chebychev's theorem at least 75% of the delivery times would be between 26 and 46 days. We find that the median is also 36. The empirical rule is preferred, giving the result that, approximately 95% of the time, it will take between 26 and 46 days for delivery. It is unlikely that it would take 2 months for a delivery, as 60 days would be an extreme outlier.

Coefficient of Variation

The *coefficient of variation* expresses the standard deviation as a percentage of the mean.

Coefficient of Variation

The **coefficient of variation, CV**, is a measure of relative dispersion that expresses the standard deviation as a percentage of the mean (provided the mean is positive).

The *population coefficient of variation* is

$$CV = \frac{\sigma}{\mu} \times 100\% \qquad \text{if } \mu > 0 \tag{3.10}$$

The *sample coefficient of variation* is

$$CV = \frac{s}{\bar{x}} \times 100\% \qquad \text{if } \bar{x} > 0 \tag{3.11}$$

If the standard deviations in sales for large and small stores selling similar goods are compared, the standard deviation for large stores will almost always be greater. A simple explanation is that a large store could be modeled as a number of small stores. Comparing variation using the standard deviation would be misleading. The coefficient of variation overcomes this problem by adjusting for the scale of units in the population.

Example 3.8 Stock Purchase Comparison (Coefficient of Variation)

In Example 3.6 two different investments with the same mean rate of return were considered. Now, the owners are considering purchasing shares of stock A or shares of stock B, both listed on the New York Stock Exchange. From the closing prices of both stocks over the last several months the standard deviations were found to be considerably different, with $s_A = \$2.00$ and $s_B = \$8.00$. Should stock A be purchased, since the standard deviation of stock B is larger?

Solution We might think that stock B is more volatile than stock A. The mean closing prices for the two stocks are $\bar{x}_A = \$4.00$ and $\bar{x}_B = \$80.00$. Next, the coefficients of variation are computed to measure and compare the risk of these competing investment opportunities:

$$CV_A = \frac{\$2.00}{\$4.00} \times 100\% = 50\% \quad \text{and} \quad CV_B = \frac{\$8.00}{\$80.00} \times 100\% = 10\%$$

Notice that the market value of stock A fluctuates more from period to period than does that of stock B.

For large data sets we recommend using the computer to obtain the numerical measures discussed in this chapter. We conclude this section by considering again mobile phone usage (see Example 2.6) and the data stored in the data file **Mobile Usage**.

Mobile Usage

Example 3.9 Mobile Phone Usage (Computer Output)

Records of minutes used by a sample of 110 subscribers to a mobile phone company's low-end user plan (250 peak minutes per month) are stored in the data file **Mobile Usage** (see Example 2.6). Describe the data numerically.

Solution To describe the data numerically, we calculate the mean, median, mode, range, variance, standard deviation, skewness, coefficient of variation, and five-number summary. The mean of 261 minutes is slightly less than the median of 263 minutes, and from Figure 3.3 skewness is close to 0. The modal time is

Figure 3.3
Mobile Phone Usage
(Excel Output)

Minutes Used	
Mean	**261.0636**
Standard Error	1.669741
Median	263
Mode	252
Standard Deviation	**17.5124**
Sample Variance	**306.684**
Kurtosis	−0.33805
Skewness	**0.001613**
Range	77
Minimum	222
Maximum	299
Sum	28717
Count	110

252 minutes, and the data range from a high of 299 minutes to a low of 222 minutes. The standard deviation is 17.5 minutes. Figure 3.4 includes the coefficient of variation, five-number summary, and interquartile range.

Figure 3.4 Mobile Phone Usage (Minitab Output)

Descriptive Statistics: Minutes/April

Variable	N	N*	Mean	SE Mean	StDev	Variance	CoefVar	Minimum
Minutes	110	0	261.06	1.67	17.51	306.68	6.71	222.00

Variable	Q1	Median	Q3	Maximum	Range	IQR	Skewness
Minutes	251.75	263.00	271.25	299.00	77.00	19.50	0.00

EXERCISES

Basic Exercises

3.12 Compute the variance and standard deviation of the following sample data:

6   8   7   10   3   5   9   8

3.13 Compute the variance and standard deviation of the following sample data:

3   0   −2   −1   5   10

3.14 Calculate the coefficient of variation for the following sample data:

10   8   11   7   9

3.15 The time (in seconds) that a random sample of employees took to complete a task is

23	35	14	37	28	45
12	40	27	13	26	25
37	20	29	49	40	13
27	16	40	20	13	66

a. Find the mean time.
b. Find the standard deviation.
c. Find the five-number summary.
d. Find the coefficient of variation.

3.16 The following stem-and-leaf display contains sample data:

Stem unit:

3	0 1
4	5 8 8
5	0 3 4 5 7 8 9
6	1 4 7 9
7	3 6 9
8	0 3 7

a. Calculate *IQR*.
b. Find the 8th decile.
c. Find the 92nd percentile.

3.17 A random sample of data has a mean of 75 and a variance of 25.

a. Use Chebychev's theorem to determine the percent of observations between 65 and 85.
b. If the data are mounded, use the empirical rule to find the approximate percent of observations between 65 and 85.

3.18 Use Chebychev's theorem to approximate each of the following observations if the mean is 250 and the standard deviation of 20. Approximately what proportion of the observations is

a. Between 190 and 310?
b. Between 210 and 290?
c. Between 230 and 270?

3.19 A set of data is mounded, with a mean of 450 and a variance of 625. Approximately what proportion of the observations is

a. Greater than 425?
b. Less than 500?
c. Greater than 525?

Application Exercises

3.20 The annual percentage returns on common stocks over a 7-year period were as follows:

4.0%   14.3%   19.0%   −14.7%   −26.5%   37.2%   23.8%

Over the same period the annual percentage returns on U.S. Treasury bills were as follows:

6.5%   4.4%   3.8%   6.9%   8.0%   5.8%   5.1%

a. Compare the means of these two population distributions.
b. Compare the standard deviations of these two population distributions.

3.21 A sample of eight U.S. corporations showed the following percentage changes in earnings per share in the current year compared with the previous year:

13.6%	25.5%	43.6%	−19.8%
12.0%	36.3%	14.3%	−13.8%

Find the sample mean percentage change in earnings per share.

3.22 ● The operations manager at a plant that bottles natural spring water wants to be sure that the filling process for 1-gallon bottles is operating properly. A random sample of 75 bottles is selected and the contents are measured. The volume of each bottle is contained in the data file **Water**.

a. Find the range, variance, and standard deviation of the volumes.
b. Find the five-number summary of the volumes.
c. Find and interpret the interquartile range for the data.
d. Find the value of the coefficient of variation.

3.23 ● The test scores of 40 students are stored in the data file **Scores**.

a. Find the mean grade on this test.
b. Find the standard deviation in test scores.
c. Find the coefficient of variation.
d. Find and interpret the interquartile range.

3.24 ● The assessment rates (in percentages) assigned to a random sample of 40 commercially zoned parcels of land in the year 2005 are stored in the data file **Rates**.

a. What is the standard deviation in the assessment rates?
b. Approximately what proportion of the rates will be within ± 2 standard deviations of the mean?

3.25 ● Calculate the mean dollar amount and the standard deviation for the dollar amounts charged to a Visa account at Florin's Flower Shop. Data are stored in the data file **Florin**.

3.3 WEIGHTED MEAN AND MEASURES OF GROUPED DATA

Some situations require a special type of mean called a *weighted mean*.

Weighted Mean
The **weighted mean** of a set of data is

$$\bar{x} = \frac{\sum\limits_{i=1}^{n} w_i x_i}{\sum w_i} = \frac{w_1 x_1 + w_2 x_2 + \cdots + w_n x_n}{\sum w_i} \tag{3.12}$$

where w_i = weight of ith observation.

One important situation that requires the use of a weighted mean is the calculation of grade point average (GPA).

Example 3.10   Grade Point Average (Weighted Mean)

Suppose that a student who completed 15 credit hours during his first semester of college received one A, one B, one C, and one D. Suppose that a value of 4 is used for an A, 3 for a B, 2 for a C, 1 for a D, and 0 for an F. Calculate the student's semester GPA.

Solution   GPA calculated by the simple mean is

$$\bar{x} = \frac{\sum\limits_{i=1}^{n} x_i}{n} = \frac{x_1 + x_2 + \cdots + x_n}{n} = \frac{4 + 3 + 2 + 1}{4} = 2.5$$

Table 3.3 Semester Academic Record

Course	Grade	Value	Credit Hours	(Value) × Credit Hours
English	A	4	3	12
Math	B	3	3	9
Biology lab	C	2	4	8
Spanish	D	1	5	5
Total			15	34

But this is not the correct GPA. In computing simple mean we assume that each course is of equal importance or "weight," but this assumption ignores the fact that the number of credit hours are not the same for all courses. That is, the A was earned in a *three*-credit-hour English course, and the B was earned in a *three*-credit-hour math course, but the C was earned in a *four*-credit-hour biology lab course, and the D grade, unfortunately, was earned in a *five*-credit-hour Spanish class. This information is summarized in Table 3.3.

Using the credit hours as weights—that is, w_i = number of credit hours, and, $\Sigma w_i = 15$, the correct GPA is 2.267 and not 2.5.

$$\bar{x} = \frac{\sum_{i=1}^{n} w_i x_i}{\sum w_i} = \frac{w_1 x_1 + w_2 x_2 + \cdots + w_n x_n}{\sum w_i} = \frac{3(4) + 3(3) + 4(2) + 5(1)}{15} = \frac{34}{15} = 2.267$$

Per capita personal income is total personal income divided by total midyear population. Economists use a weighted mean to calculate the *average* per capita personal income for a given year. Data concerning personal income, income and employment, and state economic profiles are available through the Bureau of Economic Analysis Regional Economic Information System (www.bea.doc.gov). Midyear population estimates are based on data provided by the Bureau of the Census.

Example 3.11 Per Capita Personal Income 2002 (Weighted Mean)

Population size and per capita personal income for a random sample of five states are given in Table 3.4. Calculate the mean per capita personal income for 2002 (References 1, 2).

Solution Since the population size varies for each state, the mean per capita personal income for 2002 is calculated by a weighted mean, using the state populations as the weights.

$$\text{Weighted Mean:} \frac{\sum_{i=1}^{n} w_i x_i}{\sum w_i} = \frac{35,001,986(\$32,989) + \cdots + 616,408(\$29,764)}{57,968,797}$$
$$= \$31.986.12$$

Table 3.4 Population and Per Capita Personal Income, 2002

STATE	POPULATION	PER CAPITA PERSONAL INCOME
California	35,001,986	$ 32,989
Florida	16,691,701	29,758
Minnesota	5,024,791	33,322
North Dakota	633,911	26,852
Vermont	616,408	29,764
Total	57,968,797	$ 152,685

Thus, the mean per capita personal income for 2002 is $31,986.12 and not $30,537, as calculated by a simple arithmetic mean.

A survey may ask respondents to select an age category such as "18 to 25," rather than giving their specific age. In these situations *exact* values of the mean and variance are not possible. However, we are able to approximate the mean and the variance.

Approximate Mean and Variance for Grouped Data

Suppose that data are grouped into K classes, with frequencies $f_1, f_2, \ldots, f_K$. If the midpoints of these classes are $m_1, m_2, \ldots, m_K$, then the population mean and population variance of the grouped data are estimated in the following manner:

(a) For a *population* of N observations, so that

$$N = \sum_{i=1}^{K} f_i$$

the mean is

$$\mu = \frac{\sum_{i=1}^{K} f_i m_i}{N} \tag{3.13}$$

and the variance is

$$\sigma^2 = \frac{\sum_{i=1}^{K} f_i (m_i - \mu)^2}{N} \tag{3.14}$$

(b) For a *sample* of n observations, so that

$$n = \sum_{i=1}^{K} f_i$$

the mean is

$$\bar{x} = \frac{\sum_{i=1}^{K} f_i m_i}{n} \tag{3.15}$$

and the variance is

$$s^2 = \frac{\sum_{i=1}^{K} f_i(m_i - \bar{x})^2}{n - 1} \tag{3.16}$$

Example 3.12   Chemical Tested for Concentration of Impurities (Mean and Variance for Grouped Values)

A sample of 20 batches of a chemical was tested for concentration of impurities. The results obtained were

Percentage impurities	0 < 2	2 < 4	4 < 6	6 < 8	8 < 10
Batches	2	3	6	5	4

Find the sample mean and standard deviation of these percentage impurity levels.

Solution   The computations are set out in Table 3.5.

Table 3.5   Chemical Batches (Grouped Data Computation)

CLASSES	m_i	f_i	$m_i f_i$	$(m_i - \bar{x})$	$(m_i - \bar{x})^2$	$f_i(m_i - \bar{x})^2$
0 < 2	1	2	2	−4.6	21.16	42.32
2 < 4	3	3	9	−2.6	6.76	20.28
4 < 6	5	6	30	−0.6	0.36	2.16
6 < 8	7	5	35	1.4	1.96	9.8
8 < 10	9	4	36	3.4	11.56	46.24
	Sums	20	112			120.8

From Table 3.5,

$$\sum_{i=1}^{K} f_i = n = 20 \qquad \sum_{i=1}^{K} f_i m_i = 112$$

The sample mean is estimated by

$$\bar{x} = \frac{\sum_{i=1}^{K} f_i m_i}{n} = \frac{112}{20} = 5.6$$

Since these are sample data, the variance is estimated by

$$s^2 = \frac{\sum_{i=1}^{K} f_i(m_i - \bar{x})^2}{n - 1} = \frac{120.8}{19} = 6.3579$$

Hence, the sample standard deviation is estimated as

$$s = \sqrt{s^2} = \sqrt{6.3579} = 2.52$$

Therefore, for this sample the mean impurity concentration is estimated to be 5.6%, and the sample standard deviation is estimated to be 2.52%.

EXERCISES

Basic Exercises

3.26 Consider the following sample of five values and corresponding weights:

x_i	w_i
4.6	8
3.2	3
5.4	6
2.6	2
5.2	5

a. Calculate the arithmetic mean of the x_i values without weights.
b. Calculate the weighted mean of the x_i values.

3.27 Consider the following frequency distribution for a sample of 40 observations:

Class	Frequency
0–4	5
5–9	8
10–14	11
15–19	9
20–24	7

a. Calculate the sample mean.
b. Calculate the sample variance and sample standard deviation.

Application Exercises

3.28 Find the weighted mean per capita personal income for the following random sample of seven states for 2003 (References 1, 2):

State	Population	Per Capita Personal Income
Alabama	4,500,752	26,338
Georgia	8,684,715	29,442
Illinois	12,653,544	33,690
Indiana	6,195,643	28,783
New York	19,190,115	36,574
Pennsylvania	12,365,455	31,998
Tennessee	5,841,748	28,455

3.29 A manufacturer of portable radios obtained a sample of 50 radios from a week's output. The radios were thoroughly checked and the number of defects was recorded as follows:

Number of defects	0	1	2	3
Number of radios	12	15	17	6

Calculate the standard deviation.

3.30 A random sample of 50 personal property insurance policies showed the following number of claims over the past two years.

Number of claims	0	1	2	3	4	5	6
Number of policies	21	13	5	4	2	3	2

a. Find the mean number of claims per day.
b. Find the sample variance and standard deviation.

3.31 For a random sample of 25 students from a large class, the accompanying table shows the amount of time (in hours) spent studying for a test.

Study time	$0 < 4$	$4 < 8$	$8 < 12$	$12 < 16$	$16 < 20$
Number of students	3	7	8	5	2

a. Estimate the sample mean study time.
b. Estimate the sample standard deviation.

3.32 A sample of 20 financial analysts was asked to provide forecasts of earnings per share of a corporation for next year. The results are summarized in the following table:

Forecast ($ per share)	$9.95 < 10.45$	$10.45 < 10.95$	$10.95 < 11.45$	$11.45 < 11.95$	$11.95 < 12.45$
Number of analysts	2	8	6	3	1

a. Estimate the sample mean forecast.
b. Estimate the sample standard deviation.

3.33 A publisher receives from a printer a copy of a 500-page textbook. The page proofs are carefully read, and the number of errors on each page is recorded, producing the data in the following table:

Number of errors	0	1	2	3	4	5
Number of pages	102	138	140	79	33	8

Find the mean and standard deviation in number of errors per page.

3.34 The mean and standard deviation of minutes used by a random sample of mobile phone customers were calculated in Example 3.9. Now calculate and compare the mean and standard deviation based only on the frequency distribution given in Table 2.6.

3.4 MEASURES OF RELATIONSHIPS BETWEEN VARIABLES

We introduced scatter plots in Chapter 2 as a graphical way to describe a relationship between two variables. In this section we introduce *covariance* and *correlation*, numerical ways to describe a linear relationship, giving more attention to these concepts in Chapters 12 to 14. Covariance is a measure of the *direction* of a linear relationship between two variables.

Covariance

Covariance (Cov) is a measure of the linear relationship between two variables. A positive value indicates a direct or increasing linear relationship, and a negative value indicates a decreasing linear relationship.

A *population covariance* is

$$Cov(x, y) = \sigma_{xy} = \frac{\sum_{i=1}^{N} (x_i - \mu_x)(y_i - \mu_y)}{N} \quad (3.17)$$

where x_i and y_i are the observed values, μ_x and μ_y are the population means, and N is the populations size.

A *sample covariance* is

$$Cov(x, y) = s_{xy} = \frac{\sum_{i=1}^{n} (x_i - \bar{x})(y_i - \bar{y})}{n - 1} \quad (3.18)$$

where x_i and y_i are the observed values, $\bar{x}$ and $\bar{y}$ are the sample means, and n is the sample size.

The sample correlation coefficient will give us a standardized measure of the linear relationship between two variables. It is generally a more useful measure, as it provides both the *direction* and the *strength* of a relationship. The covariance and corresponding correlation coefficient have the same sign (both are positive or both are negative).

Correlation Coefficient

The **correlation coefficient** is computed by dividing the covariance by the product of the standard deviations of the two variables.

A *population correlation coefficient*, ρ, is

$$\rho = \frac{Cov(x, y)}{\sigma_x \sigma_y} \quad (3.19)$$

where σ_x and σ_y are the population standard deviations of the two variables.

A *sample correlation coefficient, r,* is

$$r = \frac{Cov(x, y)}{s_x s_y}$$ (3.20)

where s_x and s_y are the sample standard deviations of the two variables. A useful rule of thumb is that a relationship exists if

$$|r| \geq \frac{2}{\sqrt{n}}$$ (3.21)

The correlation coefficient ranges from –1 to +1. The closer r is to +1, the closer the data points are to an increasing straight line indicating a *positive* linear relationship. The closer r is to –1, the closer the data points are to a decreasing straight line indicating a *negative* linear relationship. When $r = 0$, there is no *linear* relationship between x and y but not necessarily a lack of relationship. In Chapter 2 we presented scatter plots as a graphical measure to determine relationship. Figure 3.5 presents some examples of scatter plots and their corresponding correlation coefficients. Figure 3.6 is a plot of quarterly sales for a major retail company. Note that sales vary by quarter of the year, reflecting consumers' purchasing patterns. The correlation coefficient between the time variable and quarterly sales is zero. We can see a very definite seasonal relationship, but the relationship is not linear.

Figure 3.5   Scatter Plots and Correlation

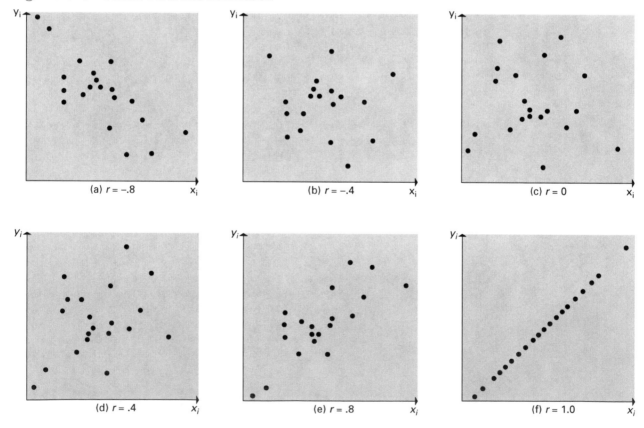

Figure 3.6
Retail Sales by
Quarter

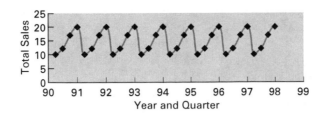

Rising Hills

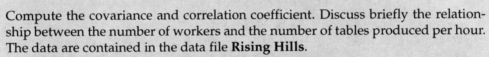

Example 3.13 Manufacturing Plant (Covariance and Correlation Coefficient)

Rising Hills Manufacturing Inc. wishes to study the relationship between the number of workers, X, and the number of tables, Y, produced in its Redwood Falls plant. It has obtained a random sample of 10 hours of production. The following (x, y) combinations of points were obtained:

(12,20)   (30,60)   (15,27)   (24,50)   (14,21)
(18,30)   (28,61)   (26,54)   (19,32)   (27,57)

Compute the covariance and correlation coefficient. Discuss briefly the relationship between the number of workers and the number of tables produced per hour. The data are contained in the data file **Rising Hills**.

Solution   The computations are set out in the Table 3.6.

Table 3.6 Computations for Covariance and Correlation

x	y	$(x_i - \bar{x})$	$(x_i - \bar{x})^2$	$(y_i - \bar{y})$	$(y_i - \bar{y})^2$	$(x_i - \bar{x})(y_i - \bar{y})$
12	20	−9.3	86.49	−21.2	449.44	197.16
30	60	8.7	75.69	18.8	353.44	163.56
15	27	−6.3	39.69	−14.2	201.64	89.46
24	50	2.7	7.29	8.8	77.44	23.76
14	21	−7.3	53.29	−20.2	408.04	147.46
18	30	−3.3	10.89	−11.2	125.44	36.96
28	61	6.7	44.89	19.8	392.04	132.66
26	54	4.7	22.09	12.8	163.84	60.16
19	32	−2.3	5.29	−9.2	84.64	21.16
27	57	5.7	32.49	15.8	249.64	90.06
Σ = 213	**Σ = 412**		**Σ = 378.1**		**Σ = 2505.6**	**Σ = 962.4**

From Equation 3.18,

$$Cov(x, y) = s_{xy} = \frac{\sum_{i=1}^{n}(x_i - \bar{x})(y_i - \bar{y})}{n-1} = \frac{962.4}{9} = 106.93$$

From Equation 3.20,

$$r = \frac{Cov(x, y)}{s_x s_y} = \frac{106.93}{\sqrt{42.01}\sqrt{278.4}} = 0.989$$

From Equation 3.21,

$$|0.989| \geq \frac{2}{\sqrt{10}} \cong 0.64$$

We conclude that there is a strong positive relationship between number of workers and number of tables produced per hour.

Example 3.14   Analysis of Stock Portfolios (Correlation Coefficient Analysis)

Alice Wong, financial analyst for Integrated Securities, is considering a number of different stocks for a new mutual fund she is developing. One of her questions concerns the correlation coefficients between prices of different stocks. To determine the patterns of stock prices, she prepared a series of scatter plots and computed the sample correlation coefficient for each plot. What information does Figure 3.7 provide Alice?

Solution   Alice sees that it is possible to control the variation in the average mutual fund price by combining various stocks into a portfolio. The portfolio variation is increased if stocks with positive correlation coefficients are included because the prices tend to increase together. In contrast, the portfolio variation is decreased if stocks with negative correlation coefficients are included. When the

Figure 3.7   Relationships Between Various Stock Prices

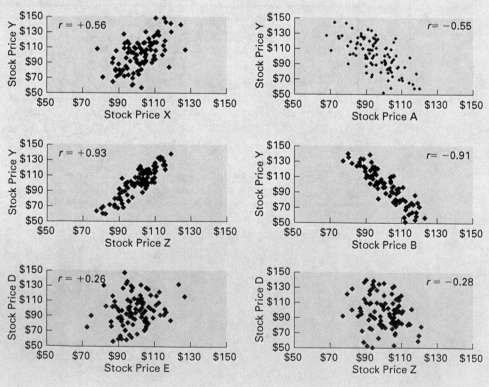

price of one stock increases, the price of the other decreases, and the combined price is more stable. Experienced observers of stock prices might question the possibility of very large negative correlation coefficients. Our objective here is to illustrate graphically the correlation coefficients for certain patterns of observed data and not to accurately describe a particular market. After examining these correlation coefficients, Alice is ready to begin constructing her portfolio. In Chapter 6 we will show precisely how correlation coefficients between stock prices affect the variation of the entire portfolio.

Minitab, Excel, SPSS, SAS, and many other statistical packages can be used to compute descriptive measures such as the sample covariance and the sample correlation coefficient. Figure 3.8 is the Minitab output for covariance and correlation.

Special care must be taken if we use Excel to compute covariance. Notice that the value in the Excel output in Figure 3.9 gives covariance = 96.24; yet we know that sample covariance = 106.93 for this data. Excel (XP or 2000) automatically calculates the population covariance as stated in Equation 3.17. We obtain the sample covariance by multiplying the population covariance of 96.24 times the factor $n/(n-1)$:

$$(96.24)\frac{n}{n-1} = (96.24)\frac{10}{9} = 106.93$$

Figure 3.8 Covariance and Correlation: Workers, Tables (Minitab Output)

Covariances: Workers, Tables

	Workers	Number of Tables
X, workers	42.0111	
Y, tables	106.9333	278.4000

Correlations: Workers, Tables

Pearson correlation of x and y = 0.989
P-Value = 0.000

Figure 3.9 Covariance and Correlation: Workers, Tables (Excel Output)

Covariance: Workers, Tables

	Workers	Tables
Workers	37.81	
Tables	96.24	250.56

Correlation: Workers, Tables

	Workers	Tables
Workers	1	
Tables	0.988773	1

EXERCISES

Basic Exercises

3.35 Following is a random sample of seven (x, y) pairs of data points:

(1, 5) (3, 7) (4, 6) (5, 8) (7, 9) (3, 6) (5, 7)

a. Compute the covariance.
b. Compute the correlation coefficient.

3.36 Following is a random sample of five (x, y) pairs of data points:

(12, 200) (30, 600) (15, 270) (24, 500) (14, 210)

a. Compute the covariance.
b. Compute the correlation coefficient.

3.37 Following is a random sample of price per piece of plywood, X, and quantity sold, Y (in thousands):

Price per Piece (X)	Thousands of Pieces Sold (Y)
$6	80
7	60
8	70
9	40
10	0

a. Compute the covariance.
b. Compute the correlation coefficient.

Application Exercises

3.38 River Hills Hospital is interested in determining the effectiveness of a new drug for reducing the time required for complete recovery from knee surgery. Complete recovery is measured by a series of strength tests that compare the treated knee with the untreated knee. The drug was given in varying amounts to 18 patients over a 6-month period. For each patient the number of drug units, X, and the days for complete recovery, Y, are given by the following (x, y) data:

(5, 53) (21, 65) (14, 48) (11, 66) (9, 46) (4, 56)
(7, 53) (21, 57) (17, 49) (14, 66) (9, 54) (7, 56)
(9, 53) (21, 52) (13, 49) (14, 56) (9, 59) (4, 56)

a. Compute covariance.
b. Compute the correlation coefficient.
c. Briefly discuss the relationship between the number of drug units and the recovery time. What dosage should we recommend based on this initial analysis?

3.39 Acme Delivery offers three different shipping rates for packages less than 5 pounds delivered from Maine to the West Coast: regular, $3; fast, $5; and lightning, $10. To test the quality of these services, a major mail-order retailer shipped 15 packages at randomly selected times from Maine to Tacoma, Washington. The packages were shipped in groups of three by the three services at the same time to reduce variation resulting from the shipping day. The following data show the shipping cost, X, and the number of days, Y, in (x, y) pairs:

(3, 7) (5, 5) (10, 2) (3, 9) (5, 6) (10, 5) (3, 6) (5, 6) (10, 1)
(3, 10) (5, 7) (10, 4) (3, 5) (5, 6) (10, 4)

a. Describe the data numerically (covariance and correlation).
b. Discuss the value of the higher-priced services in terms of quicker delivery.

3.5 OBTAINING LINEAR RELATIONSHIPS

We have now seen how the relationship between two variables can be described by using sample data. Scatter plots provide a picture of the relationship, and correlation coefficients provide a numerical measure. In many economic and business problems a specific functional relationship is desired.

- What mean level of sales can be expected if the price is set at $10 per unit?
- If 250 workers are employed, how many units should be expected?
- If a developing country increases its fertilizer production by 1,000,000 tons, how much increase in grain production should be expected?

Economic models use specific functional relationships to indicate the effect on a dependent variable, Y, that results from various changes in an independent or input variable, X. In many cases we can adequately approximate the desired functional relationships by a linear equation:

$$Y = \beta_0 + \beta_1 X$$

where Y is the dependent variable, X is the independent variable, β_0 is the Y-intercept, and β_1 is the slope of the line, or the change in Y for every unit change in X. The nominal assumption made in our applications is that different values of X can be set, and there will be a corresponding mean value of Y that results because of the underlying linear relationship in the process being studied. The linear equation model computes the mean of Y for every value of X. This idea is the basis for obtaining many economic and business relationships, including demand functions, production functions, consumption functions, and sales forecasts.

We use regression to determine the best relationship between Y and X for a particular application. This requires us to find the best values for the coefficients β_0 and β_1. Generally, we use the data available from the process to compute "estimates" or numerical values for the coefficients β_0 and β_1. These estimates—defined as

Figure 3.10
Linear Function
and Data Points

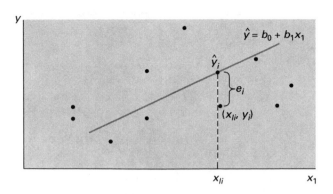

b_0 and b_1—are generally computed by using *least squares regression*, a technique widely implemented in statistical packages such as Minitab and in spreadsheets such as Excel. Least-squares is a procedure that selects the best-fit line, given a set of data points. Consider a typical plot of points from a process that has a linear relationship, as shown in Figure 3.10.

The linear equation represented by the line is the best-fit linear equation. We see that individual data points are above and below the line and that the line has points with both positive and negative deviations. The distance of each point (x_i, y_i) from the linear equation is defined as the residual, e_i. We would like to choose the equation so that some function of the positive and negative residuals is as small as possible. This implies finding estimates for the coefficients β_0 and β_1.

Early mathematicians struggled with the problem of developing a procedure for estimating the coefficients for the linear equation. Simply minimizing the deviations was not useful because the deviations have both positive and negative signs. Various procedures using absolute values have also been developed, but none has proven as useful or as popular as least-squares regression. We will learn later that those coefficients developed using this procedure have very useful statistical properties. One important caution for least-squares is that extreme outlier points can have such a strong influence on the regression line that the whole line is directed toward this point. Thus, we should always examine scatter plots to be sure that the regression relationship is not based on just a few extreme points.

Equations to compute these estimates are developed using the least-squares regression procedure that will be developed further in Chapter 12. Least-squares regression chooses b_0 and b_1 such that the sum of the squared residuals is minimized.

Least-Squares Regression

The least-squares regression line based on sample data is

$$\hat{y} = b_0 + b_1 x \qquad (3.22)$$

b_1 is the slope of the line, or the change in *y* for every unit change in *x*, and is calculated as

$$b_1 = \frac{Cov(x, y)}{s_x^2} = r\frac{s_y}{s_x} \qquad (3.23)$$

where b_0 is the *y*-intercept and is calculated as

$$b_0 = \bar{y} - b_1\bar{x} \qquad (3.24)$$

Rising Hills

Example 3.15 Manufacturing Plant (Regression Line)

The number of workers, X, and the number of tables produced per hour, Y, for a sample of 10 workers were presented in Example 3.13. If management decides to employ 25 workers, estimate the expected number of tables that are likely to be produced. The data are contained in the data file **Rising Hills**.

Solution We computed covariance and correlation for this sample data in Example 3.13:

$$Cov(x, y) = 106.93$$
$$r = 0.989$$

From the covariance we see that the direction of the relationship is *positive*; the high correlation of 0.989 also indicates that the sample data points are very close to some increasing straight line, as seen in Figure 3.11.

From the data in Table 3.6, we compute the sample regression coefficients:

$$b_1 = \frac{Cov(x, y)}{s_x^2} = \frac{106.93}{42.01} = 2.545$$

$$b_0 = \bar{y} - b_1\bar{x} = 41.21 - 2.545(21.3) = -13.02$$

From this, the sample regression line is

$$\hat{y} = b_0 + b_1 x = -13.02 + 2.545x$$

For 25 employees we would expect to produce

$$\hat{y} = -13.02 + 2.545(25) = 50.62$$

or approximately 51 tables.

We can also use a statistical software package such as Minitab or a spreadsheet such as Excel to obtain the same regression coefficients and regression line. The Minitab computer-generated output for the data is given in Figure 3.12.

Figure 3.11   Regression Line: Workers, Tables (Minitab Output)

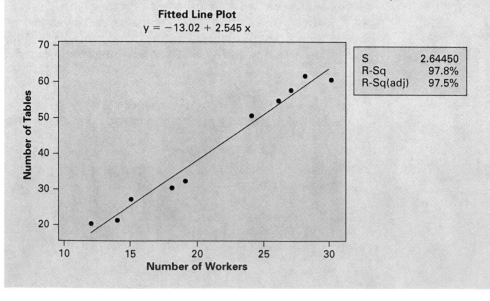

Figure 3.12 Regression Analysis: Number of Tables Versus Number of Workers (Minitab Output)

The regression equation is

Number of Tables = −13.0 + 2.55 (Number of Workers)

Predictor	Coef	SE Coef	T	P
Constant	−13.016	3.015	−4.32	0.003
Number of Workers	2.5454	0.1360	18.72	0.000

S = 2.64450   R-Sq = 97.8%   R-Sq(adj) = 97.5%

We do not intend to suggest that we can *always* substitute *any* value for x into a least-squares line and make a meaningful decision. Sometimes the relationship is merely spurious, or the value of x may be outside an acceptable range of values. For example, since the number of workers in the Rising Hills manufacturing plant ranged from 12 to 30, we cannot predict the number of tables produced per hour if 100 workers were employed.

As with this entire chapter, our objective is to learn how to describe data numerically and not how to perform sophisticated statistical analysis of linear regression models. The latter will come as we move to Chapter 12 and beyond. We will use the computer to obtain regression coefficients for most realistic data, as the sample size generally makes computation tedious.

EXERCISES

Basic Exercises

3.40 For these (x, y) pairs of data points:

(1,5)   (3,7)   (4,6)   (5,8)   (7,9)

a. Compute b_1.
b. Compute b_0.
c. What is the equation of the regression line?

3.41 The following data give X, the price charged per piece of plywood, and Y, the quantity sold (in thousands):

Price per Piece (X)	Thousands of Pieces Sold (Y)
$6	80
7	60
8	70
9	40
10	0

a. Compute the covariance.
b. What information does the correlation coefficient provide?
c. Compute and interpret b_1.
d. Compute b_0.
e. What quantity of plywood should we expect to sell if the price is $7 per piece?

3.42 A random sample for 7 days of operation produced the following (price, quantity) data values:

Price per Gallon of Paint (X)	Quantity Sold (Y)
10	100
8	120
5	200
4	200
10	90
7	110
6	150

a. Describe the data numerically (compute the covariance and correlation).
b. Compute and interpret b_1.
c. Compute and interpret b_0.
d. How many gallons of paint should we expect to sell if the price is $7 per gallon?

Application Exercises

3.43 A consumer goods company has been studying the effect of advertising on total profits. As part of this study, data on advertising expenditures (1000s) and total sales (1000s) were collected for a five-month period and are as follows:

(10, 100)   (15, 200)   (7, 80)   (12, 120)   (14, 150)

The first number is advertising expenditures and the second is total sales.

a. Plot the data and compute the correlation coefficient.

b. Do these results provide evidence that advertising has a positive effect on sales?

c. Compute the regression coefficients, b_0 and b_1.

3.44 The president of Floor Coverings Unlimited wants information concerning the relationship between retail experience (years) and weekly sales (in hundreds of dollars). He obtained the following random sample on experience and weekly sales:

(2, 5) (4, 10) (3, 8) (6, 18) (3, 6) (5, 15) (6, 20) (2, 4)

The first number for each observation is years of experience and the second is weekly sales.

a. Compute the covariance and correlation.

b. Compute the regression coefficients, b_0 and b_1.

c. Write a short explanation of the regression equation that explains how the equation might be used to predict sales. Include an indication of the range over which the equation might be applied.

3.45 A random sample of 12 college baseball players participated in a special weight-training program in an attempt to improve their batting averages. The program lasted for 20 weeks immediately prior to the start of the baseball season. The average number of hours per week and the change in their batting averages from the preceding season are as follows:

(8.0, 10) (20.0, 100) (5.4, –10) (12.4, 79) (9.2, 50)
(15.0, 89) (6.0, 34) (8.0, 30) (18.0, 68) (25.0, 110)
(10.0, 34) (5.0, 10)

a. Plot the data. Does it appear that the weight-training program was successful?

b. Estimate the regression equation.

SUMMARY

The focus of this chapter was numerical measures used to describe data. Central tendency was described by the mean, median, and mode; variability was described by the range, interquartile range, variance, standard deviation, and coefficient of variation. Both Chebychev's theorem and the empirical rule were introduced as methods to determine an approximate proportion of data within a certain range of the mean.

Approximations of the mean and variance for grouped data were discussed. Finally, we briefly introduced two numbers, covariance and correlation coefficient, as numerical measures of relationships between variables. We also discussed the method of least-squares regression. Graphical ways to describe data were presented in Chapter 2. Numerical ways to describe data were presented in Chapter 3.

KEY WORDS

- arithmetic mean
- coefficient of variation
- correlation coefficient
- covariance
- empirical rule
- first quartile
- five-number summary
- geometric mean
- interquartile range (IQR)
- median
- mode
- range
- skewed
- standard deviation
- symmetry
- third quartile
- variance

CHAPTER EXERCISES AND APPLICATIONS

3.46 A major airport recently hired consultant John Cadariu to study the problem of air traffic delays. He recorded the number of minutes planes were late for a sample of flights in the following table:

Minutes late	0 < 10	10 < 20	20 < 30	30 < 40	40 < 50	50 < 60
Number of flights	30	25	13	6	5	4

a. Estimate the mean number of minutes late.

b. Estimate the sample variance and standard deviation.

3.47 Snappy Lawn Inc. keeps records of charges for its professional lawn care services. A random sample of charges is stored in the data file **Snappy**. Describe the data numerically.

3.48 The data file **Cotton** contains information for the production of cotton fiber.

a. Plot cotton production versus wholesale price. Sketch an approximate linear relationship.

b. Find the constant and slope for the regression equation. What is the marginal effect on quantity produced for each unit change in price?

c. Estimate the relationship between exported cotton fabric and the production of cotton fiber.

3.49 ● From the data file **Cotton**,

a. Plot cotton production versus amount of exported cotton fabric. Sketch an approximate linear relationship.

b. Compute the constant and slope for the regression equation. What is the marginal effect on quantity produced for each unit change in exported fabric?

3.50 Are SAT mathematics scores a good indicator of college success? In Example 2.8 we described graphically (scatter plot) the variables SAT math scores and corresponding GPAs at the time of college graduation for a random sample of 11 students. These data are given in the following table:

SAT Math	GPA
450	3.25
480	2.60
500	2.88
520	2.85
560	3.30
580	3.10
590	3.35
600	3.20
620	3.50
650	3.59
700	3.95

a. Describe the direction and strength of a relationship between these two variables.

b. Compute and interpret b_1.

c. Compute b_0.

d. If a student's SAT math score is 530, predict this student's college GPA at the time of graduation.

e. Based on the data, can we predict the graduating GPA for a student who scored 375 on the SAT math?

3.51 Describe the following data numerically:

(5, 53)   (21, 65)   (14, 48)   (11, 66)   (9, 46)   (4, 56)
(7, 53)   (21, 57)   (17, 49)   (14, 66)   (9, 54)   (7, 56)
(9, 53)   (21, 52)   (13, 49)   (14, 56)   (9, 59)   (4, 56)

3.52 ● Graduation GPAs versus entering SAT verbal scores are contained in the data file **Student GPA** for a random sample of 67 students.

a. Describe the data graphically.

b. Describe the data numerically.

c. Estimate a graduation GPA for a student with a verbal score of 520.

3.53 Consider the following four populations:

- 1, 2, 3, 4, 5, 6, 7, 8
- 1, 1, 1, 1, 8, 8, 8, 8
- 1, 1, 4, 4, 5, 5, 8, 8,
- −6, −3, 0, 3, 6, 9, 12, 15

All of these populations have the same mean. *Without doing the calculations*, arrange the populations according to the magnitudes of their variances, from smallest to largest. Then calculate each of the variances manually.

3.54 An auditor finds that the values of a corporation's accounts receivable have a mean of $295 and a standard deviation of $63.

a. Find a range in which it can be guaranteed that 60% of these values lie.

b. Find a range in which it can be guaranteed that 84% of these values lie.

3.55 In one year, earnings growth of the 500 largest U.S. corporations averaged 9.2%; the standard deviation was 3.5%.

a. Find a range in which it can be guaranteed that 84% of these earnings growth figures lie.

b. Using the empirical rule, find a range in which it can be estimated that approximately 68% of these earnings growth figures lie.

3.56 Tires of a particular brand have a lifetime mean of 29,000 miles and a standard deviation of 3,000 miles.

a. Find a range in which it can be guaranteed that 75% of the lifetimes of tires of this brand lie.

b. Using the empirical rule, find a range in which it can be estimated that approximately 95% of the lifetimes of tires of this brand lie.

Appendix

1. GEOMETRIC MEAN

Another measure of central tendency that is important in business and economics, but often overlooked, is the *geometric mean*. Business analysts and economists who are interested in growth over a number of time periods use the geometric mean. Applications of the geometric mean in finance include compound interest over several years, total sales growth, and population growth. An important question concerns the average growth each year that will result in a certain total growth over several years.

> ## Geometric Mean
> The **Geometric Mean**, $\bar{x}_g$, is the *n*th root of the product of *n* numbers:
>
> $$\bar{x}_g = \sqrt[n]{(x_1 \bullet x_2 \bullet \cdots \bullet x_n)} = (x_1 \bullet x_2 \bullet \cdots \bullet x_n)^{1/n} \qquad (3.25)$$

The geometric mean is used to obtain mean growth over several periods, given compounded growth from each period.

For example, the geometric mean of

1.05	1.02	1.10	1.06

is

$$\bar{x}_g = \left[(1.05)(1.02)(1.10)(1.06)\right]^{1/4} = 1.0571$$

Example 3.16   Annual Growth Rate (Geometric Mean)

Find the annual growth rate if sales have grown 25% over 5 years.

Solution   The intuitive but naive temptation is simply to divide total growth, 25%, by the number of time periods, 5, and conclude that the average annual growth rate is 5 percent. This result is incorrect because it ignores the compound effect of growth.

Suppose that the annual growth rate is actually 5%; then the total growth over 5 years will be

$$(1.05)(1.05)(1.05)(1.05)(1.05) = 1.2763$$

or 27.63%. However, the annual growth rate, *r*, that would yield 25% over 5 years must satisfy this equation:

$$(1+r)^5 = 1.25$$

First, solve for the geometric mean:

$$\bar{x}_g = 1 + r = (1.25)^{1/5} = 1.046$$

The growth rate is $r = 0.046$, or 4.6%.

2. SKEWNESS

> ## Skewness
> **Skewness** is
>
> $$\text{Skewness} = \frac{1}{n} \frac{\sum_{i=1}^{n}(x_i - \bar{x})^3}{s^3} \qquad (3.26)$$

The important part of this expression is the numerator; the denominator serves the purpose of standardization, making units of measurement irrelevant. Positive skewness will result if a distribution is skewed to the right, since average cubed discrepancies about the mean are positive. Skewness will be negative for distributions skewed to the left and 0 for distributions, such as the normal, that are symmetric about their mean.

REFERENCES

1. Bureau of Economic Analysis, http://www.bea.doc.gov/bea/regional/spi/default.cfm, Table SA1-3—Per Capita Personal Income, May 28, 2004.

2. Bureau of Economic Analysis, http://www.bea.doc.gov/bea/regional/spi/default.cfm, Table SA1-3—Population, May 28, 2004.

3. Susan G. Komen Breast Cancer Foundation, About Komen, http://www.komen.org, May 19, 2004.

Topic 4

Probability

Chapter 4

Probability

Introduction

In this chapter we develop probability models that can be used to study business and economic problems for which future outcomes are unknown.

Consider the problem faced by George Smith, president of Advanced Systems Development, Inc. (ASD). The company has submitted five separate project proposals for the next year. George knows that the company will have to complete up to five projects over the next year. At present the company staff can handle up to two projects, and personnel could be hired to staff a third project. But if four or five projects are awarded to ASD, there will be a need for subcontracting or major staff expansion. In this chapter we develop probability concepts that George can use to determine the likely occurrence of the possible events—0, 1, 2, 3, 4, or 5 projects awarded. The probability of each event is a number from 0 to 1, such that the probabilities of all six events sum to exactly 1.0. The larger the probability of an event, the more likely it will occur, compared to the others. If the probability of exactly two contracts being awarded is 0.80, then George will be more confident of that event, compared to the case where the probability is 0.20. But in either case George cannot be certain that the event will occur.

City Hospital knows from past experience that a mean of 1.0 emergency room admissions per hour occurs on Saturday evenings. The emergency room has three acute-care rooms. If this pattern continues into the future, the hospital would like to know the probability that more than three people will be admitted to the emergency room in any hour. If the probability of that event is high, then the hospital will need to provide additional acute-care rooms to meet patient demand. But if the probability of more than three admissions is low, then expensive care facilities would be idle most of the time, and the resources could be better used for some other medical purpose. The probabilities of these events are thus very important for deciding how many rooms to provide.

We will show how probability models are used to study the variation in observed data so that inferences about the underlying process can be developed. Our objective, both in this chapter and in the next two chapters, is to understand probabilities and how they can be determined.

4.1 RANDOM EXPERIMENT, OUTCOMES, EVENTS

For the manager the probability of a future event presents a level of knowledge. The manager could know with certainty that the event will occur—e.g., a legal contract will exist. Or the manager may have no idea if the event will occur—e.g., the event could occur or not occur as part of a new business opportunity. In most business situations we cannot be certain about the occurrence of a future event, but if the probability of the event is known, then we have a better chance of making the best possible decision, compared to having no idea about the likely occurrence of the event. Business decisions and policies are often based on an implicit or assumed set of probabilities.

In order to make probability statements about the uncertain problem environment, we need to develop definitions and concepts, such as sample space, outcomes, and events. These are the basic building blocks for defining and computing probabilities.

For our study of probability we will be concerned with processes that can have two or more outcomes, with uncertainty about which outcome will occur.

> **Random Experiment**
> A **random experiment** is a process leading to two or more possible outcomes, with uncertainty as to which outcome will occur.

Examples of random experiments include the following:

1. A coin is tossed and the outcome is either a head or a tail.
2. In the ASD example, the company has the possibility of receiving 0 to 5 contract awards.
3. Some number of persons will be admitted to a hospital emergency room during any hour.

4. A customer enters a store and either purchases a shirt or does not.
5. The daily change in an index of stock market prices is observed.
6. A bag of cereal is selected from a packaging line and weighed to determine if the weight is above or below the stated package weight.
7. A six-sided die is rolled.

In each of the random experiments listed we can specify the possible outcomes, defined as *basic outcomes*. For example, a customer either purchases a shirt or does not.

Sample Space
The possible outcomes of a random experiment are called the **basic outcomes**, and the set of all basic outcomes is called the **sample space**. The symbol *S* will be used to denote the sample space.

We must define the basic outcomes in such a way that no two outcomes can occur simultaneously. In addition, the random experiment must necessarily lead to the occurrence of one of the basic outcomes.

Example 4.1   Roll of a Single Die (Sample Space)

What is the sample space for the roll of a single six-sided die?

Solution   The basic outcomes are the six possible face numbers, and the sample space is

$$S = [1, 2, 3, 4, 5, 6]$$

The sample space contains six basic outcomes. No two outcomes can occur together, and one of the six must occur.

Example 4.2   Investment Outcomes (Sample Space)

An investor follows the Dow-Jones Industrial index. What are the possible basic outcomes at the close of the trading day?

Solution   The sample space for this experiment is

$$S = [\{1. \text{ The index will be higher than at yesterday's close}\},$$
$$\{2. \text{ The index will not be higher than at yesterday's close}\}]$$

One of these two outcomes must occur. They cannot occur simultaneously. Thus, these two outcomes constitute a sample space.

In many cases we are interested in some subset of the basic outcomes and not the individual outcomes. For example, for the roll of a die we might be interested in whether the outcome is even—that is, 2, 4, or 6.

Event
An **event**, E, is any subset of basic outcomes from the sample space. An event occurs if the random experiment results in one of its constituent basic outcomes. The null event represents the absence of a basic outcome and is denoted by Ø.

In some applications we are interested in the simultaneous occurrence of two or more events. For example, if a die is thrown, two events that might be considered are "Number resulting is even" and "Number resulting is at least 4." One possibility is that all the events of interest might occur. That will be the case if the basic outcome of the random experiment belongs to all these events. The set of basic outcomes belonging to every event in a group of events is called the *intersection* of these events. The intersection for the events "Number resulting is even" and "Number resulting is at least 4" would be die faces equal to 4 or 6.

Intersection of Events
Let A and B be two events in the sample space S. Their **intersection**, denoted $A \cap B$, is the set of all basic outcomes in S that belong to both A and B. Hence, the intersection $A \cap B$ occurs if and only if both A and B occur. We will use the term **joint probability** of A and B to denote the probability of the intersection of A and B.

More generally, given K events $E_1, E_2, \ldots, E_K$, their intersection, $E_1 \cap E_2 \cap \cdots \cap E_K$, is the set of all basic outcomes that belong to every E_i ($i = 1, 2, \ldots, K$).

It is possible that the intersection of two events is the empty set.

Mutually Exclusive
If the events A and B have no common basic outcomes, they are called **mutually exclusive**, and their intersection, $A \cap B$, is said to be the empty set indicating that $A \cap B$ cannot occur.

More generally, the K events $E_1, E_2, \ldots, E_K$ are said to be mutually exclusive if every pair (E_i, E_j) is a pair of mutually exclusive events.

Figure 4.1 illustrates intersections using a Venn diagram. In part (a) of Figure 4.1 the rectangle S represents the sample space, and the two closed figures represent the

Figure 4.1
Venn Diagrams for the Intersection of Events A and B: (a) $A \cap B$ Is the Shaded Area; (b) A and B Are Mutually Exclusive

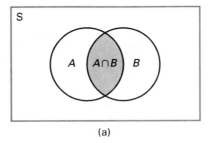
(a)

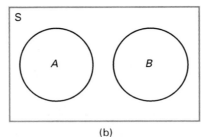
(b)

events A and B. Basic outcomes belonging to A are within the circle labeled A, and basic outcomes belonging to B are in the corresponding B circle. The intersection of A and B, $A \cap B$, is indicated by the shaded area where the figures intersect. We see that a basic outcome is in $A \cap B$ if and only if it is in both A and B. Thus, in rolling a die, the outcomes 4 and 6 both belong to the two events "Even number results" and "Number at least 4 results." In Figure 4.1(b) the figures do not intersect, indicating that events A and B are mutually exclusive. For example, if a set of accounts is audited, the events "Less than 5% contain material errors" and "More than 10% contain material errors" are mutually exclusive.

When we consider jointly several events, another possibility of interest is that at least one of them will occur. This will happen if the basic outcome of the random experiment belongs to at least one of the events. The set of basic outcomes belonging to at least one of the events is called their *union*. For example, when throwing a die, the basic outcomes 2, 4, 5, and 6 all belong to at least one of the events "Even number results" or "Odd number results."

Union

Let A and B be two events in the sample space, S. Their **union**, denoted $A \cup B$, is the set of all basic outcomes in S that belong to at least one of these two events. Hence, the union $A \cup B$ occurs if and only if either A or B or both occur.

More generally, given the K events $E_1, E_2, \ldots, E_K$, their union, $E_1 \cup E_2 \cup \cdots \cup E_K$, is the set of all basic outcomes belonging to at least one of these K events.

The Venn diagram in Figure 4.2 shows the union, from which it is clear that a basic outcome will be in $A \cup B$ if and only if it is in either A or B or both.

If the union of several events covers the entire sample space, S, we say that these events are *collectively exhaustive*. Since every basic outcome is in S, it follows that every outcome of the random experiment will be in at least one of these events. For example, if a die is thrown, the events "Result is at least 3" and "Result is at most 5" are together collectively exhaustive.

Collectively Exhaustive

Given the K events $E_1, E_2, \ldots, E_K$ in the sample space, S, if $E_1 \cup E_2 \cup \cdots \cup E_K = S$, these K events are said to be **collectively exhaustive**.

Figure 4.2 Venn Diagram for the Union of Events A and B

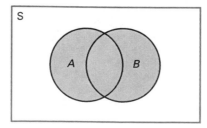

Figure 4.3 Venn Diagram for the Complement of Event A

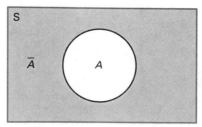

We can see that the set of all basic outcomes contained in a sample space is both mutually exclusive and collectively exhaustive. We have already noted that these outcomes are such that one must occur, but no more than one can simultaneously occur.

Next, let A be an event. Suppose that our interest is all of the basic outcomes not included in A.

Complement
Let A be an event in the sample space, S. The set of basic outcomes of a random experiment belonging to S but not to A is called the **complement** of A and is denoted by $\overline{A}$.

Clearly, events A and $\overline{A}$ are mutually exclusive—no basic outcome can belong to both—and collectively exhaustive—every basic outcome must belong to one or the other. Figure 4.3 shows the complement of A using a Venn diagram.

We have now defined three important concepts—the intersection, the union, and the complement—that will be important in our development of probability. The following examples help to illustrate these concepts.

Example 4.3 Roll of a Single Die (Unions, Intersections, and Complements)

A die is rolled. Let A be the event "Number resulting is even" and B the event "Number resulting is at least 4." Then

$$A = [2, 4, 6] \quad \text{and} \quad B = [4, 5, 6]$$

Find the complement of each event, the intersection and the union of A and B, and the intersection of $\overline{A}$ and B.

Solution The complements of these events are, respectively,

$$\overline{A} = [1, 3, 5] \quad \text{and} \quad \overline{B} = [1, 2, 3]$$

The intersection of A and B is the event "Number resulting is both even and at least 4" and so

$$A \cap B = [4, 6]$$

The union of A and B is the event "Number resulting is either even or at least 4, or both" and so

$$A \cup B = [2, 4, 5, 6]$$

Note also that the events A and $\overline{A}$ are mutually exclusive, since their intersection is the empty set, and collectively exhaustive, because their union is the sample space S; that is,

$$A \cup \overline{A} = [1, 2, 3, 4, 5, 6] = S$$

The same statements apply for events B and $\overline{B}$.

Consider another intersection of the two events $\overline{A}$ and B. Since the only outcome that is both "not even" and "at least 4" is 5, it follows that $\overline{A} \cap B = [5]$.

Example 4.4 Dow-Jones Industrial Average (Unions, Intersections, and Complements)

We will designate four basic outcomes for the Dow-Jones Industrial average over 2 consecutive days:

O_1: Dow-Jones average rises on both days.
O_2: Dow-Jones average rises on the first day but does not rise on the second day.
O_3: Dow-Jones average does not rise on the first day but rises on the second day.
O_4: Dow-Jones average does not rise on either day.

Clearly, one of these outcomes must occur, but not more than one can occur at the same time. We can therefore write the sample space as $S = [O_1, O_2, O_3, O_4]$. Now, we will consider these two events:

A: Dow-Jones average rises on the first day.
B: Dow-Jones average rises on the second day.

Find the intersection, union, and complement of A and B.

Solution   We see that A occurs if either O_1 or O_2 occurs, and, thus,

$$A = [O_1, O_2] \quad \text{and} \quad B = [O_1, O_3]$$

The intersection of A and B is the event "Dow-Jones average rises on the first day and rises on the second day." This is the set of all basic outcomes belonging to both A and B, $A \cap B = [O_1]$.

The union of A and B is the event "Dow-Jones average rises on at least one of the two days." This is the set of all outcomes belonging to either A or B, or both. Thus,

$$A \cup B = [O_1, O_2, O_3]$$

Finally, the complement of A is the event "Dow-Jones average does not rise on the first day." This is the set of all basic outcomes in the sample space, S, that do not belong to A. Hence,

$$\overline{A} = [O_3, O_4] \quad \text{and, similarly,} \quad \overline{B} = [O_2, O_4]$$

Figure 4.4 shows the intersection of events $\overline{A}$ and B. This intersection contains all outcomes that belong in both $\overline{A}$ and B. Clearly, $\overline{A} \cap B = [O_3]$.

Figure 4.4   Venn Diagram for the Intersection of $\overline{A}$ and B

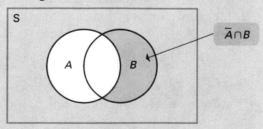

The Venn diagrams in Figures 4.5, 4.6, and 4.7 illustrate three results involving unions and intersections of events.

Result 1

Let A and B be two events. Then the events $A \cap B$ and $\overline{A} \cap B$ are mutually exclusive, and their union is B, as illustrated in the Venn diagram in Figure 4.5. Clearly,

$$(A \cap B) \cup (\overline{A} \cap B) = B \tag{4.1}$$

Result 2

Let A and B be two events. The events A and $\overline{A} \cap B$ are mutually exclusive, and their union is $A \cup B$, as illustrated in the Venn diagram in Figure 4.6. That is,

$$A \cup (\overline{A} \cap B) = A \cup B \tag{4.2}$$

Result 3

Let $E_1, E_2, \ldots, E_K$ be K mutually exclusive and collectively exhaustive events, and let A be some other event. Then the K events $E_1 \cap A$, $E_2 \cap A, \ldots, E_K \cap A$ are mutually exclusive, and their union is A. That is,

$$(E_1 \cap A) \cup (E_2 \cap A) \cup \cdots \cup (E_K \cap A) = A \tag{4.3}$$

Figure 4.5 Venn Diagram for Result 1: $(A \cap B) \cup (\overline{A} \cap B) = B$

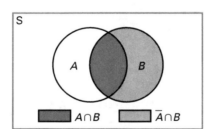

Figure 4.6 Venn Diagram for Result 2: $A \cup (\overline{A} \cap B) = A \cup B$

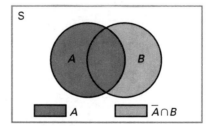

Figure 4.7 Venn Diagram for Result 3: $(E_1 \cap A) \cup (E_2 \cap A) \cup \cdots \cup (E_K \cap A) = A$

	E_1	E_2	E_3	E_4	E_5	....	E_K
A	$E_1 \cap A$	$E_2 \cap A$	$E_3 \cap A$	$E_4 \cap A$	$E_5 \cap A$	....	$E_K \cap A$
$\overline{A}$							

We can better understand the third statement by examining the Venn diagram in Figure 4.7. The large rectangle indicates the entire sample space and is divided into smaller rectangles depicting K mutually exclusive and collectively exhaustive events, $E_1, E_2, \ldots, E_K$. The event A is represented by the closed figure. We see that the events composed of the intersection of A and each of the E events are indeed exclusive and that their union is simply the event A. We can therefore write

$$(E_1 \cap A) \cup (E_2 \cap A) \cup \cdots \cup (E_K \cap A) = A$$

Example 4.5 Single Die (Results 1 and 2)

Consider the die-rolling experiment in Example 4.3, with $A = [2, 4, 6]$ and $B = [4, 5, 6]$. Show the following:

a. $(A \cap B) \cup (\overline{A} \cap B) = B$
b. $A \cup (\overline{A} \cap B) = A \cup B$

Solution We know that

$$\overline{A} = [1, 3, 5]$$

It follows that

$$A \cap B = [4, 6] \quad \text{and} \quad \overline{A} \cap B = [5]$$

Then $A \cap B$ and $\overline{A} \cap B$ are mutually exclusive, and their union is $B = [4, 5, 6]$; that is,

$$(A \cap B) \cup (\overline{A} \cap B) = [4, 5, 6] = B \qquad \text{(result 1)}$$

Also, A and $\overline{A} \cap B$ are mutually exclusive, and their union is

$$A \cup (\overline{A} \cap B) = [2, 4, 5, 6] = A \cup B \qquad \text{(result 2)}$$

Example 4.6 Single Die (Result 3)

Consider a die-rolling experiment with events A, E_1, E_2, and E_3 given by

$$A = [2, 4, 6] \quad E_1 = [1, 2] \quad E_2 = [3, 4] \quad E_3 = [5, 6]$$

Show that $E_1 \cap A$, $E_2 \cap A$, and $E_3 \cap A$ are mutually exclusive and that their union is A.

Solution First, we notice that E_1, E_2, and E_3 are mutually exclusive and collectively exhaustive. Then

$$E_1 \cap A = [2] \quad E_2 \cap A = [4] \quad E_3 \cap A = [6]$$

Clearly, these three events are mutually exclusive, and their union is

$$(E_1 \cap A) \cup (E_2 \cap A) \cup (E_3 \cap A) = [2, 4, 6] = A$$

EXERCISES

Basic Exercises

For exercises 4.1–4.4 use the sample space S defined as follows:

$$S = [E_1, E_2, E_3, E_4, E_5, E_6, E_7, E_8, E_9, E_{10}]$$

4.1 Given $A = [E_1, E_3, E_6, E_9]$, define $\overline{A}$.

4.2 Given $A = [E_1, E_3, E_7, E_9]$ and $B = [E_2, E_3, E_8, E_9]$,

    a. What is A intersection B?

    b. What is the union of A and B?

    c. Is the union of A and B collectively exhaustive?

4.3 Given $\overline{A} = [E_1, E_3, E_7, E_9]$ and $\overline{B} = [E_2, E_3, E_8, E_9]$,

    a. What is A intersection B?

    b. What is the union of A and B?

    c. Is the union of A and B collectively exhaustive?

4.4 Given $A = [E_3, E_5, E_6, E_{10}]$ and $B = [E_3, E_4, E_6, E_9]$,

    a. What is A intersection B?

    b. What is the union of A and B?

    c. Is the union of A and B collectively exhaustive?

Application Exercises

4.5 A corporation takes delivery of some new machinery that must be installed and checked before it becomes available to use. The corporation is sure that it will take no more than 7 days for this installation and check to take place. Let A be the event "It will be more than 4 days before the machinery becomes available" and B the event "It will be less than 6 days before the machinery becomes available."

    a. Describe the event that is the complement of event A.

    b. Describe the event that is the intersection of events A and B.

    c. Describe the event that is the union of events A and B.

    d. Are events A and B mutually exclusive?

    e. Are events A and B collectively exhaustive?

    f. Show that $(A \cap B) \cup (\overline{A} \cap B) = B$.

    g. Show that $A \cup (\overline{A} \cap B) = A \cup B$.

4.6 Consider Example 4.4, with the following four basic outcomes for the Dow-Jones Industrial Average over 2 consecutive days:

    O_1: Dow-Jones average rises on both days.

    O_2: Dow-Jones average rises on the first day but does not rise on the second day.

    O_3: Dow-Jones average does not rise on the first day but rises on the second day.

    O_4: Dow-Jones average does not rise on either day.

Let events A and B be the following:

    A: Dow-Jones average rises on the first day.

    B: Dow-Jones average rises on the second day.

    a. Show that $(A \cap B) \cup (\overline{A} \cap B) = B$.

    b. Show that $A \cup (\overline{A} \cap B) = A \cup B$.

4.7 Florin Frenti operates a small used car lot that has three Mercedes (M_1, M_2, M_3) and two Toyotas (T_1, T_2). Two customers, Cezara and Anda, come to his lot, and each selects a car. The customers do not know each other, and there is no communication between them. Let the events A and B be defined as follows:

    A: The customers select at least one Toyota.

    B: The customers select two cars of the same model.

    a. Identify the pairs of cars in the sample space.

    b. Describe event A.

    c. Describe event B.

    d. Describe the complement of A.

    e. Show that $(A \cap B) \cup (\overline{A} \cap B) = B$.

    f. Show that $A \cup (\overline{A} \cap B) = A \cup B$.

4.2 PROBABILITY AND ITS POSTULATES

Now, we are ready to use the language and concepts developed in the previous section to determine how to obtain an actual probability for a process of interest. Suppose that a random experiment is to be carried out and we want to determine the probability that a particular event will occur. Probability is measured over the range from 0 to 1. A probability of 0 indicates that the event will not occur, and a probability of 1 indicates that the event is certain to occur. Neither of these extremes is typical in applied problems. Thus, we are interested in assigning probabilities between 0 and 1 to uncertain events. To do this, we need to utilize any information that might be available. For example; if incomes are high, then sales of luxury automobiles will occur more often. An experienced sales manager may be able to establish a probability that future sales will exceed the company's profitability goal. In this section we consider three definitions of probability:

1. Classical probability
2. Relative frequency probability
3. Subjective probability

Classical Probability

Classical Probability

Classical probability is the proportion of times that an event will occur, assuming that all outcomes in a sample space are equally likely to occur. Dividing the number of outcomes in the sample space that satisfy the event by the total number of outcomes in the sample space determines the probability of an event. The probability of an event A is

$$P(A) = \frac{N_A}{N}$$ (4.4)

where N_A is the number of outcomes that satisfy the condition of event A and N is the total number of outcomes in the sample space. The important idea here is that one can develop a probability from fundamental reasoning about the process.

The classical statement of probability requires that we count outcomes in the sample space. Then we use the counts to determine the required probability. The following example indicates how classical probability can be used in a relatively simple problem.

Example 4.7   Computer Purchase Selection (Classical Probability)

Karlyn Akimoto operates a small computer store. On a particular day she has three Gateway and two Compaq computers in stock. Suppose that Susan Spencer comes into the store to purchase two computers. Susan is not concerned about which brand she purchases—they all have the same operating specifications—so Susan selects the computers purely by chance: Any computer on the shelf is equally likely to be selected. What is the probability that Susan will purchase one Gateway and one Compaq computer?

Solution   The answer can be obtained using classical probability. To begin, the sample space is defined as all possible pairs of two computers that can be selected from the store. The number of pairs is then counted, as is the number of outcomes that meet the condition—one Gateway and one Compaq. Define the three Gateway computers as, G_1, G_2, and G_3 and the two Compaq computers as C_1 and C_2. The sample space, S, contains the following pairs of computers:

$$S = \{G_1C_1, G_1C_2, G_2C_1, G_2C_2, G_3C_1, G_3C_2, G_1G_2, G_1G_3, G_2G_3, C_1C_2\}$$

The number of outcomes in the sample space is 10. If A is the event "One Gateway and one Compaq computer are chosen," then the number, N_A, of outcomes that have one Gateway and one Compaq computer is 6. Therefore, the required probability of event A—one Gateway and one Compaq—is

$$P(A) = \frac{N_A}{N} = \frac{6}{10} = 0.6$$

Counting all of the outcomes would be very time-consuming if we first had to identify every possible outcome. However, from previous courses many of you may have learned the basic formula to compute *the number of combinations* of n items taken k at a time.

Formula for Determining the Number of Combinations

The counting process can be generalized by using the following equation to compute the **number of combinations** of n items taken k at a time:

$$C_k^n = \frac{n!}{k!\,(n-k)!} \qquad 0! = 1 \qquad\qquad (4.5)$$

The appendix at the end of this chapter develops combinations, and you should study that appendix if you need to learn about or review your understanding of combinations.

We illustrate the combination equation, Equation 4.5, by noting that in Example 4.7 the number of combinations of the five computers taken two at a time is the number of elements in the sample space:

$$C_2^5 = \frac{5!}{2!\,(5-2)!} = \frac{5\cdot4\cdot3\cdot2\cdot1}{2\cdot1(3\cdot2\cdot1)} = 10$$

In Example 4.8 we will apply classical probability to a more difficult problem.

Example 4.8   Computer Selection Revised (Classical Probability)

Suppose that Karlyn's store now contains 10 Gateway Computers, 5 Compaq Computers, and 5 Acer computers. Susan enters the store and wants to purchase 3 computers. The computers are selected purely by chance from the shelf. Now what is the probability that 2 Gateway computers and 1 Compaq computer are selected?

Solution   The classical definition of probability will be used. But in this example the combinations formula will be used to determine the number of outcomes in the sample space and the number of outcomes that satisfy the condition A: [2 Gateways and 1 Compaq].

The total number of outcomes in the sample space is

$$N = C_3^{20} = \frac{20!}{3!\,(20-3)!} = 1,140$$

The number of ways that we can select 2 Gateway computers from the 10 available is computed by

$$C_2^{10} = \frac{10!}{2!\,(10-2)!} = 45$$

Similarly, the number of ways that we can select 1 Compaq computer from the 5 available is computed by

$$C_1^5 = \frac{5!}{1!\,(5-1)!} = 5$$

Therefore, the number of outcomes that satisfy event A is

$$N_A = C_2^{10} \times C_1^5 = 45 \times 5 = 225$$

Finally, the probability of $A = [2 \text{ Gateways and 1 Compaq}]$ is

$$P_A = \frac{N_A}{N} = \frac{C_2^{10} \times C_1^5}{C_3^{20}} = \frac{45 \times 5}{1{,}140} = 0.197$$

Relative Frequency

We often use relative frequency to determine probabilities for a particular population. The *relative frequency probability* is the number of events in the population that meet the condition divided by the total number in the population. These probabilities indicate how often an event will occur compared to other events. For example, if event A has a probability of 0.40, we know that it will occur 40% of the time. This is more often than event B if event B has only a 0.30 probability of occurrence. But we do not know which event, A or B, will occur next.

Relative Frequency Probability

The **relative frequency probability** is the limit of the proportion of times that event A occurs in a large number of trials, n:

$$P(A) = \frac{n_A}{n} \qquad (4.6)$$

where n_A is the number of A outcomes and n is the total number of trials or outcomes. The probability is the limit as n becomes large (or approaches infinity).

Example 4.9 Probability of Incomes Above \$50,000 (Relative Probability)

Sally Olson is considering an opportunity to establish a new car dealership in Dakota County, which has a population of 150,000 people. Experience from many other dealerships indicates that in similar areas a dealership will be successful if at least 40% of the households have annual incomes over $50,000. She has asked Paul Smith, a marketing consultant, to estimate the proportion of family incomes above $50,000, or the probability of such incomes.

Solution   After considering the problem, Paul decides that the probability should be based on the relative frequency. He first examines the most recent census data and finds that there were 54,345 households in Dakota County and that 31,496 had incomes above $50,000. Paul computed the probability for event A, "Family income greater than $50,000," as

$$P(A) = \frac{n_A}{n} = \frac{31,496}{54,345} = 0.580$$

Since Paul knows that there are various errors in census data, he also consulted similar data published by *Sales Management* magazine. From this source he found 55,100 households, with 32,047 having incomes above $50,000. Paul computed the probability of event A from this source as

$$P(A) = \frac{n_A}{n} = \frac{32,047}{55,100} = 0.582$$

Since these numbers are close, he could report either. Paul chose to report the probability as 0.58.

This example shows that probabilities based on the relative frequency approach often can be obtained using existing data sources. It also indicates that different results can and do occur and that experienced analysts and managers will seek to verify their results by using more than one source. Experience and good judgment are needed to decide if confirming data is close enough.

Subjective Probability

Subjective Probability
Subjective probability expresses an individual's degree of belief about the chance that an event will occur. These subjective probabilities are used in certain management decision procedures.

We can understand the subjective probability concept by using the concept of fair bets. For example, if I assert that the probability of a stock price rising in the next week is 0.5, then I believe that the stock price is just as likely to increase as it is to decrease. In assessing this subjective probability I am not necessarily thinking in terms of repeated experimentation, but instead I am thinking about a stock price over the next week. My subjective probability assessment implies that I would view as fair a bet in which I paid $1 if the price decreased and I would be paid $1 if the price increased. If I would receive more than $1 for a price increase, then I would regard the bet as being in my favor. Similarly, if I believe that the probability of a horse's winning a particular race is 0.4, I am asserting the personal view that there is a 40-to-60 chance of its winning. Given this belief, I would regard as fair a bet in which I would gain $3 if the horse won and lose $2 if the horse lost.

We emphasize that subjective probabilities are personal. There is no requirement that different individuals arrive at the same probabilities for the same event. In the stock price example most people would conclude that the appropriate probability of a stock increase is 0.50. However, an individual with more information about the stock might believe otherwise. In the horse race example it is likely that two bettors will reach different subjective probabilities. They may not have the same information, and, even if they do, they may interpret the information differently. We know that individual investors do not all hold the same views on the future behavior of the stock market. Their subjective probabilities might be thought of as depending on the knowledge they have and the way they interpret it. Managers of different firms have different subjective probabilities about the potential sales opportunities in a given regional market, and, thus, they make different decisions.

Probability Postulates

We need to develop a framework for assessing and manipulating probabilities. To do this, we will first set down three rules (or postulates) that probabilities will be required to obey and show that these requirements are "reasonable."

Probability Postulates

Let S denote the sample space of a random experiment, O_i the basic outcomes, and A an event. For each event A of the sample space, S, we assume that $P(A)$ is defined and we have the following **probability postulates**:

1. If A is any event in the sample space, S,

$$0 \leq P(A) \leq 1$$

2. Let A be an event in S, and let O_i denote the basic outcomes. Then

$$P(A) = \sum_A P(O_i)$$

where the notation implies that the summation extends over all the basic outcomes in A.

3. $P(S) = 1$

The first postulate requires that the probability lie between 0 and 1. The second postulate can be understood in terms of relative frequencies. Suppose that a random experiment is repeated N times. Let N_i be the number of times the basic outcome O_i occurs, and let N_A be the number of times event A occurs. Then, since the basic outcomes are mutually exclusive, N_A is just the sum of N_i for all basic outcomes in A; that is,

$$N_A = \sum_A N_i$$

and, on dividing by the number of trials, N, we obtain

$$\frac{N_A}{N} = \sum_A \frac{N_i}{N}$$

But under the relative frequency concept of probability, N_A/N tends to $P(A)$, and each N_i/N tends to $P(O_i)$ as N becomes infinitely large. Thus, the second postulate can be seen as a logical requirement when probability is viewed in this way.

The third postulate can be paraphrased as "When a random experiment is carried out, something has to happen." Replacing A by the sample space, S, in the second postulate gives

$$P(S) = \sum_S P(O_i)$$

where the summation extends over all the basic outcomes in the sample space. But since $P(S) = 1$ by the third postulate, it follows that

$$\sum_S P(O_i) = 1$$

That is, the sum of the probabilities for all basic outcomes in the sample space is 1.

Consequences of the Postulates

We now list and illustrate some immediate consequences of the three postulates.

1. If the sample space, S, consists of n equally likely basic outcomes, $E_1, E_2, \ldots, E_n$, then

$$P(E_i) = \frac{1}{n} \qquad i = 1, 2, \ldots, n$$

This follows because the n outcomes cover the sample space and are equally likely. For example, if a fair die is rolled, the probability for each of the six basic outcomes is $1/6$.

2. If the sample space, S, consists of n equally likely basic outcomes and event A consists of n_A of these outcomes, then

$$P(A) = \frac{n_A}{n}$$

This follows from consequence 1 and postulate 2. Every basic outcome has the probability $1/n$, and, by postulate 2, $P(A)$ is just the sum of the probabilities of the n_A basic outcomes in A. For example, if a fair die is rolled and A is the event "Even number results," there are $n = 6$ basic outcomes, and $n_A = 3$ of these are in A. Thus, $P(A) = 3/6 = 1/2$.

3. Let A and B be mutually exclusive events. Then the probability of their union is the sum of their individual probabilities; that is,

$$P(A \cup B) = P(A) + P(B)$$

In general, if $E_1, E_2, \ldots, E_K$ are mutually exclusive events,

$$P(E_1 \cup E_2 \cup \cdots \cup E_K) = P(E_1) + P(E_2) + \cdots + P(E_K)$$

This result is a consequence of postulate 2. The probability of the union of A and B is

$$P(A \cup B) = \sum_{A \cup B} P(O_i)$$

where the summation extends over all basic outcomes in $A \cup B$. But since A and B are mutually exclusive, no basic outcome belongs to both, so

$$\sum_{A \cup B} P(O_i) = \sum_A P(O_i) + \sum_B P(O_i) = P(A) + P(B)$$

4. If $E_1, E_2, \ldots, E_K$ are collectively exhaustive events, the probability of their union is

$$P(E_1 \cup E_2 \cup \cdots \cup E_K) = 1$$

Since the events are collectively exhaustive, their union is the whole sample space, S, and the result follows from postulate 3.

Example 4.10   Lottery (Probability)

A charitable organization sells 1,000 lottery tickets. There are 10 major prizes and 100 minor prizes, all of which must be won. The process of choosing winners is such that at the outset each ticket has an equal chance of winning a major prize, and each has an equal probability of winning a minor prize. No ticket can win more than one prize. What is the probability of winning a major prize with a single ticket? What is the probability of winning a minor prize? What is the probability of winning some prize?

Solution   Of the 1,000 tickets, 10 will win major prizes, 100 will win minor prizes, and 890 will win no prize. Our single ticket is selected from the 1,000. Let A be the event "Selected ticket wins a major prize," and let B be the event "Selected ticket wins a minor prize." The probabilities are

$$P(A) = \frac{10}{1,000} = 0.01$$

$$P(B) = \frac{100}{1,000} = 0.10$$

The event "Ticket wins some prize" is the union of events A and B. Since only one prize is permitted, these events are mutually exclusive, and

$$P(A \cup B) = P(A) + P(B) = 0.01 + 0.10 = 0.11$$

Example 4.11   Dow-Jones Revisited (Probability)

In Example 4.4 we considered the course of the Dow-Jones Industrial Average over 2 days and defined four basic outcomes:

O_1: Dow-Jones average rises on both days.
O_2: Dow-Jones average rises on the first day but does not rise on the second day.

O_3: Dow-Jones average does not rise on the first day but rises on the second day.
O_4: Dow-Jones average does not rise on either day.

Suppose that we assume these four basic outcomes are equally likely. In that case what is the probability that the market will rise on at least 1 of the 2 days?

Solution The event of interest, "Market rises on at least 1 of the 2 days," contains three of the four basic outcomes—O_1, O_2, and O_3. Since the basic outcomes are all equally likely, it follows that the probability of this event is 3/4, or 0.75.

Example 4.12   Oil Well Drilling (Probability)

In the early stages of the development of the Hibernia oil site in the Atlantic Ocean, the Petroleum Directorate of Newfoundland estimated the probability to be 0.1 that economically recoverable reserves would exceed 2 billion barrels. The probability for reserves in excess of 1 billion barrels was estimated to be 0.5. Given this information, what is the estimated probability of reserves between 1 and 2 billion barrels?

Solution Let A be the event "Reserves exceed 2 billion barrels" and B the event "Reserves between 1 and 2 billion barrels." These are mutually exclusive, and their union, $A \cup B$, is the event "Reserves exceed 1 billion barrels." We therefore have

$$P(A) = 0.1 \qquad P(A \cup B) = 0.5$$

Then, since A and B are mutually exclusive,

$$P(B) = P(A \cup B) - P(A) = 0.5 - 0.1 = 0.4$$

EXERCISES

Basic Exercises

4.8 The sample space contains 5 A's and 7 B's. What is the probability that a randomly selected set of 2 will include 1 A and 1 B?

4.9 The sample space contains 6 A's and 4 B's. What is the probability that a randomly selected set of 3 will include 1 A and 2 B's?

4.10 The sample space contains 10 A's and 6 B's. What is the probability that a randomly selected set of 4 will include 2 A's and 2 B's?

4.11 In a city of 120,000 people there are 20,000 Norwegians. What is the probability that a randomly selected person from the city will be Norwegian?

4.12 In a city of 180,000 people there are 20,000 Norwegians. What is the probability that a random sample of 2 people from the city will contain 2 Norwegians?

Application Exercises

4.13 Recall the corporation in Exercise 4.5. Its new machinery must be installed and checked before it becomes operational. The accompanying table shows a manager's probability assessment for the number of days required before the machinery becomes operational.

Number of days	3	4	5	6	7
Probability	0.08	0.24	0.41	0.20	0.07

Let A be the event "It will be more than 4 days before the machinery becomes operational," and let B be the event "It will be less than 6 days before the machinery becomes available."

a. Find the probability of event A.
b. Find the probability of event B.
c. Find the probability of the complement of event A.

d. Find the probability of the intersection of events A and B.

e. Find the probability of the union of events A and B.

4.14 A fund manager is considering investing in the stock of a health care provider. The manager's assessment of probabilities for rates of return on this stock over the next year is summarized in the accompanying table. Let A be the event "Rate of return will be more than 10%" and B the event "Rate of return will be negative."

Rate of return	Less than −10%	−10% to 0%	0% to 10%	10% to 20%	More than 20%
Probability	0.04	0.14	0.28	0.33	0.21

a. Find the probability of event A.
b. Find the probability of event B.
c. Describe the event that is the complement of A.
d. Find the probability of the complement of A.
e. Describe the event that is the intersection of A and B.
f. Find the probability of the intersection of A and B.
g. Describe the event that is the union of A and B.
h. Find the probability of the union of A and B.
i. Are A and B mutually exclusive?
j. Are A and B collectively exhaustive?

4.15 A manager has available a pool of eight employees who could be assigned to a project-monitoring task. Four of the employees are women and four are men. Two of the men are brothers. The manager is to make the assignment at random so that each of the eight employees is equally likely to be chosen. Let A be the event "Chosen employee is a man" and B the event "Chosen employee is one of the brothers."

a. Find the probability of A.
b. Find the probability of B.
c. Find the probability of the intersection of A and B.

4.16 If two events are mutually exclusive, we know that the probability of their union is the sum of their individual probabilities. However, this is *not* the case for events that are not mutually exclusive. Verify this assertion by considering the events A and B of Exercise 4.2.

4.17 A department store manager has monitored the number of complaints received per week about poor service. The probabilities for numbers of complaints in a week, established by this review, are shown in the following table. Let A be the event "There will be at least 1 complaint in a week" and B the event "There will be less than 10 complaints in a week."

Number of complaints	0	1 to 3	4 to 6	7 to 9	10 to 12	More than 12
Probability	0.14	0.39	0.23	0.15	0.06	0.03

a. Find the probability of A.
b. Find the probability of B.
c. Find the probability of the complement of A.
d. Find the probability of the union of A and B.
e. Find the probability of the intersection of A and B.
f. Are A and B mutually exclusive?
g. Are A and B collectively exhaustive?

4.18 A corporation receives a particular part in shipments of 100. Research indicated the probabilities shown in the accompanying table for numbers of defective parts in a shipment.

Number defective	0	1	2	3	More than 3
Probability	0.29	0.36	0.22	0.10	0.03

a. What is the probability that there will be less than 3 defective parts in a shipment?
b. What is the probability that there will be more than 1 defective part in a shipment?
c. The five probabilities in the table sum to 1. Why must this be so?

4.3 PROBABILITY RULES

We now develop some important rules for computing probabilities for compound events. The development begins by defining A as an event in the sample space, S, with A and its complement, $\overline{A}$, being mutually exclusive and collectively exhaustive.

$$P(A \cup \overline{A}) = P(A) + P(\overline{A}) = 1$$

This is the *complement rule*.

Complement Rule

Let A be an event and $\overline{A}$ its complement. Then the **complement rule** is

$$P(\overline{A}) = 1 - P(A) \qquad (4.7)$$

For example, when a die is rolled, the probability of obtaining a 1 is $1/6$, and, thus, by the complement rule the probability of not getting a 1 is $5/6$. This result is important because in some problems it may be easier to find $P(\overline{A})$ and then obtain $P(A)$, as seen in Example 4.13.

Example 4.13   Personnel Selection (Complement Rule)

Fairselect Inc. is hiring managers to fill four key positions. The candidates are five men and three women. Assuming that every combination of men and women is equally likely to be chosen, what is the probability that at least one woman will be selected?

Solution   We will solve this problem by first computing the probability of the complement of A, "No woman is selected," and then using the complement rule to compute the probability of A, "At least one woman is selected." This will be easier than computing the probabilities of one through three women being selected. Using the method of classical probability,

$$P(\overline{A}) = \frac{C_4^5}{C_4^8} = \frac{1}{14}$$

and, therefore, the required probability is

$$P(A) = 1 - P(\overline{A}) = 1 - \frac{1}{14} = \frac{13}{14}$$

Previously, we showed that if two events are mutually exclusive, then the probability of their union is the sum of the probabilities of each event:

$$P(A \cup B) = P(A) + P(B)$$

Next, we want to determine the result when events A and B are not mutually exclusive. In Section 4.1 we noted that events A and $\overline{A} \cap B$ are mutually exclusive—review result 2 and Figure 4.6—and, thus,

$$P(A \cup B) = P(A) + P(\overline{A} \cap B)$$

In addition, events $A \cap B$ and $\overline{A} \cap B$ are mutually exclusive, and their union is B—review result 1 and Figure 4.5:

$$P(B) = P(A \cap B) \cup P(\overline{A} \cap B)$$

From this we can derive the result

$$P(\overline{A} \cap B) = P(B) - P(A \cap B)$$

Figure 4.8   Venn Diagram for Addition Rule: $P(A \cup B) = P(A) + P(B) - P(A \cap B)$

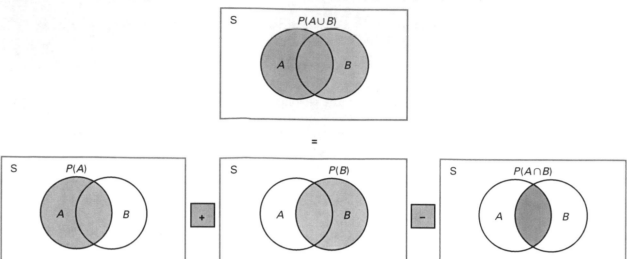

Combining these two results, we obtain the *addition rule of probabilities*.

The Addition Rule of Probabilities
Let A and B be two events. Using the **addition rule of probabilities**, the probability of their union is

$$P(A \cup B) = P(A) + P(B) - P(A \cap B)$$ (4.8)

The Venn diagram in Figure 4.8 provides an intuitive understanding of the addition rule. The larger rectangle, S, represents the entire sample space. The smaller circles, A and B, represent events A and B. We can see that the area where A and B overlap represents the intersection of the two probabilities, $P(A \cap B)$. To compute the probability of the union of events A and B, we first add the events' probabilities, $P(A) + P(B)$. However, notice that the probability of the intersection, $P(A \cap B)$, is counted twice and thus must be subtracted once.

Example 4.14   Product Selection (Addition Rule)

A hamburger chain found that 75% of all customers use mustard, 80% use ketchup, and 65% use both. What is the probability that a customer will use at least one of these?

Solution   Let A be the event "Customer uses mustard" and B the event "Customer uses ketchup." Thus, we have

$$P(A) = 0.75 \qquad P(B) = 0.80 \qquad \text{and} \qquad P(A \cap B) = 0.65$$

The required probability is

$$P(A \cup B) = P(A) + P(B) - P(A \cap B)$$
$$= 0.75 + 0.80 - 0.65 = 0.90$$

Conditional Probability

Consider a pair of events, *A* and *B*. Suppose that we are concerned about the probability of *A*, given that *B* has occurred. This problem can be approached using the concept of *conditional probability*. The basic idea is that the probability of any event's occurring often depends on whether or not other events have occurred. For example, a manufacturer planning to introduce a new brand may test-market the product in a few selected stores. This manufacturer will be much more confident about the brand's success in the wider market if it is well accepted in the test market than if it is not. The firm's assessment of the probability of high sales will therefore be conditioned by the test-market outcome.

If I knew that interest rates would fall over the next year, I would be far more bullish about the stock market than if I believed they would rise. What I know, or believe, about interest rates conditions my probability assessment of the course of stock prices. Next, we give a formal statement of conditional probability that can be used to determine the effect of prior results on a probability.

Conditional Probability
Let *A* and *B* be two events. The **conditional probability** of event *A*, given that event *B* has occurred, is denoted by the symbol *P(A|B)* and is found to be

$$P(A|B) = \frac{P(A \cap B)}{P(B)} \quad \text{provided } P(B) > 0 \tag{4.9}$$

Similarily,

$$P(B|A) = \frac{P(A \cap B)}{P(A)} \quad \text{provided } P(A) > 0$$

We can better understand these results and those that follow by considering Table 4.1. The conditional probability, *P(A|B)*, is the ratio of the joint probability, *P(A∩B)*, divided by the probability of the conditional variable, *P(B)*. This conditional probability could be thought of as using only the first row of the table that deals only with condition *B*. A similar analysis could be made for the conditional probability *P(B|A)*.

Relative frequencies can also help us understand conditional probability. Suppose that we repeat a random experiment *n* times, with n_B occurrences of event *B* and $n_{A \cap B}$ occurrences of *A* and *B* together. Then the proportion of times that *A* occurs, when *B* has occurred, is $n_{A \cap B}/n_B$, and one can think of the conditional probability of *A*, given *B*, as the limit of this proportion as the number of replications of the experiment becomes infinitely large:

$$\frac{n_{A \cap B}}{n_B} = \frac{n_{A \cap B}/n}{n_B/n}$$

Table 4.1
Joint Probability
of *A* and *B*

	A	$\overline{A}$	
B	$P(A \cap B)$	$P(\overline{A} \cap B)$	$P(B)$
$\overline{B}$	$P(A \cap \overline{B})$	$P(\overline{A} \cap \overline{B})$	$P(\overline{B})$
	$P(A)$	$P(\overline{A})$	1.0

and then, as n becomes large, the numerator and denominator of the right-hand side of this expression approach $P(A \cap B)$ and $P(B)$, respectively.

Example 4.15   Product Choice: Ketchup and Mustard (Conditional Probability)

In Example 4.14 we noted that 75% of the chain's customers use mustard, 80% use ketchup, and 65% use both. What are the probabilities that a ketchup user uses mustard and that a mustard user uses ketchup?

Solution   From Example 4.14 we know that $P(A) = 0.75$, $P(B) = 0.80$, and $P(A \cap B) = 0.65$. The probability that a ketchup user uses mustard is the conditional probability of event A, given event B.

$$P(A|B) = \frac{P(A \cap B)}{P(B)} = \frac{0.65}{0.80} = 0.8125$$

In the same way, the probability that a mustard user uses ketchup is

$$P(B|A) = \frac{P(A \cap B)}{P(A)} = \frac{0.65}{0.75} = 0.8667$$

These calculations can also be developed using Table 4.2, which has a format similar to that of Table 4.1. Note that the conditional probability that a ketchup user also uses mustard is the joint probability, 0.65, divided by the probability of a ketchup user, 0.80. A similar calculation can be made for the other conditional probability. We have found that many people find that using a table such as Table 4.2 provides better motivation and success in solving the conditional probability and related problems that follow. Using the table correctly will provide exactly the same results as using the equations. You can feel perfectly comfortable with using tables to solve the problems.

Table 4.2   Joint Probability for Mustard and Ketchup in Example 4.15

	MUSTARD	NO MUSTARD	
Ketchup	0.65	0.15	0.80
No ketchup	0.10	0.10	0.20
	0.75	0.25	1.0

An immediate consequence of conditional probability is the *multiplication rule of probabilities*, which expresses the probability of an intersection in terms of the probabilities for individual events and conditional probabilities.

The Multiplication Rule of Probabilities

Let *A* and *B* be two events. Using the **multiplication rule of probabilities**, the probability of their intersection can be derived from conditional probability as

$$P(A \cap B) = P(A|B)\,P(B) \qquad (4.10)$$

Also,

$$P(A \cap B) = P(B \mid A) \, P(A)$$

Example 4.16   Product Choice: Ketchup and Mustard II (Multiplication Rule)

When the conditional probability of mustard usage, given ketchup usage,

$$P(A|B) = \frac{0.65}{0.80} = 0.8125$$

is multiplied by the probability of ketchup usage, then we have the joint probability of both mustard and ketchup usage:

$$P(A \cap B) = (0.8125)(0.80) = 0.65$$

In the following example we see an interesting application of the multiplication rule of probabilities. We also tie together some ideas introduced previously.

Example 4.17   Sensitive Questions (Multiplication Rule)

Suppose that a survey was carried out in New York, and each respondent was faced with the following two questions:

   a. Is the last digit of your Social Security number odd?
   b. Have you ever lied on an employment application?

The second question is, of course, quite sensitive, and for various reasons we might expect that a number of people would not answer the question honestly, especially if their response was yes. To overcome this potential bias, respondents were asked to flip a coin and then to answer question (a) if the result was "head" and (b) otherwise. A "yes" response was given by 37% of all respondents. What is the probability that a respondent who was answering the sensitive question, (b), replied "yes"?

Solution   We define the following events:

   A: Respondent answers "yes."
   E_1: Respondent answers question (a).
   E_2: Respondent answers question (b).

From the problem discussion we know that $P(A) = 0.37$. We also know that the choice if question was determined by a flip of a coin and that $P(E_1) = 0.50$ and $P(E_2) = 0.50$. In addition, we know the answers to question (a). Since half of all Social Security numbers have an odd last digit, it must be that the probability of a "yes" answer, given that question (a) has been answered, is 0.50—that is, $P(A|E_1) = 0.50$.

However, we require $P(A|E_2)$, the conditional probability of a "yes" response, given that question (b) was answered. We can obtain this probability by using two results from previous sections. We know that E_1 and E_2 are mutually exclusive and collectively exhaustive. We also know that intersections $E_1 \cap A$ and $E_2 \cap A$ are mutually exclusive and that their union is A. It therefore follows that the sum of the probabilities of these two intersections is the probability of A, so

$$P(A) = P(E_1 \cap A) + P(E_2 \cap A)$$

Next, we use the multiplication rule to obtain

$$P(E_1 \cap A) = P(A|E_1)\, P(E_1) = (0.50)\,(0.50) = 0.25$$

And

$$P(E_2 \cap A) = P(A) - P(E_1 \cap A) = 0.37 - 0.25 = 0.12$$

Then we can solve for the conditional probability:

$$P(A|E_2) = \frac{P(E_2 \cap A)}{P(E_2)} = \frac{0.12}{0.50} = 0.24$$

From this result, we estimate that 24% of the surveyed population has lied on some employment application.

Statistical Independence

Statistical independence is a special case for which the conditional probability of A, given B, is the same as the unconditional probability of A. That is, $P(A|B) = P(A)$. In general, this result is not true, but when it is, we see that knowing that event B has occurred does not change the probability of event A.

Statistical Independence
Let A and B be two events. These events are said to be **statistically independent** if and only if

$$P(A \cap B) = P(A)\, P(B)$$

From the multiplication rule it also follows that

$$P(A|B) = P(A) \qquad (\text{if } P(B) > 0)$$
$$P(B|A) = P(B) \qquad (\text{if } P(A) > 0)$$

More generally, the events $E_1, E_2, \ldots, E_K$ are mutually statistically independent if and only if

$$P(E_1 \cap E_2 \cap \cdots \cap E_K) = P(E_1)\, P(E_2) \cdots P(E_K)$$

The logical basis for the definition of statistical independence is best seen in terms of conditional probabilities and is most appealing from a subjective view of probability. Suppose that I believe the probability that event A will occur is $P(A)$. Then I am given the information that event B has occurred. If this new information does not change my view of the probability of A, then $P(A) = P(A \mid B)$, and the information about the occurrence of B is of no value in determining $P(A)$. This definition of statistical independence

Table 4.3
Joint Probability for Mustard and Ketchup When They Are Independent

	MUSTARD	NO MUSTARD	
Ketchup	0.60	0.20	0.80
No ketchup	0.15	0.05	0.20
	0.75	0.25	1.0

agrees with a commonsense notion of "independence." To help understand independence, we present in Table 4.3 a revised version of our mustard and ketchup problem. In this case the marginal probabilities of ketchup and mustard are the same, but their usage is independent. Note how the above definitions for independence yield a conclusion of independence for Table 4.3, but not for Table 4.2.

In our following discussions we will refer to events being "independent." For example, the events "Dow-Jones will rise" and "Neckties are wider" are independent. Whatever I believe about the likelihood of the latter will not influence my judgment of the chances of the former. Example 4.18 illustrates a test for independence.

Example 4.18   Probability of College Degrees (Statistical Independence)

Suppose that women obtain 48% of all bachelor degrees in a particular country and that 17.5% of all bachelor degrees are in business. Also, 6% of all bachelor degrees go to women majoring in business. Are the events "Bachelor degree holder is a woman" and "Bachelor degree is in business" statistically independent?

Solution   Let A denote the event "Bachelor degree holder is a woman" and B the event "Bachelor degree is in business," and we have

$$P(A) = 0.48 \qquad P(B) = 0.175 \qquad P(A \cap B) = 0.06$$

Since

$$P(A)\,P(B) = (0.48)\,(0.175) = 0.084 \neq 0.06 = P(A \cap B)$$

these events are not independent. The dependence can be seen from the conditional probability:

$$P(A|B) = \frac{P(A \cap B)}{P(B)} = \frac{0.06}{0.175} = 0.343 \neq 0.48 = P(A)$$

Thus, in the country of interest only 34.3% of business degrees go to women, whereas women constitute 48% of all degree recipients.

It is also important to distinguish between the terms *mutually exclusive* and *independent*. Two events are mutually exclusive if they cannot occur jointly; that is, the probability of their intersection is 0. For independent events the probability of their intersection is the product of their individual probabilities, and, in general, that probability is not 0 (unless the probability of one of the events is 0, and that result is not very interesting). Also note that, if we know two events are mutually exclusive, then if one occurs, the other cannot, and the events are not independent.

In some circumstances independence can be deduced, or at least reasonably inferred, from the nature of a random experiment. For example, if we toss a fair coin two or more times, the probability of a "head" is the same for each toss and is not influenced by the outcome of the previous toss. Then the probability of the intersection can be computed from the product of individual probabilities. This is particularly useful in the case of repeated trials that are logically independent.

Example 4.19 Computer Repair (Independence)

The experience for a particular computer model is that 90% of the computers will operate for at least 1 year before repair is required. A manager purchases three of these computers. What is the probability that all three will work for 1 year without requiring any repair?

Solution In this case it is reasonable to assume that computer failures are independent for the three computers. They were all produced on the same production line, and their use in the company is likely to be similar. Given the assumption of independence, let E_i be "The ith computer works for 1 year without needing repair." The assumption of independence then leads to

$$P(E_1 \cap E_2 \cap E_3) = P(E_1)\, P(E_2)\, P(E_3) = 0.90^3 = 0.729$$

We must emphasize that events are not always independent. In Example 4.19 the computers might have their power supply from the same electrical circuit, and that circuit may not be protected against electrical surges. In that case a power surge that increases the probability of failure for one computer would result in an increase for all computers. Therefore, the events are not independent. The condition that the events are independent is an assumption and should be used only after careful analysis of the process that is being analyzed.

The following two examples illustrate how we can often simplify the determination of the probability of an event by first computing the probability of the complement and then using the probability of the complement to obtain the probability of the event of interest.

Example 4.20 The Birthday Problem (Complement Rule)

A great question for a party is "What is the probability that at least two people in this room have the same birthday?" Unfortunately, it will be difficult for you to share the solution procedure at the party.

To make the problem manageable, we assign all those born on February 29 to March 1 and assume that all 365 possible birthdays are equally likely in the population at large. We also assume that the people in the room are a random sample, with respect to birthdays, of the larger population. (These simplifications have only very small effects on the numerical results.)

Solution Let M be the number in the group and A the event "At least one pair has a common birthday." Now, to find the probability of A directly would be very tedious, since we would have to take into account the possibility of more than one pair of matching birthdays. It is easier to find the probability that "All M people have different birthdays." This is $\overline{A}$.

Since there are 365 possible birthdays for each person, and each can be associated with every possible birthday of other individuals, the total number of equally likely distinct arrangements for M people is 365^M. Next, we ask how many of these outcomes are contained in event $\overline{A}$—that is, how many pairs that involve the M individuals have different birthdays. This is precisely the same as asking in how many ways M birthdays can be selected from 365 possible birthdays and arranged in order. The first person's birthday can occur on any of 365 days, the second on any of 364 days, the third on any of 363 days, and so forth. Thus, for M people the number of different birthdays is

$$(365)\,(364)\,(363)\cdots(365-M+1)$$

The number of possible birthdays for M people is 365^M. Hence, the probability that all M birthdays will be different is

$$P(\overline{A}) = \frac{(365)(364)\cdots(365-M+1)}{365^M}$$

The required probability of at least two persons is the complement

$$P(A) = 1 - P(\overline{A}) = 1 - \frac{(365)(364)\cdots(365-M+1)}{365^M}$$

Probabilities for selected numbers of people, M, are

M	10	20	22	23	30	40	60
$P(A)$	0.117	0.411	0.476	0.507	0.706	0.891	0.994

If at least 23 people are in the group, the probability of at least one pair with the same birthday exceeds 0.50. This probability rises sharply as the group size increases until, with 60 people in the group, we are almost certain to find at least one pair. This result is surprising to most people. The probability that any given pair of people will have the same birthday is 1/365. But as the group size increases, the number of possible matches increases until the probability of at least one match becomes quite large. Here, we have the union of events that are individually unlikely, but when the events are considered together, the probability is quite large. Careful analysis using the rather simple probability rules sometimes leads to surprising results.

Example 4.21 Winning Airline Tickets (Complement Rule)

In a promotion for a particular airline, customers and potential customers were given vouchers. A 1/325 proportion of these were worth a free round-trip ticket anywhere this airline flies. How many vouchers would an individual need to collect in order to have a 50% chance of winning at least one free trip?

Solution The event of interest, A, is "At least one free trip is won from M vouchers." Again, it is easier to find first the probability of the complement, $\overline{A}$, where $\overline{A}$ is the event "No free trips are won with M vouchers." The probability of a win with one voucher is 1/325, and, thus, the probability of not winning is 324/325. If the individual has M vouchers, the event that none of these wins is just the intersection of the "No win" events for each of the vouchers. Moreover, these events are independent, and, thus,

$$P(\overline{A}) = \left(\frac{324}{325}\right)^M$$

and the probability of at least one win is

$$P(A) = 1 - P(\overline{A}) = 1 - \left(\frac{324}{325}\right)^M$$

In order for $P(A)$ to be at least 0.5, the individual needs at least $M = 225$ vouchers.

Again, this result is surprising. One might guess that, if the probability of a win for a single voucher was 1/325, then 163 vouchers would be enough to ensure a 50% chance of a win. However, in that case one would be implicitly assuming that the probability of a union is the sum of the individual probabilities, neglecting to subtract for double counting in the intersections (which in this case would involve more than one win from M vouchers).

EXERCISES

Basic Exercises

4.19 The probability of A is 0.60 and the probability of B is 0.45 and the probability of either is 0.80. What is the probability of both A and B?

4.20 The probability of A is 0.40 and the probability of B is 0.45 and the probability of either is 0.85. What is the probability of both A and B?

4.21 The probability of A is 0.60 and the probability of B is 0.40 and the probability of either is 0.76. What is the probability of both A and B?

4.22 The probability of A is 0.60 and the probability of B is 0.45 and the probability of both is 0.30. What is the probability of either A and B?

4.23 The probability of A is 0.60 and the probability of B is 0.45 and the probability of both is 0.30. What is the conditional probability of A, given B? Are A and B independent in a probability sense?

4.24 The probability of A is 0.80 and the probability of B is 0.10 and the probability of both is 0.08. What is the conditional probability of A, given B? Are A and B independent in a probability sense?

4.25 The probability of A is 0.30 and the probability of B is 0.40 and the probability of both is 0.30. What is the conditional probability of A given B? Are A and B independent in a probability sense?

4.26 The probability of A is 0.70 and the probability of B is 0.80 and the probability of both is 0.50. What is the conditional probability of A, given B? Are A and B independent in a probability sense?

Application Exercises

4.27 A company knows that a rival is about to bring out a competing product. It believes that this rival has three possible packaging plans (superior, normal, cheap) in mind and that all are equally likely. Also, there are three equally likely possible marketing strategies (intense media advertising, price discounts, and use of a coupon to reduce the price of future purchases). What is the probability that the rival will employ superior packaging in conjunction with an intense media advertising campaign? Assume that packaging plans and marketing strategies are determined independently.

4.28 A financial analyst was asked to evaluate earnings prospects for seven corporations over the next year and to rank them in order of predicted earnings growth rates.

a. How many different rankings are possible?
b. If, in fact, a specific ordering is the result of a guess, what is the probability that this guess will turn out to be correct?

4.29 A company has 50 sales representatives. It decides that the most successful representative during the previous year will be awarded a January vacation in Hawaii, while the second most successful will win a vacation in Las Vegas. The other representatives will be required to attend a conference on modern sales methods in Buffalo. How many outcomes are possible?

4.30 A securities analyst claims that, given a specific list of six common stocks, it is possible to predict, in the correct order, the three that will perform best during the coming year. What is the probability of making the correct selection by chance?

4.31 A student committee has six members—four undergraduate and two graduate students. A subcommittee of three members is to be chosen randomly so that each possible combination of three of the six students is equally likely to be selected. What is the probability that there will be no graduate students on the subcommittee?

4.32 The Little League in one community has five teams. You are required to predict, in order, the top three teams at the end of the season. Ignoring the possibility of ties, calculate the number of different predictions you could make. What is the probability of making the correct prediction by chance?

4.33 A manager has four assistants—John, George, Mary, and Jean—to assign to four tasks. Each assistant will be assigned to one of the tasks, with one assistant for each task.

a. How many different arrangements of assignments are possible?

b. If assignments are made at random, what is the probability that Mary will be assigned to a specific task?

4.34 The senior management of a corporation has decided that in the future it wishes to divide its advertising budget between two agencies. Eight agencies are currently being considered for this work. How many different choices of two agencies are possible?

4.35 You are one of seven female candidates auditioning for two parts—the heroine and her best friend—in a play. Before the auditions you know nothing of the other candidates, and you assume all candidates have equal chances for the parts.

a. How many distinct choices are possible for casting the two parts?

b. In how many of the possibilities in part (a) would you be chosen to play the heroine?

c. In how many of the possibilities in part (a) would you be chosen to play the best friend?

d. Use the results in parts (a) and (b) to find the probability you will be chosen to play the heroine. Indicate a more direct way of finding this probability.

e. Use the results in parts (a), (b), and (c) to find the probability you will be chosen to play one of the two parts. Indicate a more direct way of finding this probability.

4.36 A work crew for a building project is to be made up of two craftsmen and four laborers selected from a total of five craftsmen and six laborers.

a. How many different combinations are possible?

b. The brother of one of the craftsmen is a laborer. If the crew is selected at random, what is the probability that both brothers will be selected?

c. What is the probability that neither brother will be selected?

4.37 A mutual fund company has six funds that invest in the U.S. market and four that invest in international markets. A customer wants to invest in two U.S. funds and two international funds.

a. How many different sets of funds from this company could the investor choose?

b. Unknown to this investor, one of the U.S. funds and one of the international funds will seriously underperform next year. If the investor selects funds for purchase at random, what is the probability that at least one of the chosen funds will seriously underperform next year?

4.38 It was estimated that 30% of all seniors on a campus were seriously concerned about employment prospects, 25% were seriously concerned about grades, and 20% were seriously concerned about both. What is the probability that a randomly chosen senior from this campus is seriously concerned about at least one of these two things?

4.39 A music store owner finds that 30% of the customers entering the store ask an assistant for help and that 20% of the customers make a purchase before leaving. It is also found that 15% of all customers both ask for assistance and make a purchase. What is the probability that a customer does at least one of these two things?

4.40 Refer to the information in Exercise 4.39, and consider the two events "Customer asks for assistance" and "Customer makes purchase." In answering the following questions, provide reasons expressed in terms of probabilities of relevant events.

a. Are the two events mutually exclusive?

b. Are the two events collectively exhaustive?

c. Are the two events statistically independent?

4.41 A local public-action group solicits donations by telephone. For a particular list of prospects it was estimated that for any individual the probability was 0.05 of an immediate donation by credit card, 0.25 of no immediate donation but a request for further information through the mail, and 0.7 of no expression of interest. Information is mailed to all people requesting it, and it is estimated that 20% of these people will eventually donate. An operator makes a sequence of calls, the outcomes of which can be assumed to be independent.

a. What is the probability that no immediate credit card donation will be received until at least four unsuccessful calls have been made?

b. What is the probability that the first call leading to any donation (either immediately or eventually after a mailing) is preceded by at least four unsuccessful calls?

4.42 A mail-order firm considers three possible events in filling an order:

  A: The wrong item is sent.
  B: The item is lost in transit.
  C: The item is damaged in transit.

Assume that A is independent of both B and C and that B and C are mutually exclusive. The individual event probabilities are $P(A) = 0.02$, $P(B) = 0.01$, and $P(C) = 0.04$. Find the probability that at least one of these foul-ups occurs for a randomly chosen order.

4.43 A coach recruits for a college team a star player who is currently a high school senior. In order to play next year the senior must both complete high school with adequate grades and pass a standardized test. The coach estimates that the probability the athlete will fail to obtain adequate high school grades is 0.02, that the probability the athlete will not pass the standardized test is 0.15, and that these are independent events. According to these estimates, what is the probability that this recruit will be eligible to play in college next year?

4.44 Market research in a particular city indicated that during a week 18% of all adults watch a television program oriented to business and financial issues, 12% read a publication oriented to these issues, and 10% do both.

  a. What is the probability that an adult in this city who watches a television program oriented to business and financial issues reads a publication oriented to these issues?

  b. What is the probability that an adult in this city who reads a publication oriented to business and financial issues watches a television program oriented to these issues?

4.45 An inspector examines items coming from an assembly line. A review of her record reveals that she accepts only 8% of all defective items. It was also found that 1% of all items from the assembly line are both defective and accepted by the inspector. What is the probability that a randomly chosen item from this assembly line is defective?

4.46 An analyst is presented with lists of four stocks and five bonds. He is asked to predict, in order, the two stocks that will yield the highest return over the next year and the two bonds that will have the highest return over the next year. Suppose that these predictions are made randomly and independently of each other. What is the probability that the analyst will be successful in at least one of the two tasks?

4.47 A bank classifies borrowers as high-risk or low-risk. Only 15% of its loans are made to those in the high-risk category. Of all its loans, 5% are in default, and 40% of those in default were made to high-risk borrowers. What is the probability that a high-risk borrower will default?

4.48 A conference began at noon with two parallel sessions. The session on portfolio management was attended by 40% of the delegates, while the session on chartism was attended by 50%. The evening session consisted of a talk titled "Is the Random Walk Dead?" This was attended by 80% of all delegates.

  a. If attendance at the portfolio management session and attendance at the chartism session are mutually exclusive, what is the probability that a randomly chosen delegate attended at least one of these sessions?

  b. If attendance at the portfolio management session and attendance at the evening session are statistically independent, what is the probability that a randomly chosen delegate attended at least one of these sessions?

  c. Of those attending the chartism session, 75% also attended the evening session. What is the probability that a randomly chosen delegate attended at least one of these two sessions?

4.49 A stock market analyst claims expertise in picking stocks that will outperform the corresponding industry norms. This analyst is presented with a list of five high-technology stocks and a list of five airline stocks, and she is invited to nominate, in order, the three stocks that will do best on each of these two lists over the next year. The analyst claims that success in just one of these two tasks would be a substantial accomplishment. If, in fact, the choices are made randomly and independently, what is the probability of success in at least one of the two tasks merely by chance? Given this result, what do you think of the analyst's claim?

4.50 A quality control manager found that 30% of work-related problems occurred on Mondays and that 20% occurred in the last hour of a day's shift. It was also found that 4% of worker-related problems occurred in the last hour of Monday's shift.

  a. What is the probability that a worker-related problem that occurs on a Monday does not occur in the last hour of the day's shift?

  b. Are the events "Problem occurs on Monday" and "Problem occurs in the last hour of the day's shift" statistically independent?

4.51 A corporation was concerned about the basic educational skills of its workers and decided to offer a selected group of them separate classes in reading and practical mathematics. Of these workers 40% signed up for the reading classes and 50% for the practical mathematics classes. Of those signing up for the reading classes 30% signed up for the mathematics classes.

a. What is the probability that a randomly selected worker signed up for both classes?
b. What is the probability that a randomly selected worker who signed up for the mathematics classes also signed up for the reading classes?
c. What is the probability that a randomly chosen worker signed up for at least one of these two classes?
d. Are the events "Signs up for reading classes" and "Signs up for mathematics classes" statistically independent?

4.52 A lawn-care service makes telephone solicitations, seeking customers for the coming season. A review of the records indicates that 15% of these solicitations produce new customers and that, of these new customers, 80% had used some rival service in the previous year. It is also estimated that, of all solicitation calls made, 60% are to people who had used a rival service the previous year. What is the probability that a call to a person who had used a rival service the previous year will produce a new customer for the lawn-care service?

4.53 An editor may use all, some, or none of three possible strategies to enhance the sales of a book:

a. An expensive prepublication promotion
b. An expensive cover design
c. A bonus for sales representatives who meet predetermined sales levels

In the past these three strategies have been applied simultaneously to only 2% of the company's books. Twenty percent of the books have had expensive cover designs, and, of these, 80% have had expensive prepublication promotion. A rival editor learns that a new book is to have both an expensive prepublication promotion and an expensive cover design and now wants to know how likely it is that a bonus scheme for sales representatives will be introduced. Compute the probability of interest to the rival editor.

4.4 BIVARIATE PROBABILITIES

In this section we introduce a class of problems that involve two distinct sets of events, which we label $A_1, A_2, \ldots, A_h$ and $B_1, B_2, \ldots, B_k$. These problems have broad application in business and economics. They can be studied by constructing two-way tables that develop intuition for problem solutions. The events A_i and B_j are mutually exclusive and collectively exhaustive within their sets, but intersections $(A_i \cap B_j)$ can occur between all events from the two sets. These intersections can be regarded as basic outcomes of a random experiment. Two sets of events, considered jointly in this way, are called *bivariate*, and the probabilities are called *bivariate probabilities*.

We also consider situations where it is difficult to obtain desired conditional probabilities, but where alternative conditional probabilities are available. It may be difficult to obtain probabilities because the costs of enumeration are high or because some critical, ethical, or legal restriction prevents direct collection of probabilities.

Table 4.4 illustrates the outcomes of bivariate events labeled $A_1, A_2, \ldots, A_h$ and $B_1, B_2, \ldots, B_k$. If probabilities can be attached to all intersections $(A_i \cap B_j)$, then the whole probability structure of the random experiment is known, and other probabilities of interest can be calculated.

As a discussion example, consider a potential advertiser who wants to know both income and other relevant characteristics of the audience for a particular television show. Families may be categorized, using A_i, as to whether they regularly, occasionally, or never watch a particular series. In addition, they can be categorized, using B_j, according to low-, middle-, and high-income subgroups. Then the nine possible cross-classifications can be set out in the form of Table 4.4, with $h = 3$ and $k = 3$. The subsetting of the population can also be displayed using a tree diagram, as shown in Figure 4.9. Beginning at the left, we have the entire population of families. This population is separated into three branches, depending on their television viewing frequency. In turn, each of these branches is separated into three sub-branches, according to the family income level. As a result, there are nine sub-branches corresponding to all combinations of viewing frequency and income level.

Table 4.4
Outcomes for
Bivariate Events

	B_1	B_2	$\ldots$	B_K
A_1	$P(A_1 \cap B_1)$	$P(A_1 \cap B_2)$	$\ldots$	$P(A_1 \cap B_k)$
A_2	$P(A_2 \cap B_1)$	$P(A_2 \cap B_2)$	$\ldots$	$P(A_2 \cap B_k)$
.	.	.	.	.
.	.	.	.	.
.	.	.	.	.
A_h	$P(A_h \cap B_1)$	$P(A_h \cap B_2)$	$\ldots$	$P(A_h \cap B_k)$

Figure 4.9
Tree Diagram for
Television Viewing
and Income
Example

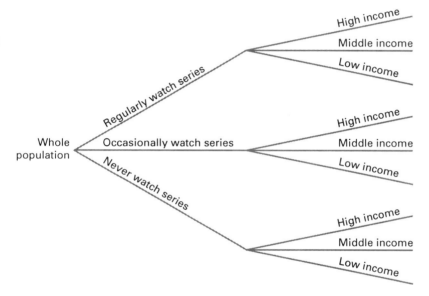

Now it is necessary to obtain the probabilities for each of the event intersections. These probabilities, as obtained from viewer surveys, are all presented in Table 4.5. For example, 10% of the families have high incomes and occasionally watch the series. These probabilities are developed using the relative frequency concept of probability, assuming that the survey is sufficiently large so that proportions can be approximated as probabilities. On this basis, the probability that a family chosen at random from the population has a high income and occasionally watches the show is 0.10.

Table 4.5
Probabilities for
Television Viewing
and Income
Example

VIEWING FREQUENCY	HIGH INCOME	MIDDLE INCOME	LOW INCOME	TOTALS
Regular	0.04	0.13	0.04	0.21
Occasional	0.10	0.11	0.06	0.27
Never	0.13	0.17	0.22	0.52
Totals	0.27	0.41	0.32	1.00

> ## Joint and Marginal Probabilities
> In the context of bivariate probabilities the intersection probabilities, $P(A_i \cap B_j)$, are called joint probabilities. The probabilities for individual events, $P(A_i)$ or $P(B_j)$, are called **marginal probabilities**. Marginal probabilities are at the margin of a table such as Table 4.5 and can be computed by summing the corresponding row or column.

To obtain the marginal probabilities for an event, we merely sum the corresponding mutually exclusive joint probabilities:

$$P(A_i) = P(A_i \cap B_1) + P(A_i \cap B_2) + \ldots + P(A_i \cap B_k)$$

Note that this would be equivalent to summing the probabilities for a particular row in Table 4.5. An analogous argument shows that the probabilities for B_j are the column totals.

Continuing with the example, define the television watching subgroups as A_1, "Regular"; A_2, "Occasional"; and A_3, "Never." Similarly define the income subgroups as B_1, "High"; B_2, "Middle"; and B_3, "Low." Then the probability that a family is an occasional viewer is

$$P(A_2) = P(A_2 \cap B_1) + P(A_2 \cap B_2) + P(A_2 \cap B_3)$$
$$= 0.10 + 0.11 + 0.06 = 0.27$$

Similarly, we can add the other rows in Table 4.5 to obtain $P(A_1) = 0.21$ and $P(A_3) = 0.52$. We can also add the columns in Table 4.5 to obtain

$$P(B_1) = 0.27 \qquad P(B_2) = 0.41 \qquad \text{and} \qquad P(B_3) = 0.32$$

Marginal probabilities can also be obtained from tree diagrams such as Figure 4.10, which has the same branches as Figure 4.9. The right-hand side contains all of the joint probabilities, and the marginal probabilities for the three viewing frequency events

Figure 4.10
Tree Diagram for the Television Viewing–Income Example, Showing Joint and Marginal Probabilities

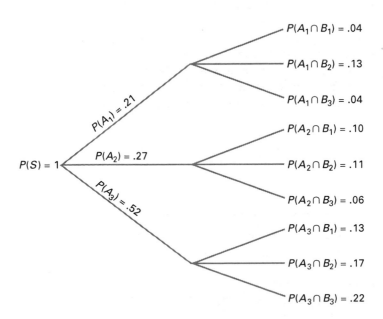

A_1: Regularly watch
A_2: Occasionally watch
A_3: Never watch
B_1: High income
B_2: Middle income
B_3: Low income
S : Sample space

Table 4.6

Conditional Probabilities of Viewing Frequencies, Given Income Levels

VIEWING FREQUENCY	HIGH INCOME	MIDDLE INCOME	LOW INCOME
Regular	0.15	0.32	0.12
Occasional	0.37	0.27	0.19
Never	0.48	0.41	0.69

are entered on the main branches by adding the probabilities on the corresponding sub-branches. The tree-branch model is particularly useful when there are more than two events of interest. In this case, for example, the advertiser might also be interested in the age of head of household or the number of children. The marginal probabilities for the various events sum to 1 because those events are mutually exclusive and mutually exhaustive.

In many applications we find that the conditional probabilities are of more interest than the marginal probabilities. An advertiser may be more concerned about the probability that a high-income family is watching than the probability of any family watching. The conditional probability can be obtained easily from the table because we have all of the joint probabilities and the marginal probabilities. For example, the probability of a high-income family regularly watching the show is

$$P(A_1|B_1) = \frac{P(A_1 \cap B_1)}{P(B_1)} = \frac{0.04}{0.27} = 0.15$$

Table 4.6 shows the probability of the viewer groups conditional on income levels. Note that the conditional probabilities with respect to a particular income group always add up to 1, as seen for the three columns in Table 4.6. This will always be the case, as seen by the following:

$$\sum_{i=1}^{h} P(A_i|B_j) = \sum_{i=1}^{h} \frac{P(A_i \cap B_j)}{P(B_j)} = \frac{P(B_j)}{P(B_j)} = 1$$

The conditional probabilities for the income groups, given viewing frequencies, can also be computed, as shown in Table 4.7, using the definition for conditional probability and the joint and marginal probabilities.

To obtain the conditional probabilities with respect to income groups in Table 4.5 we divide each of the joint probabilities in a row by the marginal probability in the right-hand column. For example,

$$P(\text{Low Income}|\text{Occasional Viewer}) = \frac{0.06}{0.27} = 0.22$$

Table 4.7

Conditional Probabilities of Income Levels, Given Viewing Frequencies

VIEWING FREQUENCY	HIGH INCOME	MIDDLE INCOME	LOW INCOME
Regular	0.19	0.62	0.19
Occasional	0.37	0.41	0.22
Never	0.25	0.33	0.42

We can also check, by using a two-way table, whether or not paired events are statistically independent. Recall that events A_i and B_j are independent if and only if their joint probability is the product of their marginal probabilities—that is, if

$$P(A_i \cap B_j) = P(A_i) \, P(B_j)$$

In Table 4.5 joint events A_2 ("Occasionally watch") and B_1 ("High Income") have a probability

$$P(A_2 \cap B_1) = 0.10$$

and

$$P(A_2) = 0.27 \qquad P(B_1) = 0.27$$

The product of these marginal probabilities is 0.0729 and thus not equal to the joint probability of 0.10. Hence, events A_2 and B_1 are not statistically independent.

> **Independent Events**
> Let A and B be a pair of events, each broken into mutually exclusive and collectively exhaustive event categories denoted by labels $A_1, A_2, \ldots, A_h$ and $B_1, B_2, \ldots, B_k$. If every event A_i is statistically independent of every event B_j, then A and B are **independent events**.

Since A_2 and B_1 are not statistically independent, it follows that the events "Viewing frequency" and "Income" are not independent.

In many practical applications the joint probabilities will not be known precisely. A sample from a population is obtained, and estimates of the joint probabilities are made from the sample data. We want to know, based on this sample evidence, if these events are independent of one another. We will develop a procedure for conducting such a test later in the book.

Odds

Odds are used to communicate probability information in some situations. For example, a sports analyst might report that the odds in favor of team A winning over team B are 2 to 1. Odds can be converted directly to probabilities, and probabilities can be converted to odds using the following equation.

> **Odds**
> The **odds** in favor of a particular event are given by the ratio of the probability of the event divided by the probability of its complement. The odds in favor of A are
>
> $$\text{Odds} = \frac{P(A)}{1 - P(A)} = \frac{P(A)}{P(\bar{A})} \qquad (4.11)$$

Therefore, the odds of 2 to 1 can be converted to the probability of A winning:

$$\frac{2}{1} = \frac{P(A)}{1 - P(A)}$$

and by basic algebra

$$2 \times (1 - P(A)) = P(A)$$

giving

$$P(A) = 0.67$$

Similarly, if the odds in favor of winning are 3 to 2, then the probability of winning is 0.60. Note that 0.60/0.40 is equal to 3/2.

Overinvolvement Ratios

There are a number of situations where it is difficult to obtain desired conditional probabilities, but alternative conditional probabilities are available. It may be difficult to obtain probabilities because the costs of enumeration are high or because some critical, ethical, or legal restriction prevents direct collection of probabilities. In some of those cases it may be possible to use basic probability relationships to derive desired probabilities from available probabilities. In this section we develop one such approach based on the use of overinvolvement ratios (Reference 3).

We will start by considering a simple example. Suppose that we know 60% of the purchasers of our product have seen our advertisement, but only 30% of the nonpurchasers have seen the advertisement. The ratio of 60% to 30% is the overinvolvement of the event "Seen our advertisement" in the purchasers group, compared to the nonpurchasers group. In the analysis to follow we show how an overinvolvement ratio greater than 1.0 provides evidence that, for example, advertising influences purchase behavior.

An overinvolvement ratio, presented in Equation 4.12, is the ratio of the probability of an event—such as viewing an advertisement—that occurs under two mutually exclusive and complementary outcome conditions, such as a product sale or not a product sale. If the ratio of the conditional probabilities is not equal to 1.0, then the event has an influence on the outcome condition. These ratios have applications in a number of business situations, including marketing, production, and accounting. In this section we develop the theory and application of *overinvolvement ratios*.

Overinvolvement Ratios
The probability of event A_1, conditional on event B_1, divided by the probability of A_1, conditional on event B_2, is defined as the **overinvolvement ratio**:

$$\frac{P(A_1 \mid B_1)}{P(A_1 \mid B_2)} \tag{4.12}$$

An overinvolvement ratio greater than 1:

$$\frac{P(A_1 \mid B_1)}{P(A_1 \mid B_2)} > 1.0$$

implies that event A_1 increases the conditional odds ratio in favor of B_1:

$$\frac{P(B_1 \mid A_1)}{P(B_2 \mid A_1)} > \frac{P(B_1)}{P(B_2)}$$

Consider a company that wishes to determine the effectiveness of a new advertisement. An experiment is conducted in which the advertisment is shown to one customer group and not to another, followed by observation of the purchase behavior of both groups. Studies of this type have a high probability of error; they can be biased because people who are watched closely often behave differently than they do when not being observed. It is possible, however, to measure the percentage of buyers who have seen an ad and to measure the percentage of nonbuyers who have seen the ad. Let us consider how those study data can be analyzed to determine the effectiveness of the new advertisement.

Advertising effectiveness is determined using the following analysis. The population is divided into

B_1: Buyers
B_2: Nonbuyers

and into

A_1: Those who have seen the advertisement
A_2: Those who have not seen the advertisement

The odds in favor of the buyer in this problem are

$$\frac{P(B_1)}{P(B_2)}$$

Similarly, we can define the conditional odds, in which we use the ratio of the probabilities that are both conditional on the same event. For this problem the odds of a buyer conditional on "Have seen an advertisement" are

$$\frac{P(B_1 | A_1)}{P(B_2 | A_1)}$$

If the conditional odds are greater than the unconditional odds, the conditioning event is said to have an influence on the event of interest. Thus, advertising would be considered effective if

$$\frac{P(B_1 | A_1)}{P(B_2 | A_1)} > \frac{P(B_1)}{P(B_2)}$$

The left-hand terms are equal to

$$P(B_1 | A_1) = \frac{P(A_1 | B_1)P(B_1)}{P(A_1)}$$

$$P(B_2 | A_1) = \frac{P(A_1 | B_2)P(B_2)}{P(A_1)}$$

By substituting these later terms, the first equation becomes

$$\frac{P(A_1 | B_1)P(B_1)}{P(A_1 | B_2)P(B_2)} > \frac{P(B_1)}{P(B_2)}$$

Dividing both sides by the right-hand ratio, we obtain

$$\frac{P(A_1 | B_1)}{P(A_1 | B_2)} > 1.0$$

This result shows that, if a larger percent of buyers have seen the advertisement, compared to nonbuyers, then the odds in favor of purchasing conditional on having seen the advertisement are greater than the unconditional odds. Therefore, we have evidence that the advertising is associated with an increased probability of purchase.

From the original problem, 60 percent of the purchasers and 30 percent of the non-purchasers had seen the advertisement. The overinvolvement ratio is 2.0 (60/30), and, thus, we conclude that the advertisement increases the probability of purchase. Market researchers use this result to evaluate the effectiveness of advertising and other sales promotion activities. Purchasers of products are asked whether they have seen certain advertisements. This is combined with random sample surveys of households from which the percentage of nonpurchasers who have seen an advertisement is determined.

Consider another situation in which it is difficult, illegal, or unethical to obtain probability results.

Example 4.22   Alcohol and Highway Crashes (Overinvolvement Ratios)

Researchers at the National Highway Traffic Safety Administration in the U.S. Department of Transportation wished to determine the effect of alcohol on high-way crashes. Clearly, it would be unethical to provide one group of drivers with alcohol and then compare their crash involvement with that of a group that did not have alcohol. However, researchers did find that 10.3% of the nighttime drivers in a specific county had been drinking and that 32.4% of the single-vehicle-accident drivers during the same time and in the same county had been drinking. Single-vehicle accidents were chosen to ensure that any driver error could be assigned to only one driver, whose alcohol usage had been measured. Based on these results they wanted to know if there was evidence to conclude that accidents increased at night when drivers had been drinking. Use the data to determine if alcohol usage leads to an increased probability of crashes (Reference 2).

Solution   Using the overinvolvement ratios can solve this problem. First, the events in the sample space need to be defined:

A_1: Driver had been drinking.
A_2: Driver had not been drinking.
C_1: Driver was involved in a crash.
C_2: Driver was not involved in a crash.

We know that alcohol, A_1, increases the probability of a crash if

$$\frac{P(A_1|C_1)}{P(A_1|C_2)} > 1.0$$

From the research the conditional probabilities are

$$P(A_1|C_1) = 0.324$$
$$P(A_1|C_2) = 0.103$$

Using these results, the overinvolvement ratio is

$$\frac{P(A_1|C_1)}{P(A_1|C_2)} = \frac{0.324}{0.103} = 3.15$$

Based on this analysis there is evidence to conclude that alcohol increases the probability of automobile crashes.

The overinvolvement ratio is a good example of how mathematical manipulations of probabilities can be used to obtain results that are useful for business decisions. The wide usage of automated methods of data collection, including bar code scanners, audience segmentation, and census data on tapes and disks, provides the possibility to compute many different probabilities, conditional probabilities, and overinvolvement ratios. As a result, analyses similar to those presented in this chapter have become part of the daily routine for marketing analysts and product managers.

EXERCISES

Basic Exercises
Basic exercises 4.54 through 4.60 refer to Table 4.8.

4.54 What is the joint probability of "High income" and "Never"?

4.55 What is the joint probability of "Low income" and "Regular"?

4.56 What is the joint probability of "Middle income" and "Never"?

4.57 What is the joint probability of "Middle income" and "Occasional"?

4.58 What is the conditional probability of "High income," given "Never"?

4.59 What is the conditional probability of "Low income," given "Occasional"?

4.60 What is the conditional probability of "Regular," given "High income"?

4.61 The probability of a sale is 0.80. What are the odds in favor of a sale?

4.62 The probability of a sale is 0.50. What are the odds in favor of a sale?

4.63 Consider two groups of students: B_1, students who received high scores on tests; and B_2, students who received low scores on tests. In group B_1, 80% study more than 25 hours per week, and in group B_2, 40% study more than 25 hours per week. What is the overinvolvement ratio for high study levels in high test scores over low test scores?

4.64 Consider two groups of students: B_1, students who received high scores on tests; and B_2, students who received low scores on tests. In group B_1, 40% study more than 25 hours per week, and in group B_2, 20% study more than 25 hours per week. What is the overinvolvement ratio for high study levels in high test scores over low test scores?

4.65 Consider two groups of students: B_1, students who received high scores on tests; and B_2, students who received low scores on tests. In group B_1, 20% study more than 25 hours per week, and in group B_2, 40% study more than 25 hours per week. What is the overinvolvement ratio for high study levels in high test scores over low test scores?

Application Exercises

4.66 A survey carried out for a supermarket classified customers according to whether their visits to the store are frequent or infrequent and whether they often, sometimes, or never purchase generic products. The accompanying table gives the proportions of people surveyed in each of the six joint classifications.

Frequency of Visit	Purchase of Generic Products		
	Often	Sometimes	Never
Frequent	0.12	0.48	0.19
Infrequent	0.07	0.06	0.08

a. What is the probability that a customer both is a frequent shopper and often purchases generic products?

b. What is the probability that a customer who never buys generic products visits the store frequently?

c. Are the events "Never buys generic products" and "Visits the store frequently" independent?

d. What is the probability that a customer who infrequently visits the store often buys generic products?

e. Are the events "Often buys generic products" and "Visits the store infrequently" independent?

Table 4.8 Probabilities for Television Viewing and Income

VIEWING FREQUENCY	HIGH INCOME	MIDDLE INCOME	LOW INCOME	TOTALS
Regular	0.10	0.15	0.05	0.30
Occasional	0.10	0.20	0.10	0.40
Never	0.05	0.05	0.20	0.30
Totals	0.25	0.40	0.35	1.00

f. What is the probability that a customer frequently visits the store?

g. What is the probability that a customer never buys generic products?

h. What is the probability that a customer either frequently visits the store or never buys generic products or both?

4.67 A consulting organization predicts whether corporations' earnings for the coming year will be unusually low, unusually high, or normal. Before deciding whether to continue purchasing these forecasts, a stockbroker compares past predictions with actual outcomes. The accompanying table shows proportions in the nine joint classifications.

	Prediction		
Outcome	Unusually High	Normal	Unusually Low
Unusually high	0.23	0.12	0.03
Normal	0.06	0.22	0.08
Unusually low	0.01	0.06	0.19

a. What proportion of predictions have been for unusually high earnings?

b. What proportion of outcomes have been for unusually high earnings?

c. If a firm were to have unusually high earnings, what is the probability that the consulting organization would correctly predict this event?

d. If the organization predicted unusually high earnings for a corporation, what is the probability that these would materialize?

e. What is the probability that a corporation for which unusually high earnings had been predicted will have unusually low earnings?

4.68 Subscribers to a local newspaper were asked whether they regularly, occasionally, or never read the business section and also whether they had traded common stocks (or shares in a mutual fund) over the last year. The table given here shows proportions of subscribers in six joint classifications.

Traded Stocks	Read Business Section		
	Regularly	Occasionally	Never
Yes	0.18	0.10	0.04
No	0.16	0.31	0.21

a. What is the probability that a randomly chosen subscriber never reads the business section?

b. What is the probability that a randomly chosen subscriber has traded stocks over the last year?

c. What is the probability that a subscriber who never reads the business section has traded stocks over the last year?

d. What is the probability that a subscriber who traded stocks over the last year never reads the business section?

e. What is the probability that a subscriber who does not regularly read the business section traded stocks over the last year?

4.69 A corporation regularly takes deliveries of a particular sensitive part from three subcontractors. It found that the proportion of parts that are good or defective from the total received were as shown in the following table:

	Subcontractor		
Part	A	B	C
Good	0.27	0.30	0.33
Defective	0.02	0.05	0.03

a. If a part is chosen randomly from all those received, what is the probability that it is defective?

b. If a part is chosen randomly from all those received, what is the probability it is from subcontractor B?

c. What is the probability that a part from subcontractor B is defective?

d. What is the probability that a randomly chosen defective part is from subcontractor B?

e. Is the quality of a part independent of the source of supply?

f. In terms of quality, which of the three subcontractors is most reliable?

4.70 Students in a business statistics class were asked what grade they expected in the course and whether they worked additional problems beyond those assigned by the instructor. The following table gives proportions of students in each of eight joint classifications.

Worked Problems	Expected Grade			
	A	B	C	Below C
Yes	0.12	0.06	0.12	0.02
No	0.13	0.21	0.26	0.08

a. Find the probability that a randomly chosen student from this class worked additional problems.

b. Find the probability that a randomly chosen student from this class expects an A.

c. Find the probability that a randomly chosen student who worked additional problems expects an A.

d. Find the probability that a randomly chosen student who expects an A worked additional problems.

e. Find the probability that a randomly chosen student who worked additional problems expects a grade below B.

f. Are "Worked additional problems" and "Expected grade" statistically independent?

4.71 The accompanying table shows proportions of computer salespeople classified according to marital status and whether they left their jobs or stayed over a period of 1 year.

Marital Status	Stayed 1 Year	Left
Married	0.64	0.13
Single	0.17	0.06

a. What is the probability that a randomly chosen salesperson was married?

b. What is the probability that a randomly chosen salesperson left the job within the year?

c. What is the probability that a randomly chosen single salesperson left the job within the year?

d. What is the probability that a randomly chosen salesperson who stayed in the job over the year was married?

4.72 The accompanying table shows proportions of adults in nonmetropolitan areas, categorized as to whether they are readers or nonreaders of newspapers and whether or not they voted in the last election.

Voted	Readers	Nonreaders
Yes	0.63	0.13
No	0.14	0.10

a. What is the probability that a randomly chosen adult from this population voted?

b. What is the probability that a randomly chosen adult from this population reads newspapers?

c. What is the probability that a randomly chosen adult from this population who did not read newspapers did not vote?

4.73 A campus student club distributed material about membership to new students attending an orientation meeting. Of those receiving this material 40% were men and 60% were women. Subsequently, it was found that 7% of the men and 9% of the women who received this material joined the club.

a. Find the probability that a randomly chosen new student who receives the membership material will join the club.

b. Find the probability that a randomly chosen new student who joins the club after receiving the membership material is a woman.

4.74 An analyst attempting to predict a corporation's earnings next year believes that the corporation's business is quite sensitive to the level of interest rates. She believes that, if average rates in the next year are more than 1% higher than this year, the probability of significant earnings growth is 0.1. If average rates next year are more than 1% lower than this year, the probability of significant earnings growth is estimated to be 0.8. Finally, if average interest rates next year are within 1% of this year's rates, the probability for significant earnings growth is put at 0.5. The analyst estimates that the

probability is 0.25 that rates next year will be more than 1% higher than this year and 0.15 that they will be more than 1% lower than this year.

a. What is the estimated probability that both interest rates will be 1% higher and significant earnings growth will result?

b. What is the probability that this corporation will experience significant earnings growth?

c. If the corporation exhibits significant earnings growth, what is the probability that interest rates will have been more than 1% lower than in the current year?

4.75 Forty-two percent of a corporation's blue-collar employees were in favor of a modified health care plan, and 22% of its blue-collar employees favored a proposal to change the work schedule. Thirty-four percent of those favoring the health plan modification favored the work schedule change.

a. What is the probability that a randomly selected blue-collar employee is in favor of both the modified health care plan and the changed work schedule?

b. What is the probability that a randomly chosen blue-collar employee is in favor of at least one of the two changes?

c. What is the probability that a blue-collar employee favoring the work schedule change also favors the modified health plan?

4.76 The grades of a freshman college class, obtained after the first year of college, were analyzed. Seventy percent of the students in the top quarter of the college class had graduated in the upper 10% of their high school class, as had 50% of the students in the middle half of the college class and 20% of the students in the bottom quarter of the college class.

a. What is the probability that a randomly chosen freshman graduated in the upper 10% of his or her high school class?

b. What is the probability that a randomly chosen freshman who graduated in the upper 10% of his or her high school class will be in the top quarter of the college class?

c. What is the probability that a randomly chosen freshman who did not graduate in the upper 10% of his or her high school class will not be in the top quarter of the college class?

4.77 Before books aimed at preschool children are marketed, reactions are obtained from a panel of preschool children. These reactions are categorized as "favorable," "neutral," or "unfavorable." Subsequently, book sales are categorized as "high," "moderate," or "low," according to the norms of this market. Similar panels have evaluated 1,000 books in the past. The accompanying table shows their reactions and the resulting market performance of the books.

Sales	Panel Reaction		
	Favorable	Neutral	Unfavorable
High	173	101	61
Moderate	88	211	70
Low	42	113	141

a. If the panel reaction is favorable, what is the probability that sales will be high?
b. If the panel reaction is unfavorable, what is the probability that sales will be low?
c. If the panel reaction is neutral or better, what is the probability that sales will be low?
d. If sales are low, what is the probability that the panel reaction was neutral or better?

4.78 A manufacturer produces boxes of candy, each containing 10 pieces. Two machines are used for this purpose. After a large batch has been produced, it is discovered that one of the machines, which produces 40% of the total output, has a fault that has led to the introduction of an impurity into 10% of the pieces of candy it makes. From a single box of candy, one piece is selected at random and tested. If that piece contains no impurity, what is the probability that the faulty machine produced the box from which it came?

4.79 A student feels that 70% of his college courses have been enjoyable and the remainder have been boring. This student has access to student evaluations of professors and finds out that professors who had previously received strong positive evaluations from their students have taught 60% of his enjoyable courses and 25% of his boring courses. Next semester the student decides to take three courses, all from professors who have received strongly positive student evaluations. Assume that this student's reactions to the three courses are independent of one another.

a. What is the probability that this student will find all three courses enjoyable?
b. What is the probability that this student will find at least one of the courses enjoyable?

4.5 Bayes' Theorem

In this section we introduce an important result that has many applications to management decision making. Bayes' theorem provides a way of revising conditional probabilities by using available information. It also provides a procedure for determining how probability statements should be adjusted, given additional information.

Reverend Thomas Bayes (1702–1761) developed Bayes' theorem, originally published in 1763 after his death and again in 1958 (Reference 1). Because games of chance and hence probability were considered to be works of the devil, the results were not widely publicized. Since World War II a major area of statistics and a major area of management decision theory have developed, based on the original works of Thomas Bayes. We begin our development with an example problem followed by a more formal development.

Example 4.23 Drug Screening (Bayes' Theorem)

A number of corporations use routine screening tests to determine if prospective employees are drug users or have various medical conditions or both. Jennifer Smith, president of Fairweather Industries Inc., has requested an analysis to determine the feasibility of screening prospective employees to determine if they are HIV positive. The potential future medical costs for such persons can dramatically raise the cost of health insurance for employees of the company, and Jennifer would like to minimize the chances of such costs. Suppose that 10% of the potential job applicants are HIV positive. In addition, a test is available that correctly identifies a person's condition 90% of the time. If a person is HIV positive, the probability is 0.90 that the person is correctly identified by the test as HIV positive. Similarly, if the person is not HIV positive, the probability is 0.90 that the person is correctly identified as not HIV positive.

We should note that there are potential ethical and possible legal questions concerning the denial of employment based on a person's medical condition. Of course, such concerns are a very important part of the decision concerning the use of a testing procedure. Here, we are concerned about the feasibility of using such a test if one has decided that such a test is proper, given the legal and value systems.

Solution   The first step in the analysis is to identify the events in the sample space:

H_1: The person is HIV positive.
H_2: The person is not HIV positive.

The proposed test indicates positive or negative results:

T_1: Test says that the person is HIV positive.
T_2: Test says that the person is not HIV positive.

From the information provided the following probabilities can be defined:

$$P(H_1) = 0.10 \qquad P(H_2) = 0.90$$
$$P(T_1 | H_1) = 0.90 \qquad P(T_2 | H_1) = 0.10$$
$$P(T_1 | H_2) = 0.10 \qquad P(T_2 | H_2) = 0.90$$

Using these probabilities, a two-way table containing the joint probabilities can be constructed:

$$P(H_1 \cap T_1) = P(T_1 | H_1)P(H_1) = 0.90 \times 0.10 = 0.09$$
$$P(H_1 \cap T_2) = P(T_2 | H_1)P(H_1) = 0.10 \times 0.10 = 0.01$$
$$P(H_2 \cap T_1) = P(T_1 | H_2)P(H_2) = 0.10 \times 0.90 = 0.09$$
$$P(H_2 \cap T_2) = P(T_2 | H_2)P(H_2) = 0.90 \times 0.90 = 0.81$$

From Table 4.9 we can easily determine the conditional probability of HIV positive, given that the test says HIV positive, by dividing the joint probability of H_1 and T_1 (0.09) by the marginal probability of T_1 (0.18):

$$P(H_1 | T_1) = \frac{P(H_1 \cap T_1)}{P(T_1)} = \frac{0.09}{0.18} = 0.50$$

Similarly, the probability of not HIV positive, given that the test says not HIV positive, can be obtained from the second column of Table 4.9:

$$P(H_2 | T_2) = \frac{P(H_2 \cap T_2)}{P(T_2)} = \frac{0.81}{0.82} = 0.988$$

From these results we see that, if the test says a person is not HIV positive, the probability is very high that the test result is correct. However, if the test says that the person is HIV positive, the probability is only 0.50 that the person is HIV positive. This is a large increase over a probability of 0.10 for a randomly selected person. However, it is clear that the company would not want to reject prospective employees merely on the results of this screening test. The potential for unethical hiring procedures and serious legal action would be too great. The best strategy would be to

Table 4.9   Drug Test Subgroups

	T_1 (Test Says HIV)	T_2 (Test Says Not HIV)	Total
H_1 (HIV positive)	0.09	0.01	0.10
H_2 (not HIV positive)	0.09	0.81	0.90
Total	0.18	0.82	1.0

use a second independent test to further screen the people identified as HIV positive by the first test. We stress again that there may be serious ethical and medical concerns if people are rejected for employment because they are HIV positive.

Given this background, we will now provide a more formal development of Bayes' theorem. To begin, we first review the multiplication rule, Equation 4.10:

$$P(A \cap B) = P(A \mid B)P(B) = P(B \mid A)P(A)$$

Bayes' theorem follows from this rule.

Bayes' Theorem
Let *A* and *B* be two events. Then **Bayes' theorem** states that

$$P(B \mid A) = \frac{P(A \mid B)P(B)}{P(A)} \tag{4.13}$$

and

$$P(A \mid B) = \frac{P(B \mid A)P(A)}{P(B)}$$

An interesting interpretation of Bayes' theorem has been developed in the context of subjective probabilities. Suppose that an individual is interested in event *B* and forms a subjective view of the probability that *B* will occur; in this context the probability $P(B)$ is called a *prior* probability. If the individual then acquires an additional piece of information—namely, that event *A* has occurred—this may cause a modification of the initial judgment as to the likelihood of the occurrence of *B*. Since *A* is known to have happened, the relevant probability for *B* is now the conditional probability of *B*, given *A*, and is termed the *posterior* probability. Viewed in this way, Bayes' theorem can be thought of as a mechanism for updating a prior probability to a posterior probability when the information that *A* has occurred becomes available. The theorem then states that the updating is accomplished through the multiplication of the prior probability by $P(A \mid B)/P(A)$.

We know that people commonly form and subsequently modify subjective probability assessments. For example, an important part of an auditor's work is to determine whether or not the account balances are correct. Before examining a particular account, the auditor will have formed an opinion, based on previous audits, of the probability that there is an error. However, if the balance is found to be substantially different from what might be expected on the basis of the last few years' figures, the auditor will believe that the probability of an error is higher and therefore give the account particularly close attention. Here, the prior probability has been updated in the light of additional information.

Example 4.24   Auditing Business Records (Bayes' Theorem)

Based on an examination of past records of a corporation's account balances, an auditor finds that 15% have contained errors. Of those balances in error 60% were regarded as unusual values based on historical figures. Of all the account balances 20% were unusual values. If the figure for a particular balance appears unusual on this basis, what is the probability that it is in error?

Solution   Let A be "Error in account balance" and B be "Unusual value based on historical figures." Then from the available information

$$P(A) = 0.15 \qquad P(B) = 0.20 \qquad P(B|A) = 0.60$$

Using Bayes' theorem,

$$P(A|B) = \frac{P(B|A)P(A)}{P(B)} = \frac{(0.60)(0.15)}{0.20} = 0.45$$

Thus, given the information that the account balance appears unusual, the probability that it is in error is modified from the prior 0.15 to the posterior 0.45.

Bayes' theorem is often expressed in a different, but equivalent, form that uses more detailed information. Let $E_1, E_2, \ldots, E_K$ be K mutually exclusive and collectively exhaustive events, and let A be some other event. We can find the probability of E_i, given A, by using Bayes' theorem:

$$P(E_i|A) = \frac{P(A|E_i)P(E_i)}{P(A)}$$

The denominator can be expressed in terms of the probabilities of A, given the various E_i's, by using the intersections and the multiplication rule:

$$P(A) = P(A \cap E_1) + P(A \cap E_2) + \ldots + P(A \cap E_K)$$
$$= P(A|E_1) P(E_1) + P(A|E_2) P(E_2) + \ldots + P(A|E_K) P(E_K)$$

These results can be combined to provide a second form of Bayes' theorem.

Bayes' Theorem (Alternative Statement)
Let $E_1, E_2, \ldots, E_K$ be K mutually exclusive and collectively exhaustive events, and let A be some other event. The conditional probability of E_i, given A, can be expressed as Bayes' Theorem:

$$P(E_i|A) = \frac{P(A|E_i)P(E_i)}{P(A)}$$
$$= \frac{P(A|E_i)P(E_i)}{P(A|E_1)P(E_1) + P(A|E_2)P(E_2) + \ldots + P(A|E_k)P(E_k)} \tag{4.14}$$

where

$$P(A) = P(A \cap E_1) + P(A \cap E_2) + \ldots + P(A \cap E_k)$$
$$= P(A|E_1)P(E_1) + P(A|E_2)P(E_2) + \ldots + P(A|E_k)P(E_k)$$

The advantage of this restatement of the theorem lies in the fact that the probabilities it involves are often precisely those that are directly available.

This process for solving conditional probability and/or Bayes' problems can be summarized as follows.

Solution Steps for Bayes' Theorem

1. Define the subset events from the problem.
2. Define the probabilities for the events defined in Step 1.
3. Compute the complements of the probabilities.
4. Apply Bayes' theorem to compute the probability for the problem solution.

Here, we apply these solution steps to a problem that requires careful analysis. We consider Example 4.23 again. The first task is to identify the events in the sample space. The sample space in Example 4.23 consists of prospective employees separated into H_1, HIV positive, and H_2, not HIV positive. This required an independent judgment of which people were actually HIV positive and which were not. These events cover the sample space. Events were also identified by their test classification. Events are T_1, the test indicates HIV positive, and T_2, the test indicates non–HIV positive. These events also cover the sample space. Note that a test result T_1, which indicates HIV positive, does not guarantee that the person is HIV positive, H_1.

After the events have been defined, we need to determine the capability of the procedure to predict, using the data. Thus, in Example 4.23 the test was given to a group of known HIV positives and to a group of known non–HIV positives. These test results provided the conditional probabilities of the test results, given either HIV positive or not. The data were converted to information concerning the quality of the screening test predictions by using Bayes' theorem. The final task is to express one or more questions in the form of Bayes' theorem. In Example 4.23 we were interested in the probability that a prospective employee was HIV positive, given that the person obtained a positive result on the test. We also realized that it was important to know the probability that a person was not HIV positive, given a positive test result.

Example 4.25   Automobile Sales Incentive (Bayes' Theorem)

A car dealership knows from past experience that 10% of the people who come into the showroom and talk to a salesperson will eventually purchase a car. To increase the chances of success, you propose to offer a free dinner with a salesperson for all people who agree to listen to a complete sales presentation. You know that some people will do anything for a free dinner even if they do not intend to purchase a car. However, some people would rather not spend a dinner with a car salesperson. Thus, you wish to test the effectiveness of this sales promotion incentive. The project is conducted for six months, and 40% of the people who purchased cars had a free dinner. In addition, 10% of the people who did not purchase cars had a free dinner.

The specific questions to be answered are these:

a. Do people who accept the dinner have a higher probability of purchasing a new car?

b. What is the probability that a person who does not accept a free dinner will purchase a car?

Solution

Step 1. Define the subset events from the problem:

D_1: Customer has dinner with the salesperson.
D_2: Customer does not have dinner with the salesperson.
P_1: Customer purchases a car.
P_2: Customer does not purchase a car.

Step 2. Define the probabilities for the events defined in Step 1:

$$P(P_1) = 0.10 \qquad P(D_1|P_1) = 0.40 \qquad P(D_1|P_2) = 0.10$$

Step 3. Compute the complements of the probabilities:

$$P(P_2) = 0.90 \qquad P(D_2|P_1) = 0.60 \qquad P(D_2|P_2) = 0.90$$

Step 4. Apply Bayes' theorem to compute the probability for the problem solution.

a. We know that the sales promotion plan has increased the probability of a car purchase if more than 10% of those that had dinner purchased a car. Specifically, we ask if

$$P(P_1|D_1) > P(P_1)$$
$$P(P_1|D_1) > 0.10$$

Using Bayes' theorem, we find that

$$P(P_1|D_1) = \frac{P(D_1|P_1)P(P_1)}{P(D_1|P_1)P(P_1) + P(D_1|P_2)P(P_2)}$$
$$= \frac{0.40 \times 0.10}{0.40 \times 0.10 + 0.10 \times 0.90}$$
$$= 0.308$$

Therefore, the probability of purchase is higher, given the dinner with the salesperson.

b. This question asks that we compute the probability of purchase, P_1, given that the customer does not have dinner with the salesperson, D_2. We again apply Bayes' theorem to compute

$$P(P_1|D_2) = \frac{P(D_2|P_1)P(P_1)}{P(D_2|P_1)P(P_1) + P(D_2|P_2)P(P_2)}$$
$$= \frac{0.60 \times 0.10}{0.60 \times 0.10 + 0.90 \times 0.90}$$
$$= 0.069$$

We see that those who refuse the dinner have a lower probability of purchase. To provide additional evaluation of the sales program, we might also wish to compare the 6-month sales experience with that of other dealers and with previous sales experience, given similar economic conditions.

We have presented a logical step-by-step or linear procedure for solving Bayes' problems. This procedure works very well for persons experienced in solving this type of problem. The procedure can also help you to organize Bayes' problems. However, most real problem solving in new situations does not follow a step-by-step or linear procedure. Thus, you are likely to move back to previous steps and revise your initial definitions. In some cases you may find it useful to write out Bayes' theorem before you define the probabilities. The mathematical form defines the probabilities that must be obtained from the problem description. Alternatively, you may want to construct a two-way table, as we did in Example 4.23. As you are learning to solve these problems, use the structure, but learn to be creative and willing to go back to previous steps.

EXERCISES

Basic Exercises

The following basic exercises use a sample space defined by events A_1, A_2, B_1, and B_2.

4.80 Given $P(A_1) = 0.40$, $P(B_1|A_1) = 0.60$, and $P(B_1|A_2) = 0.70$, what is the probability of $P(A_1|B_1)$?

4.81 Given $P(A_1) = 0.80$, $P(B_1|A_1) = 0.60$, and $P(B_1|A_2) = 0.20$, what is the probability of $P(A_1|B_1)$?

4.82 Given $P(A_1) = 0.50$, $P(B_1|A_1) = 0.40$, and $P(B_1|A_2) = 0.70$, what is the probability of $P(A_1|B_2)$?

4.83 Given $P(A_1) = 0.40$, $P(B_1|A_1) = 0.60$, and $P(B_1|A_2) = 0.70$, what is the probability of $P(A_2|B_2)$?

4.84 Given $P(A_1) = 0.60$, $P(B_1|A_1) = 0.60$, and $P(B_1|A_2) = 0.40$, what is the probability of $P(A_1|B_1)$?

Application Exercises

4.85 A publisher sends advertising materials for an accounting text to 80% of all professors teaching the appropriate accounting course. Thirty percent of the professors who received this material adopted the book, as did 10% of the professors who did not receive the material. What is the probability that a professor who adopts the book has received the advertising material?

4.86 A stock market analyst examined the prospects of the shares of a large number of corporations. When the performance of these stocks was investigated one year later, it turned out that 25% performed much better than the market average, 25% much worse, and the remaining 50% about the same as the average. Forty percent of the stocks that turned out to do much better than the market were rated "good buys" by the analyst, as were 20% of those that did about as well as the market and 10% of those that did much worse. What is the probability that a stock rated a "good buy" by the analyst performed much better than the average?

SUMMARY

In this chapter we introduced the basic ideas of probability. A rigorous set of definitions and rules provides the capability to develop procedures for solving the core of probability problems that occur in economic and business settings. We developed these problem-solving procedures using joint probabilities, marginal probabilities, independence, conditional probabilities, overinvolvement ratios, and Bayes' theorem. Problem-solving methods include the use of equations, Venn diagrams, and two-way tables.

KEY WORDS

- addition rule of probabilities
- basic outcomes
- Bayes' theorem
- Bayes' theorem (alternative statement)
- classical probability
- collectively exhaustive
- combination
- complement
- complement rule
- conditional probability
- event
- independent events
- intersection
- joint probabilities
- marginal probabilities
- multiplication rule of probabilities
- mutually exclusive
- number of combinations
- odds
- overinvolvement ratios
- permutations
- probability postulates

- random experiment
- relative frequency probability
- sample space
- solution steps for Bayes' theorem
- statistical independence
- subjective probability
- union

CHAPTER EXERCISES AND APPLICATIONS

4.87 Suppose that you have an intelligent friend who has not studied probability. How would you explain to your friend the distinction between mutually exclusive events and independent events? Illustrate your answer with suitable examples.

4.88 State, with reasons, whether each of the following statements is true or false:

a. The complement of the union of two events is the intersection of their complements.
b. The sum of the probabilities of collectively exhaustive events must equal 1.
c. The number of combinations of x objects chosen from n is equal to the number of combinations of $(n - x)$ objects chosen from n, where $1 \leq x \leq (n - 1)$.
d. If A and B are two events, the probability of A, given B, is the same as the probability of B, given A, if the probability of A is the same as the probability of B.
e. If an event and its complement are equally likely to occur, the probability of that event must be 0.5.
f. If A and B are independent, then $\overline{A}$ and $\overline{B}$ must be independent.
g. If A and B are mutually exclusive, then $\overline{A}$ and $\overline{B}$ must be mutually exclusive.

4.89 Explain carefully the meaning of conditional probability. Why is this concept important in discussing the chance of an event's occurrence?

4.90 "Bayes' theorem is important, as it provides a rule for moving from a prior probability to a posterior probability." Elaborate on this statement so that it would be well understood by a fellow student who has not yet studied probability.

4.91 State, with reasons, whether each of the following statements is true or false:

a. The probability of the union of two events cannot be less than the probability of their intersection.
b. The probability of the union of two events cannot be more than the sum of their individual probabilities.
c. The probability of the intersection of two events cannot be greater than either of their individual probabilities.
d. An event and its complement are mutually exclusive.
e. The individual probabilities of a pair of events cannot sum to more than 1.

f. If two events are mutually exclusive, they must also be collectively exhaustive.
g. If two events are collectively exhaustive, they must also be mutually exclusive.

4.92 Distinguish among joint probability, marginal probability, and conditional probability. Provide some examples to make the distinctions clear.

4.93 State, giving reasons, whether each of the following claims is true or false:

a. The conditional probability of A, given B, must be at least as large as the probability of A.
b. An event must be independent of its complement.
c. The probability of A, given B, must be at least as large as the probability of the intersection of A and B.
d. The probability of the intersection of two events cannot exceed the product of their individual probabilities.
e. The posterior probability of any event must be at least as large as its prior probability.

4.94 Show that the probability of the union of events A and B can be written

$$P(A \cup B) = P(A) + P(B) [1 - P(A|B)]$$

4.95 An insurance company estimated that 30% of all automobile accidents were partly caused by weather conditions and that 20% of all automobile accidents involved bodily injury. Further, of those accidents that involved bodily injury, 40% were partly caused by weather conditions.

a. What is the probability that a randomly chosen accident both was partly caused by weather conditions and involved bodily injury?
b. Are the events "Partly caused by weather conditions" and "Involved bodily injury" independent?
c. If a randomly chosen accident was partly caused by weather conditions, what is the probability that it involved bodily injury?
d. What is the probability that a randomly chosen accident both was not partly caused by weather conditions and did not involve bodily injury?

4.96 A company places a rush order for wire of two thicknesses. Consignments of each thickness are to be sent immediately when they are available. Previous experience suggests that the probability is

0.8 that at least one of these consignments will arrive within a week. It is also estimated that, if the thinner wire arrives within a week, the probability is 0.4 that the thicker wire will also arrive within a week. Further, it is estimated that, if the thicker wire arrives within a week, the probability is 0.6 that the thinner wire will also arrive within a week.

a. What is the probability that the thicker wire will arrive within a week?
b. What is the probability that the thinner wire will arrive within a week?
c. What is the probability that both consignments will arrive within a week?

4.97 Based on a survey of students on a large campus, it was estimated that 35% of the students drink at least once a week in local bars and that 40% of all students have grade point averages of B or better. Further, of those who drink at least once a week in local bars, 30% have a B average or better.

a. What is the probability that a randomly chosen student both drinks at least once a week in local bars and has a B average or better?
b. What is the probability that a randomly chosen student who has a B average or better drinks at least once a week in local bars?
c. What is the probability that a randomly chosen student has at least one of these characteristics: "Drinks at least once a week in local bars" and "Has B average or better"?
d. What is the probability that a randomly chosen student who does not have a B average or better does not drink at least once a week in local bars?
e. Are the events "Drinks at least once a week in local bars" and "Has B average or better" independent?
f. Are the events "Drinks at least once a week in local bars" and "Has B average or better" mutually exclusive?
g. Are the events "Drinks at least once a week in local bars" and "Has B average or better" collectively exhaustive?

4.98 In a campus restaurant it was found that 35% of all customers order hot meals and that 50% of all customers are students. Further, 25% of all customers who are students order hot meals.

a. What is the probability that a randomly chosen customer both is a student and orders a hot meal?
b. If a randomly chosen customer orders a hot meal, what is the probability that the customer is a student?
c. What is the probability that a randomly chosen customer both does not order a hot meal and is not a student?

d. Are the events "Customer orders a hot meal" and "Customer is a student" independent?
e. Are the events "Customer orders a hot meal" and "Customer is a student" mutually exclusive?
f. Are the events "Customer orders a hot meal" and "Customer is a student" collectively exhaustive?

4.99 It is known that 20% of all farms in a state exceed 160 acres and that 60% of all farms in that state are owned by persons over 50 years old. Of all farms in the state exceeding 160 acres, 55% are owned by persons over 50 years old.

a. What is the probability that a randomly chosen farm in this state both exceeds 160 acres and is owned by a person over 50 years old?
b. What is the probability that a farm in this state either is bigger than 160 acres or is owned by a person over 50 years old (or both)?
c. What is the probability that a farm in this state, owned by a person over 50 years old, exceeds 160 acres?
d. Are size of farm and age of owner in this state statistically independent?

4.100 In a large corporation 80% of the employees are men and 20% are women. The highest levels of education obtained by the employees are graduate training for 10% of the men, undergraduate training for 30% of the men, and high school training for 60% of the men. The highest levels of education obtained are also graduate training for 15% of the women, undergraduate training for 40% of the women, and high school training for 45% of the women.

a. What is the probability that a randomly chosen employee will be a man with only a high school education?
b. What is the probability that a randomly chosen employee will have graduate training?
c. What is the probability that a randomly chosen employee who has graduate training is a man?
d. Are gender and level of education of employees in this corporation statistically independent?
e. What is the probability that a randomly chosen employee who has not had graduate training is a woman?

4.101 A large corporation organized a ballot for all its workers on a new bonus plan. It was found that 65% of all night-shift workers favored the plan and that 40% of all female workers favored the plan. Also, 50% of all employees are night-shift workers and 30% of all employees are women. Finally, 20% of all night-shift workers are women.

a. What is the probability that a randomly chosen employee is a woman in favor of the plan?

b. What is the probability that a randomly chosen employee is either a woman or a night-shift worker (or both)?

c. Is employee gender independent of whether the night shift is worked?

d. What is the probability that a female employee is a night-shift worker?

e. If 50% of all male employees favor the plan, what is the probability that a randomly chosen employee both does not work the night shift and does not favor the plan?

4.102 A jury of 12 members is to be selected from a panel consisting of 8 men and 8 women.

a. How many different jury selections are possible?

b. If the choice is made randomly, what is the probability that a majority of the jury members will be men?

4.103 A consignment of 12 electronic components contains 1 component that is faulty. Two components are chosen randomly from this consignment for testing.

a. How many different combinations of 2 components could be chosen?

b. What is the probability that the faulty component will be chosen for testing?

4.104 Of 100 patients with a certain disease 10 were chosen at random to undergo a drug treatment that increases the cure rate from 50% for those not given the treatment to 75% for those given the drug treatment.

a. What is the probability that a randomly chosen patient both was cured and was given the drug treatment?

b. What is the probability that a patient who was cured had been given the drug treatment?

c. What is the probability that a specific group of 10 patients was chosen to undergo the drug treatment? (Leave your answer in terms of factorials.)

4.105 Subscriptions to a particular magazine are classified as gift, previous renewal, direct mail, and subscription service. In January 8% of expiring subscriptions were gift; 41%, previous renewal; 6%, direct mail; and 45%, subscription service. The percentages of renewals in these four categories were 81%, 79%, 60%, and 21%, respectively. In February of the same year 10% of expiring subscriptions were gift; 57%, previous renewal; 24%, direct mail; and 9%, subscription service. The percentages of renewals were 80%, 76%, 51%, and 14%, respectively.

a. Find the probability that a randomly chosen subscription expiring in January was renewed.

b. Find the probability that a randomly chosen subscription expiring in February was renewed.

c. Verify that the probability in part (b) is higher than that in part (a). Do you believe that the editors of this magazine should view the change from January to February as a positive or negative development?

4.106 In a large city 8% of the inhabitants have contracted a particular disease. A test for this disease is positive in 80% of people who have the disease and is negative in 80% of people who do not have the disease. What is the probability that a person for whom the test result is positive has the disease?

4.107 A life insurance salesman finds that, of all the sales he makes, 70% are to people who already own policies. He also finds that, of all contacts for which no sale is made, 50% already own life insurance policies. Furthermore, 40% of all contacts result in sales. What is the probability that a sale will be made to a contact who already owns a policy?

4.108 A professor finds that she awards a final grade of A to 20% of the students. Of those who obtain a final grade of A, 70% obtained an A on the midterm examination. Also, 10% of the students who failed to obtain a final grade of A earned an A on the midterm exam. What is the probability that a student with an A on the midterm examination will obtain a final grade of A?

4.109 The accompanying table shows, for 1,000 forecasts of earnings per share made by financial analysts, the numbers of forecasts and outcomes in particular categories (compared with the previous year).

| | Forecast | | |
Outcome	Improvement	About the Same	Worse
Improvement	210	82	66
About the Same	106	153	75
Worse	75	84	149

a. Find the probability that, if the forecast is for a worse performance in earnings, this outcome will result.

b. If the forecast is for an improvement in earnings, find the probability that this outcome fails to result.

4.110 A dean has found that 62% of entering freshmen and 78% of community college transfers eventually graduate. Of all entering students, 73% are freshmen and the remainder are community college transfers.

a. What is the probability that a randomly chosen entering student is a freshman who will eventually graduate?

b. Find the probability that a randomly chosen entering student will eventually graduate.

c. What is the probability that a randomly chosen entering student either is a freshmen or will eventually graduate (or both)?

d. Are the events "Eventually graduates" and "Enters as community college transfer" statistically independent?

4.111 A market research group specializes in providing assessments of the prospects of sites for new clothing stores in shopping centers. The group assesses prospects as good, fair, or poor. The records of assessments made by this group were examined, and it was found that, for all stores that turned out to be successful, the assessments were good for 70%, fair for 20%, and poor for 10%. For all stores that turned out to be unsuccessful, the assessments were good for 20%, fair for 30%, and poor for 50%. It is known that 60% of new clothing stores are successful and 40% are unsuccessful.

a. For a randomly chosen store what is the probability that prospects will be assessed as good?

b. If prospects for a store are assessed as good, what is the probability that it will be successful?

c. Are the events "Prospects assessed as good" and "Store is successful" statistically independent?

d. Suppose that five stores are chosen at random. What is the probability that at least one of them will be successful?

4.112 A restaurant manager classifies customers as well dressed, moderately dressed, or poorly dressed and finds that of all customers 50%, 40%, and 10%, respectively, fall into these categories. The manager found that wine was ordered by 70% of the well-dressed customers, by 50% of the moderately dressed, and by 30% of the poorly dressed.

a. What is the probability that a randomly chosen customer orders wine?

b. If wine is ordered, what is the probability that the person ordering is well dressed?

c. If wine is ordered, what is the probability that the person ordering is not well dressed?

4.113 A record store owner assesses customers entering the store as high school age, college age, or older and finds that of all customers 30%, 50%, and 20%, respectively, fall into these categories. The owner also found that purchases were made by 20% of high school age customers, by 60% of college age customers, and by 80% of older customers.

a. What is the probability that a randomly chosen customer entering the store will make a purchase?

b. If a randomly chosen customer makes a purchase, what is the probability that this customer is high school age?

4.114 Note that this exercise represents a completely imaginary situation. Suppose that a statistics class contained exactly 8 men and 8 women. You have discovered that the teacher decided to assign 5 F's on an exam by randomly selecting names from a hat. He concluded that this would be easier than actually grading all those papers and that his students are all equally skilled in statistics—but someone has to get an F. What is the probability that all 5 F's were given to male students?

4.115 A robbery has been committed and McGuff, the crime-fighting dog, has been called in to investigate. He discovers that Sally Coldhands was seen wearing gloves in the neighborhood shortly after the crime, and, thus, he concludes that she should be arrested. From past experience you know that 50 percent of the people that McGuff says should be arrested for robbery are actually guilty. Before making the arrest, you order some additional investigation. From a large population of convicted robbers you find that 60% wore gloves at the time of the crime and continued to wear them for an interval after the crime. Further investigation reveals that 80% of the people in the neighborhood of the crime were wearing gloves around the time of the crime.

a. Based on the fact that Sally was wearing gloves, what is the probability that Sally actually committed the crime?

b. If you charged her with the crime, do you think a jury would convict her based on the glove evidence? Explain why or why not.

4.116 You are responsible for detecting the source of the error when the computer system fails. From your analysis you know that the source of error is the disk drive, the computer memory, or the operating system. You know that 50% of the errors are disk drive errors, 30% are computer memory errors, and the remainder are operating system errors. From the component performance standards you know that, when a disk drive error occurs, the probability of failure is 0.60; when a computer memory error occurs, the probability of failure is 0.7; and when an operating system error occurs, the probability of failure is 0.4. Given the information from the component performance standards, what is the probability of a disk drive error, given that a failure occurred?

4.117 After meeting with the regional sales managers, Lauretta Anderson, president of Cowpie Computers Inc., believes that the probability that sales will grow by 10% in the next year is 0.70. After coming to this conclusion, she receives a report that John Cadariu of Minihard Software Inc. has just announced a new operating system that will be available for customers in 8 months. From past history she knows that, in situations where growth has eventually occurred, new operating systems have been announced 30% of the time. However, in situations where growth has not eventually occurred, new operating systems have been announced 10% of the time. Based on all of these facts, what is the probability that sales will grow by 10%?

Appendix: Permutations and Combinations

A practical difficulty that sometimes arises in computing the probability of an event is counting the numbers of basic outcomes in the sample space and the event of interest. For some problems the use of *permutations* or *combinations* can be helpful.

1. NUMBER OF ORDERINGS

We begin with the problem of ordering. Suppose that we have some number x of objects that are to be placed in order. Each object may be used only once. How many different sequences are possible? We can view this problem as a requirement to place one of the objects in each of x boxes arranged in a row.

Beginning with the left box in Figure 4.11, there are x different ways to fill it. Once an object is put in that box, there are $(x - 1)$ objects remaining, and so $(x - 1)$ ways to fill the second box. That is, for each of the x ways to place an object in the first box, there are $(x - 1)$ possible ways to fill the second box, so the first two boxes can be filled in a total of $x \times (x - 1)$ ways. Given that the first two boxes are filled, there are now $(x - 2)$ ways of filling the third box, so the first three boxes can be filled in a total of $x \times (x - 1) \times (x - 2)$ ways. When we arrive at the last box, there is only one object left to put in it. Finally, we arrive at the number of possible orderings.

> ### Number of Possible Orderings
> The total number of possible ways of arranging x objects in order is given by
>
> $$x(x - 1)(x - 2) \cdots (2)(1) = x! \tag{4.15}$$
>
> where $x!$ is read "x factorial."

2. PERMUTATIONS

Suppose that now we have a number n of objects with which the x *ordered* boxes could be filled (with $n > x$). Each object may be used only once. The number of possible orderings is called the number of *permutations* of x objects chosen from n and is denoted by the symbol P_x^n.

Now, we can argue precisely as before, except that there will be n ways to fill the first box, $(n - 1)$ ways to fill the second box, and so on, until we come to the final box. At this point there will be $(n - x + 1)$ objects left, each of which could be placed in that box, as illustrated in Figure 4.12.

**Figure 4.11
The Orderings of
x Objects**

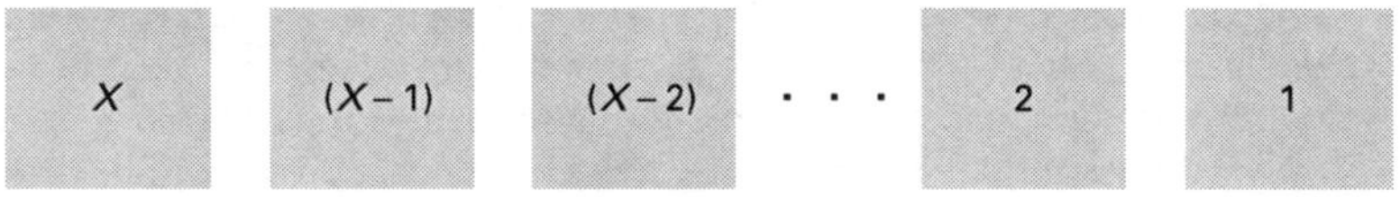

| X | $(X-1)$ | $(X-2)$ | $\cdots$ | 2 | 1 |

Figure 4.12
The Permutations
of x Objects
Chosen from n

| n | $(n-1)$ | $(n-2)$ | $\cdots$ | $(n-x+2)$ | $(n-x+1)$ |

$(n-x)$ objects left over

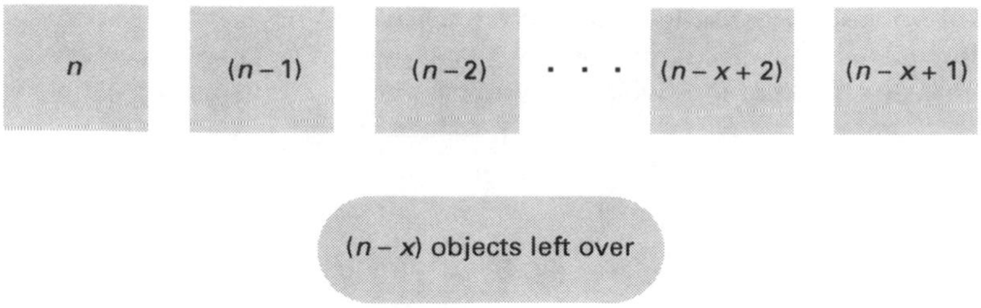

Permutations

The total number of **permutations** of x objects chosen from n, P_x^n, is the number of possible arrangements when x objects are to be selected from a total of n and arranged in order.

$$P_x^n = n(n-1)(n-2)\cdots(n-x+1) \tag{4.16}$$

Multiplying and dividing Equation 4.16 by

$$(n-x)(n-x-1)\cdots(2)(1) = (n-x)!$$

gives

$$P_x^n = \frac{n(n-1)(n-2)\cdots(n-x+1)(n-x)(n-x-1)\cdots(2)(1)}{(n-x)(n-x-1)\cdots(2)(1)}$$

or

$$P_x^n = \frac{n!}{(n-x)!} \tag{4.17}$$

Example 4.26 Five Letters (Permutations)

Suppose that two letters are to be selected from A, B, C, D, and E and arranged in order. How many permutations are possible?

Solution The number of permutations, with $n = 5$ and $x = 2$, is

$$P_2^5 = \frac{5!}{3!} = 20$$

These are

AB	AC	AD	AE	BC
BA	CA	DA	EA	CB
BD	BE	CD	CE	DE
DB	EB	DC	EC	ED

3. Combinations

Finally, suppose that we are interested in the number of different ways that x objects can be selected from n (where no object may be chosen more than once) but are *not concerned about the order*. Notice in Example 4.26 that the entries in the second and fourth rows are just rearrangements of those directly above them and may therefore be ignored. Thus, there are only 10 possibilities for selecting 2 objects from a group of 5 if order is not important. The number of possible selections is called the number of *combinations* and is denoted C_x^n where x objects are to be chosen from n. To find this number, note first that the number of possible permutations is P_x^n. However, many of these will be rearrangements of the same x objects and so are irrelevant. In fact, since x objects can be ordered in $x!$ ways, we are concerned with only a proportion $1/x!$ of the permutations. This leads us to a previously stated outcome—namely, Equation 4.5 in Section 4.2, which we repeat here for completeness.

Number of Combinations

The **number of combinations,** C_x^n, of x objects chosen from n is the number of possible selections that can be made. This number is

$$C_x^n = \frac{P_x^n}{x!}$$

or simply

$$C_x^n = \frac{n!}{x!\,(n-x)!} \tag{4.18}$$

Example 4.27 Probability of Employee Selection (Combinations)

A personnel officer has 8 candidates to fill 4 similar positions. Five candidates are men, and 3 are women. If, in fact, every combination of candidates is equally likely to be chosen, what is the probability that no women will be hired?

Solution   First, the total number of possible combinations of 4 candidates chosen from 8 is

$$C_4^8 = \frac{8!}{4!\,4!} = 70$$

Now, in order for no women to be hired, it follows that the 4 successful candidates must come from the available 5 men. The number of such combinations is

$$C_4^5 = \frac{5!}{4!\,1!} = 5$$

Therefore, if at the outset each of the 70 possible combinations was equally likely to be chosen, the probability that 1 of the 5 all-male combinations would be selected is $5/70 = 1/14$.

REFERENCES

1. Bayes, Thomas. "Essay Towards Solving a Problem in the Doctrine of Chance." *Biometrika* 45 (1958): pp. 293–315 (reproduction of 1763 paper).
2. Carlson, William L. "Alcohol Usage of the Night Driver." *Journal of Safety Research* 4, no. 1 (March 1972): pp. 12–29.
3. Carlson, William L., and Betty Thorne. *Applied Statistical Methods for Business and Economics.* Upper Saddle River, NJ: Prentice Hall, 1997.

Topic 5

Statistical Decision Theory

Chapter 21

Statistical Decision Theory

Introduction

The topic of this chapter could be characterized as capturing the essence of management problems in any organization. Indeed, the applicability of the subject matter extends further, touching many aspects of our everyday lives. We will consider situations in which an individual, a group, or a corporation has available several alternative feasible courses of action. The decision as to which course to follow must be made in a world in which there is uncertainty about the future behavior of the factors that will determine the consequences stemming from the action taken. In this chapter four criteria for decision making are discussed. The maximin criterion and the minimax regret criterion are nonprobabilistic decision-making criteria. That is, these decision criteria "do not take into account the probability associated with the outcomes for each alternative; they merely focus on the dollar value of the outcomes" (Reference 4). Two decision-making criteria that include information about the chances of each outcome's occurrence are the expected monetary value criterion and the expected utility criterion.

21.1 DECISION MAKING UNDER UNCERTAINTY

We are all constrained to operate in an environment whose future direction is uncertain. For example, you may consider attending a baseball game but are doubtful because of the possibility of rain. If you *knew* that it was not going to rain, you would go to the game; if you were *certain* that heavy rain was going to fall for several hours, you would not go. But you are unable to predict the weather with complete assurance, and your decision must be made while contemplating an uncertain future. As another example, at some stage during your final year in college, you will have to decide what to do upon graduation. It is possible that you will have offers of employment from several sources. Graduate school, too, may be a possibility. The decision as to initial career direction is clearly an important one. Certainly, you will have acquired information about the alternatives. You will know what starting salaries are on offer, and you will have learned something about the business operations of your future potential employers and how you might fit into these operations.

However, one really does not have a very clear picture of where one will be in a year or two if a particular offer is accepted. This important decision, then, is made in the face of uncertainty about the future.

In the business world, circumstances of this type often arise, as the following examples illustrate:

1. In a recession a company must decide whether to lay off employees. If the downturn in business activity is to be short-lived, it may be preferable to retain these workers, who might be difficult to replace when demand improves. If the recession is to be prolonged, however, their retention would be costly. Unfortunately, the art of economic forecasting has not reached the stage where it is possible to predict with great certainty the length or severity of a recession.

2. An investor may believe that interest rates are currently at a peak. In that case long-term bonds would appear to be very attractive. However, it is impossible to be sure about the future direction of interest rates, and if they were to continue to rise, the decision to tie up funds in long-term bonds would have been suboptimal.

3. Contractors are often required to submit bids for a program of work. The decision to be made is the level at which the bid should be pitched. Two areas of uncertainty may be relevant here. First, the contractor will not know how low a bid will have to be in order to secure the work. Second, the contractor can't be sure precisely how much it will cost to fulfill the contract. Again, in spite of this uncertainty, some decision must be made.

4. The cost of drilling exploratory offshore oil wells is enormous, and, in spite of excellent geological advice, oil companies will not know, before a well is drilled, whether commercially viable quantities of oil will be discovered. The decision as to whether and where to drill in a particular field is one that must be made in an uncertain environment.

Our objective is to study methods for attacking decision-making problems of the type just described. A decision maker is faced with a finite number, K, of possible *actions*, which will be labeled $a_1, a_2, \ldots, a_K$. At the time a particular action must be selected, the decision maker is uncertain about the future of some factor that will determine the consequences of the chosen action. It is assumed that a finite number, H, of possible *states of nature* can characterize the possibilities for this factor. These will be denoted $s_1, s_2, \ldots, s_H$. Finally, it is assumed that the decision maker is able to specify the monetary reward, or *payoff*, for each action–state of nature combination. Let M_{ij} represent the payoff for action a_i in the event of the occurrence of state of nature s_j. Actions, states of nature, monetary payoffs, and payoff tables are part of the general framework for any decision-making problem.

Framework for a Decision-Making Problem

1. The decision maker has available K possible courses of **action:** $a_1, a_2, \ldots, a_K$. Actions are sometimes called alternatives.
2. There are H possible uncertain **states of nature:** $s_1, s_2, \ldots, s_H$. States of nature are the possible outcomes over which the decision maker has no control. Sometimes states of nature are called events.
3. For each possible action–state of nature combination there is an associated outcome representing either profit or loss, called the monetary **payoff,** M_{ij}, that corresponds to action a_i and state of nature s_j. The table of all such outcomes for a decision problem is called a **payoff table.**

The general form of a payoff table is shown in Table 21.1.

When a decision maker is faced with alternative courses of action, the appropriate choice will depend to a considerable extent on the objectives. It is possible to describe various lines of attack that have been employed in the solution of business decision-making problems. However, it must be kept in mind that each individual problem has its own special features and that the objectives of decision makers may vary considerably and indeed be rather complex. A situation of this sort arises when one contemplates the position of a middle manager in a large corporation. In practice, this manager's objectives may differ somewhat from those of the corporation. In making decisions the manager is very likely to be conscious of his or her own position as well as the overall good of the corporation.

In spite of the individual nature of decision-making problems, it may be possible to eliminate some actions from further consideration under any circumstances.

Table 21.1 Payoff Table for a Decision Problem with K Possible Actions and H Possible States of Nature

ACTION	STATE OF NATURE			
a_i/s_i	s_1	s_2	$\ldots$	s_H
a_1	M_{11}	M_{12}	$\ldots$	M_{1H}
a_2	M_{21}	M_{22}	$\ldots$	M_{2H}
.	.	.	.	.
.	.	.	.	.
.	.	.	.	.
a_K	M_{K1}	M_{K2}	$\ldots$	M_{KH}

Admissible and Inadmissible Actions

If the payoff for action a_j is at least as high as that for a_i, whatever the state of nature, and if the payoff for a_j is higher than that for a_i for at least one state of nature, then action a_j is said to *dominate* action a_i. Any action that is dominated in this way is said to be **inadmissible**. Inadmissible actions are removed from the list of possibilities prior to further analysis of a decision-making problem. Any action that is not dominated by some other action and is therefore not inadmissible is said to be **admissible**.

The following example is used throughout this chapter.

Example 21.1 Cellular Phone Manufacturer (Admissible Actions)

Consider a manufacturer planning to introduce a new cellular phone. The manufacturer has available four alternative production processes, denoted A, B, C, and D, ranging in scope from a relatively minor modification of existing facilities to a quite major extension of the plant. The decision as to which course of action to follow must be made at a time when the eventual demand for the product will be unknown. For convenience, this potential demand is characterized as "low," "moderate," or "high." It will also be assumed that the manufacturer is able to calculate, for each production process, the profit over the lifetime of the investment for each of the three levels of demand. Table 21.2 shows these profit levels (in dollars) for each production process–level of demand combination. Determine if there are any inadmissible actions.

Solution   In this example there are four possible actions corresponding to the four possible production processes and three possible states of nature corresponding to the three possible levels of demand for the product.

Referring to Table 21.2, consider production process D. The payoff from this process will be precisely the same as that from process C if there is a low level of demand and lower than that from process C if the level of demand is either moderate or high. It therefore makes no sense to choose option D, since there is another available choice through which the payoffs can be no lower and could be higher. Since action C is necessarily at least as rewarding as and possibly more rewarding than action D, then action C is said to *dominate* action D. Since production process D is dominated by another available alternative, production process C, production

Table 21.2 Estimated Profits of a Cellular Phone Manufacturer for Different Process-Demand Combinations

ACTION	STATE OF NATURE		
PRODUCTION PROCESS	LOW DEMAND	MODERATE DEMAND	HIGH DEMAND
A	70,000	120,000	200,000
B	80,000	120,000	180,000
C	100,000	125,000	160,000
D	100,000	120,000	150,000

process D is said to be *inadmissible*. This action should be removed from further consideration, as it would be suboptimal to adopt it. Accordingly, this possibility will be dropped from further consideration, and, in our subsequent analysis of this problem, only the possibility of adoption of process A, B, or C is considered.

The decision-making problem as outlined is essentially discrete in character. That is to say, there are only a finite number of available alternatives and a finite number of possible states of nature. However, many practical problems are continuous. The state of nature, for instance, may be more appropriately measured on a continuum than depicted by a number of discrete possibilities. In the cellular phone manufacturer example it may be possible to anticipate a range of potential demand levels rather than simply to specify three levels. Also, in some problems the available actions are most appropriately represented by a continuum. This would be the case, for example, when a contractor must decide on the level at which to bid for a contract. The remainder of this chapter focuses on the discrete case. The *principles* involved in the analysis of the continuous case are no different. However, the details of that analysis are based on calculus and will not be considered further here.

EXERCISES

Basic Exercises

21.1   An investor is considering three alternatives—a certificate of deposit, a low-risk stock fund, and a high-risk stock fund—for a \$20,000 investment. She considers three possible states of nature:

s_1:   Strong stock market
s_2:   Moderate stock market
s_3:   Weak stock market

The payoff table (in dollars) is as follows:

Action	State of Nature		
Possible Investment Alternative	s_1	s_2	s_3
Certificate of deposit	1,200	1,200	1,200
Low-risk stock fund	4,300	1,200	–600
High-risk stock fund	6,600	800	–1,500

Are any of these actions inadmissible?

21.2   A manufacturer of deodorant is about to expand production capacity to make a new product. Four alternative production processes are available. The accompanying table shows estimated profits, in dollars, for these processes for each of three possible demand levels for the product.

Action	State of Nature		
Production Process	Low Demand	Moderate Demand	High Demand
A	100,000	350,000	900,000
B	150,000	400,000	700,000
C	250,000	400,000	600,000
D	250,000	400,000	550,000

Are any of these actions inadmissible?

21.2 SOLUTIONS NOT INVOLVING SPECIFICATION OF PROBABILITIES: MAXIMIN CRITERION, MINIMAX REGRET CRITERION

Before deciding which production process to employ, our manufacturer of cellular phones is likely to ask, "What are the chances of each of these levels of demand actually materializing?" The bulk of this chapter discusses solutions to a decision-making problem that require the specification of outcome probabilities for the various states of

Table 21.3   Maximin Criterion Output for Example 21.1

ACTION	STATE OF NATURE			MINIMUM PAYOFF
PRODUCTION PROCESS	LOW DEMAND	MODERATE DEMAND	HIGH DEMAND	MINIMUM PAYOFF FOR EACH PROCESS
A	70,000	120,000	200,000	70,000
B	80,000	120,000	180,000	80,000
C	100,000	125,000	160,000	100,000 (Maximum)

nature. However, in this section two choice criteria that are not based on such probabilities and, in fact, have no probabilistic content are presented. Rather, these approaches (and others of the same type) depend only on the structure of the payoff table.

The two procedures considered in this section are called the *maximin criterion* and the *minimax regret criterion*. Each criterion is discussed in relation to the payoff table for the cellular phone manufacturer in Example 21.1, with the inadmissible strategy of choosing production process D ignored. The manufacturer must therefore select from among three available actions, faced with three possible states of nature.

Maximin Criterion

Consider the worst possible outcome for each action, whatever state of nature materializes. This *worst outcome* is simply the smallest payoff that could conceivably result. The **maximin criterion** selects the action for which the minimum payoff is highest—that is, we *maximize* the *minimum* payoff.

For the cellular phone manufacturer's problem, the smallest payoff, whatever production process is used, occurs at the low level of demand. Clearly, as set out in Table 21.3, the maximum value of these minimum payoffs is $100,000. This will occur if production process C is used. Thus, maximin criterion selects production process C.

Since the maximum value of the minimum payoff for each production process is $100,000, it follows that production process C is selected as the course of action under the maximin criterion.

Example 21.2   Investment Opportunity (Maximin)

An investor wishes to choose between investing $10,000 for one year at an assured interest rate of 12% and investing the same amount over that period in a portfolio of common stocks. If the fixed-interest choice is made, the investor will be assured of a payoff of $1,200. If the portfolio of stocks is chosen, the return will depend on the performance of the market over the year. If the market is buoyant, a profit of $2,500 is expected; if the market is steady, the expected profit is $500; and for a depressed market, a loss of $1,000 is expected. Set up the payoff table for this investor, and find the maximin choice of action.

Solution   Table 21.4 shows the payoffs (in dollars), with a negative payoff indicating a loss.

The minimum payoff for the fixed-interest investment is $1,200, as this will occur whatever happens in the stock market. The minimum payoff from the stock

Table 21.4 Maximin Criterion Output for Example 21.2

ACTION	STATE OF NATURE			MINIMUM PAYOFF
INVESTMENT OPTION	BUOYANT STATE	STEADY STATE	DEPRESSED STATE	MINIMUM PAYOFF FOR EACH INVESTMENT OPTION
Fixed interest	1,200	1,200	1,200	**1,200 (Maximum)**
Stock Portfolio	2,500	500	−1,000	−1,000

portfolio is a loss of $1,000, or −$1,000, which occurs when the market is depressed. Since the largest minimum payoff arises from the fixed-interest investment, it follows that fixed interest is selected as the course of action under the maximin criterion.

From these illustrations the general form of the decision rule based on the maximin criterion is clear. The objective of the maximin criterion is to *maximize* the *minimum* payoff.

Decision Rule Based on Maximin Criterion

Suppose that a decision maker has to choose from K admissible actions $a_1, a_2, \ldots, a_K$, given H possible states of nature $s_1, s_2, \ldots, s_H$. Let M_{ij} denote the payoff corresponding to the ith action and jth state of nature. For each action seek the smallest possible payoff. For the action a_1, for example, this is the smallest of $M_{11}, _{12}, \ldots, M_{1H}$. Let us denote this minimum M_1^* where

$$M_1^* = \text{Min} \, (M_{11}, M_{12}, \ldots, M_{1H})$$

More generally, the smallest possible payoff for action a_i is given by

$$M_i^* = (M_{i1}, M_{i2}, \ldots, M_{iH})$$

The **maximin criterion** then selects the action a_i for which the corresponding M_1^* is largest (that is, the action for which the minimum payoff is highest).

The positive feature of the maximin criterion for decision making is that it produces the largest possible payoff that can be *guaranteed*. If production process C is used, the cellular phone manufacturer is *assured* a payoff of at least $100,000, whatever the level of demand turns out to be. Similarly, for the investor of Example 21.2, the choice of fixed interest makes a *certain* profit of $1,200. In neither example can any available alternative action *guarantee* as much.

However, it is precisely within this guarantee that reservations about the maximin criterion arise because one must often pay a price for such a guarantee. The price here lies in the forgoing of opportunities to receive a larger payoff, through the choice of some other action, *however unlikely* the worst-case situation seems to be. Thus, for example, the cellular phone manufacturer may be virtually certain that a high level of demand will result, in which case production process C would be a poor choice, since it yields the lowest payoff at this demand level.

The maximin criterion, then, can be thought of as providing a very cautious strategy for choosing among alternative actions. Such a strategy may, in certain circumstances, be appropriate, but only an extreme pessimist would use it invariably. For this reason it is sometimes called the *criterion of pessimism*. "Maximin is often used in situations where the planner feels he or she cannot afford to be wrong. (Defense planning might be an example, as would investing your life savings.) The planner chooses a decision that does as well as possible in the worst possible (most pessimistic) case" (Reference 1).

Minimax Regret Criterion

The decision maker wanting to use the *minimax regret criterion* must imagine being in the position where a choice of action has been made and one of the states of nature has occurred. He or she can look back on the choice made either with satisfaction or with disappointment because, as things turned out, some alternative action would have been preferable. The decision maker then determines the *regret*, or *opportunity loss*, of not making the best decision for a given state of nature and establishes a regret table.

> ### Regret or Opportunity Loss Table
> Suppose that a payoff table is arranged as a rectangular array, with rows corresponding to actions and columns to states of nature. If each payoff in the table is subtracted from the largest payoff *in its column*, the resulting array is called a **regret table**, or an **opportunity loss table**.

By considering the difference between the actual monetary payoff that occurs for a decision and the optimal payoff for the same state of nature, the decision maker can select the action that *minimizes* the *maximum* loss or regret.

> ### Decision Rule Based on Minimax Regret Criterion
> Given the regret table, the actions dictated by the **minimax regret criterion** are found as follows:
>
> 1. For each row (action), find the maximum regret.
> 2. Choose the action corresponding to the *minimum* of these *maximum* regrets.
>
> The **minimax regret criterion** selects the action for which the maximum regret is smallest; that is, the minimax regret criterion produces the smallest possible opportunity loss that can be guaranteed.

Consider again the cellular phone manufacturer in Example 21.1. It will be shown that process B is selected by the minimax regret criterion. Suppose that the level of demand for the new product turns out to be low. In that case the best choice of action would have been production process C, yielding a payoff of $100,000. Had this choice been made, the manufacturer would have had 0 regret. Had process A been chosen, the resulting profit would have been only $70,000. The extent of the manufacturer's regret, in this eventuality, is the difference between the best payoff

Table 21.5 Minimax Regret Criterion Output for Example 21.1

ACTION	STATE OF NATURE			REGRET
PRODUCTION PROCESS	LOW DEMAND	MODERATE DEMAND	HIGH DEMAND	MAXIMUM REGRET FOR EACH PROCESS
A	30,000	5,000	0	30,000
B	20,000	5,000	20,000	20,000 (Minimum)
C	0	0	40,000	40,000

that could have been obtained ($100,000) and that resulting from what turned out to be an inferior choice of action. Thus, the regret would be $100,000 – $70,000 = $30,000. Similarly, given low demand, if process B had been chosen, the regret would be

$$\$100,000 - \$80,000 = \$20,000$$

Continuing in this way the regrets involved for moderate and high levels of demand are calculated. In each case the regret is 0 for what would have turned out to be the best choice of action (process C for moderate demand and process A for high demand). These regrets, or opportunity losses from not making the best decision for a given state of nature, are given in Table 21.5, with the largest amount of regret for a given process included in the last column.

Clearly, the minimax regret criterion selects production process B, since the maximum regret for this process is the smallest of processes A, B, and C.

Neither the maximin criterion nor the minimax regret criterion allows the decision maker to inject personal views as to the likelihood of occurrence of states of nature into the decision-making process. Since most practical business problems occur in an environment with which the decision maker is at least moderately familiar, this represents a waste of expertise. The probabilities associated with the outcomes for each alternative action are considered in the next section.

EXERCISES

Basic Exercises

21.3   Consider Exercise 21.1, where an investor is considering three alternatives—a certificate of deposit, a low-risk stock fund, and a high-risk stock fund—for a $20,000 investment. She considers three possible states of nature:

s_1:   Strong stock market
s_2:   Moderate stock market
s_3:   Weak stock market

The payoff table (in dollars) is as follows:

Action	State of Nature		
Possible Investment Alternative	s_1	s_2	s_3
Certificate of deposit	1,200	1,200	1,200
Low-risk stock fund	4,300	1,200	–600
High-risk stock fund	6,600	800	–1,500

a. Which action is selected by the maximin criterion?

b. Which action is selected by the minimax regret criterion?

21.4   Consider the manufacturer of deodorant in Exercise 21.2, who is about to expand production capacity to make a new product. Four alternative production processes are available. The accompanying table shows estimated profits, in dollars, for these processes for each of three possible demand levels for the product.

Action	State of Nature		
Production Process	Low Demand	Moderate Demand	High Demand
A	100,000	350,000	900,000
B	150,000	400,000	700,000
C	250,000	400,000	600,000
D	250,000	400,000	550,000

a. Which action is chosen by the maximin criterion?

b. Which action is chosen by the minimax regret criterion?

21.5 Another criterion for selecting a decision is the *maximax criterion*, sometimes known as the *criterion of optimism*. This criterion chooses the action with the largest possible payoff.

    a. What action would be chosen by the cellular phone manufacturer, with the payoffs of Table 21.2, according to this criterion?

    b. The investor of Example 21.2 according to this criterion would choose what action?

Application Exercises

21.6 The cellular phone manufacturer in Example 21.1 has three admissible actions—processes A, B, and C. When these are considered together, process B is chosen by the minimax regret criterion. Suppose now that a fourth admissible alternative, production process E, is available. Estimated payoffs for this action are $60,000 under low demand, $115,000 for moderate demand, and $220,000 for high demand. Show that when production processes A, B, C, and E are considered together, process A is chosen by the minimax regret criterion. Thus, while adding process E to the available actions does not result in the selection of that process, it does lead to the choice of a different action than would otherwise have been the case. Comment on the intuitive appeal of the minimax regret criterion in light of this example.

21.7 Consider a decision problem with two possible actions and two states of nature.

    a. Give an example of a payoff table where both actions are admissible and the same action is chosen by both the maximin criterion and the minimax regret criterion.

    b. Give an example of a payoff table according to which different actions are chosen by the maximin criterion and the minimax regret criterion.

21.8 Consider a decision problem with two admissible actions and two possible states of nature. Formulate a description of the form that the payoff table must take for the same action to be chosen by the maximin criterion and by the minimax regret criterion.

21.9 The prospective operator of a shoe store has the opportunity to locate in an established and successful shopping center. Alternatively, at lower cost, he can locate in a new center, whose development has recently been completed. If the new center turns out to be very successful, it is expected that annual store profits from location in it would be $130,000. If the center is only moderately successful, annual profits would be $60,000. If the new center is unsuccessful, an annual loss of $10,000 would be expected. The profits to be expected from location in the established center will also depend to some extent on the degree of success of the new center, as potential customers may be drawn to it. If the new center was unsuccessful, annual profits for the shoe store located in the established center would be expected to be $90,000. However, if the new center was moderately successful, the expected profits would be $70,000, while they would be $30,000 if the new center turned out to be very successful.

    a. Set up the payoff table for the decision-making problem of this shoe store operator.

    b. Which action is chosen by the maximin criterion?

    c. Which action is chosen by the minimax regret criterion?

21.3 EXPECTED MONETARY VALUE; TREEPLAN

An important ingredient in the analysis of many business decision-making problems is likely to be the decision maker's assessment of the chances that various states of nature relevant in the determination of the eventual payoff will occur. The criteria discussed in Section 21.2 do not allow the incorporation of this kind of assessment into the decision-making process. However, a manager will almost invariably have a good feeling for the environment in which the decision is to be made and will want this expertise to be taken into account before deciding on a course of action. The discussion in this section assumes that a *probability* of occurrence can be attached to each state of nature, and it will be shown how these probabilities are employed in arriving at an eventual decision.

In general, when there are H possible states of nature, a probability must be attached to each. These probabilities are denoted by $P_1, P_2, \ldots, P_H$, so that probability

Table 21.6   Payoffs with State-of-Nature Probabilities

ACTION	STATE OF NATURE			
a_i/s_j	$s_1(P_1)$	$s_2(P_2)$	$\ldots$	$s_H(P_H)$
a_1	M_{11}	M_{12}	$\ldots$	M_{1H}
a_2	M_{21}	M_{22}	$\ldots$	M_{2H}
$\cdot$	$\cdot$	$\cdot$	$\cdot$	$\cdot$
$\cdot$	$\cdot$	$\cdot$	$\cdot$	$\cdot$
$\cdot$	$\cdot$	$\cdot$	$\cdot$	$\cdot$
a_K	M_{K1}	M_{K2}	$\ldots$	M_{KH}

P_j corresponds to state of nature s_j. The general setup for this decision-making problem is shown in Table 21.6.

Since one, and only one, of the states of nature must occur, these probabilities necessarily sum to 1, so that

$$\sum_{j=1}^{H} P_j = 1$$

When choosing an action, the decision maker will see each particular choice as having a specific probability of receiving the associated payoff and will therefore be able to calculate the *expected payoff* arising from each action. The expected payoff for this action is then the sum of the individual payoffs, weighted by their associated probabilities. These expected payoffs are often called the **expected monetary values** of the actions.

Expected Monetary Value (*EMV*) Criterion
Suppose that a decision maker has K possible actions, $a_1, a_2, \ldots, a_K$, and is faced with H states of nature. Let M_{ij} denote the payoff corresponding to the ith action and jth state and P_j the probability of occurrence of the jth state of nature, with $\sum_{j=1}^{H} P_j = 1$. The **expected monetary value** of action a_i, *EMV*(a_i), is

$$EMV(a_i) = P_1 M_{i1} + P_2 M_{i2} + \cdots + P_H M_{iH} = \sum_{j=1}^{H} P_j M_{ij} \qquad (21.1)$$

The **expected monetary value criterion** adopts the action with the largest expected monetary value; that is, given a choice among alternative actions, the *EMV* criterion dictates the choice of the action for which the *EMV* is highest.

Let's return to the cellular phone manufacturer in Example 21.1 and calculate the *EMV* for each of the production processes. The cellular phone manufacturer will presumably have some experience with the market for his product and, on the basis of

Table 21.7   Payoffs and State-of-Nature Probabilities for Cellular Phone Manufacturer in Example 21.1

ACTION	STATE OF NATURE		
PRODUCTION PROCESS	LOW DEMAND ($P = 0.10$)	MODERATE DEMAND ($P = 0.50$)	HIGH DEMAND ($P = 0.40$)
A	70,000	120,000	200,000
B	80,000	120,000	180,000
C	100,000	125,000	160,000

that experience, will be able to form a view as to the likelihood of occurrence of low, moderate, or high demand. Suppose that the cellular phone manufacturer knows that, of all previous introductions of this type of product, 10% have had low demand, 50% moderate demand, and 40% high demand. In the absence of any further information it is then reasonable to postulate, for this particular market introduction, the following probabilities for the states of nature:

$$P_1 = P(s_1) = \text{Probability of Low Demand} = 0.1$$
$$P_2 = P(s_2) = \text{Probability of Moderate Demand} = 0.5$$
$$P_3 = P(s_3) = \text{Probability of High Demand} = 0.4$$

Since one, and only one, of the states of nature must occur, these probabilities necessarily sum to 1; that is, the states of nature are mutually exclusive and collectively exhaustive. These probabilities are added to the payoff table (Table 21.2), giving Table 21.7.

If the cellular phone manufacturer adopts production process A, he will receive a payoff of $70,000 with probability 0.1, $120,000 with probability 0.5, and $200,000 with probability 0.4. For the cellular phone manufacturer the expected monetary values for the three admissible actions are as follows:

$$EMV \text{ (Process A)} = (0.1)(70,000) + (0.5)(120,000) + (0.4)(200,000) = \$147,000$$
$$EMV \text{ (Process B)} = (0.1)(80,000) + (0.5)(120,000) + (0.4)(180,000) = \$140,000$$
$$EMV \text{ (Process C)} = (0.1)(100,000) + (0.5)(125,000) + (0.4)(160,000) = \$136,500$$

The cellular phone manufacturer would choose production process A. It is interesting to note that neither the maximin criterion nor the minimax regret criterion led to this particular choice. However, the information that a high level of demand appears much more likely than a low level has been added. This renders process A a relatively attractive option.

Decision Trees

The analysis of a decision problem by means of the expected monetary value criterion can be conveniently set out diagrammatically through a mechanism called a **decision tree**. When faced with analyzing decisions under risk, the tree diagram is a graphical device that forces the decision maker "to examine all possible outcomes, including unfavorable ones. He or she is also forced to make decisions in a logical, sequential manner" (Reference 4). Decision trees are especially helpful when a sequence of decisions must be made. All decision trees contain

☐ **Decision (or action) nodes.** These squares indicate that a decision must be made and are sometimes called square nodes.

○ **Event (state of nature) nodes**. These circular junctions, from which *branches* emerge, represent a possible state of nature, to which the associated probability is attached. These nodes are sometimes called circular nodes.

| **Terminal nodes.** A vertical bar represents the end of the decision-event branch. Originally, a triangle was used to designate this point. Sometimes no designation is given.

After carefully defining a problem, the decision maker draws the decision tree, assigns probabilities to the possible events (states of nature), and estimates the pay-off for each possible decision-event combination (every combination of action and state of nature). Now the decision maker is ready to find the optimal decision. This is called "solving the tree" (Reference 1). To solve a decision tree, one must work backward (called *folding back* the tree). Compute the expected monetary value (*EMV*) for each state of nature by starting at the far right of the decision tree and working back to decision nodes on the left.

A tree diagram for the cellular phone manufacturer is given in Figure 21.1. The following steps were taken to choose the action with the largest *EMV*:

1. Beginning at the left-hand side of the figure, branches emerge from the **decision node** (square junction) representing the three possible actions: process A, process B, and process C. Next, come **event nodes** (circular junctions), from which branches representing possible states of nature (levels of demand emerge).

2. The *associated probability* is attached to each state of nature (low, moderate, or high).

Figure 21.1
Decision Tree for
Cellular Phone
Manufacturer
(*Action with
Maximum *EMV*)

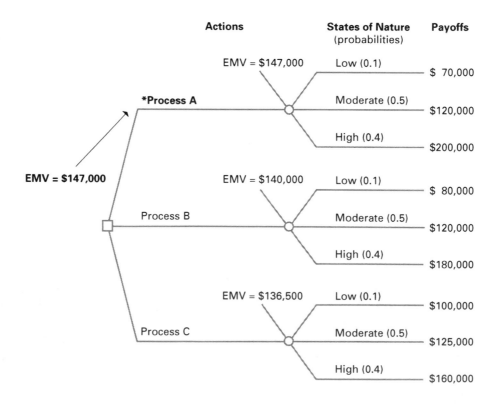

3. The *payoffs* corresponding to the action–state of nature combinations are inserted at the far right of the tree.
4. The computations proceed from *right to left*, beginning with these payoffs. For each circular junction the sum of the probability times the payoff for each emerging branch is found. This provides the *EMV for each action*.
5. The *optimal decision* has the highest *EMV* and is indicated at the left square junction. Process A is therefore chosen by the expected monetary value criterion. This choice of action results in an expected monetary value, or expected profit, of $147,000 for the cellular phone manufacturer.

Using TreePlan to Solve a Decision Tree

Developed by Michael Middleton (Reference 3) and included with this text, TreePlan is an Excel add-in that can be used to draw decision trees. The *EMV*s will be computed, giving the optimal decision. Check the Web site www.treeplan.com for both documentation and details to continue use of this add-in beyond this course (Reference 5).

Example 21.3   Investment Opportunity (*EMV* Criterion)

The investor in Example 21.2 needed to decide between a fixed-interest-rate investment and a portfolio of stocks. Let us assume that this investor is, in fact, very optimistic about the future course of the stock market, believing that the probability of a buoyant market is 0.6, while the probability is 0.2 for each of the other two states. The payoffs and state-of-nature probabilities are therefore those given in the accompanying table:

	State of Nature		
Action Investment	Buoyant State ($P = 0.60$)	Steady State ($P = 0.20$)	Depressed State ($P = 0.20$)
Fixed interest	1,200	1,200	1,200
Stock portfolio	2,500	500	−1,000

Which investment should be chosen according to the expected monetary value criterion?

Solution   Since a payoff of $1,200 will result from the fixed-interest investment, whatever happens in the stock market, the expected monetary value of this investment is $1,200. The *EMV* for the stock portfolio is

$$EMV \text{ (Stock Portfolio)} = (0.6)(2,500) + (0.2)(500) + (0.2)(-1,000) = \$1,400$$

Since this is the higher expected monetary value, the investor would choose the *portfolio of common stocks*, according to the expected monetary value criterion.

Now let's solve this example with TreePlan. Once TreePlan is installed, the simplest way to access TreePlan is to open a new Excel spreadsheet and hit Ctrl-t (the tree will begin wherever the cursor appears. Be sure to leave enough space for the decision table and the tree). Click on "New Tree" and the default tree with two decision nodes (Figure 21.2) will appear. The completed decision tree is Figure 21.3.

A problem that requires a *sequence* of decisions is considered next.

Figure 21.2   Beginning TreePlan

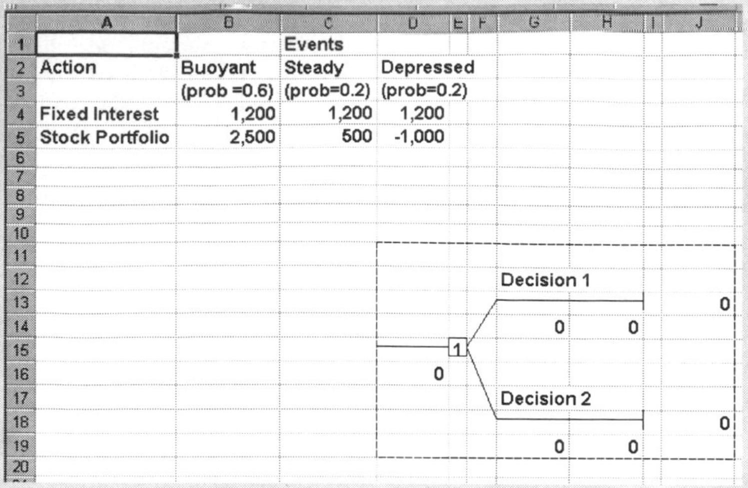

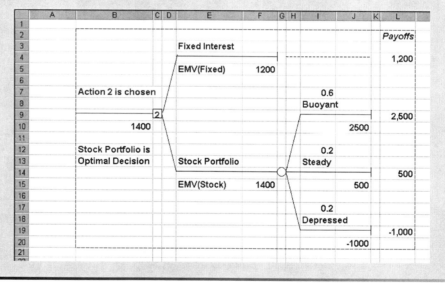

	Events		
Action	Buoyant	Steady	Depressed
	(prob =0.6)	(prob=0.2)	(prob=0.2)
Fixed Interest	1,200	1,200	1,200
Stock Portfolio	2,500	500	-1,000

Figure 21.3   Decision Tree for Example 21.3 Using TreePlan; Optimal Decision: Select the Stock Portfolio

Example 21.4   Drug Manufacturer (*EMV* Criterion)

A drug manufacturer holds the patent rights to a new formula for lowering cholesterol levels. The manufacturer is able to sell the patent for $50,000 or to proceed with intensive tests of the drug's efficacy. The cost of carrying out these tests is $10,000. If the drug is found to be ineffective, it will not be marketed, and the cost of the tests will be written off as a loss. In the past, tests of drugs of this type have shown 60% to be effective and 40% ineffective.

If the tests should now reveal the drug to be effective, the manufacturer again has two options available. He can sell the patent rights and test results for $120,000, or he can market the drug himself. If the drug is marketed, it is estimated that profits on sales (exclusive of the cost of the tests) will amount to $180,000 if the sales campaign is highly successful but only $90,000 if it is just moderately successful. It is estimated that these two levels of market penetration are equally likely. According to the expected monetary value criterion, how should the drug manufacturer proceed?

Solution   It is best to attack this problem through the construction of a decision tree. The completed tree is shown in Figure 21.4.

The manufacturer may decide either to sell the patent, in which case there is nothing further to be done, or to retain it and carry out tests on the drug's efficacy. There are two possible states of nature—the drug is either effective (with probability 0.6) or ineffective (with probability 0.4). In the latter case, the story ends. However, if the drug proves to be effective, a second decision must be made— whether to market it or to sell the patent rights and test results. If the former option is adopted, then the level of marketing success determines the eventual outcome, which could be either moderate or high (each with probability 0.5).

Next, the payoffs resulting from all action–state of nature combinations are considered. Begin at the bottom of the decision tree. If the manufacturer's original decision is to sell the patent, he receives $50,000. If the patent is kept but the drug turns out to be ineffective, the manufacturer sustains a loss of $10,000, the cost of carrying out the tests. This is shown as a negative payoff in that amount. If the drug is found to be effective and the patent and test results are then sold, the manufacturer receives $120,000, from which must be subtracted the cost of the tests,

Figure 21.4   Decision Tree for Example 21.4; Optimal Decision: Retain Patent, and, If Test Shows Drug to Be Effective, Then Market the Drug (*EMV* = $71,000)

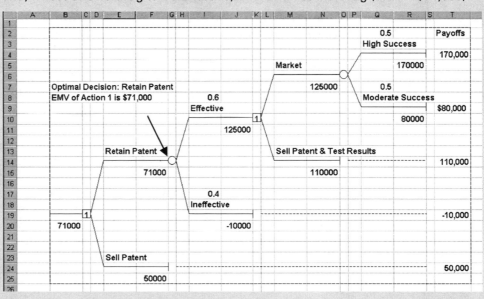

leaving a payoff of $110,000. Finally, if the drug is marketed, the payoffs for moderate and high success are, respectively, $90,000 and $180,000, less the cost of the tests, leaving $80,000 and $170,000, respectively.

Having reached this point, the decision problem is solved by working backward from right to left along the tree. This is necessary because the appropriate action at the first decision point cannot be determined until the expected monetary value of the best available option at the second decision point is found.

Therefore, begin by supposing that initially the patent was retained and that the tests proved the drug to be effective. If the patent and test results are sold, then a profit of $110,000 will result. The expected monetary value from marketing the drug is

$$EMV = (0.5)(170,000) + (0.5)(80,000) = \$125,000$$

Since this exceeds $110,000, the better option at this stage, by the expected monetary value criterion, is to market the drug. This amount is therefore entered at the square junction of the second decision point and is treated as the payoff that results if the manufacturer's initial decision is to retain the patent and the tests indicate that the drug is effective. Hence, for the initial decision the payoff table with state-of-nature probabilities is as shown here. The expected monetary value of selling the patent is the assured $50,000, while the expected monetary value of retaining it is $(0.6)(125,000) + (0.4)(-10,000) = \$71,000$. Then, by the expected monetary value criterion, the patent should be retained.

Action	State of Nature	
	Effective Drug ($P = 0.60$)	Ineffective Drug ($P = 0.40$)
Retain patent	125,000	-10,000
Sell patent	50,000	50,000

If the manufacturer's objective is to maximize expected monetary value (that is, expected profit), then the manufacturer should retain the patent. If the tests prove the drug to be effective, then the manufacturer should market it. This strategy yields an expected profit of $71,000.

By use of TreePlan, the same result appears in Figure 21.4.

Sensitivity Analysis

For the cellular phone manufacturer, production process A was selected by the expected monetary value criterion. This decision was based on the estimated payoff for each action–state of nature combination and on the estimated probability of occurrence for each state of nature. However, often a decision maker will be uncertain about such estimates, so it is useful to ask under what range of specifications of a decision problem a particular action will be optimal under the expected monetary value criterion. **Sensitivity analysis** seeks to answer such questions, the most straightforward case being where a single problem specification is allowed to vary, while all other specifications are held fixed.

To illustrate, suppose that the cellular phone manufacturer agrees with the assessment that the probability of high demand is 0.4 but is less sure of the assessments for the other two states of nature. Let P denote the probability of low demand, so that the probability of moderate demand must be $(0.6 - P)$. According to the expected monetary value criterion, under what range of values of P would the adoption of process A be optimal? Using the payoffs of Table 21.7, the expected monetary values are

$$EMV(A) = (P)(70,000) + (0.6 - P)(120,000) + (0.4)(200,000) = 152,000 - 50,000P$$
$$EMV(B) = (P)(80,000) + (0.6 - P)(120,000) + (0.4)(180,000) = 144,000 - 40,000P$$
$$EMV(C) = (P)(100,000) + (0.6 - P)(125,000) + (0.4)(160,000) = 139,000 - 25,000P$$

Choice of process A will remain optimal provided the associated *EMV* is higher than that of each of the other two processes. Thus, for process A to be preferred to process B, it must follow that

$$152,000 - 50,000P \geq 144,000 - 40,000P$$

or

$$8,000 \geq 10,000P$$

so

$$P \leq 0.8$$

This must be so, since, by our assumptions, the probability of low demand cannot exceed 0.6. Similarly, for process A to be preferred to process C, then

$$152,000 - 50,000P \geq 139,000 - 25,000P$$

or

$$13,000 \geq 25,000P$$

so

$$P \leq .52$$

If the payoffs are as postulated in Table 21.7 and the probability of high demand is 0.4, then production process A is the best choice under the expected monetary value criterion, provided that the probability of low demand does not exceed 0.52.

Now suppose that the cellular phone manufacturer is uncertain about the estimated payoff of $200,000 for process A under high demand. Consider under what range of payoffs process A will be the optimal choice, when all other problem specifications are kept at their initial levels, given in Table 21.7. If M is the payoff for process A under high demand, then the expected monetary value for this process is

$$EMV(A) = (0.1)(70,000) + (0.5)(120,000) + 0.4M = 67,000 + 0.4M$$

The expected monetary values for processes B and C are, as before, $140,000 and $136,500. Therefore, process A will be the best choice according to the expected monetary value criterion, provided that

$$67,000 + 0.4M \geq 140,000$$

or

$$0.4M \geq 73,000$$

or

$$M \geq 182,500$$

If all other specifications are as originally given in Table 21.7, then production process A will be selected by the expected monetary value criterion, provided that the payoff for process A under high demand is at least $182,500.

EXERCISES

Application Exercises

21.10 A student already has offers of employment. She must now decide whether to visit another potential employer for further interviews. She views the time and effort of doing so as having a cost of $500, which will be incurred whether or not she takes a job with this employer. If the employer offers a position preferable to her other alternatives, this would be viewed as a benefit worth $5,000 (from which the $500 cost must be subtracted). Otherwise, her time and effort would have been wasted.

   a. Set up the payoff table for the student's decision-making problem.

   b. Suppose the student believes that the probability is 0.05 that she would be offered a position preferable to her other alternatives by this employer. According to the expected monetary value criterion, should she visit this potential employer?

21.11 A manager has to choose between two actions, a_1 and a_2. There are two possible states of nature, s_1 and s_2. The payoffs are shown in the accompanying table. If the manager believes that each state of nature is equally likely to occur, which action should be chosen, according to the expected monetary value criterion?

Action	State of Nature s_1	s_2
a_1	72,000	51,000
a_2	78,000	47,000

21.12 The investor of Exercise 21.1 believes that the probability of a strong stock market is 0.2, the probability of a moderate stock market is 0.5, and the probability of a weak stock market is 0.3.

   a. Which action should be chosen, according to the expected monetary value criterion?

   b. Draw the decision tree for the investor's problem.

21.13 The deodorant manufacturer in Exercise 21.2 knows that historically 30% of new products of this type have met high demand, 40% moderate demand, and 30% low demand.

   a. According to the expected monetary value criterion, which production process should be used?

   b. Draw the decision tree for this manufacturer's problem.

21.14 Consider a decision problem with two admissible actions and two possible states of nature, each of which is equally likely to occur.

   a. Determine whether each of the following statements is true or false for such problems:

     i. The action chosen by the expected monetary value criterion will always be the same as the action chosen by the maximin criterion.

     ii. The action chosen by the expected monetary value criterion will always be the same as the action chosen by the minimax regret criterion.

     iii. The action chosen by the expected monetary value criterion will always be that for which the average possible payoff is higher.

   b. Would your answer regarding statement (iii) in part (a) be the same if the two states of nature were not equally likely to occur?

21.15 A decision problem has K possible actions and H possible states of nature. If one of these actions is inadmissible, show that it cannot be chosen by the expected monetary value criterion.

21.16 The shoe store operator of Exercise 21.9 believes that the probability is 0.4 that the new shopping center will be very successful, 0.4 that it will be moderately successful, and 0.2 that it will be unsuccessful.

   a. According to the expected monetary value criterion, where should the shoe store be located?

   b. Draw the decision tree.

21.17 Refer to the decision-making problem in Exercises 21.1, 21.3, and 21.12. This investor is comfortable with the assessment of a probability of 0.2 for a strong market. However, she is less sure of the probability assessments for the other two states of nature. Under what range of probabilities for a weak stock market does the expected monetary value criterion give the choice of action found in Exercise 21.12?

21.18 Refer to the problem of the deodorant manufacturer of Exercises 21.2, 21.4, and 21.13.

   a. The manufacturer is comfortable with an assessment that the probability of low demand is 0.3 but is less secure about the probabilities for the other two demand levels. Under what range of probabilities for moderate demand will the expected monetary value criterion yield the choice of action found in Exercise 21.13?

   b. Take the remaining problem specifications to be as given in Exercises 21.2 and 21.13. Under what range of profits for high demand when process A is used will the expected monetary value criterion give the choice of action found in Exercise 21.13?

21.19 Refer to the problem of the shoe store operator of Exercises 21.9 and 21.16.

    a. The shoe store operator is happy with the assessment that the probability is 0.2 that the new shopping center will be unsuccessful but is less sure about the probability assessments for the other two states of nature. Under what range of probabilities that the new shopping center will be very successful will the expected monetary value criterion lead to the choice of action found in Exercise 21.16?

    b. Assuming that the other problem specifications are as in Exercises 21.9 and 21.16, under what range of profit levels for location in the new center if it turns out to be very successful will the expected monetary value criterion lead to the choice of action found in Exercise 21.16?

21.20 A manufacturer receives regular contracts for large consignments of parts for the automobile industry. This manufacturer's production process is such that, when it is operating correctly, 10% of all parts produced do not meet industry specifications. However, the production process is prone to a particular malfunction, whose presence can be checked at the beginning of a production run. When the process is operated with this malfunction, 30% of the parts produced fail to meet industry specifications. The manufacturer supplies parts under a contract that will yield a profit of $20,000 if only 10% of the parts are defective and a profit of $12,000 if 30% of the parts are defective. The cost of checking for the malfunction is $1,000, and, if it turns out that repair is needed, this costs a further $2,000. If incurred, these costs must be subtracted from the profit of the contract. Historically, it has been found that the production process functions correctly 80% of the time. The manufacturer must decide whether to check the process at the beginning of a production run.

    a. According to the expected monetary value criterion, what is the optimal decision?

    b. Draw the decision tree.

    c. Suppose that the proportion of occasions on which the production process operates correctly is unknown. Under what range of values for this proportion would the decision selected in part (a) be optimal, according to the expected monetary value criterion?

21.21 A contractor has to decide whether to submit a bid for a construction project. It will cost $16,000 to prepare the bid. This cost would be incurred whether or not the bid was accepted. The contractor intends to bid at a level that will produce a $110,000 profit (less the cost of preparing the bid).

The contractor knows that 20% of bids prepared in this way have been successful.

    a. Set up the payoff table.

    b. Should a bid be prepared and submitted, according to the expected monetary value criterion?

    c. Under what range of probabilities that the bid will be successful should a bid be prepared and submitted, according to the expected monetary value criterion?

21.22 On Thursday evening the manager of a small branch of a car rental agency finds that he has available six cars for rental on the following day. However, he is able to request delivery of additional cars at a cost of $20 each from the regional depot. Each car that is rented produces an expected profit of $40. (The cost of delivery of the car must be subtracted from this profit.) Each potential customer requesting a car when none is available is counted as a $10 loss in goodwill. On reviewing his records for previous Fridays, the manager finds that the number of cars requested has ranged from 6 to 10; the percentages are shown in the accompanying table. The manager must decide how many cars, if any, to order from the regional depot.

Number of requests	6	7	8	9	10
Percent	10	30	30	20	10

    a. Set up the payoff table.

    b. If the expected monetary value criterion is used, how many cars should be ordered?

21.23 A contractor has decided to place a bid for a project. Bids are to be set in multiples of $20,000. It is estimated that the probability that a bid of $240,000 will secure the contract is 0.2, the probability that a bid of $220,000 will be successful is 0.3, and the probability that a bid of $200,000 will be accepted is 0.5. It is thought that any bid under $200,000 is certain to succeed and any bid over $240,000 is certain to fail. If the manufacturer wins the contract, he must solve a design problem with two possible choices at this stage. He can hire outside consultants, who will guarantee a satisfactory solution, for a price of $80,000. Alternatively, he can invest $30,000 of his own resources in an attempt to solve the problem internally; if this effort fails, he must then engage the consultants. It is estimated that the probability of successfully solving the problem internally is 0.6. Once this problem has been solved, the additional cost of fulfilling the contract is $140,000.

    a. Potentially, this contractor has two decisions to make. What are they?

    b. Draw the decision tree.

c. What is the optimal course of action, according to the expected monetary value criterion?

21.24 Consider a decision problem with two actions, a_1 and a_2, and two states of nature, s_1 and s_2. Let M_{ij} denote the payoff corresponding to action a_i and state of nature s_j. Assume that the probability of occurrence of state of nature s_1 is P, so the probability of state s_2 is $(1 - P)$.

a. Show that action a_1 is selected by the *EMV* criterion if

$$P(M_{11} - M_{21}) > (1 - P)(M_{22} - M_{12})$$

b. Hence, show that if a_1 is an admissible action, there is some probability, P, for which it will be chosen. However, if a_1 is not admissible, it cannot be chosen, whatever the value of P.

21.4 SAMPLE INFORMATION: BAYESIAN ANALYSIS AND VALUE

Decisions made in the business world can often involve considerable amounts of money, and the cost of making a suboptimal choice may turn out to be substantial. This being the case, it could well pay the decision maker to make an effort to obtain as much relevant information as possible before the decision is made. In particular, he or she will want to become as thoroughly informed as possible about the chances of occurrence of the various states of nature that determine the eventual payoff.

This feature of any careful analysis of a decision problem has not been apparent in our discussion so far. The cellular phone manufacturer, in Section 21.3, assessed the probabilities of low, moderate, and high levels of demand for a new cellular phone as 0.1, 0.5, and 0.4, respectively. However, this assessment reflected no more than the historical proportions achieved by previous products. In practice, he might well want to carry out some market research on the prospects for the new product. Given such research, these initial or *prior probabilities* may be modified, yielding new probabilities, called *posterior probabilities*, for the three demand levels. The information (in this case the market research results) leading to the modification of probabilities for the states of nature will be referred to as *sample information*.

Use of Bayes' Theorem

In Chapter 4 the mechanism for modifying prior probabilities to produce posterior probabilities was given. This is accomplished through **Bayes' theorem**, which, for convenience, is restated in the framework of our decision-making problem.

Bayes' Theorem

Let $s_1, s_2, \ldots, s_H$ be H mutually exclusive and collectively exhaustive events, corresponding to the H states of nature of a decision problem. Let A be some other event. Denote the conditional probability that s_i will occur, given that A occurs, by $P(s_i|A)$ and the probability of A, given s_i, by $P(A|s_i)$. **Bayes' theorem** states that the conditional probability of s_i, given A, can be expressed as

$$P(s_i \mid A) = \frac{P(A \mid s_i)P(s_i)}{P(A)}$$

$$= \frac{P(A \mid s_i)P(s_i)}{P(A \mid s_1)P(s_1) + P(A \mid s_2)P(s_2) + \ldots + P(A \mid s_H)P(s_H)} \quad (21.2)$$

In the terminology of this section $P(s_i)$ is the **prior probability** of s_i and is modified to the **posterior probability**, $P(s_i|A)$, given the **sample information** that event A has occurred.

Now, suppose that the cellular phone manufacturer hires a market research organization to predict the level of demand for his new product. Of course, there will be a fee for this service. Later in this chapter the question of whether the return merits the cost involved is discussed. The organization provides a rating of "poor," "fair," or "good," on the basis of its research. A review of the market research company's records reveals the quality of its past predictions in this field. Table 21.8 shows, for each level of demand outcome, the proportion of poor, fair, and good assessments.

For example, on 10% of occasions that demand was high, the assessment was "poor." Thus, in the notation of conditional probability, denoting low, moderate, and high demand levels by s_1, s_2, and s_3, respectively, it follows that

$$P(\text{Poor}\,|\,s_1) = 0.6 \qquad P(\text{Poor}\,|\,s_2) = 0.3 \qquad P(\text{Poor}\,|\,s_3) = 0.1$$

It is only a coincidence that the sum of $P(\text{Poor}\,|\,s_1) = 0.6$, $P(\text{Poor}\,|\,s_2) = 0.3$, and $P(\text{Poor}\,|\,s_3) = 0.1$ is 1.0. These conditional probabilities do not have to sum to 1. Take "fair," for example; notice that the sum of $P(\text{Fair}\,|\,s_1) = 0.2$, $P(\text{Fair}\,|\,s_2) = 0.4$, and $P(\text{Fair}\,|\,s_3) = 0.2$ is only 0.8 and not 1.0.

Suppose now that the market research firm is consulted and produces an assessment of "poor" for the prospects of the cellular phone. Given this new information, the prior probabilities

$$P(s_1) = 0.1 \qquad P(s_2) = 0.5 \qquad P(s_3) = 0.4$$

for the three demand levels can be modified using Bayes' theorem. For a low level of demand, the posterior probability is

$$P(s_1|\text{Poor}) = \frac{P(\text{Poor}|s_1)P(s_1)}{P(\text{Poor}|s_1)P(s_1) + P(\text{Poor}|s_2)P(s_2) + P(\text{Poor}|s_3)P(s_3)}$$
$$= \frac{(0.6)(0.1)}{(0.6)(0.1) + (0.3)(0.5) + (0.1)(0.4)} = \frac{0.06}{0.25} = 0.24$$

Similarly, for the other two demand levels the posterior probabilities are

$$P(s_2|\text{Poor}) = \frac{(0.3)(0.5)}{0.25} = 0.6$$
$$P(s_3|\text{Poor}) = \frac{(0.1)(0.4)}{0.25} = 0.16$$

Table 21.8   Proportion of Assessments of Each Type Provided by Market Research Organization for Cellular Phones Achieving Given Levels of Demand

ACTION	STATE OF NATURE		
ASSESSMENT	LOW DEMAND (s_1)	MODERATE DEMAND (s_2)	HIGH DEMAND (s_3)
Poor	0.6	0.3	0.1
Fair	0.2	0.4	0.2
Good	0.2	0.3	0.7

Table 21.9 Payoffs for Cellular Phone Manufacturer and Posterior Probabilities for States of Nature, Given an Assessment of "Poor" by Market Research Organization

ACTION	STATE OF NATURE		
PRODUCTION PROCESS	LOW DEMAND $(P = 0.24)*$	MODERATE DEMAND $(P = 0.60)*$	HIGH DEMAND $(P = 0.16)*$
A	70,000	120,000	200,000
B	80,000	120,000	180,000
C	100,000	125,000	160,000

*Posterior probabilities

The posterior probabilities can then be employed to calculate the expected monetary values. Table 21.9 shows the payoffs (without the fee of the organization), together with the posterior probabilities for the three demand levels. This is simply a modification of Table 21.7, with the posterior probabilities replacing the prior probabilities of that table.

The expected monetary values for the three production processes can be found in precisely the same manner as before. These are as follows:

EMV (Process A) = (0.24)(70,000) + (0.60)(120,000) + (0.16)(200,000) = $120,800
EMV (Process B) = (0.24)(80,000) + (0.60)(120,000) + (0.16)(180,000) = $120,000
EMV (Process C) = (0.24)(100,000) + (0.60)(125,000) + (0.16)(160,000) = $124,600

If the assessment of market prospects is "poor," then, according to the expected monetary value criterion, production process C should be used. The market research group's assessment has rendered low demand much more likely and high demand considerably less likely than was previously the case. This shift in the view of market prospects is sufficient to induce the cellular phone manufacturer to switch preference from process A (based on the prior probabilities) to process C.

Following the same line of argument, one can determine the decisions that would be made if the prospects for the cellular phone's market success were rated either "fair" or "good." Again, the posterior probabilities for the three levels of demand can be obtained through Bayes' theorem. For a "fair" assessment, these are

$$P(s_1|\text{Fair}) = \frac{1}{15} \qquad P(s_2|\text{Fair}) = \frac{10}{15} \qquad P(s_3|\text{Fair}) = \frac{4}{15}$$

For a "good" assessment

$$P(s_1|\text{Good}) = \frac{2}{45} \qquad P(s_2|\text{Good}) = \frac{15}{45} \qquad P(s_3|\text{Good}) = \frac{28}{45}$$

Using these posterior probabilities, we obtained via Excel calculations the expected monetary values of each of the production processes for each given assessment. Table 21.10 contains these EMVs. The calculated EMVs in Table 21.10 could vary depending on the number of decimal places used to express the posterior probabilities.

As has been shown previously, if the assessment is "poor," then process C is preferred by the expected monetary value criterion. If any other assessment is made, then production process A would be chosen, according to this criterion.

Table 21.10   *EMVs* for Cellular Phone Manufacturer for Three Possible Assessments by Market Research Firm

ACTION	STATE OF NATURE		
PRODUCTION PROCESS	POOR ASSESSMENT	FAIR ASSESSMENT	GOOD ASSESSMENT
A	120,800	138,000	167,556
B	120,000	133,333	155,556
C	124,600	132,667	145,667

Recall that, for the cellular phone manufacturer's problem when the prior probabilities for levels of demand were used, the optimal decision according to the expected monetary value criterion was to use process A. It can be the case (if an assessment of "poor" is obtained) that a different decision will be made when these prior probabilities are modified by sample information. Hence, it turns out that consulting the market research organization could be valuable for the manufacturer. Of course, if the choice of process A had proved optimal, whatever the assessment, the sample information could not possibly be of value.

Example 21.5   Drug Manufacturer Revisited (Expected Monetary Value)

In Example 21.4 a drug manufacturer had to decide whether to sell the patent for a cholesterol-lowering formula before subjecting the drug to thorough testing. (Subsequently, if the patent was retained and the drug was found to be effective, a second decision—to market the drug or to sell the patent and test results—also had to be made.) For the initial decision, the two states of nature were s_1: Drug is effective; and s_2: Drug is ineffective. The associated prior probabilities, formed on the basis of previous experience, are

$$P(s_1) = 0.6 \quad \text{and} \quad P(s_2) = 0.4$$

The drug manufacturer has the option of carrying out, at modest cost, an initial test before the first decision is made. The test is not infallible. For drugs that have subsequently proved effective, the preliminary test result was positive on 60% of occasions and negative on the remainder. For ineffective drugs a positive preliminary test result was obtained 30% of the time, the other results being negative. Given the results of the preliminary test, how should the drug manufacturer proceed? Assume that it is still possible to sell the patent for $50,000 if the preliminary test result is negative.

Solution   First, notice that, if the patent is retained and the exhaustive tests prove the drug to be effective, then in the absence of any sample information on market conditions, the optimal decision at this stage, as in Example 21.4, is to market the drug. The information provided by the preliminary test is irrelevant in that particular decision. However, it could conceivably influence the initial decision as to whether to sell the patent. Accordingly, only this decision is considered.

The conditional probabilities of the sample outcomes, given the states of nature, are

$$P(\text{Positive}\,|\,s_1) = 0.6 \qquad P(\text{Negative}\,|\,s_1) = 0.4$$
$$P(\text{Positive}\,|\,s_2) = 0.3 \qquad P(\text{Negative}\,|\,s_2) = 0.7$$

If the result of the preliminary test is positive, then the posterior probability for the state s_1 (effective), given this information, is

$$P(s_1\,|\,\text{Positive}) = \frac{P(\text{Positive}\,|\,s_1)P(s_1)}{P(\text{Positive}\,|\,s_1)P(s_1) + P(\text{Positive}\,|\,s_2)P(s_2)} = \frac{(0.6)(0.6)}{(0.6)(0.6) + (0.3)(0.4)} = 0.75$$

Further, since the two posterior probabilities must sum to 1, then $P(s_2\,|\,\text{Positive}) = 0.25$. The accompanying payoff table is the same as in Example 21.4, with these posterior probabilities added.

	State of Nature	
Action	Effective Drug ($P = 0.75$)*	Ineffective Drug ($P = 0.25$)*
Retain patent	125,000	−10,000
Sell patent	50,000	50,000

*Posterior probabilities

The expected monetary value, if the patent is sold, is $50,000, while if the patent is retained, the expected monetary value is

$$(0.75)(125,000) + (0.25)(-10,000) = \$91,250$$

Therefore, if the initial test result is positive, the patent should be retained, according to this criterion.

Next, consider the case where the preliminary test result is negative. The posterior probability for the state s_1 is, by Bayes' theorem,

$$P(s_1\,|\,\text{Negative}) = \frac{P(\text{Negative}\,|\,s_1)P(s_1)}{P(\text{Negative}\,|\,s_1)P(s_1) + P(\text{Negative}\,|\,s_2)P(s_2)} = \frac{(0.4)(0.6)}{(0.4)(0.6) + (0.7)(0.4)} = 0.4615$$

Hence, the posterior probability for the state s_2 is

$$P(s_2\,|\,\text{Negative}) = 0.5385$$

Once more, if the patent is sold, the expected monetary value is the $50,000 that will be received. If the patent is retained, the expected monetary value of this decision is

$$(0.4615)(125,000) + (0.5385)(-10,000) = \$52,302.50$$

Thus, even if the preliminary test result is negative, the optimal decision, by the expected monetary value criterion, is to retain the patent.

In this particular example, then, whatever the sample information, the chosen action is the same. The manufacturer should retain the patent in the event of either result emerging from the preliminary test. Since the sample information cannot possibly affect the decision, there is, of course, no point in gathering it. In fact, since performing the preliminary test will not be costless, it will be suboptimal to do so. Thus, according to the expected monetary value criterion, the drug manufacturer should retain the patent, and if the thorough tests prove the drug to be effective, then the manufacturer should market it. The preliminary test should not be carried out.

The Value of Sample Information

It has been shown how sample information can be incorporated into the decision-making process. The potential value of such information lies, of course, in its provision of a better feel for the chances of occurrence of the relevant states of nature. This, in turn, can provide firmer ground on which to base a decision. This section shows how a *monetary* value can be attached to the sample information. This is important, since there will typically be some cost involved in obtaining the sample information, and the decision maker will want to know whether the expected benefits exceed this cost.

Example 21.5 illustrates a situation where the same action was optimal, whatever the sample result. In such a case the sample information clearly has no value, since the same action would have been taken without it. This is a general rule: If the sample information cannot affect the choice of action, then it has value 0.

Accordingly, the remainder of this section concerns only circumstances in which the sample result can affect the choice of action. Our example of the cellular phone manufacturer planning to introduce a new product is such a case. This manufacturer has to choose from three production processes and is faced with three states of nature, representing different levels of demand for the product. Section 21.3 showed that, in the absence of sample information and using only the prior probabilities, process A with an expected monetary value of $147,000 is selected.

Now, in practice, having obtained sample information, the decision maker will typically not know which state of nature will occur but will have more firmly grounded probabilistic assessments for these states. However, before discussing the value of sample information in this general framework, it is useful to consider the extreme case where **perfect information** is obtainable—that is, the case where the decision maker is able to gain information that will tell *with certainty* which state will occur. What is the value to the decision maker of having such perfect information?

Expected Value of Perfect Information, *EVPI*

Suppose that a decision maker has to choose from among *K* possible actions in the face of *H* states of nature, $s_1, s_2, \ldots, s_H$. **Perfect information** corresponds to knowledge of which state of nature will arise. The expected value of perfect information is obtained as follows:

1. Determine which action will be chosen if only the prior probabilities $P(s_1), P(s_2), \ldots, P(s_H)$ are used.
2. For each possible state of nature, s_i, find the difference, W_i, between the payoff for the best choice of action, if it was known that state would arise, and the payoff for the action chosen if only the prior probabilities were used. This is the **value of perfect information**, when it is known that s_i will occur.
3. The **expected value of perfect information**, *EVPI*, is then

$$EVPI = P(s_1)W_1 + P(s_2)W_2 + \cdots + P(s_H)W_H \qquad (21.3)$$

Let's return again to the cellular phone manufacturer and calculate the *EVPI*. In the context of this manufacturer perfect information corresponds to knowledge of which of the three possible demand levels will actually result. In the absence of any sample information and on the basis of the prior probabilities only, process A will be chosen. However, referring to Table 21.7, if the level of demand is low, then the best choice will be process C. Since this has a payoff that exceeds by $30,000 that of process A, the value of knowing that demand will be low is $30,000. Similarly, if it is known that moderate demand will result, process C will again be chosen. Here, the payoff from the best available choice exceeds that of process A by $5,000, which is, accordingly, the value of knowing that demand will be moderate. If it is known that high demand will occur, then process A will be chosen. Thus, this particular knowledge is of no value, since the same decision would have been made without it. The value of perfect information depends on the information. Using the prior probabilities of the various states of nature, the expected value of perfect information is found.

For the cellular phone manufacturer, the prior probabilities are 0.1 for low, 0.5 for moderate, and 0.4 for high demand. It therefore follows that to this manufacturer the value of perfect information is $30,000 with probability 0.1, $5,000 with probability 0.5, and $0 with probability 0.4. The expected value of perfect information is, accordingly,

$$EVPI = (0.1)(30{,}000) + (0.5)(5{,}000) + (0.4)(0) = \$5{,}500$$

This dollar amount, then, represents the expected value to the cellular phone manufacturer of knowing what level of demand will result.

For more complex problems, software is available to obtain $EVPI$.

Although perfect information will not be available typically, the calculation of the expected value of perfect information can be useful. Since, of course, no sample information can be better than perfect, its expected value cannot be higher than that of the expected value of perfect information. Thus, the expected value of perfect information provides an *upper limit* for the expected value of any sample information. For example, if the cellular phone manufacturer is offered information at a cost of $6,000, it is not necessary to inquire further about the quality of this information. It should not be purchased, however reliable, according to the expected monetary value criterion, since its expected value cannot be more than $5,500.

Consider now the more general problem of assessing the value of sample information that is not necessarily perfect. Again, consider the decision-making problem of the cellular phone manufacturer, who has the option of obtaining an assessment from a market research organization of the prospects for the new cellular phone. These prospects will be rated "poor," "fair," or "good." In Section 21.4 it was shown that, in the last two of the three eventualities, process A will still be chosen. Thus, if a "fair" or "good" rating is obtained, the initial choice of action will remain unchanged, and nothing will have been gained from consulting the market research company.

However, if the prospects are rated "poor," then Table 21.10 shows that the optimal choice is process C. This optimal choice would yield an expected monetary value of $124,600, whereas process A, which otherwise would have been used, gives an expected monetary value of $120,800. The difference in these amounts, $3,800, represents the gain from the sample information *if the assessment is "poor."* The gains from the sample information are $0 for ratings of "good" or "fair" and $3,800 for a rating of "poor."

We now need to know how likely these gains are to materialize, so in our example we must find the probability of a "poor" assessment. In general, if A denotes a piece of sample information and $s_1, s_2, \ldots, s_H$ the H possible states of nature, then

$$P(A) = P(A \mid s_1)P(s_1) + P(A \mid s_2)P(s_2) + \cdots + P(A \mid s_H)P(s_H)$$

For the cellular phone example, with s_1, s_2, and s_3 denoting low, moderate, and high levels of demand, respectively, then

$$P(s_1) = 0.1 \qquad P(s_2) = 0.5 \qquad P(s_3) = 0.4$$
$$P(\text{Poor} \mid s_1) = 0.6 \qquad P(\text{Poor} \mid s_2) = 0.3 \qquad P(\text{Poor} \mid s_3) = 0.1$$

Therefore, the probability of a "poor" assessment is

$$P(\text{Poor}) = P(\text{Poor} \,|\, s_1)\, P(s_1) + P(\text{Poor} \,|\, s_2)P(s_2) + P(\text{Poor} \,|\, s_3)P(s_3)$$
$$= (0.6)(0.1) + (0.3)(0.5) + (0.1)(0.4) = 0.25$$

In the same way, using the conditional probabilities of Table 21.8, the probabilities for the other two assessments are

$$P(\text{Fair}) = 0.30 \qquad P(\text{Good}) = 0.45$$

Thus, the value of the sample information is \$3,800 with probability 0.25, \$0 with probability 0.30, and \$0 with probability 0.45. It therefore follows that the **expected value of the sample information** is

$$EVSI = (0.25)(3,800) + (0.30)(0) + (0.45)(0) = \$950$$

This dollar amount, then, represents the expected value of the sample information to the decision maker. In terms of the expected monetary value criterion this sample information will be worth acquiring if its cost is less than its expected value. The **expected net value of sample information** is the difference between its expected value and its cost.

Suppose that the market research group charges a fee of \$750 for its assessment. The expected net value of this assessment to the cellular phone manufacturer is then \$950 − \$750 = \$200. Thus, the manufacturer's expected payoff will be \$200 higher if the sample information is purchased than if it is not. This amount represents the expected worth of having that information, taking into account its cost. In this case the manufacturer's optimal strategy is to purchase the market research report and then use production process A if the assessment is either "good" or "fair" and process C if the assessment is "poor." The *EMV* of this strategy is \$147,200—that is, the \$147,000 that would result from no sample information plus the expected net value of the sample information.

Expected Value of Sample Information, *EVSI*

Suppose that a decision maker has to choose from *K* possible actions in the face of *H* states of nature, $s_1, s_2, \ldots, s_H$. The decision maker may obtain sample information. Let there be *M* possible sample results, $A_1, A_2, \ldots, A_M$.

The expected value of sample information is obtained as follows.

1. Determine which action would be chosen if only the prior probabilities were used.
2. Determine the probabilities of obtaining each sample result:

$$P(A_i) = P(A_i \,|\, s_1)P(s_1) + P(A_i \,|\, s_2)P(s_2) + \cdots + P(A_i \,|\, s_H)P(s_H)$$

3. For each possible sample result A_i, find the difference, V_i, between the expected monetary value for the optimal action and that for the action chosen if only prior probabilities are used. This is the **value of the sample information**, given that A_i was observed.
4. The **expected value of sample information, *EVSI*,** is then

$$EVSI = P(A_1)V_1 + P(A_2)V_2 + \cdots + P(A_M)V_M \qquad (21.4)$$

The Value of Sample Information Viewed by Means of Decision Trees

The expected value of sample information can be computed in an alternative (but equivalent) manner, which is arithmetically slightly more cumbersome but does provide a convenient way of representing the problem in terms of a sequence of decisions through the construction of a decision tree. The first decision to make is whether to obtain the sample information. Next, it is necessary to decide which of the alternative actions should be followed.

To illustrate, consider again the problem of the cellular phone manufacturer. Figure 21.5 shows the decision trees following from the three possible market research appraisals. These trees have the same general structure as Figure 21.1. The essential difference is that the probabilities associated with the three states of nature are the appropriate *posterior probabilities*, given the specific sample information. These posterior probabilities were found in Section 21.4. The payoffs are now weighted by the posterior probabilities, yielding the expected monetary value of each action, given each possible sample result. These are the expected monetary values shown in Table 21.10. Finally, at the left of each part of Figure 21.5 is the highest possible expected monetary value for each sample outcome.

This information is transferred to the right of Figure 21.6, in which the decision whether to purchase the market research study is analyzed. If this information is not bought, then the bottom part of Figure 21.6 shows an expected monetary value of $147,000. This results from using the prior probabilities and is taken from Figure 21.1.

We turn now to the upper part of Figure 21.6; the expected monetary value that results will depend on the sample outcome. The probabilities are 0.25 for "poor," 0.30

Figure 21.5
Decision Trees for the Cellular Phone Manufacturer, Given the Market Research Organization Assessments of (a) "Poor," (b) "Fair," and (c) "Good" (*Action with Maximum *EMV*)

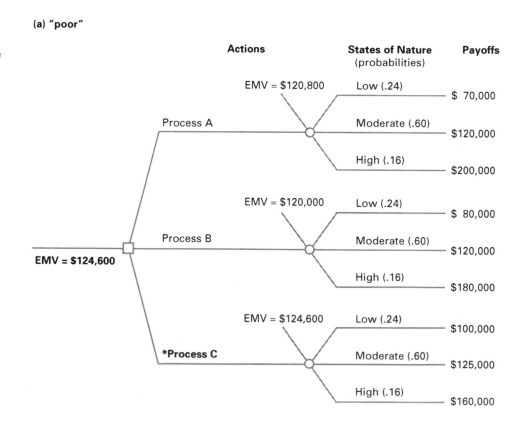

(a) "poor"

(b) "fair"

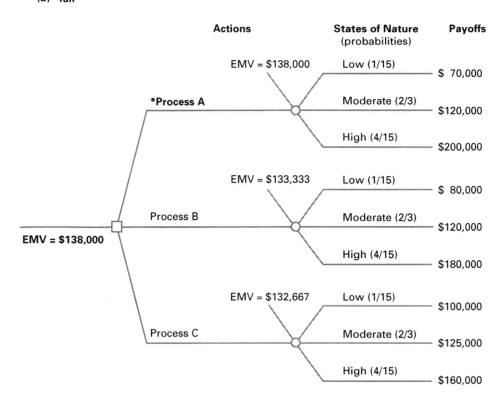

(c) "good"

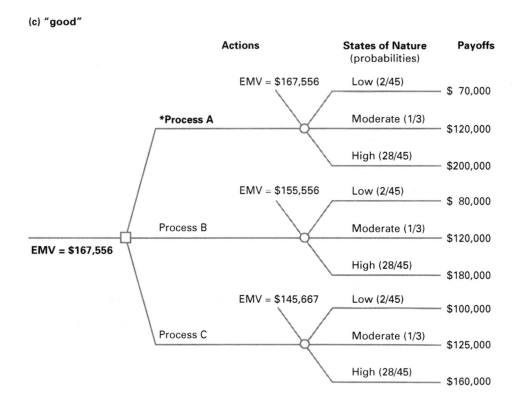

Figure 21.6
Cellular Phone Manufacturer's Decision to Purchase the Services of the Market Research Organization (*Action with Maximum *EMV*)

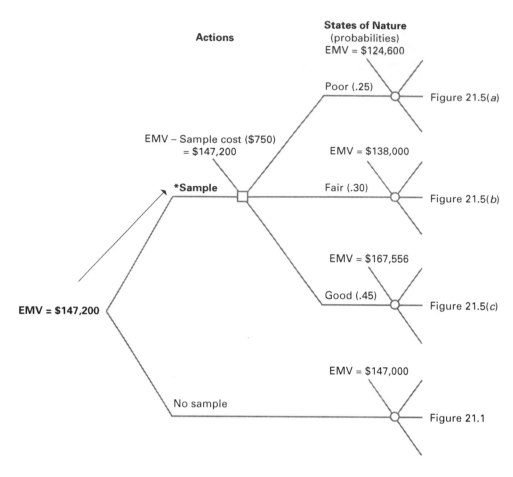

for "fair," and 0.45 for "good." Thus, since $124,600 can be expected with probability 0.25, $138,000 with probability 0.30, and $167,556 with probability 0.45, the expected payoff if the sample information is purchased is

$$(0.25)(124,600) + (0.30)(138,000) + (0.45)(167,556) = \$147,950$$

However, it is necessary to subtract from this amount the $750 cost of the sample information, leaving $147,200. Since this is more than the expected payoff when no sample information is obtained, the best strategy, according to the expected monetary value criterion, is to purchase the services of the market research group. The optimal decision has, as indicated at the left of Figure 21.6, an expected monetary value of $147,200.

EXERCISES

Application Exercises

21.25   A manufacturer must decide whether to mount, at a cost of $100,000, an advertising campaign for a product whose sales have been rather flat. It is estimated that a highly successful campaign would add $400,000 (from which the campaign's costs must be subtracted) to profits, and a moderately successful campaign would add $100,000, but an unsuccessful campaign would add nothing. Historically, 40% of all similar campaigns have been very successful, 30% moderately successful, and the remainder unsuccessful. This manufacturer consults a media consultant for a judgment on the potential effectiveness of the campaign. This consultant's record is such that she has reported favorably on 80% of campaigns that turned out to be highly successful, 40% of those that were moderately successful, and 10% of unsuccessful campaigns.

a. Find the prior probabilities for the three states of nature.
b. In the absence of any report from the media consultant, should this advertising campaign be mounted, according to the *EMV* criterion?
c. Find the posterior probabilities for the three states of nature, given that the media consultant reports favorably.
d. Given a favorable report from the consultant, should the advertising campaign be mounted, according to the *EMV* criterion?
e. Find the posterior probabilities for the three states of nature, given that the media consultant does not report favorably.
f. If the consultant's report is not favorable, should the advertising campaign be mounted, according to the *EMV* criterion?

21.26 Refer to Exercise 21.2. The deodorant manufacturer has four possible production processes from which to choose, depending on the view that is taken of future demand levels. On the basis of past experience the prior probabilities are 0.3 for high demand, 0.4 for moderate demand, and 0.3 for low demand. The accompanying table shows proportions of "poor," "fair," and "good" assessments for prospects provided by a market research group for similar products that have achieved these demand levels.

Action	State of Nature		
Assessment	Low Demand	Moderate Demand	High Demand
Poor	0.5	0.3	0.1
Fair	0.3	0.4	0.2
Good	0.2	0.3	0.7

a. If the market research group is not consulted, which action should be chosen, according to the *EMV* criterion?
b. Find the posterior probabilities of the three demand levels, given an assessment of "poor."
c. Which action should be chosen, according to the *EMV* criterion, given an assessment of "poor"?
d. Find the posterior probabilities of the three demand levels, given an assessment of "fair."

e. Which action should be chosen, according to the *EMV* criterion, given an assessment of "fair?"
f. Find the posterior probabilities of the three demand levels, given an assessment of "good."
g. Which action should be chosen, according to the *EMV* criterion, given an assessment of "good"?

21.27 The shoe store operator of Exercise 21.9 has available two courses of action. His decision is based on his view of the likely level of success of the new shopping center. Historically, 40% of new centers of this type have been very successful, 40% moderately successful, and 20% unsuccessful. A consulting group sells assessments of the prospects of this type of shopping center. The table given here shows the proportion of "good," "fair," and "poor" assessments, given the particular outcome actually resulting.

Action	State of Nature (Success Level)		
Assessment	Very Successful	Moderately Successful	Unsuccessful
Good	0.6	0.3	0.2
Fair	0.3	0.4	0.3
Poor	0.1	0.3	0.5

a. What are the prior probabilities for the three states of nature?
b. If the shoe store operator does not seek advice from the consulting group, what action should he take, according to the *EMV* criterion?
c. What are the posterior probabilities of the three states of nature, given an assessment of "good"?
d. According to the *EMV* criterion, given an assessment of "good," what course of action should the shoe store operator adopt?
e. What are the posterior probabilities of the three states of nature, given an assessment of "fair"?
f. According to the *EMV* criterion, given an assessment of "fair," which action should be chosen?
g. What are the posterior probabilities of the three states of nature, given an assessment of "poor"?
h. If the *EMV* criterion is followed, which action should be chosen, given a forecast of "poor"?

21.28 Consider the drug manufacturer of Example 21.5, who had to decide whether to sell the patent for a cholesterol-lowering drug before subjecting it to thorough testing. In the example we saw that, whatever the result of a certain preliminary test of the drug's efficacy, the optimal decision was to retain the patent. Subsequently, this manufacturer developed a superior preliminary test, which again could be carried out at modest cost. For drugs that subsequently proved effective, this new test gave a positive result 80% of the time, while a positive result was obtained for only 10% of the drugs that proved to be ineffective.

a. Find the posterior probabilities of the two states of nature, given a positive result from this new preliminary test.

b. According to the *EMV* criterion, should the patent be sold if the new test result is positive?

c. Find the posterior probabilities of the two states of nature, given a negative result from the new preliminary test.

d. According to the *EMV* criterion, should the patent be sold if the new test result is negative?

21.29 In Exercise 21.20, a supplier of parts to the automobile industry had to decide whether to check the production process for a certain malfunction before starting a production run. The two states of nature were

s_1: Repair not needed (10% of all parts produced fail to meet specifications)

s_2: Repair needed (30% of all parts produced fail to meet specifications)

The prior probabilities, derived from the historical record for this production process, are

$$P(s_1) = 0.8 \quad \text{and} \quad P(s_2) = 0.2$$

The manufacturer can, before beginning a full production run, produce a single part and check whether it meets specifications, basing a decision on whether to check the production process on the resulting sample information.

a. If the single part checked meets specifications, what are the posterior probabilities of the states of nature?

b. If the single part checked meets specifications, should the production process be checked according to the *EMV* criterion?

c. If the single part checked does not meet specifications, what are the posterior probabilities of the states of nature?

d. If the single part checked does not meet specifications, should the production process be checked, according to the *EMV* criterion?

21.30 Continuing Exercise 21.29, suppose now that, before making a decision on whether to check the production process, *two* parts are made and examined.

a. If, in fact, repair is not needed, what are the probabilities that both parts, just one part, or neither part will fail to meet specifications?

b. Compute the same probabilities as in part (a), given that repair of the production process is, in fact, needed.

c. Compute the posterior probabilities of the states of nature, and determine the optimal action under the expected monetary value criterion, given each of the following circumstances:

i. Both parts fail to meet specifications.

ii. Just one part fails to meet specifications.

iii. Neither part fails to meet specifications.

21.31 The Watts New Lightbulb Corporation ships large consignments of light bulbs to big industrial users. When the production process is functioning correctly (which is 90% of the time), 10% of all bulbs produced are defective. However, the process is susceptible to an occasional malfunction, leading to a defective rate of 20%. The Watts New Lightbulb Corporation counts the cost, in terms of goodwill, of a shipment with the higher defective rate to an industrial user as $5,000. If a consignment is suspected of containing this larger proportion of defectives, it can instead be sold to a chain of discount stores, though this involves a reduction of $600 in profits, whether or not the consignment does indeed contain a large proportion of defective bulbs. Decisions by this company are made through the *EMV* criterion.

a. A consignment is produced. In the absence of any further information should it be shipped to an industrial user or to the discount chain?

b. Suppose that a single bulb from the consignment is checked. Determine where the consignment should be shipped under each of the following circumstances:

i. This bulb is defective.

ii. This bulb is not defective.

c. Suppose that two bulbs from the consignment are checked. Determine where the consignment should be shipped for each of the following situations:

i. Both bulbs are defective.

ii. Just one bulb is defective.

iii. Neither bulb is defective.

d. Without doing the calculations indicate how the decision problem could be attacked if 100 bulbs were checked prior to shipping the consignment.

21.32 Refer to the problem of the investor of Exercise 21.1.

a. Explain what is meant by "perfect information" in the context of this investor's problem.

b. The prior probabilities are 0.2 for a strong stock market, 0.5 for a moderate stock market, and 0.3 for a weak stock market. What is the expected value of perfect information to this investor?

21.33 For the deodorant manufacturer of Exercise 21.2, the prior probabilities are 0.3 for high demand, 0.4 for moderate demand, and 0.3 for low demand. Find the *EVPI* to this manufacturer.

21.34 For the shoe store operator of Exercise 21.9, the prior probabilities are 0.4 that the new shopping center will be very successful, 0.4 that it will be moderately successful, and 0.2 that it will be unsuccessful. What is the expected value of perfect information to this shoe store operator?

21.35 The manufacturer of automobile parts of Exercise 21.20 must decide whether to check the production process before beginning a full production run. Given that the production process functions correctly 80% of the time, what is the value of perfect information to this manufacturer?

21.36 Before showing how to find the expected value of sample information, we discussed separately the determination of the expected value of perfect information. In fact, this was not necessary because perfect information is just a special kind of sample information. Given the general procedure for finding the expected value of sample information, show how to specialize this to the case of perfect information.

21.37 Refer to Exercise 21.25. The manufacturer is considering an advertising campaign and first seeks the advice of a media consultant.

a. What is the expected value to the manufacturer of the media consultant's advice?
b. The media consultant charges a fee of $5,000. What is the expected net value of the consultant's advice?
c. This manufacturer faces a two-stage decision problem. First, he must decide whether to purchase advice from the media consultant. Next, he must decide whether to mount the advertising campaign. Draw the complete decision tree, and indicate how the manufacturer should proceed.

21.38 Refer to Exercise 21.26. Find the largest fee the deodorant manufacturer should pay to the market research group, according to the expected monetary value criterion.

21.39 Refer to Exercise 21.27. Find the expected value to the shoe store operator of an assessment of the shopping center's prospects provided by the consulting group.

21.40 Refer to Exercise 21.28. Before deciding whether to sell the patent of the new cholesterol-lowering formula, the drug manufacturer carries out the new preliminary test. Find the expected value to the manufacturer of the test result.

21.41 Refer to Exercise 21.29. The supplier of automobile parts is able to produce and examine a single part before deciding whether to check the production process. What is the *EVSI*?

21.42 Consider the Watts New Lightbulb Corporation of Exercise 21.31. The corporation can check one or more light bulbs before deciding whether to ship a consignment to an industrial user or to a discount chain.

a. What is the expected value to the corporation of checking a single light bulb?
b. What is the expected value to the corporation of checking two light bulbs?
c. What is the difference between expected values of checking two bulbs and one bulb?
d. If the first bulb checked turns out to be defective, what is the expected value of checking the second?
e. If the first bulb checked turns out not to be defective, what is the expected value of checking the second?

21.5 ALLOWING FOR RISK: UTILITY ANALYSIS

The expected monetary value criterion provides a framework for decision making that has wide practical applicability. That is to say, in many instances, an individual or corporation will believe that the action offering the highest expected monetary value is the preferred course. However, this is not invariably the case, as the following examples illustrate.

1. Many individuals purchase term life insurance through which, for a relatively modest outlay, the insured person's estate is generously compensated in the event of death during the term of the policy. Now, insurance companies are able to calculate the death probability of an individual of any given age during a specified period of time. Accordingly, their rates are set in such a way that the

price of a policy exceeds the amount of money that is expected to be paid out. The amount of this excess covers the insurance company's costs and provides, on the average, a margin of profit. It then follows that, for the person insured, the expected payoff from the life insurance policy is less than its cost. Therefore, if everyone based decisions on the expected monetary value criterion, term life insurance would not be purchased. Nevertheless, many people do buy this form of insurance, demonstrating a willingness to sacrifice something in expected returns for the assurance that the heirs will be provided a financial cushion in the event of death.

2. Suppose that an investor is considering purchasing shares in one or more of a group of corporations whose prospects he regards as bright. In principle, it is possible to postulate the various states of nature that will influence the returns from investment in each of these corporations. In this way the expected monetary value of an investment of a fixed amount in each corporation could be determined. According to the expected monetary value criterion, the investor should then put all of his available capital into the corporation for which the expected monetary value is highest. In fact, a great many investors in the stock market do not follow such a strategy. Rather, they spread their cash over a portfolio of stocks. The abandonment of the option of "putting all one's eggs in a single basket," while leading to a lower expected return, provides a hedge against the possibility of losing a good deal of money if the single stock with the highest expected return happens to perform badly. In opting for a portfolio of stocks the investor is asserting a willingness to sacrifice something in expected monetary value for a smaller chance of a large financial loss.

In each of these examples, the decision maker has exhibited a preference for a criterion of choice other than expected monetary value, and in each circumstance this preference seems to be extremely reasonable. The two examples involve a common ingredient in addition to expected returns. In both cases the decision maker wants to take *risk* into account. The purchaser of term life insurance is prepared to accept a negative expected return as the price to be paid for the chance of a large positive return in the event of death. In doing so, he is expressing a **preference for risk** (of course, he is guarding against the risk that his family will be financially ill-prepared for his death). By contrast, the investor who, in spreading his investment over a portfolio of stocks, accepts a lower expected return in order to reduce the chances of a large loss is expressing an **aversion to risk**.

The expected monetary value criterion is inappropriate for decision makers who either prefer or are averse to risk. Fortunately, it is not too difficult to modify this criterion to handle situations in which risk is a relevant factor. Essentially, the idea is to replace the monetary payoffs by quantities that reflect not only the dollar amounts to be received but also the decision maker's attitude to risk.

The Concept of Utility

Example 21.3 considered the problem of an investor choosing between a guaranteed fixed-interest investment and a portfolio of stocks. The former would yield a payoff of $1,200, while gains of $2,500 and $500 would result for the latter if the stock market was buoyant or steady, but a loss of $1,000 would result if it was depressed. This investor believed that the respective probabilities for these three states of nature were 0.6, 0.2, and 0.2. In that event the expected monetary value from choosing the stock portfolio was $1,400, exceeding by $200 that of the fixed-interest investment. At this juncture we need to inquire whether this higher expected return merits the risk of losing $1,000, as would occur if the market was depressed. A very wealthy investor, who could quite comfortably sustain such a loss, would almost certainly decide that it does. However, the position of a relatively poor person, to whom a loss of $1,000 would be quite disastrous, may well be different. For such an investor the payoffs must be replaced by some other quantities that more adequately reflect the calamitous nature of a loss of $1,000. These quantities must measure the value, or *utility*, to the investor of a loss of $1,000 as compared with, for example, a gain of $500 or $2,500.

The early works of researchers such as Von Neumann and Morgenstern (Reference 6) enhanced the concept of utility, which even today plays a central role in economics. Utility analysis provides the basis for the solution of decision-making problems in the presence of risk preference or aversion. To employ it, only fairly mild and usually quite reasonable assumptions are needed. Suppose that an individual is faced with several possible payoffs, which may or may not be monetary. It is assumed that the individual can rank in order (possibly with ties) the utility, or satisfaction, that would be derived from each. Thus, if payoff A is preferred to B and B is preferred to C, A must be preferred to C.

Also assume that, if payoff A is preferred to B and B is preferred to C, then there exists a gamble, which offers A with probability P and C with probability $(1 - P)$, such that the decision maker will be indifferent between taking this gamble and receiving B with certainty. Given these and certain other, generally innocuous assumptions whose details need not detain us, it is possible to show that the rational decision maker will choose the action for which expected utility is highest. Consequently, the decision problem is analyzed precisely as in the preceding sections, *but with utilities instead of payoffs*. That is to say, a utility table rather than a payoff table is constructed, and then the state-of-nature probabilities to compare expected utilities are employed.

Now consider how the utilities corresponding to the various payoffs are determined. The possible payoffs in ascending order for our investor are –$1,000, $500, $1,200, and $2,500. The first step is to obtain a utility function.

Obtaining a Utility Function

Suppose that a decision maker may receive several alternative payoffs. The transformation from payoffs to **utilities** is made as follows:

1. The units in which utility is measured are arbitrary. Accordingly, a scale can be fixed in any convenient fashion. Let L be the lowest and H the highest of all the payoffs. Assign utility 0 to payoff L and utility 100 to payoff H.
2. Let I be any payoff between L and H. Determine the probability P such that the decision maker is indifferent between the following alternatives:

   a. Receive payoff I with certainty.
   b. Receive payoff H with probability P and payoff L with probability $(1 - P)$.

3. The utility to the decision maker of payoff I is then $100P$. The curve relating utility to payoff is called a **utility function.**

The first step is straightforward and simply provides us with a convenient metric for measuring utility. The choice of the numbers 0 and 100 to represent the utilities of the lowest and highest payoffs is entirely arbitrary. Any other pair of numbers could equally well be used, as long as the utility of the highest payoff is greater than that of the lowest, without affecting the remaining analysis.

As a practical matter, the second step is the most difficult, partly because it presupposes that the decision maker can manipulate probabilities in a coherent way. In practice, the probability must be determined by trial and error, through the asking of questions such as "Would you prefer to receive I with certainty or a gamble in which you could obtain H with probability 0.9 and L with probability 0.1?" Or perhaps, the question "Would you prefer to receive I with certainty or a gamble in which you could obtain H with probability 0.8 and L with probability 0.2?" This process is continued until the point of indifference is reached.

The logic of the final step is quite straightforward. Since H has utility 100 and L has utility 0, the *expected utility* if H is obtained with probability P and L with probability $(1 - P)$ is

$$100P + 0(1 - P) = 100P$$

Since the decision maker is indifferent between this gamble and receiving I with certainty, the utility $100P$ is associated with the payoff I.

Return now to our investor. At the first step we attach utility 0 to the lowest payoff, –$1,000, and utility 100 to the highest, $2,500.

It remains to determine the utilities for the intermediate payoffs, $500 and $1,200. This is achieved by posing to the decision maker a series of questions, such as "Would you prefer to receive $500 with certainty or a gamble in which you could obtain a gain of $2,500 with probability P and a loss of $1,000 with probability $(1 - P)$?" Different values of the probability P are tried until the value at which the decision maker is indifferent between the two alternatives is found. This process is repeated for the payoff of $1,200.

Suppose that the investor is indifferent between a payoff of $500 and the gamble with $P = 0.6$ and between a payoff of $1,200 and the gamble with $P = 0.8$. The utilities for the intermediate payoffs are then

Payoff $500:   Utility = (100)(0.6) = 60
Payoff $1,200:   Utility = (100)(0.8) = 80

The four utilities for this investor are plotted against the corresponding payoffs as points in Figure 21.7.

A curve is drawn through these points to indicate the general shape of this investor's utility function. The shape of this curve is interesting, since it characterizes

Figure 21.7
Utility Function
for an Investor

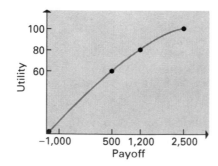

the investor's attitude to risk. As must be the case, utility increases as the payoff increases. However, notice that the *rate of increase* of utility is highest at the lowest payoffs and decreases as payoff increases. This implies a distaste for the lowest payoffs that is more than commensurate with their monetary amounts, indicating *aversion* to risk. This aversion can be seen from the investor's attitude to the gambles offered. For example, the investor is indifferent between a sure payoff of $500 and a gamble in which $2,500 might be won with probability 0.6 and $1,000 lost with probability 0.4. The expected monetary value of this gamble is

$$(0.6)(2,500) + (0.4)(-1,000) = \$1,100$$

which considerably exceeds the equally preferred sure payoff of $500. The amount of this difference provides a measure of the extent of the aversion to risk.

The shape of Figure 21.7 is typical of risk aversion.

Friedman and Savage suggested, "An important class of reactions of individuals to risk can be rationalized by a rather simple extension of orthodox utility analysis" (Reference 2). They developed graphs of utility functions similar to the three types of utility functions shown in Figure 21.8.

The function in part (a) of the figure, where utility increases at a *decreasing* rate as payoff increases, has the same shape as Figure 21.7, once again reflecting an *aversion* to risk. In part (b) of the figure, utility increases at an *increasing* rate as the payoffs become higher. This implies a taste for the highest payoffs that is more than commensurate with the monetary amounts involved, thus showing *preference* for risk. Finally, part (c) of Figure 21.8 shows the intermediate case with utility increasing at a *constant* rate for all payoffs. In this case the monetary values of the payoffs provide a true measure of their utility to the decision maker, who thus demonstrates **indifference to risk**.

The three curves of Figure 21.8 characterize aversion for, preference for, and indifference to risk. However, it is not necessarily the case that a decision maker will exhibit just one of these attitudes over the whole range of possible payoffs.

Figure 21.9 illustrates a more complex situation. Here, for payoffs in the range between M_1 and M_2 the utility function has the shape of Figure 21.8(a), indicating aversion to risk in this payoff range. However, for payoffs of monetary amounts between M_2 and M_3, this utility function has the shape of Figure 21.8(b). Hence, for

Figure 21.8 Utility functions: (a) Risk Aversion; (b) Preference for Risk; (c) Indifference to Risk

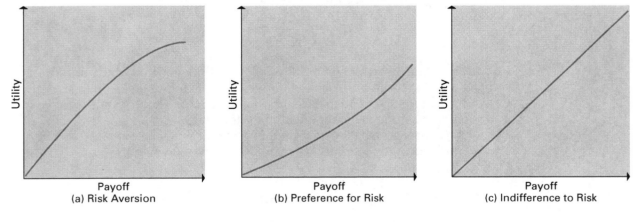

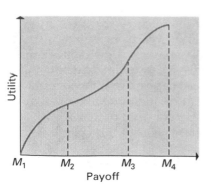

Figure 21.9
Utility Function Showing Aversion to Risk Between Payoffs M_1 and M_2 and Payoffs M_3 and M_4 and Preference for Risk Between Payoffs M_2 and M_3

this range of payoffs the decision maker exhibits a preference for risk. Finally, in the range of highest payoffs, between M_3 and M_4, the position is once again reversed, the decision maker being averse to risk in this region. Such a utility function can arise in practical problems. For example, an investor may well be averse to sustaining a substantial loss, while being prepared to accept some risk to obtain a fairly high positive return rather than a modest one. However, if a satisfactorily high return can be achieved at modest risk, the investor may be reluctant to risk much more for the possibility of an even higher return.

Expected Utility Criterion for Decision Making

Having determined the appropriate utilities, it remains only to solve the decision-making problem by finding that course of action with the highest expected utility. These expected utilities are obtained in the usual manner, employing the probabilities of the states of nature, as given in Equation 21.5.

The Expected Utility Criterion

Suppose that a decision maker has K possible actions, $a_1, a_2, \ldots, a_K$, and is faced with H states of nature. Let U_{ij} denote the utility corresponding to the ith action and jth state and P_j the probability of occurrence of the jth state of nature. Then the **expected utility**, $EU(a_i)$, of the action a_i is

$$EU(a_i) = P_1 U_{i1} + P_2 U_{i2} + \cdots + P_H U_{iH} = \sum_{j=1}^{H} P_j U_{ij} \qquad (21.5)$$

Given a choice between alternative actions, the **expected utility criterion** dictates the choice of the action for which expected utility is highest. Under generally reasonable assumptions it can be shown that the rational decision maker should adopt this criterion.

   If the decision maker is indifferent to risk, the expected utility criterion and the expected monetary value criterion are equivalent.

Table 21.11 shows the utilities and state-of-nature probabilities for our investor.

Table 21.11   Utilities and State-of-Nature Probabilities for an Investor

ACTION	STATE OF THE MARKET		
INVESTMENT	BUOYANT STATE ($P = 0.60$)	STEADY STATE ($P = 0.20$)	DEPRESSED STATE ($P = 0.20$)
Fixed interest	80	80	80
Stock portfolio	100	60	0

If the fixed-interest investment is chosen, a utility of 80 is assured, whichever state of nature prevails. For the portfolio of stocks the expected utility is

$$(0.6)(100) + (0.2)(60) + (0.2)(0) = 0.72$$

Since this is less than 80, this investor should elect to make the fixed-interest investment, according to the expected utility criterion.

In Example 21.3, investment in the portfolio of stocks was selected by the expected monetary value criterion. However, the incorporation into the analysis of another factor—the extent of this investor's aversion to risk—leads to the conclusion that the fixed-interest option is the better choice. This example serves to illustrate that on occasion, when risk is an important factor, the expected monetary value criterion is inadequate for solving decision-making problems.

The expected utility criterion is the most generally applicable and intellectually defensible of the criteria introduced for attacking decision-making problems.

Its chief drawback arises from the difficulty of eliciting information about which gambles are regarded as equally attractive as particular assured payoffs. This type of information is essential in the determination of utilities. For a wide range of problems where indifference to risk can safely be assumed, the expected monetary value criterion remains applicable. This would typically be the case, for example, in a small proportion of the corporation's total revenue. If, however (as may be the case in the development of a new commercial airliner, for example), possible losses from a project could threaten a corporation with insolvency, the utilities should appropriately reflect an aversion to risk. A company may attempt to spread this risk by forming partnerships with other firms in the industry or with possible customers.

EXERCISES

Application Exercises

21.43   A decision maker faces a problem in which the possible payoffs (in dollars) are

1,000   3,000   6,000   9,000   10,000   12,000

Utility 0 is assigned to a payoff of $1,000 and utility 100 to a payoff of $12,000. This decision maker is indifferent to risk for payoffs in this range.

a. Find the utilities for the four intermediate payoffs.
b. For each intermediate payoff, I, find the probability P such that the decision maker is indifferent between receiving I with certainty and a wager in which $12,000 is received with probability P and $1,000 with probability $(1 - P)$.

21.44   The shoe store operator of Exercise 21.9 has six possible payoffs (in dollars):

−10,000   30,000   60,000   70,000   90,000   130,000

Assign utility 0 to a loss of $10,000 and utility 100 to a profit of $130,000. For each intermediate payoff, I, the probabilities P such that the shoe store operator is indifferent between receiving I with certainty and a gamble in which $130,000 would be gained with probability P and \$10,000 lost with probability $(1 - P)$ are shown in the accompanying table.

Payoff	30,000	60,000	70,000	90,000
P	0.35	0.60	0.70	0.85

a. What are the utilities for the intermediate payoffs?

b. Suppose that the probabilities that the new shopping center will be very successful, moderately successful, and unsuccessful are 0.4, 0.4, and 0.2, respectively. Which action should be taken if expected utility is to be maximized?

21.45 The shoe store operator of Exercise 21.44 is unsure what value P to attach to indifference between receiving \$30,000 with certainty and a gamble in which \$130,000 would be gained with probability P and \$10,000 lost with probability $(1 - P)$. Assuming that the remaining problem specifications are as in Exercise 21.44, under what range of values for this probability will the expected utility criterion yield the same choice of action?

21.46 Consider the contractor of Exercise 21.21. In fact, this contractor is indifferent between submitting and not submitting a bid. What does this imply about the contractor's utility function?

SUMMARY

This chapter is intended as an introduction to decision analysis. All of us must live and work in an environment whose future is uncertain. Corporate decision making is no exception. The framework of a decision problem was considered, various criteria to select an optimal action were studied, the value of sample information was discussed, and situations where the decision maker may be more interested in taking into account risk rather than maximizing expected monetary values were examined. In the latter situation a utility function was considered. Four criteria for decision making were considered in this chapter: maximin, minimax regret, expected monetary value, and expected utility. TreePlan was used to obtain decision trees.

KEY WORDS

- action
- admissible action
- aversion to risk
- Bayes' theorem
- decision nodes
- decision trees
- EMV
- event nodes
- EVPI
- EVSI
- expected monetary value
- expected monetary value criterion
- expected net value of sample information
- expected utility criterion
- expected value of perfect information
- expected value of sample information
- inadmissible action
- indifference to risk
- maximin criterion
- minimax regret criterion
- opportunity loss table
- payoff table
- perfect information
- preference for risk
- prior probability
- regret table
- sensitivity analysis
- states of nature
- terminal nodes
- TreePlan
- utility function
- value of perfect information
- value of sample information

CHAPTER EXERCISES AND APPLICATIONS

21.47 A consultant is considering submitting detailed bids for two possible contracts. The bid for the first contract costs \$100 to prepare, while that for the second contract costs \$150 to prepare. If the bid for the first contract is accepted and the work is carried out, a profit of \$800 will result. If the bid for the second contract is accepted and the work is carried out, a profit of \$1,200 will result. Any costs of bid preparation must be subtracted from these profits. The consultant can, if he wishes, submit bids for both contracts. He does not, however, have the resources to carry out both pieces of work simultaneously. If a bid is submitted and accepted and the consultant is then unable to carry out the work, he counts this as a cost of $200 in lost goodwill. For the decision-making process, there are four possible states of nature:

s_1: Both bids rejected
s_2: Bid for the first contract accepted, bid for the second contract rejected
s_3: Bid for the second contract accepted, bid for the first contract rejected
s_4: Both bids accepted

a. The consultant has four possible courses of action. What are they?
b. Set out the payoff table for this consultant's decision-making problem.
c. Which action is chosen by the maximin criterion?
d. Which action is chosen by the minimax regret criterion?

21.48 Refer to Exercise 21.47. The consultant believes that the probability is 0.7 that a bid for the first contract would be accepted and 0.4 that a bid for the second contract would be accepted. He also believes that the acceptance of one bid is independent of acceptance of the other.

a. What are the probabilities for the four states of nature?
b. According to the expected monetary value criterion, which action should the consultant adopt, and what is the expected monetary value of this action?

c. Draw the decision tree for the consultant's problem.
d. What is the expected value of perfect information to this consultant?
e. The consultant is offered "inside information" on the prospects of the bid for the first contract. This information is entirely reliable in the sense that it would allow him to know for sure whether the bid would be accepted. However, no further information is available on the prospects of the bid for the second contract. What is the expected value of this "inside information"?

21.49 Refer to Exercises 21.47 and 21.48. There are nine possible payoffs for this consultant, as follows (in dollars):

−250 −150 −100 0 550 700 750 950 1,050

A utility of 0 is assigned to a loss of $250 and a utility of 100 to a profit of $1,050. For each intermediate payoff, I, the probabilities P such that the consultant is indifferent between payoff I with certainty and a gamble in which $1,050 is gained with probability P and $250 lost with probability $(1 − P)$ are shown in the accompanying table. According to the expected utility criterion, which action should the consultant choose, and what is the expected utility of this action?

Payoff	−150	−100	0	550	700	750	950
P	0.05	0.10	0.20	0.65	0.70	0.75	0.85

REFERENCES

1. Eppen, G. D., F. J. Gould, et al. *Introductory Management Science: Decision Modeling with Spreadsheets*, 5th ed. Upper Saddle River, NJ: Prentice Hall, 1998.
2. Friedman, Milton, and L. J. Savage. "The Utility Analysis of Choices Involving Risk." *Journal of Political Economy* 56 (1948): 279–304.
3. Middleton, Michael, Professor, University of San Francisco, www.usaf.edu/~middleton.
4. Render, Barry, and Ralph M. Stair, Jr. *Quantitative Analysis for Management*, 7th ed. Upper Saddle River, NJ: Prentice Hall, 2000.
5. TreePlan Documentation, available from *www.treeplan.com*.
6. Von Neumann, John, and Oskar Morgenstern. *The Theory of Games and Economic Behavior*, 3rd ed. Princeton, NJ: Princeton University Press, 1953.

Topic 6

Discrete Random Variables and Probability Distributions

Chapter 5

Discrete Random Variables and Probability Distributions

Introduction

In Chapter 4 we began our development of probability to represent situations with uncertain outcomes. In this chapter we use those ideas to develop probability models with an emphasis on discrete random variables. In Chapter 6 we will develop probability models for continuous random variables.

Probability models have extensive application to a number of business problems, and some of these applications will be developed here. Suppose that you have a business that rents a variety of equipment. From past experience—relative frequency—you know that 30% of the people who enter your store want to rent a trailer. Today you have three trailers available. Five completely unrelated people enter your store (the probability of one of them renting a trailer is independent of that of the others). What is the probability that these five people are seeking to rent a total of four or five trailers? If that happens, rental opportunities will be missed and customers will be disappointed. The probability of the events (number of trailers desired) can be computed using the binomial model that is developed in this chapter.

5.1 RANDOM VARIABLES

When the outcomes are numerical values, these probabilities can be conveniently summarized through the notion of a *random variable*.

Random Variable

A **random variable** is a variable that takes on numerical values determined by the outcome of a random experiment.

It is important to distinguish between a random variable and the possible values that it can take. Notationally, this is done by using capital letters, such as X, to denote the random variable and the corresponding lowercase letter, x, to denote a possible value. For example, prior to the results being observed in the throw of a die, we can use the random variable X to denote the outcome. This random variable can take the specific values $x = 1, x = 2, \ldots, x = 6$, each with probability $P(X = 2) = \cdots = P(X = 6) = \dfrac{1}{6}$.

A further important distinction is that between *discrete* and *continuous random variables*. The die throw provides us with an example of the former; there are only six possible outcomes, and a probability can be attached to each.

Discrete Random Variable

A random variable is a **discrete random variable** if it can take on no more than a countable number of values.

It follows from the definition that any random variable that can take on only a finite number of values is discrete. For example, the number of heads resulting from 10 throws of a coin is a discrete random variable. Even if the number of possible outcomes is infinite but countable, the random variable is discrete. An example is the number of throws of a coin needed before a head first appears. The possible outcomes are 1, 2, 3, . . . , and a probability can be attached to each. (A discrete random variable that can take a countably infinite number of values will be discussed in Section 5.6.) Some other examples of discrete random variables are:

1. The number of defective items in a sample of 20 items from a large shipment
2. The number of customers arriving at a checkout counter in an hour
3. The number of errors detected in a corporation's accounts
4. The number of claims on a medical insurance policy in a particular year

By contrast, suppose that we are interested in the day's high temperature. The random variable, temperature, is measured on a continuum and so is said to be *continuous*.

> **Continuous Random Variable**
> A random variable is a **continuous random variable** if it can take any value in an interval.

For continuous random variables we cannot assign probabilities to specific values. For example, the probability that today's high temperature will be precisely 77.236° Fahrenheit is 0. The temperature will certainly not be *precisely* that figure. However, probabilities may be determined for ranges, so that one could attach a probability to the event "Today's high temperature will be between 75 and 80°." Some other examples of continuous random variables include:

1. The yearly income for a family
2. The amount of oil imported into the United States in a particular month
3. The change in the price of a share of IBM common stock in a month
4. The time that elapses between the installation of a new component and its failure
5. The percentage of impurity in a batch of chemicals

The distinction that we have made between discrete and continuous random variables may appear rather artificial. After all, rarely is anything actually measured on a continuum. For example, we cannot report today's high temperature more precisely than the measuring instrument allows. Moreover, a family's income in a year will be some integer number of cents. However, we will find that it is convenient to act as if measurements had truly been made on a continuum when the differences between adjacent values are of no significance. The difference between family's incomes of $35,276.21 and $35,276.22 is of very little significance, and the attachment of probabilities to each would be a tedious and worthless exercise.

For practical purposes we treat random variables as discrete when probability statements about the individual possible outcomes have worthwhile meaning; all other random variables are regarded as continuous. Because of this distinction, we treat these two classes separately. Discrete random variables are discussed in this chapter; continuous random variables will be discussed in Chapter 6.

EXERCISES

Basic Exercises

5.1   A store sells 0 to 12 computers per day. Is the daily computer sales a discrete or continuous random variable?

5.2   A factory production process produces a small number of defective parts in its daily production. Is the number of defective parts a discrete or continuous random variable?

5.3   For each of the following indicate if a discrete or a continuous random variable provides the best definition:

a. The number of cars that arrive each day for repair in a two-person repair shop
b. The number of cars produced annually by General Motors
c. Total daily e-commerce sales in dollars
d. The number of passengers that are bumped from a specific airline flight 3 days before Christmas

5.4   An Equity actor auditions 100 times a year. Is her work schedule (number of plays) a discrete or random variable?

Application Exercises

5.5 List four examples of discrete random variables that could be observed in a new consulting business.

5.6 Define three continuous random variables that a marketing vice president should regularly examine.

5.7 A presidential election poll contacts 2,000 randomly selected people. Should the number of people that support candidate A be analyzed using discrete or continuous probability models?

5.8 A salesperson contacts 20 people each day and requests that they purchase. Should the number of daily purchases be analyzed using discrete or continuous probability models?

5.2 PROBABILITY DISTRIBUTIONS FOR DISCRETE RANDOM VARIABLES

Suppose that X is a discrete random variable and that x is one of its possible values. The probability that random variable X takes specific value x is denoted $P(X = x)$. The *probability distribution function* of a random variable is a representation of the probabilities for all the possible outcomes. This representation might be algebraic, graphical, or tabular. For discrete random variables one simple procedure is to list the probabilities of all possible outcomes according to the values of x.

Probability Distribution Function

The **probability distribution function**, $P(x)$, of a discrete random variable X expresses the probability that X takes the value x, as a function of x. That is,

$$P(x) = P(X = x), \quad \text{for all values of } x \tag{5.1}$$

We will use the term *probability distribution* to represent probability distribution functions in this book, following increasingly common practice to use these terms interchangeably.

Because the probability function takes nonzero values only at discrete points x, it is sometimes called a *probability mass function*. Once the probabilities have been calculated, the function can be graphed.

Example 5.1 Rolling a Die (Probability Function Graph)

Graph the probability distribution function for the roll of a single six-sided balanced die.

Solution Let the random variable X denote the number resulting from a single roll of a six-sided balanced die. Since

$$P(X = 1) = P(X = 2) = \cdots = P(X = 6) = \frac{1}{6}$$

the probability function is

$$P(x) = P(X = x) = \frac{1}{6} \quad \text{for } x = 1, 2, 3, \ldots, 6$$

Figure 5.1   Graph of Probability Distribution Function for Example 5.1

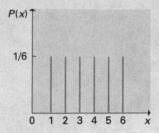

The function takes the value 0 for all other values of x, which cannot occur. The probability distribution function is graphed in Figure 5.1, where spikes of height $(X = 1) = P(X = 2) = \cdots = P(X = 6) = \dfrac{1}{6}$ represent probability masses at the points $x = 1, x = 2, \ldots, x = 6$.

The probability distribution function of a discrete random variable must satisfy the following two properties.

Required Properties of Probability Distribution Functions of Discrete Random Variables

Let X be a discrete random variable with probability distribution function $P(x)$. Then

1. $0 \leq P(x) \leq 1$ for any value x, and
2. The individual probabilities sum to 1—that is,

$$\sum_x P(x) = 1$$

where the notation indicates summation over all possible values of x.

Property 1 merely states that probabilities cannot be negative or exceed 1. Property 2 follows from the fact that the events "$X = x$," for all possible values of x, are mutually exclusive and collectively exhaustive. The probabilities for these events must therefore sum to 1. That this is, in fact, so can be verified directly. It is simply a way of saying that, when a random experiment is to be carried out, something must happen.

Another representation of discrete probability distributions is also useful.

Cumulative Probability Function

The **cumulative probability function**, $F(x_0)$, for a random variable X, expresses the probability that X does not exceed the value x_0, as a function of x_0. That is,

$$F(x_0) = P(X \leq x_0) \tag{5.2}$$

where the function is evaluated at all values of x_0.

Example 5.2 Automobile Sales (Probabilities)

Stetson Motors, Inc., is a car dealer in a small midwestern town. Based on an analysis of its sales history, the managers know that on any single day the number of Vertigo A cars sold can vary from 0 to 5. How can the probability distribution function shown in Table 5.1 be used for inventory planning?

Table 5.1 Probability Distribution Function for Automobile Sales

x	$P(x)$	$F(x)$
0	0.15	0.15
1	0.30	0.45
2	0.20	0.65
3	0.20	0.85
4	0.10	0.95
5	0.05	1.00

Solution The random variable, X, takes on the values of x indicated in the first column, and the probability function, $P(x)$, is defined in the second column. The third column contains the cumulative distribution, $F(x)$. This model could be used for planning the inventory of cars. For example, if there are only four cars in stock, Stetson Motors could satisfy customers' needs for a car 95% of the time. But if only two cars are in stock, then 35% $[(1 - 0.65) \times 100]$ of the customers would not have their needs satisfied.

For discrete random variables the cumulative probability function is sometimes called the *cumulative mass function*. It can be seen from the definition that, as x_0 increases, the cumulative probability function will change values only at those points x_0 that can be taken by the random variable with positive probability. Its evaluation at these points can be carried out in terms of the probability function.

Derived Relationship Between Probability Function and Cumulative Probability Function

Let X be a random variable with probability function $P(x)$ and cumulative probability function $F(x_0)$. Then we can show that

$$F(x_0) = \sum_{x \leq x_0} P(x) \tag{5.3}$$

where the notation implies that summation is over all possible values of x that are less than or equal to x_0.

The result in Equation 5.3 follows, since the event "$X \leq x_0$" is the union of the mutually exclusive events "$X = x$," for all possible values of x less than or equal to x_0. The probability of the union is then the sum of these individual event probabilities.

> ### Derived Properties of Cumulative Probability Functions for Discrete Random Variables
>
> Let X be a discrete random variable with cumulative probability function $F(x_0)$. Then we can show that
>
> 1. $0 \leq F(x_0) \leq 1$ for every number x_0; and
> 2. If x_0 and x_1 are two numbers with $x_0 < x_1$, then $F(x_0) \leq F(x_1)$.

Property 1 simply states that a probability cannot be less than 0 or greater than 1. For example, note the probabilities for die faces in Figure 5.1. Property 2 implies that the probability that a random variable does not exceed some number cannot be more than the probability that it does not exceed any larger number.

EXERCISES

Basic Exercises

5.9 What is the probability distribution function of the number of heads when a fair coin is tossed?

5.10 Show the probability distribution function of the number of heads in one toss of a fair coin.

5.11 Show the probability distribution function of the number of heads when three fair coins are tossed independently.

5.12 Let the random variable represent the number of times that you will miss class this semester. Prepare a table that shows the probability function and the cumulative probability function.

Application Exercises

5.13 The number of computers sold per day at Dan's Computer Works is defined by the following probability distribution:

X	0	1	2	3	4	5	6
$P(x)$	0.05	0.10	0.20	0.20	0.20	0.15	0.10

a. $P(3 \leq x < 6) = ?$
b. $P(x > 3) = ?$
c. $P(x \leq 4) = ?$
d. $P(2 < x \leq 5) = ?$

5.14 American Travel Air has asked you to study flight delays during the week before Christmas at Midway Airport. The random variable X is the number of flights delayed per hour.

X	0	1	2	3	4	5	6	7	8	9
$P(x)$	0.10	0.08	0.07	0.15	0.12	0.08	0.10	0.12	0.08	0.10

a. What is the cumulative probability distribution?
b. What is the probability of five or more delayed flights?
c. What is the probability of three through seven (inclusive) delayed flights?

5.3 PROPERTIES OF DISCRETE RANDOM VARIABLES

The probability distribution contains all the information about the probability properties of a random variable, and graphical inspection of this distribution can certainly be valuable. However, it is frequently desirable to have some summary measures of the distribution's characteristics.

Expected Value of a Discrete Random Variable

In order to obtain a measure of the center of a probability distribution, we introduce the notion of the *expectation* of a random variable. In Chapter 3 we computed the sample mean as a measure of central location for sample data. The *expected value* is the corresponding measure of central location for a random variable. Before introducing its definition, we show the fallacy of a superficially attractive alternative measure.

Consider the following example: A review of textbooks in a segment of the business area found that 81% of all pages of texts were error-free, 17% of all pages contained one error, and the remaining 2% contained two errors. We use the random variable X to denote the number of errors on a page chosen at random from one of these books, with possible values of 0, 1, and 2, and the probability distribution function

$$P(0) = 0.81 \qquad P(1) = 0.17 \qquad P(2) = 0.02$$

We could consider using the simple average of the values as the central location of a random variable. In this example the possible numbers of errors on a page are 0, 1, and 2. Their average is, then, one error. However, a moment's reflection will convince the reader that this is an absurd measure of central location. In calculating this average, we paid no attention to the fact that 81% of all pages contain no errors, while only 2% contain two errors. In order to obtain a sensible measure of central location, we *weight* the various possible outcomes by the probabilities of their occurrence.

Expected Value

The **expected value, $E(X)$,** of a discrete random variable X is defined as

$$E(X) = \mu = \sum_x xP(x) \qquad (5.4)$$

where the notation indicates that summation extends over all possible values of x.

The expected value of a random variable is also called its **mean** and is denoted μ.

We can express expected value in terms of long-run relative frequencies. Suppose that a random experiment is repeated N times and that the event "$X = x$" occurs in N_x of these trials. The average of the values taken by the random variable over all N trials will then be the sum of xN_x/N over all possible values of x. Now, as the number of replications, N, becomes infinitely large, the ratio N_x/N tends to the probability of the occurrence of the event "$X = x$"—that is, to $P(x)$. Hence, the quantity xN_x/N tends to $xP(x)$. Thus, we can view the expected value as the long-run average value that a random variable takes over a large number of trials. Recall that in Chapter 3 we used the *mean* for the average of a set of numerical observations. We use the same term for the expectation of a random variable.

Example 5.3   Errors in Textbooks (Expected Value)

Suppose that the probability function for the number of errors, X, on pages from business textbooks is

$$P(0) = 0.81 \qquad P(1) = 0.17 \qquad P(2) = 0.02$$

Find the mean number of errors per page.

Figure 5.2   Probability Function for Number of Errors per Page in Business Textbooks; Location of Population Mean, μ, for Example 5.3

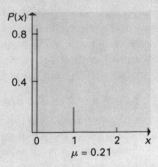

Solution   We have

$$\mu = E(X) = \sum_x xP(x) = (0)(0.81) + (1)(0.17) + (2)(0.02) = 0.21$$

From this result it is concluded that over a large number of pages, the expectation would be to find an average of 0.21 error per page. Figure 5.2 shows the probability function, with the location of the mean indicated.

Variance of a Discrete Random Variable

In Chapter 3 we found that the sample variance was one useful measure of the spread of a set of numerical observations. The sample variance is the average of the squared discrepancies of the observations from their mean. We will use this same idea to measure dispersion in the probability distribution of a random variable. We define the *variance* of a random variable as the weighted average of the squares of its possible deviations, $(x - \mu)$, from the mean; the weight associated with $(x - \mu)^2$ is the probability that the random variable takes the value x. The variance can then be viewed as the average value that will be taken by the function $(X - \mu)^2$ over a very large number of repeated trials, as defined by Equation 5.5.

Variance and Standard Deviation of a Discrete Random Variable

Let *X* be a discrete random variable. The expectation of the squared discrepancies about the mean, $(X - \mu)^2$, is called the **variance**, denoted σ^2 and given by

$$\sigma^2 = E\left[(X - \mu)^2\right] = \sum_x (x - \mu)^2 P(x) \tag{5.5}$$

The variance of a discrete random variable *X* can also be expressed as

$$\sigma^2 = E(X^2) - \mu^2$$
$$= \sum_x x^2 P(x) - \mu^2 \mu_x^2 \tag{5.6}$$

The **standard deviation**, σ_X, is the positive square root of the variance.

The concept of variance can be very useful in comparing the dispersions of probability distributions. Consider, for example, viewing as a random variable the return over a year on an investment. Two investments may have the same expected returns but will still differ in an important way if the variances of these returns are substantially different. A higher variance indicates that returns substantially different from the mean are more likely than if the variance of returns is small. In this context, then, variance of the return can be associated with the concept of the risk of an investment—the higher the variance, the greater the risk.

Taking the square root of the variance to obtain the standard deviation yields a quantity in the original units of measurement, as noted in Chapter 3.

In some practical applications an alternative, but equivalent, formula for the variance is preferable for computational purposes. That alternative formula is defined by Equation 5.6, which can be verified algebraically (see the chapter Appendix).

Example 5.4 Expected Value and Variance of Automobile Sales (Expected Value and Variance)

In Example 5.2 Stetson Motors, Inc., determined that the number of Vertigo A cars sold daily could vary from 0 to 5, with the probabilities given in Table 5.1. Find the expected value and variance for this probability distribution.

Solution   Using Equation 5.4, the expected value is

$$\mu = E(X)\sum_x xP(x) = 0(0.15) + 1(0.30) + \cdots + 5(0.05) = 1.95$$

Using Equation 5.5, the variance is

$$\sigma^2 = (0 - 1.95)^2(0.15) + (1 - 1.95)^2(0.3) + \cdots + (5 - 1.95)^2(0.05) = 1.9475$$

For more complex probability distributions Excel can be used for these computations. Figures 5.3 and 5.4 illustrate how to obtain the expected value and variance for the distribution in Table 5.1.

Figure 5.3   Expected Value for the Discrete Random Variable in Table 5.1 Computed Using Microsoft Excel

	A	B	C	D
1	Sales	P(x)	Mean	Variance
2	0	0.15	0	
3	1	0.3	0.3	
4	2	0.2	0.4	
5	3	0.2	0.6	
6	4	0.1	0.4	
7	5	0.05	0.25	
8			1.95	

Expected Value = 1.95

INSTRUCTIONS
To Obtain Expected Value

1. Enter Sales (0 to 5) in Column A and corresponding probabilities in Column B.
2. Type "Mean" in C1 and "Variance" in D1.
3. Select C2; Type "=A2*B2" and press Enter. The value "0" should appear in C2. This gives xP(x) for each row.
4. Drag the fill handle for C2 downward from C2 to C7.
5. Select C8 and click the AutoSum button (Σ) and press Enter. The Expected Value "1.95" should appear in C8.

Figure 5.4 Variance for the Discrete Random Variable in Table 5.1 Computed Using Microsoft Excel

	A	B	C	D	E	F	G	H	I	J	K	L
1	Sales	P(x)	Mean	Variance								
2	0	0.15	0	0.570375								
3	1	0.3	0.3	0.27075								
4	2	0.2	0.4	0.0005								
5	3	0.2	0.6	0.2205								
6	4	0.1	0.4	0.42025								
7	5	0.05	0.25	0.465125								
8			1.95	1.9475								

INSTRUCTIONS
To Obtain Variance

1. Select D2, Type "=(A2-C8)^2*B2" and press Enter. This is $(x-\mu_x)^2 P(x)$ for each value of x. The value "0.570375" should appear in D2.
2. Drag the fill handle for D2 downward from D2 to D7.
3. Select D8, click the AutoSum button (Σ) and press Enter. The variance "1.9475" should appear in D8.

Variance = 1.9475

Suppose that we change the probability distribution function *pdf* in Table 5.1 to reflect a higher probability of both low and high sales. The new probabilities are given in Table 5.2. Figure 5.5 indicates the change in mean and variance.

Table 5.2
Probability Distribution Function for Automobile Sales Revised

SALES	P(X)
0	0.30
1	0.20
2	0.10
3	0.05
4	0.15
5	0.20

Figure 5.5 Comparison of Means and Variances for the Discrete Random Variable in Table 5.2 Computed Using Microsoft Excel

	A	B	C	D	E	F	G	H	I	J
1		Table 5.1					Table 5.2			
2	Sales	P(x)	Mean	Variance		Sales	P(x)	Mean	Variance	
3	0	0.15	0	0.570375		0	0.3	0	1.38675	
4	1	0.3	0.3	0.27075		1	0.2	0.2	0.2645	
5	2	0.2	0.4	0.0005		2	0.1	0.2	0.00225	
6	3	0.2	0.6	0.2205		3	0.05	0.15	0.036125	
7	4	0.1	0.4	0.42025		4	0.15	0.6	0.513375	
8	5	0.05	0.25	0.465125		5	0.2	1	1.6245	
9			1.95	1.9475				2.15	3.8275	
10										
11										

		COMMENTS		
		Table 5.1	Table 5.2	Statement
Expected Value		1.95	2.15	A modest change in the means
Variance		1.9475	3.8275	Larger change in the variances

Since the variance uses the squared deviations from the mean, extreme values of the random variable have a greater effect than the values closer to the mean.

Comments

- In Table 5.2 there is a higher probability of 0 sales (0.30 rather than 0.15 from Table 5.1). Also, there is a higher probability of selling all 5 cars (0.20 rather than 0.05 from Table 5.1).
- The variance should increase because the probability of extreme values 0 and 5 increases.

Mean and Variance of Linear Functions of a Random Variable

The notion of expectation is not restricted to the random variable itself but can be applied to any function of the random variable. For example, a contractor may be uncertain of the time required to complete a contract. This uncertainty could be represented by a random variable whose possible values are the number of days elapsing from the beginning to the completion of work on the contract. However, the contractor's primary concern is not with the time taken but rather with the cost of fulfilling the contract. This cost will be a function of the time taken, so in determining expected value of the random variable "Cost," we need to find the expectation of a function of the random variable "Time to completion."

Expected Value of Functions of Random Variables

Let X be a discrete random variable with probability function $P(x)$, and let $g(X)$ be some function of X. Then the expected value, $E[g(X)]$, of that function is defined as

$$E[g(X)] = \sum_x g(x)P(x) \tag{5.7}$$

We define the expectation of a function of a random variable X by Equation 5.7. That is, the expectation can be thought of as the average value that $g(X)$ would take over a very large number of repeated trials. We now develop the expected value and variance for linear functions of a random variable. First, consider the linear function $a + bX$, where a and b are constant fixed numbers. Let X be a random variable that takes the value x with probability $P(x)$, and consider a new random variable Y, defined by

$$Y = a + bX$$

When random variable X takes the specific value x, Y must take the value $a + bx$. The mean and variance, of such variables are frequently required. The mean, variance, and standard deviation for a linear function of a random variable are derived in the chapter Appendix. The results are summarized in Equations 5.8 and 5.9.

Summary of Properties for Linear Functions of a Random Variable

Let X be a random variable with mean μ_X and variance σ_X^2, and let a and b be any constant fixed numbers. Define the random variable Y as $a + bX$. Then, the **mean and variance of Y** are

$$\mu_Y = E(a + bX) = a + b\mu_X \tag{5.8}$$

and

$$\sigma_Y^2 = \text{Var}(a + bX) = b^2\sigma_X^2 \qquad (5.9)$$

so that the standard deviation of *Y* is

$$\sigma_y = |b|\, \sigma_x \qquad (5.10)$$

Example 5.5 Total Project Cost (Computations for Functions of Random Variables)

A contractor is interested in the total cost of a project on which he intends to bid. He estimates that materials will cost \$25,000 and that his labor will be \$900 per day. If the project takes *X* days to complete, the total labor cost will be 900*X* dollars, and the total cost of the project (in dollars) will be

$$C = 25{,}000 + 900X$$

The contractor forms subjective probabilities (Table 5.3) of likely completion times for the project.

  a. Find the mean and variance for completion time *X*.
  b. Find the mean, variance, and standard deviation for total cost *C*.

Table 5.3 Probability Distribution for Completion Times

Completion time X (days)	10	11	12	13	14
Probability	0.1	0.3	0.3	0.2	0.1

Solution

  a. The mean and variance for completion time *X* can be found using Equations 5.4 and 5.5.

$$\mu = E(X) = \sum_x xP(x)$$

$$= (10)(0.1) + (11)(0.3) + (12)(0.3) + (13)(0.2) + (14)(0.1) = 11.9 \text{ days}$$

and

$$\sigma_x^2 = E\!\left[(X - \mu)^2\right] = \sum_x (x - \mu)^2 P(x)$$

$$= (10 - 11.9)^2(0.1) + (11 - 11.9)^2(0.3) + \cdots + (14 - 11.9)^2(0.1) = 1.29 \text{ days}$$

  b. The mean, variance, and standard deviation of total cost, *C*, are obtained using Equations 5.8, 5.9, and 5.10.

  The mean is

$$\mu_C = E(25{,}000 + 900X) = (25{,}000 + 900\,\mu_X)$$
$$= 25{,}000 + (900)(11.9) = \$35{,}710$$

The variance is

$$\sigma_C^2 = \text{Var}(25{,}000 + 900X) = (900)^2 \sigma_X^2$$
$$= (810{,}000)(1.29) = 1{,}044{,}900$$

The standard deviation is

$$\sigma_C = \sqrt{\sigma_C^2} = \$1{,}022.20$$

Three special examples of the linear function $W = a + bX$ are important. The first example considers a constant function, $W = a$, for any constant a. In this situation the coefficient $b = 0$. In the second example $a = 0$, giving $W = bX$. The expected value and the variance for these functions are defined by Equations 5.11 and 5.12. The third example is significant in later chapters. The mean and variance of this special linear function are defined by Equations 5.13 and 5.14. Thus, subtracting from a random variable its mean and dividing by its standard deviation yield a random variable with mean 0 and standard deviation 1.

Summary Results for the Mean and Variance of Special Linear Functions

a. Let $b = 0$ in the linear function $W = a + bX$. Then $W = a$ (for any constant a).

$$E(a) = a \quad \text{and} \quad \text{Var}(a) = 0 \tag{5.11}$$

If a random variable always takes the value a, it will have a mean a and a variance 0.

b. Let $a = 0$ in the linear function $W = a + bX$. Then $W = bX$.

$$E(bX) = b\mu_X \quad \text{and} \quad \text{Var}(bX) = b^2\sigma_X^2 \tag{5.12}$$

The Mean and Variance Of $Z = \dfrac{X - \mu_X}{\sigma_X}$

Let $a = -\mu_X/\sigma_X$ and $b = 1/\sigma_X$ in the linear function $Z = a + bX$. Then

$$Z = a + bX = \frac{X - \mu_X}{\sigma_X}$$

so that

$$E\left(\frac{X - \mu_X}{\sigma_X}\right) = -\frac{\mu_X}{\sigma_X} + \frac{1}{\sigma_X}\mu_X = 0 \tag{5.13}$$

and

$$Var\left(\frac{X - \mu_X}{\sigma_X}\right) = \frac{1}{\sigma_X^2}\sigma_X^2 = 1 \tag{5.14}$$

EXERCISES

Basic Exercises

5.15 Consider the probability distribution function

x	0	1
Probability	0.40	0.60

  a. Draw the probability distribution function.
  b. Calculate and draw the cumulative probability function.
  c. Find the mean of the random variable X.
  d. Find the variance of X.

5.16 Given the probability distribution function

x	0	1	2
Probability	0.25	0.50	0.25

  a. Draw the probability distribution function.
  b. Calculate and draw the cumulative probability function.
  c. Find the mean of the random variable X.
  d. Find the variance of X.

5.17 Consider the probability distribution function

x	0	1
Probability	0.50	0.50

  a. Draw the probability distribution function.
  b. Calculate and draw the cumulative probability function.
  c. Find the mean of the random variable X.
  d. Find the variance of X.

5.18 An automobile dealer calculates the proportion of new cars sold that have been returned various numbers of times for the correction of defects during the warranty period. The results are shown in the table.

Number of returns	0	1	2	3	4
Proportion	0.28	0.36	0.23	0.09	0.04

  a. Draw the probability distribution function.
  b. Calculate and draw the cumulative probability function.
  c. Find the mean of the number of returns of an automobile for corrections for defects during the warranty period.
  d. Find the variance of the number of returns of an automobile for corrections for defects during the warranty period.

5.19 A company specializes in installing and servicing central heating furnaces. In the prewinter period service calls may result in an order for a new furnace. The table shows estimated probabilities for the numbers of new furnace orders generated in this way in the last 2 weeks of September.

Number of orders	0	1	2	3	4	5
Probability	0.10	0.14	0.26	0.28	0.15	0.07

  a. Draw the probability distribution function.
  b. Calculate and draw the cumulative probability function.
  c. Find the probability that at least three orders will be generated in this period.
  d. Find the mean of the number of orders for new furnaces in this 2-week period.
  e. Find the standard deviation of the number of orders for new furnaces in this 2-week period.

Application Exercises

5.20 A corporation produces packages of paper clips. The number of clips per package varies, as indicated in the accompanying table.

Number of clips	47	48	49	50	51	52	53
Proportion of packages	0.04	0.13	0.21	0.29	0.20	0.10	0.03

  a. Draw the probability function.
  b. Calculate and draw the cumulative probability function.
  c. What is the probability that a randomly chosen package will contain between 49 and 51 clips (inclusive)?
  d. Two packages are chosen at random. What is the probability that at least one of them contains at least 50 clips?
  e. Use Microsoft Excel to find the mean and standard deviation of the number of paper clips per package.
  f. The cost (in cents) of producing a package of clips is $16 + 2X$, where X is the number of clips in the package. The revenue from selling the package, however many clips it contains, is $1.50. If profit is defined as the difference between revenue and cost, find the mean and standard deviation of profit per package.

5.21 A municipal bus company has started operations in a new subdivision. Records were kept on the numbers of riders from this subdivision during the early-morning service. The accompanying table shows proportions over all weekdays.

Number of riders	0	1	2	3	4	5	6	7
Proportion		0.02	0.12	0.23	0.31	0.19	0.08	0.03	0.02

  a. Draw the probability function.
  b. Calculate and draw the cumulative probability function.

c. What is the probability that on a randomly chosen weekday there will be at least four riders from the subdivision on this service?

d. Two weekdays are chosen at random. What is the probability that on both of these days there will be fewer than three riders from the subdivision on this service?

e. Find the mean and standard deviation of the number of riders from this subdivision on this service on a weekday.

f. If the cost of a ride is 50 cents, find the mean and standard deviation of the total payments of riders from this subdivision on this service on a weekday.

5.22 a. A very large shipment of parts contains 10% defectives. Two parts are chosen at random from the shipment and checked. Let the random variable X denote the number of defectives found. Find the probability function of this random variable.

b. A shipment of 20 parts contains 2 defectives. Two parts are chosen at random from the shipment and checked. Let the random variable Y denote the number of defectives found. Find the probability function of this random variable. Explain why your answer is different from that for part (a).

c. Find the mean and variance of the random variable X in part (a).

d. Find the mean and variance of the random variable Y in part (b).

5.23 A student needs to know details of a class assignment that is due the next day and decides to call fellow class members for this information. She believes that for any particular call the probability of obtaining the necessary information is 0.40. She decides to continue calling class members until the information is obtained. Let the random variable X denote the number of calls needed to obtain the information.

a. Find the probability function of X.

b. Find the cumulative probability function of X.

c. Find the probability that at least three calls are required.

5.24 A college basketball player who sinks 75% of his free throws comes to the line to shoot a "one and one" (if the first shot is successful, he is allowed a second shot, but no second shot is taken if the first is missed; one point is scored for each successful shot). Assume that the outcome of the second shot, if any, is independent of that of the first. Find the expected number of points resulting from the "one and one." Compare this with the expected number of points from a "two-shot foul," where a second shot is allowed, irrespective of the outcome of the first.

5.25 A professor teaches a large class and has scheduled an examination for 7:00 P.M. in a different classroom. She estimates the probabilities in the table for the number of students who will call her at home, in the hour before the examination, asking in which classroom it will be held.

Number of calls	0	1	2	3	4	5
Probability	0.10	0.15	0.19	0.26	0.19	0.11

Find the mean and standard deviation of the number of calls.

5.26 Students in a large accounting class were asked to rate the course by assigning a score of 1, 2, 3, 4, or 5 to the course. A higher score indicates that the students received greater value from the course. The accompanying table shows proportions of students rating the course in each category.

Rating	1	2	3	4	5
Proportion	0.07	0.19	0.28	0.30	0.16

Find the mean and standard deviation of the ratings.

5.27 A store owner stocks an out-of-town newspaper, which is sometimes requested by a small number of customers. Each copy of this newspaper costs him 70 cents, and he sells them for 90 cents each. Any copies left over at the end of the day have no value and are destroyed. Any requests for copies that cannot be met because stocks have been exhausted are considered by the store owner as a loss of 5 cents in goodwill. The probability distribution of the number of requests for the newspaper in a day is shown in the accompanying table. If the store owner defines total daily profit as total revenue from newspaper sales, less total cost of newspapers ordered, less goodwill loss from unsatisfied demand, how many copies per day should he order to maximize expected profit?

Number of requests	0	1	2	3	4	5
Probability	0.12	0.16	0.18	0.32	0.14	0.08

5.28 A factory manager is considering whether to replace a temperamental machine. A review of past records indicates the following probability distribution for the number of breakdowns of this machine in a week.

Number of breakdowns	0	1	2	3	4
Probability	0.10	0.26	0.42	0.16	0.06

a. Find the mean and standard deviation of the number of weekly breakdowns.

b. It is estimated that each breakdown costs the company $1,500 in lost output. Find the mean and standard deviation of the weekly cost to the company from breakdowns of this machine.

5.29 An investor is considering three strategies for a $1,000 investment. The probable returns are estimated as follows:

- *Strategy* 1: A profit of $10,000 with probability 0.15 and a loss of $1,000 with probability 0.85

- *Strategy* 2: A profit of $1,000 with probability 0.50, a profit of $500 with probability 0.30, and a loss of $500 with probability 0.20
- *Strategy* 3: A certain profit of $400

Which strategy has the highest expected profit? Would you necessarily advise the investor to adopt this strategy?

5.4 BINOMIAL DISTRIBUTION

We now develop the Binomial probability distribution that is used extensively in many applied business and economic problems. Our approach begins by first developing the Bernoulli model, which is a building block for the Binomial. We consider a random experiment that can give rise to just two possible mutually exclusive and collectively exhaustive outcomes, which for convenience we will label "success" and "failure." Let P denote the probability of success, so that the probability of failure is $(1 - P)$. Now, define the random variable X so that X takes the value 1 if the outcome of the experiment is success and 0 otherwise. The probability function of this random variable is then

$$P(0) = (1 - P) \quad \text{and} \quad P(1) = P$$

This distribution is known as the *Bernoulli distribution*. Its mean and variance can be found by direct application of the equations in Section 5.3.

Derivation of the Mean and Variance of a Bernoulli Random Variable
The **mean** is

$$\mu = E(X) = \sum_x xP(x) = (0)(1 - P) + (1)P = P \tag{5.15}$$

and the **variance** is

$$\sigma^2 = E\left[(X - \mu)^2\right] = \sum_x (x - \mu)^2 P(x)$$
$$= (0 - P)^2(1 - P) + (1 - P)^2 P = P(1 - P) \tag{5.16}$$

Example 5.6   Contract Sale (Compute Bernoulli Mean and Variance)

Shirley Ferguson, an insurance broker, believes that for a particular contact the probability of making a sale is 0.4. If the random variable X is defined to take the value 1 if a sale is made and 0 otherwise, then X has a Bernoulli distribution with probability of success P equal to 0.4. Find the mean and the variance of the distribution.

Solution   The probability function of X is $P(0) = 0.6$ and $P(1) = 0.4$. The mean of the distribution is $P = 0.40$, and the variance is $\sigma^2 = P(1 - P) = (0.4)(0.6) = 0.24$.

An important generalization of the Bernoulli distribution concerns the case where a random experiment with two possible outcomes is repeated several times and the repetitions are independent. We can determine the probabilities here by using the binomial distribution. Suppose again that the probability of a success in a single trial is P and that n independent trials are carried out, so that the result of any one trial has no influence on the outcome of any other. The number of successes X resulting from these n trials could be any whole number from 0 to n, and we are interested in the probability of obtaining exactly $X = x$ successes in n trials.

We develop the result in two stages. First, observe that the n trials will result in a sequence of n outcomes, each of which must be either success (S) or failure (F). One sequence with x successes and $(n - x)$ failures is

$$S, S, \ldots, S \qquad F, F, \ldots, F$$

$$(x \text{ times}) \qquad (n - x \text{ times})$$

In words, the first x trials result in success, while the remainder result in failure. Now, the probability of success in a single trial is P, and the probability of failure is $(1 - P)$. Since the n trials are independent of one another, the probability of any particular sequence of outcomes is, by the multiplication rule of probabilities (Chapter 4), equal to the product of the probabilities for the individual outcomes. Thus, the probability of observing the specific sequence of outcomes just described is

$$[P \times P \times \cdots \times P] \qquad \times \qquad [(1 - P) \times (1 - P) \times \cdots \times (1 - P)] = P^x (1 - P)^{(n - x)}$$

$$(x \text{ times}) \qquad\qquad\qquad (n - x \text{ times})$$

This line of argument establishes that the probability of observing *any specific sequence* involving x successes and $(n - x)$ failures is $P^x(1 - P)^{n-x}$. For example, suppose that there are five independent trials, each with probability of success $P = 0.60$, and the probability of exactly three successes is required. Using + to designate a success and 0 to indicate a nonsuccess, the desired outcomes could be designated as

$$+++00 \qquad \text{or} \qquad +0+0+$$

The probability of either of these specific outcomes is $(0.6)^3(0.4)^2 = 0.03456$.

The original problem concerned the determination not of the probability of occurrence of a particular sequence but of the probability of precisely x successes, regardless of the order of the outcomes. There are several sequences in which x successes could be arranged among $(n - x)$ failures. In fact, the number of such possibilities is just the number of combinations of x objects chosen from n, since any x locations can be selected from a total of n in which to place the successes and the total number of successes can be computed using Equation 5.17. Returning to the example of three successes in five trials ($P = 0.60$), the number of different sequences with three successes would be

$$C_3^5 = \frac{5!}{3!(3 - 5)!} = 10$$

The probability of three successes in five independent Bernoulli trials is thus 10 times the probability of each of the sequences that has three successes, and, thus,

$$P(X = 3) = (10)(0.03456) = 0.3456$$

Next, this result will be generalized for any combination of n and x.

Number of Sequences with x Successes in n Trials
The **number of sequences with x successes in n independent trials** is

$$C_x^n = \frac{n!}{x!\,(n-x)!} \tag{5.17}$$

where $n! = n \times (n-1) \times (n-2) \times \cdots \times 1$ and $0! = 1$.
These C_x^n sequences are mutually exclusive, since no two of them can occur at the same time. This result was developed in the Chapter 4 Appendix.

The event "x successes resulting from n trials" can occur in C_x^n mutually exclusive ways, each with probability $P^x(1-P)^{n-x}$. Therefore, by the addition rule of probabilities (Chapter 4) the probability required is the sum of these C_x^n individual probabilities. The result is given by Equation 5.18.

The Binomial Distribution
Suppose that a random experiment can result in two possible mutually exclusive and collectively exhaustive outcomes, "success" and "failure," and that P is the probability of a success in a single trial. If n independent trials are carried out, the distribution of the number of resulting successes, x, is called the **binomial distribution**. Its probability distribution function for the binomial random variable $X = x$ is

$$P(x \text{ Successes in } n \text{ Independent Trials}) = P(x)$$
$$= \frac{n!}{x!\,(n-x)!} P^x(1-P)^{(n-x)} \quad \text{for } x = 0, 1, 2, \ldots, n \tag{5.18}$$

The mean and variance are derived in the chapter Appendix, and the results are given by Equations 5.19 and 5.20.

Derived Mean and Variance of a Binomial Probability Distribution
Let X be the number of successes in n independent trials, each with probability of success P. Then X follows a binomial distribution with **mean**

$$\mu = E(X) = nP \tag{5.19}$$

and **variance**

$$\sigma^2 = E[(X-\mu)^2] = nP(1-P) \tag{5.20}$$

The binomial distribution is widely used in business and economic applications involving the probability of discrete occurrences. Before using the binomial, the specific situation must be analyzed to determine if

1. The application involves several trials, each of which has only two outcomes: yes or no, on or off, success or failure.
2. The probability of the outcome is the same for each trial.
3. The probability of the outcome on one trial does not affect the probability on other trials.

In the following examples typical applications will be provided. Binomial distribution probabilities can be obtained using:

1. Equation 5.18 (good for small values of n); see Example 5.7
2. Tables in the Appendix (good for selected value of n and P); see Example 5.8
3. Computer-generated probabilities; see Example 5.9

Example 5.7 Multiple Contract Sales (Binomial Calculations)

Suppose that the insurance broker, Shirley Ferguson, in Example 5.6 has five contacts, and she believes that for each contact the probability of making a sale is 0.40. Using Equation 5.18

a. Find the probability that she makes at most one sale.
b. Find the probability that she makes between two and four sales (inclusive).
c. Graph the probability distribution function.

Solution

a. $P(\text{At Most 1 Sale}) = P(X \le 1) = P(X = 0) + P(X = 1) = 0.078 + 0.259 = 0.337$, since

$$P(\text{No Sale}) = P(0) = \frac{5!}{0!\,5!}(0.4)^0(0.6)^5 = 0.078$$

$$P(\text{1 Sale}) = P(1) = \frac{5!}{1!\,4!}(0.4)^1(0.6)^4 = 5(0.4)(0.6)^4 = 0.259$$

b. $P(2 \le X \le 4) = P(2) + P(3) + P(4) = 0.346 + 0.230 + 0.077 = 0.653$, since

$$P(2) = \frac{5!}{2!\,3!}(0.4)^2(0.6)^3 = 10(0.4)^2(0.6)^3 = 0.346$$

$$P(3) = \frac{5!}{3!\,2!}(0.4)^3(0.6)^2 = 10(0.4)^3(0.6)^2 = 0.230$$

$$P(4) = \frac{5!}{4!\,1!}(0.4)^4(0.6)^1 = 5(0.4)^4(0.6)^1 = 0.077$$

c. The probability distribution function is shown in Figure 5.6.

Figure 5.6 Graph of Binomial Probability Function for Example 5.7 ($n = 5$, $P = 0.40$)

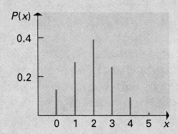

Comments

- This shape is typical for binomial probabilities when P is neither very large nor very small.
- At the extremes (0 or 5 sales), the probabilities are quite small.

Unless the number of trials n is very small, the calculation of binomial probabilities is likely to be extremely cumbersome. Binomial probabilities can also be obtained from tables in the Appendix.

Example 5.8 College Admissions (Binomial Probabilities Using Tables)

Early in August an undergraduate college discovers that it can accommodate a few extra students. Enrolling those additional students would provide a substantial increase in revenue without increasing the operating costs of the college; that is, no new classes would have to be added. From past experience the college knows that 40% of those students admitted will actually enroll.

    a. What is the probability that at most 6 students will enroll if the college offers admission to 10 more students?

    b. What is the probability that more than 12 will actually enroll if admission is offered to 20 students?

    c. If 70% of those students admitted actually enroll, what is the probability that at least 12 out of 15 students will actually enroll?

Solution

    a. This probability can be obtained using the cumulative binomial probability distribution from Table 3 in the Appendix. The probability of at most 6 students enrolling if $n = 10$ and $P = 0.40$ is

$$P(X \leq 6 \mid n = 10, P = 0.40) = 0.945$$

    b. $P(X > 12 \mid n = 20, P = 0.40) = 1 - P(X \leq 12) = 1 - 0.979 = 0.021$.

    c. The probability that at least 12 out of 15 students enroll is the same as the probability that at most 3 out of 15 students do not enroll (the probability of a student not enrolling is $1 - 0.70 = 0.30$).

$$P(X \geq 12 \mid n = 15, P = 0.70) = P(X \leq 3 \mid n = 15, P = 0.30) = 0.297$$

Most good computer packages have the capability to compute binomial and other probabilities for various probability distribution functions. Example 5.9 illustrates the procedure using Minitab, but other packages have similar capabilities.

Example 5.9 Sales of Airline Seats (Compute Binomial Probabilities using Minitab)

Have you ever agreed to give up your airplane ticket in return for a free ticket? Have you ever searched for the cheapest flight so that you could visit a special friend? The following example provides some of the analysis that leads to results such as overbooked flights and reduced fares on certain flights.

    Suppose that you are in charge of marketing airline seats for a major carrier. Four days before the flight date you have 16 seats remaining on the plane. You know from past experience data that 80% of the people that purchase tickets in this time period will actually show up for the flight.

    a. If you sell 20 extra tickets, what is the probability that you will overbook the flight or have at least one empty seat?

    b. If you sell 18 extra tickets, what is the probability that you will overbook the flight or have at least one empty seat?

Solution

a. To find $P(X > 16)$, given $n = 20$ and $P = 0.80$, use Minitab by following the instructions in Figure 5.7. With Minitab the user must select *either* Probability [such as $P(X = 16)$] *or* Cumulative Probability [$P(X = 16)$], but not both simultaneously.

Figure 5.7 Binomial Probability Dialog Box for $n = 20$, $P = 0.80$ Using Minitab

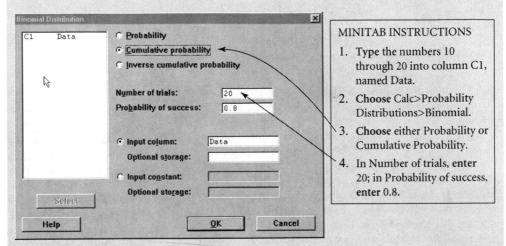

Table 5.4 Binomial Probabilities Obtained from Minitab for $n = 20$, $P = 0.80$

X	$P(X <= X)$
10	0.0026
11	0.0100
12	0.0321
13	0.0867
14	0.1958
15	0.3704
16	0.5886
17	0.7939
18	0.9308
19	0.9885
20	1.0000

Comments

- To find the probability of overbooking,

$$P(X > 16) = 1 - P(X <= 16) = 1 - 0.589 = 0.411$$

- If 20 tickets are sold, this also means that the probability that 15 or fewer people will arrive is

$$P(X <= 15) = 0.37.$$

- That is, there is a 37% chance that selling 20 tickets results in at least one empty seat!

b. To find the chance that you overbook the flight by selling 18 tickets, follow the same steps as above. The chance that you overbook the flight will be only 10%, but the probability of at least one empty seat will increase to 72.9%!

The airline management then must evaluate the cost of overbooking (providing free tickets) versus the cost of empty seats that generate no revenue. Airlines analyze data to determine the number of seats that should be sold at reduced rates to maximize the ticket revenue from each flight. This analysis is complex, but it has its starting point in analyses such as the example presented here.

EXERCISES

Basic Exercises

5.30 For a Bernoulli random variable with probability of success $P = 0.5$, compute the mean and variance.

5.31 For a binomial probability function with $P = 0.5$ and $n = 12$, find the probability that the number of successes is equal to 7 and the probability that the number of successes is less than 6.

5.32 For a binomial probability function with $P = 0.3$ and $n = 14$, find the probability that the number of successes is equal to 7 and the probability that the number of successes is less than 6.

5.33 For a binomial probability function with $P = 0.4$ and $n = 20$, find the probability that the number of successes is equal to 9 and the probability that the number of successes is less than 7.

5.34 For a binomial probability function with $P = 0.7$ and $n = 18$, find the probability that the number of successes is equal to 12 and the probability that the number of successes is less than 6.

Application Exercises

5.35 A production manager knows that 5% of components produced by a particular manufacturing process have some defect. Six of these components, whose characteristics can be assumed to be independent of each other, are examined.

a. What is the probability that none of these components has a defect?

b. What is the probability that one of these components has a defect?

c. What is the probability that at least two of these components have a defect?

5.36 A politician believes that 25% of all macroeconomists in senior positions will strongly support a proposal he wishes to advance. Suppose that this belief is correct and that five senior macroeconomists are approached at random.

a. What is the probability that at least one of the five will strongly support the proposal?

b. What is the probability that a majority of the five will strongly support the proposal?

5.37 A public interest group hires students to solicit donations by telephone. After a brief training period students make calls to potential donors and are paid on a commission basis. Experience indicates that early on these students tend to have only modest success and that 70% of them give up their jobs in their first 2 weeks of employment. The group hires six students, which can be viewed as a random sample.

a. What is the probability that at least two of the six will give up in the first 2 weeks?

b. What is the probability that at least two of the six will not give up in the first 2 weeks?

5.38 Suppose that the probability is 0.5 that the value of the U.S. dollar will rise against the Japanese yen over any given week and that the outcome in one week is independent of that in any other week. What is the probability that the value of the U.S. dollar will rise against the Japanese yen in a majority of weeks over a period of 7 weeks?

5.39 A company installs new central heating furnaces and has found that for 15% of all installations a return visit is needed to make some modifications. Six installations were made in a particular week. Assume independence of outcomes for these installations.

a. What is the probability that a return visit will be needed in all of these cases?

b. What is the probability that a return visit will be needed in none of these cases?

c. What is the probability that a return visit will be needed in more than one of these cases?

5.40 The Cubs are to play a series of five games in St. Louis against the Cardinals. For any one game it is estimated that the probability of a Cubs win is 0.4. The outcomes of the five games are independent of one another.

a. What is the probability that the Cubs will win all five games?

b. What is the probability that the Cubs will win a majority of the five games?

c. If the Cubs win the first game, what is the probability that they will win a majority of the five games?

d. Before the series begins, what is the expected number of Cubs wins in these five games?

e. If the Cubs win the first game, what is the expected number of Cubs wins in the five games?

5.41 A small commuter airline flies planes that can seat up to eight passengers. The airline has determined that the probability that a ticketed passenger will not show up for a flight is 0.2. For each flight the airline sells tickets to the first 10 people placing orders. The probability distribution for the number of tickets sold per flight is shown in the accompanying table. For what proportion of the airline's flights does the number of ticketed passengers showing up exceed the number of available seats? (Assume independence between the number of tickets sold and the probability that a ticketed passenger will show up.)

Number of tickets	6	7	8	9	10
Probability	0.25	0.35	0.25	0.10	0.05

5.42 Following a touchdown, a college football coach has the option to elect to attempt a "2-point conversion"; that is, 2 additional points are scored if the attempt is successful and none if it is unsuccessful. The coach believes that the probability is 0.4 that his team will be successful in any attempt and that outcomes of different attempts are independent of each other. In a particular game the team scores four touchdowns and 2-point conversion attempts were made each time.

a. What is the probability that at least two of these attempts will be successful?

b. Find the mean and standard deviation of the total number of points resulting from these four attempts.

5.43 An automobile dealer mounts a new promotional campaign. Purchasers of new automobiles may, if dissatisfied for any reason, return them within 2 days of purchase and receive a full refund. The cost to the dealer of such a refund is $250. The dealer estimates that 15% of all purchasers will indeed return automobiles and obtain refunds. Suppose that 50 automobiles are purchased during the campaign period.

a. Find the mean and standard deviation of the number of these automobiles that will be returned for refunds.

b. Find the mean and standard deviation of the total refund costs that will accrue as a result of these 50 purchases.

5.44 A family of mutual funds maintains a service that allows clients to switch money among accounts through a telephone call. It was estimated that 3.2% of callers either get a busy signal or are kept on hold so long that they may hang up. Fund management assesses any failure of this sort as a $10 goodwill loss. Suppose that 2,000 calls are attempted over a particular period.

a. Find the mean and standard deviation of the number of callers who will either get a busy signal or may hang up after being kept on hold.

b. Find the mean and standard deviation of the total goodwill loss to the mutual fund company from these 2,000 calls.

5.45 We have seen that, for a binomial distribution with n trials, each with probability of success P, the mean is

$$\mu_X = E(X) = nP$$

Verify this result for the data of Example 5.7 by calculating the mean directly from

$$\mu_X = \Sigma\, xP(x)$$

showing that for the binomial distribution the two formulas produce the same answer.

5.46 A campus finance officer finds that, for all parking tickets issued, fines of 78% are paid. The fine is $2. In the most recent week 620 parking tickets have been issued.

a. Find the mean and standard deviation of the number of these tickets for which the fines will be paid.

b. Find the mean and standard deviation of the amount of money that will be obtained from the payment of these fines.

5.47 A company receives a very large shipment of components. A random sample of 16 of these components will be checked, and the shipment will be accepted if fewer than 2 of these components are defective. What is the probability of accepting a shipment containing

a. 5% defectives?

b. 15% defectives?

c. 25% defectives?

5.48 The following two acceptance rules are being considered for determining whether to take delivery of a large shipment of components:

• A random sample of 10 components is checked, and the shipment is accepted only if none of them is defective.

• A random sample of 20 components is checked, and the shipment is accepted only if no more than 1 of them is defective.

Which of these acceptance rules has the smaller probability of accepting a shipment containing 20% defectives?

5.49 A company receives large shipments of parts from two sources. Seventy percent of the shipments come from a supplier whose shipments typically contain 10% defectives, while the remainder are from a supplier whose shipments typically contain 20% defectives. A manager receives a shipment but does not know the source. A random sample of 20 items from this shipment is tested, and 1 of the parts is found to be defective. What is the probability that this shipment came from the more reliable supplier? [*Hint*: Use Bayes' theorem.]

5.5 HYPERGEOMETRIC DISTRIBUTION

The binomial distribution presented in Section 5.4 assumes that the items are drawn independently, with the probability of selecting an item being constant. In many applied problems these assumptions can be met if a small sample is drawn from a large population. But here we consider a situation where it is necessary to select 5 employees from a group of 15 equally qualified applicants—a small population. In the group of 15 there are 9 women and 6 men. Suppose that, in the group of 5 selected employees, 3 are men and 2 are women. What is the probability of selecting that particular group if the selections are made randomly without bias. In the initial group of 15 the probability of selecting a woman is 9/15. If a woman is not selected in the first draw, then the probability of selecting a woman in the second draw is 9/14. Thus, the probabilities change with each selection. Because the assumptions for the binomial are not met, a different probability model must be selected. This probability distribution is the *hypergeometric probability distribution*.

We can use the binomial distribution in situations that are defined as "sampling with replacement." If the selected item is replaced in the population, then the probability of selecting that type of item remains the same and the binomial assumptions are met. In contrast, if the items are not replaced—"sampling without replacement"—the probabilities change with each selection, and, thus, the appropriate probability model is the hypergeometric distribution. If the population is large ($N > 10,000$) and the sample size is small (<1%), then the change in probability after each draw is very small. In those situations the binomial is a very good approximation and is typically used. The hypergeometric probability model is given in Equation 5.21.

Hypergeometric Distribution

Suppose that a random sample of *n* objects is chosen from a group of *N* objects, *S* of which are successes. The distribution of the number of successes, *X*, in the sample is called the **hypergeometric distribution**. Its probability function is

$$P(x) = \frac{C_x^S C_{n-x}^{N-s}}{C_n^N} = \frac{\dfrac{S!}{x!(S-x)!} \times \dfrac{(N-S)!}{(n-x)!(N-S-n+x)!}}{\dfrac{N!}{n!(N-n)!}} \qquad (5.21)$$

where *x* can take integer values ranging from the larger of 0 and [*n* − (*N* − *S*)] to the smaller of *n* and *S*.

The logic for the hypergeometric distribution was developed in Section 4.3, using the classic definition of probability and the counting formulas for combinations. In Equation 5.21 the individual components are

1. The number of possible ways that x successes can be selected for the sample out of S successes contained in the population:

$$C_x^S = \frac{S!}{x!(S-x)!}$$

2. The number of possible ways that $n - x$ nonsuccesses can be selected from the population that contains $N - S$ nonsuccesses:

$$C_{n-x}^{N-S} = \frac{(N-S)!}{(n-x)!(N-S-n+x)!}$$

3. And, finally, the total number of different samples of size n that can be obtained from a population of size N:

$$C_n^N = \frac{N!}{n!(N-n)!}$$

When these components are combined using the classical definition of probability, the hypergeometric probability distribution is obtained.

Example 5.10 Shipment of Items (Compute Hypergeometric Probability)

A company receives a shipment of 20 items. Because inspection of each individual item is expensive, it has a policy of checking a random sample of 6 items from such a shipment, and if no more than 1 sampled item is defective, the remainder will not be checked. What is the probability that a shipment of 5 defective items will not be subjected to additional checking?

Solution If "defective" is identified with "success" in this example, the shipment contains $N = 20$ items and $S = 5$ of the 20 that are successes. A sample of $n = 6$ items is selected. Then the number of successes, X, in the sample has a hypergeometric distribution with the probability function

$$P(x) = \frac{C_x^S C_{n-x}^S}{C_n^N} = \frac{C_x^5 C_{6-x}^{15}}{C_6^{20}} = \frac{\dfrac{5!}{x!(5-x)!} \times \dfrac{15!}{(6-x)!(9+x)!}}{\dfrac{20!}{6!14!}}$$

The shipment is not checked further if the sample contains either zero or one success (defective), so that the probability of its acceptance is

$$P(\text{Shipment Accepted}) = P(0) + P(1)$$

The probability of no defectives in the sample is

$$P(0) = \frac{\dfrac{5!}{0!5!} \times \dfrac{15!}{6!9!}}{\dfrac{20!}{6!14!}} = 0.129$$

The probability of 1 defective item in the sample is

$$P(1) = \frac{\dfrac{5!}{1!4!} \times \dfrac{15!}{5!10!}}{\dfrac{20!}{6!14!}} = 0.387$$

Therefore, we find that the probability that the shipment of 20 items containing 5 defectives is not checked further is P(Shipment Accepted) $= P(0) + P(1) = 0.129 + 0.387 = 0.516$. This is a high error rate, which indicates a need for process improvement.

Hypergeometric probabilities can also be computed using computer packages following a procedure similar to the procedure in Example 5.9 for the binomial.

EXERCISES

Basic Exercises

5.50 Compute the probability of 5 successes in a random sample of size $n = 12$ obtained from a population of size $N = 50$ that contains 25 successes.

5.51 Compute the probability of 7 successes in a random sample of size $n = 14$ obtained from a population of size $N = 60$ that contains 25 successes.

5.52 Compute the probability of 9 successes in a random sample of size $n = 20$ obtained from a population of size $N = 80$ that contains 42 successes.

5.53 Compute the probability of 3 successes in a random sample of size $n = 5$ obtained from a population of size $N = 40$ that contains 25 successes.

5.54 Compute the probability of 8 successes in a random sample of size $n = 15$ obtained from a population of size $N = 400$ that contains 200 successes.

Application Exercises

5.55 A company receives a shipment of 16 items. A random sample of 4 items is selected, and the shipment is rejected if any of these items proves to be defective.

a. What is the probability of accepting a shipment containing 4 defective items?

b. What is the probability of accepting a shipment containing 1 defective item?

c. What is the probability of rejecting a shipment containing 1 defective item?

5.56 A committee of eight members is to be formed from a group of eight men and eight women. If the choice of committee members is made randomly, what is the probability that precisely half of these members will be women?

5.57 A bond analyst was given a list of 12 corporate bonds. From that list she selected 3 whose ratings she felt were in danger of being downgraded in the next year. In actuality, a total of 4 of the 12 bonds on the list had their ratings downgraded in the next year. Suppose that the analyst had simply chosen 3 bonds randomly from this list. What is the probability that at least 2 of the chosen bonds would be among those whose ratings were to be downgraded in the next year?

5.58 A bank executive is presented with loan applications from 10 people. The profiles of the applicants are similar, except that 5 are minorities and 5 are not minorities. In the end the executive approves 6 of the applications. If these 6 approvals are chosen at random from the 10 applications, what is the probability that less than half the approvals will be of applications involving minorities?

5.6 THE POISSON PROBABILITY DISTRIBUTION

The *Poisson probability distribution* was first proposed by Simeon Poisson (1781–1840) in a book published in 1837. The number of applications began to increase early in the twentieth century, and the availability of the computer has brought about further applications in the twenty-first century. The Poisson probability distribution is an important discrete probability distribution for a number of applications, including:

1. The number of failures in a large computer system during a given day
2. The number of replacement orders for a part received by a firm in a given month
3. The number of ships arriving at a loading facility during a 6-hour loading period
4. The number of delivery trucks to arrive at a central warehouse in an hour
5. The number of dents, scratches, or other defects in a large roll of sheet metal used to manufacture filters
6. The number of customers to arrive for flights during each 15-minute time interval from 3:00 P.M. to 6:00 P.M. on weekdays
7. The number of customers to arrive at a checkout aisle in your local grocery store during a particular time interval

We can use the Poisson probability distribution to determine the probability of each of these random variables, which are characterized as the number of occurrences or successes of a certain event in a given continuous interval (such as time, surface area, or length).

A Poisson probability distribution is modeled according to certain assumptions.

Assumptions of the Poisson Probability Distribution

Assume that an interval is divided into a very large number of subintervals so that the probability of the occurrence of an event in any subinterval is very small. The **assumptions of a Poisson probability distribution** are as follows:

1. The probability of the occurrence of an event is constant for all subintervals.
2. There can be no more than one occurrence in each subinterval.
3. Occurrences are independent; that is, the occurrences in nonoverlapping intervals are independent of one another.

We can derive the equation for computing Poisson probabilities directly from the binomial probability distribution by taking the mathematical limits as $P \to 0$ and $n \to \infty$. With these limits the parameter $\lambda = nP$ is a constant that specifies the average number of occurrences (successes) for a particular time and/or space. The Poisson probability distribution function is given in Equation 5.22.

The Poisson Probability Distribution Function, Mean, and Variance

The random variable X is said to follow the **Poisson probability distribution** if it has the probability function

$$P(x) = \frac{e^{-\lambda}\lambda^x}{x!} \text{ for } x = 0, 1, 2 \qquad (5.22)$$

where

$P(x)$ = the probability of x successes over a given time or space, given λ
λ = the expected number of successes per time or space unit; $\lambda > 0$
$e \cong 2.71828$ (the base for natural logarithms)

The **mean and variance of the Poisson probability distribution** are

$$\mu = E(X) = \lambda \quad \text{and} \quad \sigma^2 = E[(X - \mu)^2] = \lambda$$

The sum of Poisson random variables is also a Poisson random variable. Thus, the sum of K Poisson random variables, each with mean λ, is a Poisson random variable with mean $K\lambda$.

Example 5.11 System Component Failure (Poisson Probabilities)

Andrew Whittaker, computer center manager, reports that his computer system experienced three component failures during the past 100 days.

a. What is the probability of no failures in a given day?
b. What is the probability of one or more component failures in a given day?
c. What is the probability of at least two failures in a 3-day period?

Solution   A modern computer system has a very large number of components, each of which could fail and thus result in a computer system failure. To compute the probability of failures using the Poisson distribution, assume that each of the millions of components has the same very small probability of failure. Also assume that the first failure does not affect the probability of a second failure (in some cases, these assumptions may not hold, and more complex distributions would be used).

From past experience the expected number of failures per day is 3/100, or $\lambda = 0.03$.

a.
$$P(\text{No Failures in a Given Day}) = P(X = 0 \mid \lambda = 0.03)$$
$$= \frac{e^{-0.03}\lambda^0}{0!} = 0.970446$$

b. The probability of at least one failure is the complement of the probability of 0 failures:

$$P(X \geq 1) = 1 - P(X = 0)$$
$$= 1 - \left[\frac{e^{-\lambda}\lambda^x}{x!}\right] = 1 - \left[\frac{e^{-0.03}\lambda^0}{0!}\right]$$
$$= 1 - e^{-0.03} = 1 - 0.970446 = 0.029554$$

c. $P(\text{At Least Two Failures in a 3-Day Period}) = P(X \geq 2 \mid \lambda = 0.09)$, where the average over a 3-day period is $\lambda = 3(0.03) = 0.09$:

$$P(X \geq 2 \mid \lambda = 0.09) = 1 - P(X \leq 1) = 1 - [P(X = 0) + P(X = 1)] = 1 - [0.913931 + 0.082254]$$

and, thus,

$$P(X \geq 2 \mid \lambda = 0.09) = 1 - 0.996185 = 0.003815$$

The Poisson distribution has been found to be particularly useful in *waiting line*, or *queuing*, problems. Examples include the number of customers to arrive at a checkout aisle in a grocery store, the number of delivery trucks to arrive at a central warehouse, the number of people to arrive for flights, the number of students waiting to purchase texts in the university bookstore, and so forth. In practice, it is often possible to represent arrival processes of this sort by a Poisson distribution.

Example 5.12 Customers at a Photocopying Machine (Poisson Probability)

Customers arrive at a photocopying machine at an average rate of two every 5 minutes. Assume that these arrivals are independent, with a constant arrival rate, and that this problem follows a Poisson model, with X denoting the number of arriving customers in a 5-minute period and mean $\lambda = 2$. Find the probability that more than two customers arrive in a 5-minute period.

Solution Since the mean number of arrivals in 5 minutes is two, then $\lambda = 2$. To find the probability that more than two customers arrive, first compute the probability of at most two arrivals in a 5-minute period, and then use the complement rule.

These probabilities can be found in Table 5 in the Appendix or by using a computer:

$$P(X = 0) = \frac{e^{-2}2^0}{0!} = e^{-2} = 0.1353$$

$$P(X = 1) = \frac{e^{-2}2^1}{1!} = 2e^{-2} = 0.2707$$

$$P(X = 2) = \frac{e^{-2}2^2}{2!} = 2e^{-2} = 0.2707$$

Thus, the probability of more than two arrivals in a 5-minute period is

$$P(X > 2) = 1 - P(X \le 2) = 1 - [0.135335 + 0.27067 + 0.27067] = 0.323325$$

Poisson Approximation to the Binomial Distribution

Previously, we noted that the Poisson probability distribution is obtained by starting with the Binomial probability distribution with P approaching 0 and n becoming very large. Thus, it follows that the Poisson distribution can be used to approximate the binomial probabilities when the number of trials, n, is large and at the same time the probability, P, is small (generally such that $\lambda = nP \le 7$). Examples of situations that would satisfy these conditions include the following:

* An insurance company will hold a large number of life policies on individuals of any particular age, and the probability that a single policy will result in a claim during the year is very low. Here, we have a binomial distribution with large n and small P.
* A company may have a large number of machines working on a process simultaneously. If the proability that any one of them will break down in a single day is small, the distribution of the number of daily breakdowns is binomial with large n and small P.

Poisson Approximation to the Binomial Distribution
Let X be the number of successes resulting from n independent trials, each with probability of success P. The distribution of the number of

successes, X, is binomial, with mean nP. If the number of trials, n, is large and nP is of only moderate size (preferably $nP \leq 7$), this distribution can be **approximated by the Poisson distribution** with $\lambda = nP$. The probability function of the approximating distribution is then

$$P(x) = \frac{e^{-nP}(nP)^x}{x!} \quad \text{for } x = 0, 1, 2, \cdots \tag{5.23}$$

Example 5.13   Probability of Bankruptcy (Poisson Probability)

An analyst predicted that 3.5% of all small corporations would file for bankruptcy in the coming year. For a random sample of 100 small corporations, estimate the probability that at least 3 will file for bankruptcy in the next year, assuming that the analyst's prediction is correct.

Solution   The distribution of X, the number of filings for bankruptcy, is binomial with $n = 100$ and $P = 0.035$, so that the mean of the distribution is $\mu_x = nP = 3.5$. Using the Poisson distribution to approximate the probability of at least 3 bankruptcies, we find

$$P(X \geq 3) = 1 - P(X \leq 2)$$

$$P(0) = \frac{e^{-3.5}(3.5)^0}{0!} = e^{-3.5} = 0.030197$$

$$P(1) = \frac{e^{-3.5}(3.5)^1}{1!} = (3.5)(0.030197) = 0.1056895$$

$$P(2) = \frac{e^{-3.5}(3.5)^2}{2!} = (6.125)(0.030197) = 0.1849566$$

Thus, $P(X \leq 2) = P(0) + P(1) + P(2) = 0.030197 + 0.1056895 + 0.1849566 = 0.3208431$

$$P(X \geq 3) = 1 - 0.3208431 = 0.6791569$$

The binomial probability of $X \geq 3$ is

$$P(X \geq 3) = 0.684093$$

The Poisson probability is simply an estimate of the actual binomial probability.

Comparison of the Poisson and Binomial Probability Distributions

We should indicate at this point that confusion may exist about the choice of the binomial or the Poisson probability distribution for particular applications. The choice is many cases can be made easier by carefully reviewing the assumptions for the two probability distributions. For example, if the problem uses a small sample of observations, then it is not possible to find a limiting probability with n large, and, thus, the binomial is the correct probability distribution. Further, if we have a small sample and the probability of a success for a single trial is between 0.05 and 0.95, then there is further support for choosing the binomial. If we knew or could assume that each of 10 randomly selected customers in an automobile showroom had the same probability of purchase (assume $0.05 \leq P \leq 0.95$), then the number of purchases from this group would follow a binomial probability distribution. However, if the set of cases that could be affected is very large—say, several thousand—and the mean number of "successes" over that large set of cases is small—say, less than 30—then there is strong support for choosing the Poisson probability distribution. If we wanted to compute the probability of a certain number of defective parts in a set of 100,000 parts when the mean number of 15 defectives per 100,000 parts represented a typical production cycle, then we would use the Poisson probability distribution.

In the previous discussion it was noted that, when P is less than 0.05 and n is large, we can approximate the binomial probability distribution by using the Poisson probability distribution. It can also be shown that, when $n \geq 20$ and $P \leq 0.05$ and the population mean is the same, we will find that both the binomial and the Poisson probability distributions generate approximately the same probability values.

EXERCISES

Basic Exercises

5.59 Determine the probability of exactly 7 successes for a random variable with a Poisson distribution with parameter $\lambda = 3.5$.

5.60 Determine the probability of exactly 4 successes for a random variable with a Poisson distribution with parameter $\lambda = 2.5$.

5.61 Determine the probability of more than 7 successes for a random variable with a Poisson distribution with parameter $\lambda = 4.5$.

5.62 Determine the probability of less than 6 successes for a random variable with a Poisson distribution with parameter $\lambda = 3.5$.

5.63 Determine the probability of less than or equal to 9 successes for a random variable with a Poisson distribution with parameter $\lambda = 8.0$.

Application Exercises

5.64 Customers arrive at a busy checkout counter at an average rate of three per minute. If the distribution of arrivals is Poisson, find the probability that in any given minute there will be two or fewer arrivals.

5.65 The number of accidents in a production facility has a Poisson distribution with a mean of 2.6 per month.

  a. For a given month what is the probability there will be fewer than two accidents?
  b. For a given month what is the probability there will be more than three accidents?

5.66 A professor receives, on average, 4.2 telephone calls from students the day before a final examination. If the distribution of calls is Poisson, what is the probability of receiving at least three of these calls on such a day?

5.67 Records indicate that, on average, 3.2 breakdowns per day occur on an urban highway during the morning rush hour. Assume that the distribution is Poisson.

  a. Find the probability that on any given day there will be fewer than two breakdowns on this highway during the morning rush hour.
  b. Find the probability that on any given day there will be more than four breakdowns on this highway during the morning rush hour.

5.68 The Internal Revenue Service reported that 5.5% of all taxpayers filling out the 1040 short form make mistakes. If 100 of these forms are chosen at random, what is the probability that fewer than 3 of them contain errors? Use the Poisson approximation to the binomial distribution.

5.69 A corporation has 250 personal computers. The probability that any 1 of them will require repair in a given week is 0.01. Find the probability that fewer than 4 of the personal computers will require repair in a particular week. Use the Poisson approximation to the binomial distribution.

5.70 An insurance company holds fraud insurance policies on 6,000 firms. In any given year the probability that any single policy will result in a claim is 0.001. Find the probability that at least three claims are made in a given year. Use the Poisson approximation to the binomial distribution.

5.71 A state has a law requiring motorists to carry insurance. It was estimated that, despite this law, 7.5% of all motorists in the state are uninsured. A random sample of 60 motorists was taken. Use the Poisson approximation to the binomial distribution to estimate the probability that at least 3 of the motorists in this sample are uninsured. Also indicate what calculations would be needed to find this probability exactly if the Poisson approximation was not used.

5.72 A new warehouse is being designed and a decision concerning the number of loading docks is required. There are two models for the use of this warehouse, given that loading a truck requires 1 hour. The warehouse could be serviced by one of the many thousands of independent truckers who arrive randomly to obtain a load for delivery. It is known that, on average, one of these trucks would arrive each hour. Alternatively, the company might hire a fleet of 10 trucks that are assigned full-time to shipments from this warehouse. Under that assumption the trucks would arrive randomly, but the probability of any truck arriving during a given hour is 0.1. Obtain the appropriate probability distribution for each of these assumptions and compare the results. The probability distribution values can be obtained either from Tables 2 and 5 in the Appendix or by using a computer.

5.7 JOINTLY DISTRIBUTED DISCRETE RANDOM VARIABLES

Business and economic applications of statistics are often concerned about the relationships between variables. Products at different quality levels are priced at different price intervals. Age groups have different preferences for clothing, for automobiles, and for music. The percent returns on two different stocks may tend to be related, and the probability of higher returns for both may increase when the market is growing. Alternatively, when the return on one stock is growing, the return on the other might be decreasing. When we work with probability models for problems involving relationships between variables, it is important that the effect of these relationships is included in the probability model. For example, assume that a car dealer is selling the following automobiles: (1) a red two-door compact, (2) a blue minivan, and (3) a silver full-size sedan; the probability distribution for purchasing would not be the same for women in their twenties, thirties, and fifties. Thus, it is important that probability models reflect the joint effect of variables on probabilities.

In Section 4.6 we discussed joint probabilities. We now consider the case where two or more, possibly related, discrete random variables are examined. With a single random variable, the probabilities for all possible outcomes can be summarized in a probability function, where as now we need to define the probabilities that the random variables of interest simultaneously take specific values. Consider the following example involving the use of jointly distributed discrete random variables.

Example 5.14   Market Research (Joint Probabilities)

Sally Peterson, a marketing analyst, has been asked to develop a probability model for the relationship between the sale of luxury cookware and age group. This model will be important for developing a marketing campaign for a new line of chef-grade cookware. She believes that purchasing patterns for luxury cookware are different for different age groups.

Solution   To represent the market, Sally proposes to use three age groups—16 to 25, 26 to 45, and 46 to 65—and two purchasing patterns—"buy" and "not buy." Next, she collects a random sample of persons for the age range 16 to 65 and records their age group and desire to purchase. The result of this data collection is the joint probability distribution contained in Table 5.5. Table 5.5 thus provides a summary of the probability of purchase and age group that will be a valuable resource for marketing analysis.

Table 5.5 Joint Probability Distribution of Age Group (*X*) Versus Purchase Decision (*Y*)

| PURCHASE DECISION (*Y*) | AGE GROUP (*X*) | | | |
	1 (16 TO 25)	2 (26 TO 45)	3 (46 TO 65)	$P(y)$
1 (buy)	0.10	0.20	0.10	0.40
2 (not buy)	0.25	0.25	0.10	0.60
$P(x)$	0.35	0.45	0.20	1.00

Joint Probability Function

Let *X* and *Y* be a pair of discrete random variables. Their **joint probability function** expresses the probability that simultaneously *X* takes the specific value *x* and *Y* takes the value *y*, as a function of *x* and *y*. We note that the discussion here is a direct extension of the material in Section 4.4, where we presented the probability of the intersection of two events, $P(A_i \cap B_j)$. Here, we will use random variables. The notation used is $P(x, y)$, so

$$P(x,y) = P(X = x \cap Y = y)$$

The probability functions for the individual random variables are frequently desired when dealing with jointly distributed random variables.

Derivation of the Marginal Probability Function

Let *X* and *Y* be a pair of jointly distributed random variables. In this context the probability function of the random variable *X* is called its **marginal probability function** and is obtained by summing the joint probabilities over all possible values; that is,

$$P(x) = \sum_y P(x,y) \tag{5.24}$$

Similarly, the marginal probability function of the random variable *Y* is

$$P(y) = \sum_x P(x,y) \tag{5.25}$$

An example of these marginal probability functions is shown in the lower row and the right column in Table 5.5.

Joint probability functions must have the following properties.

Properties of Joint Probability Functions of Discrete Random Variables

Let X and Y be discrete random variables with joint probability function $P(x, y)$. Then

1. $0 < P(x, y) < 1$ for any pair of values x and y.
2. The sum of the joint probabilities $P(x, y)$ over all possible pairs of values must be 1.

The *conditional probability function* of one random variable, given specified values of another, is the collection of conditional probabilities.

Conditional Probability Function

Let X and Y be a pair of jointly distributed discrete random variables. The **conditional probability function** of the random variable Y, given that the random variable X takes the value x, expresses the probability that Y takes the value y, as a function of y, when the value x is specified for X. This is denoted $P(y|x)$, and so by the definition of conditional probability

$$P(y|x) = \frac{P(x,y)}{P(x)} \tag{5.26}$$

Similarly, the conditional probability function of X, given $Y = y$, is

$$P(x|y) = \frac{P(x,y)}{P(y)} \tag{5.27}$$

For example, using the probabilities in Table 5.5, we can compute the conditional probability of purchase ($y = 1$), given age group 26 to 45 ($x = 2$), as

$$P(1|2) = \frac{P(2,1)}{P(2)} = \frac{0.20}{0.45} = 0.44$$

In Chapter 4 we discussed independence of events. This concept extends directly to random variables.

Independence of Jointly Distributed Random Variables

The jointly distributed random variables X and Y are said to be **independent** if and only if their joint probability function is the product of their marginal probability functions; that is, if and only if

$$P(x, y) = P(x)P(y)$$

for all possible pairs of values x and y. And k random variables are independent if and only if

$$P(X_1, X_2, \ldots, X_k) = P(X_1) P(X_2) \ldots P(X_k) \tag{5.28}$$

From the definition of conditional probability functions it follows that, if the random variables X and Y are independent, then the conditional probability function of Y, given X, is the same as the marginal probability function of Y; that is,

$$P(y \mid x) = P(y)$$

Similarly, it follows that

$$P(x \mid y) = P(x)$$

Example 5.15 considers the possible percent returns for two stocks, A and B, illustrates the computation of marginal probabilities and tests for independence, and finds the means and variances of two jointly distributed random variables.

Example 5.15 Stock Returns, Marginal Probability, Mean, Variance (Joint Probabilities)

Suppose that Charlotte King has two stocks, A and B. Let X and Y be random variables of possible percent returns (0%, 5%, 10%, and 15%) for each of these two stocks, with the joint probability distribution given in Table 5.6.

a. Find the marginal probabilities.
b. Determine if X and Y are independent.
c. Find the means and variances of both X and Y.

Table 5.6 Joint Probability Distribution for Random Variables X and Y

X RETURN	Y RETURN			
	0%	5%	10%	15%
0%	0.0625	0.0625	0.0625	0.0625
5%	0.0625	0.0625	0.0625	0.0625
10%	0.0625	0.0625	0.0625	0.0625
15%	0.0625	0.0625	0.0625	0.0625

Solution

a. This problem is solved using the definitions developed in this chapter. Note that, for every combination of values for X and Y, $P(x, y) = 0.0625$. That is, there is a 6.25% probability for each possible combination of x and y returns. To find the marginal probability that X has a 0% return:

$$P(X = 0) = \sum_y P(0,y) = 0.0625 + 0.0625 + 0.0625 + 0.0625 = 0.25$$

Here all the marginal probabilities of X are 25%. Notice that the sum of the marginal probabilities is 1. Similar results can be found for the marginal probabilities of Y.

b. To test for independence, we need to check if $P(x, y) = P(x)P(y)$ for all possible pairs of values x and y.

$$P(x,y) = 0.0625 \quad \text{for all possible pairs of values } x \text{ and } y$$
$$P(x) = 0.25 \quad \text{and} \quad P(y) = 0.25 \quad \text{for all possible pairs of values } x \text{ and } y$$
$$P(x,y) = 0.0625 = (0.25)(0.25) = P(x)\,P(y)$$

Therefore, X and Y are independent.

c. The mean of X is

$$\mu_X = E(X) = \sum_X x P(x)$$
$$= 0(0.25) + 0.05(0.25) + 0.10(0.25) + 0.15(0.25) = 0.075$$

Similarly, the mean of Y is $\mu_Y = E(y) = 0.075$.

The variance of X is

$$\sigma_X^2 = \sum_X (x - \mu_X)^2 P(x) = P(x) \sum_X (x - \mu_X)^2 = (0.25) \sum_x (x - \mu_X)^2$$
$$= (0.25)[(0 - 0.075)^2 + (0.05 - 0.075)^2 (0.10 - 0.075)^2 + (0.15 - 0.075)^2]$$
$$= 0.003125$$

and the standard deviation of X is $\sigma_X = \sqrt{0.003125} = 0.0559016$, or 5.59%. Follow similar steps to find the variance and standard deviation of Y.

Computer Applications

There is no add-in currently available to make the marginal probabilities, means, and variances of jointly distributed random variables easy to compute. However, we can develop formulas in Excel to simplify our efforts. To find marginal probabilities, means, and variances of jointly distributed random variables X and Y using Microsoft Excel, follow the example in Figure 5.8.

Covariance

The *covariance* is a measure of the joint variability for two random variables. The covariance can be used to compute the variance of linear combinations of random variables—such as the variance for the total value for the combination of two stocks in a portfolio. In addition, the covariance is used to compute a standardized measure of joint variability called the correlation. We first develop the definition of the covariance and then present some important applications. Suppose that X and Y are a pair of random variables that are not statistically independent. We would like some measure of the nature and strength of the relationship between them. This is rather difficult to achieve, since the random variables could conceivably be related in any number of ways. To simplify matters, attention is restricted to the possibility of linear

Figure 5.8 Marginal Probabilities, Means, and Variances of X and Y

X Return	Y Return 0%	5%	10%	15%	P(x)	Mean of	Var of X	StDev of
0%	0.0625	0.0625	0.0625	0.0625	0.25	0	0.0014063	
5%	0.0625	0.0625	0.0625	0.0625	0.25	0.0125	0.0001563	
10%	0.0625	0.0625	0.0625	0.0625	0.25	0.025	0.0001563	
15%	0.0625	0.0625	0.0625	0.0625	0.25	0.0375	0.0014063	
P(y)	0.25	0.25	0.25	0.25		0.075	0.003125	0.055902
Mean of Y	0	0.0125	0.025	0.0375	0.075			
Var of Y	0.00140625	0.00015625	0.00015625	0.00140625	0.003125			
StDev of Y					0.055902			

association. For example, a high value of X might be associated, on average, with a high value of Y, and a low value of X with a low value of Y, in such a way that, to a good approximation, a straight line might be drawn through the associated values when plotted on a graph.

Suppose that the random variable X has mean μ_X and Y has mean μ_Y, and consider the product $(X - \mu_X)(Y - \mu_Y)$. If high values of X tend to be associated with high values of Y and low values of X with low values of Y, we would expect this product to be positive, and the stronger the association, the larger the expectation of $(X - \mu_X)(Y - \mu_Y)$, defined as $E[(X - \mu_X)(Y - \mu_Y)]$. By contrast, if high values of X are associated with low values of Y and low X with high Y, the expected value for this product, $E[(X - \mu_X)(Y - \mu_Y)]$, would be negative. An expectation that $E[(X - \mu_X)(Y - \mu_Y)]$ equals 0 would imply an absence of linear association between X and Y. Thus, the expected value, $E[(X - \mu_X)(Y - \mu_Y)]$, will be used as a measure of linear association in the population.

Covariance

Let X be a random variable with mean μ_X, and let Y be a random variable with mean μ_Y. The expected value of $(X - \mu_X)(Y - \mu_Y)$ is called the **covariance** between X and Y, denoted $\text{Cov}(X, Y)$. For discrete random variables

$$\text{Cov}(X, Y) = E[(X - \mu_X)(Y - \mu_Y)] = \sum_x \sum_y (x - \mu_X)(y - \mu_Y)P(x, y) \qquad (5.29)$$

An equivalent expression is

$$\text{Cov}(X, Y) = E[XY] - \mu_X \mu_Y = \sum_x \sum_y xyP(x, y) - \mu_X \mu_Y$$

Correlation

Although the covariance provides an indication of the direction of the relationship between random variables, the covariance does not have an upper or lower bound, and its size is greatly influenced by the scaling of the numbers. A strong linear relationship is defined as a condition where the individual observation points are close to a straight line. It is difficult to use the covariance to provide a measure of the strength of a linear relationship because it is unbounded. A related measure, the correlation coefficient, provides a measure of the strength of the linear relationship between two random variables, with the measure being limited to the range from –1 to +1.

Correlation

Let X and Y be jointly distributed random variables. The **correlation** between X and Y is

$$\rho = \text{Corr}(X, Y) = \frac{\text{Cov}(X, Y)}{\sigma_X \sigma_Y} \qquad (5.30)$$

The correlation is the covariance divided by the standard deviations of the two random variables. This results in a standardized measure of relationship that varies from –1 to +1. The following interpretations are important:

1. A correlation of 0 indicates that there is no linear relationship between the two random variables. If the two random variables are independent, the correlation is equal to 0.
2. A positive correlation indicates that, if one random variable is high (low), then the other random variable has a higher probability of being high (low), and we say that the variables are positively dependent. Perfect positive linear dependency is indicated by a correlation of +1.0.
3. A negative correlation indicates that, if one random variable is high (low), then the other random variable has a higher probability of being low (high), and we say that the variables are negatively dependent. Perfect negative linear dependency is indicated by a correlation of –1.0.

The correlation is more useful for describing relationships than the covariance. With a correlation of +1 the two random variables have a perfect positive linear relationship, and, therefore, a specific value of one variable, X, predicts the other variable, Y, exactly. A correlation of –1 indicates a perfect negative linear relationship between two variables, with one variable, X, predicting the negative of the other variable, Y. A correlation of 0 indicates no linear relationship between the two variables. Intermediate values indicate that variables tend to be related, with stronger relationships occurring as the absolute value of the correlation approaches 1.

We also know that correlation is a term that has moved into common usage. In many cases correlation is used to indicate that a relationship exists. However, variables that have nonlinear relationships will not have a correlation coefficient close to 1.0. This distinction is important for us in order to avoid confusion between correlated random variables and those with nonlinear relationships.

Example 5.16   Joint Distribution of Stock Prices (Compute Covariance and Correlation)

Find the covariance and correlation for the stocks A and B from Example 5.15 with the joint probability distribution in Table 5.6.

Solution   The computation of covariance is tedious for even a problem such as this, which is simplified so that all of the joint probabilities, $P(x, y)$, are 0.0625 for all pairs of values x and y. By definition, you need to find

$$
\begin{aligned}
\text{Cov}(X,Y) &= \sum_x \sum_y xyP(x,y) - \mu_X\mu_Y \\
&= 0[(0)(0.0625) + (0.05)(0.0625) + (0.10)(0.0625) + (0.15)(0.0625)] \\
&\quad + \cdots + (0.15)[(0)(0.0625) + (0.05)(0.0625) + (0.10)(0.0625) \\
&\quad + (0.15)(0.0625)] - (0.075)(0.075) \\
&= 0.005625 - 0.005625 \\
&= 0
\end{aligned}
$$

Thus,

$$\rho = \text{Corr}(X, Y) = \frac{\text{Cov}(X, Y)}{\sigma_X \sigma_Y} = 0$$

Microsoft Excel can be used for these computations by carefully following the example in Figure 5.9.

Figure 5.9 Covariance and Correlation Using Microsoft Excel

X Return	Y Return 0%	5%	10%	15%	P(x)	Mean o	Var of X	StDev of
0%	0.0625	0.0625	0.0625	0.0625	0.25	0	0.0014063	
5%	0.0625	0.0625	0.0625	0.0625	0.25	0.0125	0.0001563	
10%	0.0625	0.0625	0.0625	0.0625	0.25	0.025	0.0001563	
15%	0.0625	0.0625	0.0625	0.0625	0.25	0.0375	0.0014063	
P(y)	0.25	0.25	0.25	0.25		0.075	0.003125	0.055902
Mean of Y	0	0.0125	0.025	0.0375	0.075			
Var of Y	0.00140625	0.00015625	0.00015625	0.00140625	0.003125			
StDev of Y					0.055902			
xyP(x)	0.0000000	0.0009375	0.0018750	0.0028125	0.0056250			
ΣΣ xyP(x)	0.0000000							

Covariance and Statistical Independence

If two random variables are **statistically independent**, the **covariance** between them is 0. However, the converse is not necessarily true.

The reason a covariance of 0 does not necessarily imply statistical independence is that covariance is designed to measure linear association, and it is possible that this quantity may not detect other types of dependency. Suppose that the random variable X has probability function

$$P(-1) = 1/4 \qquad P(0) = 1/2 \qquad P(1) = 1/4$$

Let the random variable Y be defined as

$$Y = X^2$$

Thus, knowledge of the value taken by X implies knowledge of the value taken by Y, and, hence, these two random variables are certainly not independent. Whenever $X = 0$, then $Y = 0$, and if X is either -1 or 1, then $Y = 1$. The joint probability function of X and Y is

$$P(-1, 1) = 1/4 \qquad P(0, 0) = 1/2 \qquad P(1, 1) = 1/4$$

with the probability of any other combination of values being equal to 0. It is then straightforward to verify that

$$E(X) = 0 \qquad E(Y) = 1/2 \qquad E(XY) = 0$$

The covariance between X and Y is 0.

Linear Functions of Random Variables

Previously, the expectation of a function of a single random variable was defined. This definition can now be extended to functions of several random variables.

Expected Value of Functions of Jointly Distributed Random Variables

Let X and Y be a pair of discrete random variables with joint probability function $P(x, y)$. The expectation of any function $g(X, Y)$ of these random variables is defined as

$$E[g(X, Y)] = \sum_x \sum_y g(x, y)P(x, y) \qquad (5.31)$$

To conclude the discussion of joint distributions, consider the mean and variance of a random variable that can be written as the sum or difference of other random variables. These results are summarized below and can be derived using Equation 5.31.

Summary Results for Sums and Differences of Random Variables

Let X and Y be a pair of random variables with means μ_X and μ_Y and variances σ_X^2 and σ_Y^2. The following properties hold:

1. The **expected value of their sum** is the sum of their expected values:

$$E(X + Y) = \mu_X + \mu_Y \qquad (5.32)$$

2. The **expected value of their difference** is the difference between their expected values:

$$E(X - Y) = \mu_X - \mu_Y \qquad (5.33)$$

3. If the covariance between X and Y is 0, the **variance of their sum** is the sum of their variances:

$$\text{Var}(X + Y) = \sigma_X^2 + \sigma_Y^2 \qquad (5.34)$$

but if the covariance is not 0, then

$$\text{Var}(X + Y) = \sigma_X^2 + \sigma_Y^2 + 2\text{Cov}(X, Y)$$

4. If the covariance between X and Y is 0, the **variance of their difference** is the *sum* of their variances:

$$\text{Var}(X - Y) = \sigma_X^2 + \sigma_Y^2 \qquad (5.35)$$

but if the covariance is not 0, then

$$\text{Var}(X - Y) = \sigma_X^2 + \sigma_Y^2 - 2\text{Cov}(X, Y)$$

Let $X_1, X_2, \ldots, X_K$ be K random variables with means $\mu_1, \mu_2, \ldots, \mu_K$ and variances $\sigma_1^2, \sigma_2^2, \ldots, \sigma$. The following properties hold:

5. The expected value of their sum is

$$E(X_1 + X_2 + \cdots + X_K) = \mu_1 + \mu_2 + \cdots + \mu_K \qquad (5.36)$$

6. If the covariance between every pair of these random variables is 0, the variance of their sum is

$$\text{Var}(X_1 + X_2 + \cdots + X_K) = \sigma_1^2 + \sigma_2^2 + \cdots + \sigma_K^2 \qquad (5.37)$$

Example 5.17 Simple Investment Portfolio (Means and Variances, Functions of Random Variables)

An investor has \$1,000 to invest and two investment opportunities, each requiring a minimum of \$500. The profit per \$100 from the first can be represented by a random variable X, having the following probability function:

$$P(X = -5) = 0.4 \quad \text{and} \quad P(X = 20) = 0.6$$

The profit per \$100 from the second is given by the random variable Y, whose probability function is

$$P(Y = 0) = 0.6 \quad \text{and} \quad P(Y = 25) = 0.4$$

Random variables X and Y are independent. The investor has the following possible strategies:

a. \$1,000 in the first investment
b. \$1,000 in the second investment
c. \$500 in each investment

Find the mean and variance of the profit from each strategy.

Solution Random variable X has mean

$$\mu_X = E(X) = \sum_x xP(x) = (-5)(0.4) + (20)(0.6) = \$10$$

and variance

$$\sigma_X^2 = E[(X - \mu_x)^2] = \sum_x (x - \mu_x)^2 P(x)$$

$$= (-5 - 10)^2(0.4) + (20 - 10)^2(0.6) = 150$$

Strategy (a) has mean profit of $E(10X) = 10E(X) = \$100$ and variance of

$$\text{Var}(10X) = 100\text{Var}(X) = 15,000$$

Random variable Y has mean

$$\mu_Y = E(Y) = \sum_Y yP(y) = (0)(0.6) + (25)(0.4) = \$10$$

and variance

$$\sigma_Y^2 = E[(Y - \mu_Y)^2] = \sum_Y (y - \mu_Y)^2 P(y)$$
$$= (0 - 10)^2(0.6) + (25 - 10)^2(0.4) = 150$$

Strategy (b) has mean profit $E(10Y) = 10E(Y) = \$100$ and variance of

$$\mathrm{Var}(10Y) = 100\mathrm{Var}(Y) = 15{,}000$$

Now consider strategy (c): \$500 in each investment. The return from strategy (c) is $5X + 5Y$, which has mean

$$E(5X + 5Y) = E(5X) + E(5Y) = 5E(X) + 5E(Y) = \$100$$

Thus, all three strategies have the same expected profit. However, since X and Y are independent and the covariance is 0, the variance of the return from strategy (c) is

$$\mathrm{Var}(5X + 5Y) = \mathrm{Var}(5X) + \mathrm{Var}(5Y) = 25\mathrm{Var}(X) + 25\mathrm{Var}(Y) = 7{,}500$$

This is smaller than the variances of the other strategies, reflecting the decrease in risk that follows from diversification in an investment portfolio. This investor should certainly prefer strategy (c), since it yields the same expected return as the other two, but with lower risk.

Portfolio Analysis

Investment managers spend considerable effort developing investment portfolios that consist of a set of financial instruments that each have returns defined by a probability distribution model. Portfolios are used to obtain a combined investment that has a given expected return and risk. Stock portfolios with a high risk can be constructed by combining several individual stocks whose values tend to increase or decrease together. With such a portfolio an investor will have either large gains or large losses. Stocks whose values move in opposite directions could be combined to create a portfolio with a more stable value, implying less risk. Decreases in one stock price would be balanced by increases in another stock price.

This process of portfolio construction and analysis is conducted using probability models defined by random variables and probability distribution functions. The mean value of the portfolio is the linear combination of the mean values of the two stocks in the portfolio. The variance of the portfolio value is computed using the sum of the variances and the covariance of the joint distribution of the stock values. We will develop the method using an example with a portfolio consisting of two stocks.

Consider a portfolio that consists of a shares of stock A and b shares of stock B. It is important to be able to find the mean and variance for the market value, W, of a portfolio, where W is the linear function $W = aX + bY$. The mean and variance are derived in the chapter Appendix.

The Mean and Variance for the Market Value of a Portfolio

The random variable X is the price for stock A, and the random variable Y is the price for stock B. The **portfolio market value**, W, is given by the linear function

$$W = aX + bY$$

where a is the number of shares of stock A and b is the number of shares of stock B.

The **mean value for W** is

$$\mu_w = E[W] = E[aX + bY]$$
$$= a\mu_X + b\,\mu_Y \qquad (5.38)$$

The **variance for W** is

$$\sigma_W^2 = a^2\sigma_X^2 + b^2\sigma_Y^2 + 2ab\mathrm{Cov}(X, Y) \qquad (5.39)$$

or, using the correlation,

$$\sigma_W^2 = a^2\sigma_X^2 + b^2\sigma_Y^2 + 2ab\mathrm{Corr}(X, Y)\sigma_X\sigma_Y$$

Example 5.18   Analysis of Stock Portfolios (Means and Variances, Functions of Random Variables)

George Tiao has 5 shares of stock A and 10 shares of stock B, whose price variations are modeled by the probability distribution in Table 5.7. Find the mean and variance of the portfolio.

Table 5.7   Stock A and Stock B Prices

STOCK A PRICE	STOCK B PRICE			
	$40	$50	$60	$70
$45	0.24	0.003333	0.003333	0.003333
$50	0.003333	0.24	0.003333	0.003333
$55	0.003333	0.003333	0.24	0.003333
$60	0.003333	0.003333	0.003333	0.24

Solution   The value, W, of the portfolio can be represented by the linear combination $W = 5X + 10Y$. The mean and variance for stock A are $53 and 31.3, respectively, while for stock B they are $55 and 125, respectively. The covariance is 59.17 and the correlation is 0.947. These results were obtained with Microsoft Excel, using computations similar to those in Figure 5.9.

The mean value for the portfolio is thus

$$\mu_W = E[W] = E[5X + 10Y] = 5(53) + (10)(55) = 815$$

The variance for the portfolio value is

$$\sigma_W^2 = 5^2\sigma_X^2 + 10^2\sigma_Y^2 + 2 \times 5 \times 10 \times \text{Cov}(X, Y)$$
$$= 5^2 \times 31.3 + 10^2 \times 125 + 2 \times 5 \times 10 \times 59.17 = 19{,}199.5$$

George knows that high variance implies high risk. He believes that the risk for this portfolio is too high. Thus, he asks you to prepare a portfolio that has lower risk. After some investigation you discover a different pair of stocks whose prices follow the probability model in Table 5.8.

The mean for stock C is $53, the same as for stock A. Similarly, the mean for stock D is $55, the same as for stock B. Thus, the mean value of the portfolio is not changed.

The variance for each stock is also the same, but the covariance is now –59.17. Thus, the variance for the new portfolio includes a *negative covariance* term and is

$$\sigma_W^2 = 5^2\sigma_X^2 + 10^2\sigma_Y^2 + 2 \times 5 \times 10 \times \text{Cov}(X, Y)$$
$$= 5^2 \times 31.3 + 10^2 \times 125 + 2 \times 5 \times 10 \times (-59.17) = 7{,}365.5$$

We see that the effect of the negative covariance is to reduce the variance and hence to reduce the risk of the portfolio.

Table 5.8   New Portfolio of Stock C and Stock D

STOCK C PRICE	STOCK D PRICE			
	$40	$50	$60	$70
$45	0.003333	0.003333	0.003333	0.24
$50	0.003333	0.003333	0.24	0.003333
$55	0.003333	0.24	0.003333	0.003333
$60	0.24	0.003333	0.003333	0.003333

Figure 5.10
Portfolio Variance
Versus Correlation
of Stock Prices

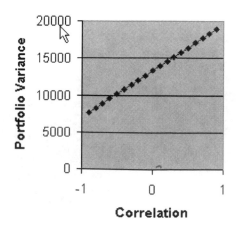

Figure 5.10 shows how portfolio variance, and hence risk, changes with different correlations between stock prices. Note that the portfolio variance is linearly related to the correlation. To help control risk, designers of stock portfolios select stocks based on the correlation between prices.

As seen in Example 5.18, the correlation between stock prices, or between any two random variables, has important effects on the portfolio value random variable. A positive correlation indicates that both prices, X and Y, increase or decrease together. Thus, large or small values of the portfolio are magnified, resulting in greater range and variance compared to a zero correlation. Conversely, a negative correlation leads to price increases for X matched by price decreases for Y. As a result, the range and variance of the portfolio are decreased compared to a zero correlation. By selecting stocks with particular combinations of correlations, fund managers can control the variance and the risk for portfolios.

EXERCISES

Basic Exercises

5.73 Consider the joint probability distribution

		X	
		1	2
Y	0	0.25	0.25
	1	0.25	0.25

a. Compute the marginal probability distributions for X and Y.
b. Compute the covariance and correlation for X and Y.

5.74 Consider the joint probability distribution

		X	
		1	2
Y	0	0.20	0.25
	1	0.30	0.25

a. Compute the marginal probability distributions for X and Y.
b. Compute the covariance and correlation for X and Y.

5.75 Consider the joint probability distribution

		X	
		1	2
Y	0	0.25	0.25
	1	0.25	0.25

a. Compute the marginal probability distributions for X and Y.
b. Compute the covariance and correlation for X and Y.
c. Compute the mean and variance for the linear function $W = X + Y$.

5.76 Consider the joint probability distribution

		X	
		0	1
Y	0	0.30	0.20
	1	0.25	0.25

a. Compute the marginal probability distributions for X and Y.
b. Compute the covariance and correlation for X and Y.
c. Compute the mean and variance for the linear function $W = 2X + Y$.

5.77 Consider the joint probability distribution

		X	
		1	2
Y	0	0.70	0.0
	1	0.0	0.30

a. Compute the marginal probability distributions for X and Y.
b. Compute the covariance and correlation for X and Y.
c. Compute the mean and variance for the linear function $W = 3X + 4Y$.

5.78 Consider the joint probability distribution

		X	
		1	2
Y	0	0.25	0.25
	1	0.25	0.25

a. Compute the marginal probability distributions for X and Y.
b. Compute the covariance and correlation for X and Y.

c. Compute the mean and variance for the linear function $W = X + Y$.

5.79 Consider the joint probability distribution

		X	
		1	2
Y	0	0.30	0.20
	1	0.25	0.25

a. Compute the marginal probability distributions for X and Y.
b. Compute the covariance and correlation for X and Y.
c. Compute the mean and variance for the linear function $W = 2X + Y$.

5.80 Consider the joint probability distribution

		X	
		1	2
Y	0	0.0	0.60
	1	0.40	0.0

a. Compute the marginal probability distributions for X and Y.
b. Compute the covariance and correlation for X and Y.
c. Compute the mean and variance for the linear function $W = 2X - 4Y$.

5.81 Consider the joint probability distribution

		X	
		1	2
Y	0	0.70	0.0
	1	0.0	0.30

a. Compute the marginal probability distributions for X and Y.
b. Compute the covariance and correlation for X and Y.
c. Compute the mean and variance for the linear function $W = 10X - 8Y$.

Application Exercises

5.82 A researcher suspected that the number of between-meal snacks eaten by students in a day during final examinations might depend on the number of tests a student had to take on that day. The accompanying table shows joint probabilities, estimated from a survey.

Number of	Number of Tests (X)			
Snacks (Y)	0	1	2	3
0	0.07	0.09	0.06	0.01
1	0.07	0.06	0.07	0.01
2	0.06	0.07	0.14	0.03
3	0.02	0.04	0.16	0.04

a. Find the probability function of X and hence the mean number of tests taken by students on that day.
b. Find the probability function of Y and hence the mean number of snacks eaten by students on that day.
c. Find and interpret the conditional probability function of Y, given $X = 3$.
d. Find the covariance between X and Y.
e. Are number of snacks and number of tests independent of each other?

5.83 A real estate agent is interested in the relationship between the number of lines in a newspaper advertisement for an apartment and the volume of inquiries from potential renters. Let volume of inquiries be denoted by the random variable X, with the value 0 for little interest, 1 for moderate interest, and 2 for strong interest. The real estate agent estimated the joint probability function shown in the accompanying table.

Number of	Number of Enquiries (X)		
Lines (Y)	0	1	2
3	0.09	0.14	0.07
4	0.07	0.23	0.16
5	0.03	0.10	0.11

a. Find the joint cumulative probability function at $X = 1$, $Y = 4$, and interpret your result.
b. Find and interpret the conditional probability function for Y, given $X = 0$.
c. Find and interpret the conditional probability function for X, given $Y = 5$.
d. Find and interpret the covariance between X and Y.
e. Are number of lines in the advertisement and volume of inquiries independent of one another?

5.84 The accompanying table shows, for credit card holders with one to three cards, the joint probabilities for number of cards owned (X) and number of credit purchases made in a week (Y).

Number of	Number of Purchases in Week (Y)				
Cards (X)	0	1	2	3	4
1	0.08	0.13	0.09	0.06	0.03
2	0.03	0.08	0.08	0.09	0.07
3	0.01	0.03	0.06	0.08	0.08

a. For a randomly chosen person from this group, what is the probability function for number of purchases made in a week?
b. For a person in this group who has three cards, what is the probability function for number of purchases made in the week?
c. Are number of cards owned and number of purchases made statistically independent?

5.85 A market researcher wants to determine whether a new model of a personal computer that had been advertised on a late-night talk show had achieved more brand-name recognition among people who watched the show regularly than among people who did not. After conducting a survey, it was found that 15% of all people both watched the show regularly and could correctly identify the product. Also, 16% of all people regularly watched the show and 45% of all people could correctly identify the product. Define a pair of random variables as follows:

$X = 1$	if regularly watch the show	$X = 0$	otherwise
$Y = 1$	if product correctly identified	$Y = 0$	otherwise

   a. Find the joint probability function of X and Y.
   b. Find the conditional probability function of Y, given $X = 1$.
   c. Find and interpret the covariance between X and Y.

5.86 A college bookseller makes calls at the offices of professors and forms the impression that professors are more likely to be away from their offices on Friday than any other working day. A review of the records of calls, one-fifth of which are on Fridays, indicates that for 16% of Friday calls, the professor is away from the office, while this occurs for only 12% of calls on every other working day. Define the random variables as follows:

$X = 1$	if call is made on a Friday	$X = 0$	otherwise
$Y = 1$	if professor is away from the office	$Y = 0$	otherwise

   a. Find the joint probability function of X and Y.
   b. Find the conditional probability function of Y, given $X = 0$.
   c. Find the marginal probability functions of X and Y.
   d. Find and interpret the covariance between X and Y.

5.87 A restaurant manager receives occasional complaints about the quality of both the food and the service. The marginal probability functions for the number of weekly complaints in each category are shown in the accompanying table. If complaints about food and service are independent of each other, find the joint probability function.

Number of Food Complaints	Probability	Number of Service Complaints	Probability
0	0.12	0	0.18
1	0.29	1	0.38
2	0.42	2	0.34
3	0.17	3	0.10

5.88 Refer to the information in Exercise 5.87. Find the mean and standard deviation of the total number of complaints received in a week. Having reached this point, you are concerned that the numbers of food and service complaints may not be independent of each other. However, you have no information about the nature of their dependence. What can you now say about the mean and standard deviation of the total number of complaints received in a week?

5.89 A company has 5 representatives covering large territories and 10 representatives covering smaller territories. The probability distributions for the numbers of orders received by each of these types of representatives in a day are shown in the accompanying table. Assuming that the number of orders received by any representative is independent of the number received by any other, find the mean and standard deviation of the total number of orders received by the company in a day.

Numbers of Orders (Large Territory)	Probability	Numbers of Orders (Smaller Territory)	Probability
0	0.08	0	0.18
1	0.16	1	0.26
2	0.28	2	0.36
3	0.32	3	0.13
4	0.10	4	0.07
5	0.06		

SUMMARY

In this chapter we have presented discrete probability models. These models are defined by a random variable and by a probability distribution function. We also developed expected values and variances for these models. Three important discrete probability models—the binomial, the Poisson, and the hypergeometric—were developed along with potential applications. Finally, we developed joint discrete probability distributions and indicated how to compute the covariance for these models. We showed how joint probability models can be used to determine the mean and variance for linear combinations of random variables, with particular application to stock portfolios.

KEY WORDS

- Bernoulli random variable mean and variance
- binomial distribution
- conditional probability function
- continuous random variable
- correlation
- covariance
- cumulative probability function
- derivation of the marginal probability function
- differences between random variables
- discrete random variable
- expected value
- expected value of functions of jointly distributed random variables

- expected value for functions of random variables
- hypergeometric distribution
- independence of jointly distributed random variables
- joint probability function
- marginal probability function
- mean
- mean of binomial distribution
- mean of functions of random variables
- Poisson approximation to the binomial distribution
- Poisson probability distribution
- portfolio analysis
- portfolio market value
- probability distribution function
- properties of cumulative probability functions

- properties of joint probability functions
- properties of probability distribution functions
- random variable
- relationship between probability function and cumulative probability function
- standard deviation for a discrete random variable
- sums of random variables
- variance for a binomial distribution
- variance for a discrete random variable
- variance for a discrete random variable (alternate formula)
- variance for functions of random variables

CHAPTER EXERCISES AND APPLICATIONS

5.90 As an investment advisor, you tell a client that an investment in a mutual fund has (over the next year) a higher expected return than an investment in the money market. The client then asks the following questions:

a. Does that imply that the mutual fund will certainly yield a higher return than the money market?

b. Does it follow that I should invest in the mutual fund rather than in the money market?

How would you reply?

5.91 A contractor estimates the probabilities for the number of days required to complete a certain type of construction project as follows:

Time (days)	1	2	3	4	5
Probability	0.05	0.20	0.35	0.30	0.10

a. What is the probability that a randomly chosen project will take less than 3 days to complete?

b. Find the expected time to complete a project.

c. Find the standard deviation of time required to complete a project.

d. The contractor's project cost is made up of two parts—a fixed cost of $20,000, plus $2,000 for each day taken to complete the project. Find the mean and standard deviation of total project cost.

e. If three projects are undertaken, what is the probability that at least two of them will take at least 4 days to complete, assuming independence of individual project completion times?

5.92 A car salesman estimates the following probabilities for the number of cars that he will sell in the next week:

Number of cars	0	1	2	3	4	5
Probability	0.10	0.20	0.35	0.16	0.12	0.07

a. Find the expected number of cars that will be sold in the week.

b. Find the standard deviation of the number of cars that will be sold in the week.

c. The salesman receives for the week a salary of $250, plus an additional $300 for each car sold. Find the mean and standard deviation of his total salary for the week.

d. What is the probability that the salesman's salary for the week will be more than $1,000?

5.93 A multiple-choice test has nine questions. For each question there are four possible answers from which to select. One point is awarded for each correct answer, and points are not subtracted for incorrect answers. The instructor awards a bonus point if the student spells his or her name correctly. A student who has not studied for this test decides to choose at random an answer for each question.

a. Find the expected number of correct answers for the student on these nine questions.

b. Find the standard deviation of the number of correct answers for the student on these nine questions.

c. The student spells his name correctly:

    i. Find the expected total score on the test for this student.

    ii. Find the standard deviation of his total score on the test.

5.94 Develop realistic examples of pairs of random variables for which you would expect to find

    a. Positive covariance.

    b. Negative covariance.

    c. Zero covariance.

5.95 A long-distance taxi service owns four vehicles. These are of different ages and have different repair records. The probabilities that, on any given day, each vehicle will be available for use are 0.95, 0.90, 0.90, and 0.80. Whether one vehicle is available is independent of whether any other vehicle is available.

    a. Find the probability function for the number of vehicles available for use on a given day.

    b. Find the expected number of vehicles available for use on a given day.

    c. Find the standard deviation of the number of vehicles available for use on a given day.

5.96 Students in a college were classified according to years in school (X) and number of visits to a museum in the last year ($Y = 0$ for no visits, 1 for one visit, 2 for more than one visit). The joint probabilities in the accompanying table were estimated for these random variables.

Number of Visits (Y)	Years in School (X)			
	1	2	3	4
0	0.07	0.05	0.03	0.02
1	0.13	0.11	0.17	0.15
2	0.04	0.04	0.09	0.10

    a. Find the probability that a randomly chosen student has not visited a museum in the last year.

    b. Find the means of the random variables X and Y.

    c. Find and interpret the covariance between the random variables X and Y.

5.97 A basketball team's star 3-point shooter takes six 3-point shots in a game. Historically, he makes 40% of all 3-point shots taken in a game. State at the outset what assumptions you have made.

    a. Find the probability that at least two shots will be made.

    b. Find the probability that exactly three shots will be made.

    c. Find the mean and standard deviation of the number of shots made.

    d. Find the mean and standard deviation of the total number of points scored as a result of these shots.

5.98 It is estimated that 55% of the freshmen entering a particular college will graduate from that college in four years.

    a. For a random sample of five entering freshmen, what is the probability that exactly three will graduate in four years?

    b. For a random sample of five entering freshmen, what is the probability that a majority will graduate in four years?

    c. Eighty entering freshmen are chosen at random. Find the mean and standard deviation of the proportion of these 80 that will graduate in four years.

5.99 The World Series of baseball is to be played by team A and team B. The first team to win four games wins the series. Suppose that team A is the better team, in the sense that the probability is 0.6 that team A will win any specific game. Assume also that the result of any game is independent of that of any other.

    a. What is the probability that team A will win the series?

    b. What is the probability that a seventh game will be needed to determine the winner?

    c. Suppose that, in fact, each team wins two of the first four games.

      i. What is the probability that team A will win the series?

      ii. What is the probability that a seventh game will be needed to determine the winner?

5.100 Using detailed cash flow information, a financial analyst claims to be able to spot companies that are likely candidates for bankruptcy. The analyst is presented with information on the past records of 15 companies and told that, in fact, 5 of these have failed. He selects as candidates for failure 5 companies from the group of 15. In fact, 3 of the 5 companies selected by the analyst were among those that failed. Evaluate the financial analyst's performance on this test of his ability to detect failed companies.

5.101 A team of five analysts is about to examine the earnings prospects of 20 corporations. Each of the five analysts will study 4 of the corporations. These analysts are not equally competent. In fact, one of them is a star, having an excellent record of anticipating changing trends. Ideally, management would like to allocate to this analyst the 4 corporations whose earnings will deviate most from past trends. However, lacking this information, management allocates corporations to analysts randomly. What is the probability that at least 2 of the 4 corporations whose earnings will deviate most from past trends are allocated to the star analyst?

Table 5.9   Joint Probability Distribution for Stock Prices

STOCK C PRICE	STOCK D PRICE			
	$40	$50	$60	$70
$45	0.00	0.00	0.05	0.20
$50	0.05	0.00	0.05	0.10
$55	0.10	0.05	0.00	0.05
$60	0.20	0.10	0.05	0.00

Table 5.10   Joint Distribution of Automobile and Steel Prices

PRICE OF STEEL (Y)	PRICE OF AUTOMOBILES (X)		
	$3	$4	$5
$4	0.10	0.15	0.05
$6	0.10	0.20	0.10
$8	0.05	0.15	0.10

5.102 On average, 2.4 customers per minute arrive at an airline check-in desk during the peak period. Assume that the distribution of arrivals is Poisson.

   a. What is the probability that there will be no arrivals in a minute?
   b. What is the probability that there will be more than three arrivals in a minute?

5.103 A recent estimate suggested that, of all individuals and couples reporting income in excess of $200,000, 6.5% either paid no federal tax or paid tax at an effective rate of less than 15%. A random sample of 100 of those reporting income in excess of $200,000 was taken. What is the probability that more than 2 of the sample members either paid no federal tax or paid tax at an effective rate of less than 15%.

5.104 A company has two assembly lines, each of which stalls an average of 2.4 times per week according to a Poisson distribution. Assume that the performances of these assembly lines are independent of one another. What is the probability that at least one line stalls at least once in any given week?

5.105 George Allen has asked you to analyze his stock portfolio, which contains 10 shares of stock D and 5 shares of stock C. The joint probability distribution of the stock prices is shown in Table 5.9. Compute the mean and variance for the total value of his stock portfolio.

5.106 Consider a country that imports steel and exports automobiles. The value per unit of cars exported is measured in units of thousands of dollars per car by the random variable X. The value per unit of steel imported is measured in units of thousands of dollars per ton of steel by the random variable Y. Suppose that the country annually exports 10 cars and 5 tons of steel. Compute the mean and variance of the trade balance where the trade balance is the total dollars received for all cars exported minus the total dollars spent for all steel imported. The joint probability distribution for the prices of cars and steel is shown in Table 5.10.

Appendix: Verifications

1. VERIFICATION OF AN ALTERNATIVE FORMULA FOR THE VARIANCE OF A DISCRETE RANDOM VARIABLE (EQUATION 5.6)

Begin with the original definition of variance:

$$\sigma_X^2 = \sum_x (x - \mu_X)^2 P(x) = \sum_x (x^2 - 2\mu_X x + \mu_X^2) P(x)$$
$$= \sum_x x^2 P(x) - 2\mu_X \sum_x x P(x) + \mu_X^2 \sum_x P(x)$$

But we have seen that

$$\sum_x x P(x) = \mu_X \quad \text{and} \quad \sum_x P(x) = 1$$

Thus

$$\sigma_X^2 = \sum_x x^2 P(x) - 2\mu_X^2 + \mu_X^2$$

and, finally,

$$\sigma_X^2 = \sum_x x^2 P(x) - \mu_X^2$$

2. VERIFICATION OF THE MEAN AND VARIANCE OF A LINEAR FUNCTION OF A RANDOM VARIABLE (EQUATIONS 5.8 AND 5.9)

It follows from the definition of expectation that if Y takes the values $a + bx$ with probabilities $P_X(x)$, its mean is

$$E(Y) = \mu_Y = \sum_x (a + bx)P(x)$$
$$= a \sum_x P(x) + b \sum_x xP(x)$$

Then, since the first summation on the right-hand side of this equation is 1 and the second summation is the mean of X, we have

$$E(Y) = a + b\mu_X \qquad \text{as in Equation 5.8}$$

Further, the variance of Y is, by definition,

$$\sigma_Y^2 = E[(Y - \mu_Y)^2] = \sum_X [(a + bx) - \mu_Y]^2 P(x)$$

Substituting $a + b\mu_X$ for μ_Y then gives

$$\sigma_Y^2 = \sum_X (bx - b\mu_X)^2 P(x) = b^2 \sum_X (x - \mu_X)^2 P(x)$$

Since the summation on the right-hand side of this equation is, by definition, the variance of X, the result in Equation 5.9 follows:

$$\sigma_Y^2 = \text{Var}(a + bX) = b^2 \sigma_X^2$$

3. VERIFICATION OF THE MEAN AND VARIANCE OF THE BINOMIAL DISTRIBUTION (EQUATIONS 5.19 AND 5.20)

To find the mean and variance of the binomial distribution, it is convenient to return to the Bernoulli distribution. Consider n independent trials, each with probability of success P, and let $X_i = 1$ if the ith trial results in success and 0 otherwise. The random variables $X_1, X_2, \ldots, X_n$ are therefore n independent Bernoulli variables, each with probability of success P. Moreover, the total number of successes X is

$$X = X_1 + X_2 + \cdots + X_n$$

Thus, the binomial random variable can be expressed as the sum of independent Bernoulli random variables.

The mean and the variance for Bernoulli random variables can be used to find the mean and variance of the binomial distribution. Using Equation 5.15, we know that

$$E(X_i) = P \quad \text{and} \quad \sigma_{xi}^2 = P(1-P) \quad \text{for all } i = 1, 2, \ldots, n$$

Then, for the binomial distribution

$$E(X) = E(X_1 + X_2 + \cdots + X_n) = E(X_1) + E(X_2) + \cdots + E(X_n) = nP$$

Since the Bernoulli random variables are independent, the covariance between any pair of them is zero, and

$$\begin{aligned}
\sigma_X^2 &= \sigma^2(X_1 + X_2 + \cdots + X_n) \\
&= \sigma^2(X_1) + \sigma^2(X_2) + \cdots + \sigma^2(X_n) \\
&= nP(1-P)
\end{aligned}$$

4. VERIFICATION OF THE MEAN AND VARIANCE OF THE MARKET VALUE, *W*, OF A PORTFOLIO (EQUATIONS 5.38 AND 5.39)

You are given a linear combination, W, of random variables X and Y, where $W = aX + bY$ and a and b are constants. The mean of W is

$$\begin{aligned}
\mu_W &= E[W] = E[aX + bY] \\
&= a\,\mu_X + b\,\mu_Y
\end{aligned}$$

and the variance of W is

$$\begin{aligned}
\sigma_W^2 &= E[(W - \mu_W)^2] \\
&= E[((aX + bY) - (a\mu_X + b\mu_Y))^2] \\
&= E[(a(X - \mu_X) + b(Y - \mu_Y))^2] \\
&= E[a^2(X - \mu_X)^2 + b^2(Y - \mu_Y)^2 + 2ab(X - \mu_X)(Y - \mu_Y)] \\
&= a^2 E[(X - \mu_X)^2] + b^2 E[(Y - \mu_Y)^2] + 2ab E[(X - \mu_X)(Y - \mu_Y)] \\
&= a^2 \sigma_X^2 + b^2 \sigma_Y^2 + 2ab\,\mathrm{Cov}(X, Y)
\end{aligned}$$

Topic 7

Continuous Random Variables and Probability Distributions

Chapter 6

Continuous Random Variables and Probability Distributions

Introduction

In Chapter 5 we developed discrete random variables and probability distributions. Here, we extend the probability concepts to continuous random variables and probability distributions. The concepts and insights for discrete random variables also apply to continuous random variables, so we are building directly on the previous chapter. Many economic and business measures such as sales, investment, consumption, costs, and revenues can be represented by continuous random variables. In addition, measures of time, distance, temperature, and weight fit into this category. Probability statements for continuous random variables are specified over ranges. The probability that sales are between 140 and 190 or greater than 200 is a typical example. Mathematical theory leads us to conclude that, in reality, random variables for all applied problems are discrete because measurements are rounded to some value. But for us the important fact is that continuous random variables and probability distributions provide good approximations for many applied problems. Thus, these models are very important and provide excellent tools for business and economic applications.

6.1 CONTINUOUS RANDOM VARIABLES

Here, we again define X as a random variable and x as a specific value of the random variable. We begin by defining the *cumulative distribution function*. Then we will define the probability density function, which is analogous to the probability distribution function used for discrete random variables.

> ### Cumulative Distribution Function
> The **cumulative distribution function**, $F(x)$, for a continuous random variable X expresses the probability that X does not exceed the value of x, as a function of x
>
> $$F(x) = P(X \le x) \tag{6.1}$$

We illustrate the cumulative distribution function by using a simple probability structure. Consider a gasoline station that has a 1,000-gallon storage tank that is filled each morning at the start of the business day. Analysis of past history indicates that it is not possible to predict the amount of gasoline sold on any particular day, but the lower limit is 0 and the upper limit is, of course, 1,000 gallons, the size of the tank. In addition, past history indicates that any demand in the interval from 1 to 1,000 gallons is equally likely. The random variable X indicates the gasoline sales in gallons for a particular day. We are concerned with the probability of various levels of daily gasoline sales, where the probability of a specific number of gallons sold is the same over the range from 0 to 1,000 gallons. The distribution of X is said to follow a **uniform probability distribution**, and the cumulative distribution is

$$F(x) = \begin{cases} 0 & \text{if} \cdots x < 0 \\ 0.001x & \text{if} \cdots 0 \le x \le 1{,}000 \\ 1 & \text{if} \cdots x > 1{,}000 \end{cases}$$

This function is graphed as a straight line between 0 and 1,000, as shown in Figure 6.1. From this we see that the probability of sales between 0 and 400 gallons is

$$P(X \le 400) = F(400) = (0.001)(400) = 0.40$$

To obtain the probability that a continuous random variable X falls in a specified range, we find the difference between the cumulative probability at the upper end of the range and the cumulative probability at the lower end of the range.

> ### Probability of a Range Using a Cumulative Distribution Function
> Let X be a continuous random variable with a cumulative distribution function $F(x)$, and let a and b be two possible values of X, with $a < b$. The **probability that X lies between a and b** is
>
> $$P(a < X < b) = F(b) - F(a) \tag{6.2}$$

Figure 6.1
Cumulative Distribution Function for a Random Variable over 0 to 1,000 with a Uniform Probability Distribution

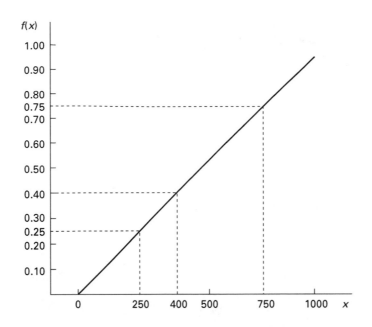

For continuous random variables, it does not matter whether we write "less than" or "less than or equal to" because the probability that X is precisely equal to b is 0.

For the random variable that is distributed uniformly in the range 0 to 1,000, the cumulative distribution function in that range is $F(x) = 0.001x$. Therefore, if a and b are two numbers between 0 and 1,000 with $a < b$,

$$P(a < X < b) = F(b) - F(a) = 0.001(b - a)$$

For example, the probability of sales between 250 and 750 gallons is

$$P(250 < X < 750) = (0.001)(750) - (0.001)(250) = 0.75 - 0.25 = 0.50$$

as shown in Figure 6.1.

We have seen that the probability that a continuous random variable lies between any two values can be expressed in terms of its cumulative distribution function. This function therefore contains all the information about the probability structure of the random variable. However, for many purposes a different function is more useful. In Chapter 5 we discussed the probability function for discrete random variables, which expresses the probability that a discrete random variable takes any specific value. Since the probability of a specific value is 0 for continuous random variables, that concept is not directly relevant here. However, a related function, called the *probability density function*, can be constructed for continuous random variables, allowing for graphical interpretation of their probability structure.

Probability Density Function
Let X be a continuous random variable, and let x be any number lying in the range of values this random variable can take. The **probability**

density function, $f(x)$, of the random variable is a function with the following properties:

1. $f(x) > 0$ for all values of x.
2. The area under the probability density function, $f(x)$, over all values of the random variable, X, is equal to 1.0.
3. Suppose that this density function is graphed. Let a and b be two possible values of random variable X, with $a < b$. Then the probability that X lies between a and b is the area under the density function between these points.
4. The cumulative distribution function, $F(x_0)$, is the area under the probability density function, $f(x)$, up to x_0:

$$F(x_0) = \int_{x_m}^{x_0} f(x)\, dx$$

where x_m is the minimum value of the random variable X.

The probability density function can be approximated by a discrete probability distribution with many discrete values close together, as seen in Figure 6.2.

Figure 6.3 shows the plot of an arbitrary probability density function for some continuous random variable. Two possible values, a and b, are shown, and the shaded area under the curve between these points is the probability that the random variable lies in the interval between them (see the Chapter Appendix).

Figure 6.2   Approximation of a Probability Density Function by a Discrete Probability Distribution

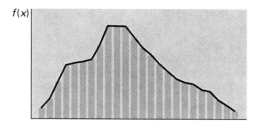
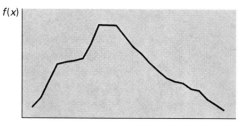

Figure 6.3
Shaded Area Is
·the Probability
That X Is Between
a and b

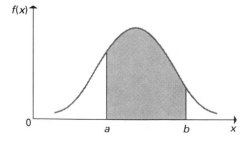

Figure 6.4
Properties of
the Probability
Density Function

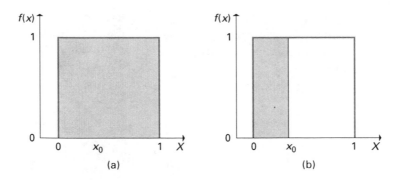

These results are shown in Figure 6.4, with Figure 6.4(a) showing that the entire area under the probability density function is equal to 1 and Figure 6.4(b) indicating the area to the left of x_0.

The Uniform Distribution

Now, we consider a probability density function that represents a probability distribution over the range of 0 to 1. Figure 6.5 is a graph of the uniform probability density function. This is the probability density function for the gasoline sales example. Since the probability is the same for any interval of the sales range from 0 to 1, we deduce that the probability density function is constant over the range from 0 to 1,000 and can be defined as the uniform probability density function, which can be written as

$$f(x) = \begin{cases} 0.001 & \text{if } 0 \le x \le 1{,}000 \\ 0 & \text{else} \end{cases}$$

For any uniform random variable defined over the range from a to b, the probability density function is

$$f(x) = \begin{cases} \dfrac{1}{b-a} & \text{if } a \le x \le b \\ 0 & \text{else} \end{cases}$$

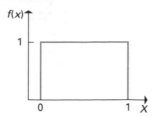

Figure 6.5 Probability Density Function for a Uniform Random Variable over 0 to 1

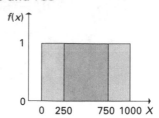

Figure 6.6 Density Function Showing the Probability That X Is Between 250 and 750

This probability density function can be used to find the probability that the random variable falls within a specific range. For example, the probability that sales are between 250 gallons and 750 gallons is shown in Figure 6.6. Since the height of the density function is $f(x) = 0.001$, the area under the curve between 250 and 750 is equal to 0.50, which is the required probability. Note that this is the same result obtained previously using the cumulative probability function.

We have seen that the probability that a random variable lies between a pair of values is the area under the probability density function between these two values. There are two important results worth noting. The area under the entire probability density function is 1, and the cumulative probability, $F(x_0)$, is the area under the density function to the left of x_0.

Example 6.1 Probability of Pipeline Failure (Cumulative Distribution Function)

A repair team is responsible for a stretch of oil pipeline 2 miles long. The distance (in miles) at which any fracture occurs can be represented by a uniformly distributed random variable, with probability density function

$$f(x) = 0.5$$

Find the cumulative distribution function and the probability that any given fracture occurs between 0.5 mile and 1.5 miles along this stretch of pipeline.

Solution Figure 6.7 shows a plot of the probability density function, with the shaded area indicating $F(x_0)$, the cumulative distribution function evaluated at x_0. Thus, we see that

$$F(x_0) = 0.5x_0 \quad \text{for } 0 < x_0 < 2$$

The probability that a fracture occurs between 0.5 mile and 1.5 miles along the pipe is

$$P(0.5 < X < 1.5) = F(1.5) - F(0.5)$$

$$= (0.5)(1.5) - (0.5)(0.5) = 0.5$$

This is the area under the probability density function from $x = 0.5$ to $x = 1.5$.

Figure 6.7 Probability Density Function for Example 6.1

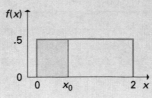

EXERCISES

Basic Exercises

6.1 Using the uniform probability density function shown in Figure 6.7, find the probability that the random variable X is between 1.4 and 1.8.

6.2 Using the uniform probability density function shown in Figure 6.7, find the probability that the random variable X is between 1.0 and 1.9.

6.3 Using the uniform probability density function shown in Figure 6.7, find the probability that the random variable X is less than 1.4.

6.4 Using the uniform probability density function shown in Figure 6.7, find the probability that the random variable X is greater than 1.3.

Application Exercises

6.5 An analyst has available two forecasts, F_1 and F_2, of earnings per share of a corporation next year. He intends to form a compromise forecast as a weighted average of the two individual forecasts. In forming the compromise forecast, weight X will be given to the first forecast and weight $(1 - X)$ to the second, so that the compromise forecast is $XF_1 + (1 - X)F_2$. The analyst wants to choose a value between 0 and 1 for the weight X, but he is quite uncertain of what will be the best choice. Suppose that what eventually emerges as the best possible choice of the weight X can be viewed as a random variable uniformly distributed between 0 and 1, having probability density function

$$f(x) = \begin{cases} 1 & \text{for } 0 \le x \le 1 \\ 0 & \text{for all other values of } x \end{cases}$$

a. Draw the probability density function.
b. Find and draw the cumulative distribution function.
c. Find the probability that the best choice of the weight X is less than 0.25.
d. Find the probability that the best choice of the weight X is more than 0.75.
e. Find the probability that the best choice of the weight X is between 0.2 and 0.8.

6.6 The jurisdiction of a rescue team includes emergencies occurring on a stretch of river that is 4 miles long.

Experience has shown that the distance along this stretch, measured in miles from its northernmost point, at which an emergency occurs can be represented by a uniformly distributed random variable over the range 0 to 4 miles. Then, if X denotes the distance (in miles) of an emergency from the northernmost point of this stretch of river, its probability density function is

$$f(x) = \begin{cases} 0.25 & \text{for } 0 < x < 4 \\ 0 & \text{for all other } x \end{cases}$$

a. Draw the probability density function.
b. Find and draw the cumulative distribution function.
c. Find the probability that a given emergency arises within 1 mile of the northernmost point of this stretch of river.
d. The rescue team's base is at the midpoint of this stretch of river. Find the probability that a given emergency arises more than 1.5 miles from this base.

6.7 The incomes of all families in a particular suburb can be represented by a continuous random variable. It is known that the median income for all families in this suburb is $60,000 and that 40% of all families in the suburb have incomes above $72,000.

a. For a randomly chosen family, what is the probability that its income will be between $60,000 and $72,000?
b. Given no further information, what can be said about the probability that a randomly chosen family has an income below $65,000?

6.8 At the beginning of winter, a homeowner estimates that the probability is 0.4 that her total heating bill for the three winter months will be less than $380. She also estimates that the probability is 0.6 that the total bill will be less than $460.

a. What is the probability that the total bill will be between $380 and $460?
b. Given no further information, what can be said about the probability that the total bill will be less than $400?

6.2 EXPECTATIONS FOR CONTINUOUS RANDOM VARIABLES

In Section 5.2 we presented the concepts of expected value of a discrete random variable and the expected value of a function of that random variable. Here, we will extend those ideas to continuous random variables. Because the probability of any specific value is 0 for a continuous random variable, we need to use Equation 6.3.

Rationale for Expectations of Continuous Random Variables

Suppose that a random experiment leads to an outcome that can be represented by a continuous random variable. If N independent replications of this experiment are carried out, then the **expected value** of the random variable is the average of the values taken, as the number of replications becomes infinitely large. The expected value of a random variable is denoted by $E(X)$.

Similarly, if $g(X)$ is any function of the random variable X, then the expected value of this function is the average value taken by the function over repeated independent trials, as the number of trials becomes infinitely large. This expectation is denoted $E[g(X)]$.

By using calculus we can define expected values for continuous random variables similar to those used for discrete random variables:

$$E[g(x)] = \int_x g(x)f(x)\,dx \tag{6.3}$$

These concepts can be clearly presented if one understands integral calculus, as shown in the chapter Appendix. Using Equation 6.3, we can obtain the mean and variance for continuous random variables. Equations 6.4 and 6.5 present the mean and variance for continuous random variables.

Mean, Variance, and Standard Deviation for Continuous Random Variables

Let X be a continuous random variable. There are two important expected values that are used routinely to define continuous probability distributions.

1. The **mean of X**, denoted by μ_X, is defined as the expected value of X:

$$\mu_X = E(X) \tag{6.4}$$

2. The **variance of X**, denoted by σ_X^2, is defined as the expectation of the squared deviation, $(X - \mu_X)^2$, of the random variable from its mean:

$$\sigma_X^2 = E[(X - \mu_X)^2] \tag{6.5}$$

or an alternative expression can be derived:

$$\sigma_X^2 = E(X^2) - \mu_X^2 \tag{6.6}$$

The **standard deviation of X**, σ_X, is the square root of the variance.

The mean and variance provide two important pieces of summary information about a probability distribution. The mean provides a measure of the center of the distribution. Consider a physical interpretation as follows: Cut out the graph of a probability density function. The point along the x-axis at which the figure exactly balances on one's finger is the mean of the distribution. For example, in Figure 6.4 the uniform distribution is symmetric about $x = 0.5$, and, thus, $\mu_X = 0.5$ is the mean of the random variable.

The variance—or its square root, the standard deviation—provides a measure of the dispersion or spread of a distribution. Thus, if we compare two uniform distributions with the same mean, $\mu_X = 1$—one over the range 0.5 to 1.5 and the other over the range 0 to 2—we will find that the latter has a larger variance because it is spread over a greater range.

For a *uniform distribution* defined over the range from a to b, we have the following results:

$$f(x) = \frac{1}{b-a}$$
$$a \leq X \leq b$$

$$\mu_x = E[X] = \frac{a+b}{2}$$

$$\sigma_x^2 = E[(X - \mu_x)^2] = \frac{(b-a)^2}{12}$$

In Section 5.3 we showed how to obtain the means and variances of linear functions of discrete random variables. The results are the same for continuous random variables because the derivations make use of the expected value operator. The summary results from Chapter 5 are repeated here.

Linear Functions of Random Variables

Let X be a continuous random variable with mean μ_X and variance σ_X^2, and let a and b be any constant fixed numbers. Define the random variable W as

$$W = a + bX$$

Then the mean and variance of W are

$$\mu_W = E(a + bX) = a + b\mu_X \tag{6.7}$$

and

$$\sigma_W^2 = \text{Var}(a + bX) = b^2 \sigma_X^2 \tag{6.8}$$

and the standard deviation of W is

$$\sigma_W = |b| \sigma_X \tag{6.9}$$

An important special case of these results is the standardized random variable

$$Z = \frac{X - \mu_X}{\sigma_X} \tag{6.10}$$

which has mean 0 and variance 1.

Example 6.2   Home Heating Costs (Mean and Standard Deviation)

A homeowner estimates that within the range of likely temperatures her January heating bill, Y, in dollars, will be

$$Y = 290 - 5T$$

where T is the average temperature for the month, in degrees Fahrenheit. If the average January temperature can be represented by a random variable with mean 24 and standard deviation 4, find the mean and standard deviation of this homeowner's January heating bill.

Solution   The random variable T has mean $\mu_T = 24$ and standard deviation $\sigma_T = 4$. Therefore, the expected heating bill is

$$\mu_Y = 290 - 5\,\mu_T$$
$$= 290 - (5)(24) = \$170$$

The standard deviation is

$$\sigma_Y = |-5|\,\sigma_T = (5)(4) = \$20$$

EXERCISES

Basic Exercises

6.9 The total cost for a production process is equal to $1,000 plus 2 times the number of units produced. The mean and variance for the number of units produced are 500 and 900, respectively. Find the mean and variance of the total cost.

6.10 The profit for a production process is equal to $1,000 minus 2 times the number of units produced. The mean and variance for the number of units produced are 50 and 90, respectively. Find the mean and variance of the profit.

6.11 The profit for a production process is equal to $2,000 minus 2 times the number of units produced. The mean and variance for the number of units produced are 500 and 900, respectively. Find the mean and variance of the profit.

6.12 The profit for a production process is equal to $6,000 minus 3 times the number of units produced. The mean and variance for the number of units produced are 1,000 and 900, respectively. Find the mean and variance of the profit.

Application Exercises

6.13 An author receives from a publisher a contract, according to which she is to be paid a fixed sum of $10,000 plus $1.50 for each copy of her book sold. Her uncertainty about total sales of the book can be represented by a random variable with mean 30,000

and standard deviation 8,000. Find the mean and standard deviation of the total payments she will receive.

6.14 A contractor submits a bid on a project, for which more research and development work needs to be done. It is estimated that the total cost of satisfying the project specifications will be $20 million plus the cost of the further research and development work. The contractor views the cost of this work as a random variable with mean $4 million and standard deviation $1 million. The contractor wishes to submit a bid such that his expected profit will be 10% of his expected costs. What should be the bid? If this bid is accepted, what will be the standard deviation of the profit made by the project?

6.15 A charitable organization solicits donations by telephone. Employees are paid $60 plus 20% of the money their calls generate each week. The amount of money generated in a week can be viewed as a random variable with mean $700 and standard deviation $130. Find the mean and standard deviation of an employee's total pay in a week.

6.16 A salesman receives an annual salary of $6,000 plus 8% of the value of the orders he takes. The annual value of these orders can be represented by a random variable with mean $600,000 and standard deviation $180,000. Find the mean and standard deviation of the salesman's annual income.

6.3 THE NORMAL DISTRIBUTION

In this section we present the normal probability distribution, which is the continuous random variable probability distribution used most often for economics and business applications. An example of the normal probability density function is shown in Figure 6.8.

There are many reasons for its wide application.

1. The normal distribution closely approximates the probability distributions of a wide range of random variables. For example, the dimensions of parts and the weights of food packages often follow a normal distribution. This leads to quality control applications. Total sales or production often follows a normal distribution, which leads us to a large family of applications in marketing and production management. The patterns of stock and bond prices are often modeled using the normal distribution in large computer-based financial trading models. Economic models use the normal distribution for a number of economic measures.
2. Distributions of sample means approach a normal distribution, given a "large" sample size.
3. Computation of probabilities is direct and elegant.
4. The most important reason is that the normal probability distribution has led to good business decisions for a number of applications.

A formal definition of the normal probability density function is given by Equation 6.11.

Probability Density Function of the Normal Distribution

The **probability density function for a normally distributed random variable X** is

$$f(x) = \frac{1}{\sqrt{2\pi\sigma^2}}\, e^{-(x-\mu)^2/2\sigma^2} \quad \text{for } -\infty < x < \infty \tag{6.11}$$

where μ and σ^2 are any numbers such that $-\infty < \mu < \infty$ and $0 < \sigma^2 < \infty$ and where e and π are physical constants, $e = 2.71828\ldots$ and $\pi = 3.14159\ldots$.

The normal probability distribution represents a large family of distributions, each with a unique specification for the parameters μ and σ^2. These parameters have a very convenient interpretation.

Figure 6.8
Probability
Density Function
for a Normal
Distribution

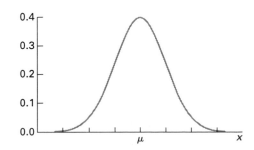

Properties of the Normal Distribution

Suppose that the random variable X follows a normal distribution with parameters μ and σ^2. Then the following properties hold:

1. The mean of the random variable is μ:

$$E(X) = \mu$$

2. The variance of the random variable is σ^2:

$$Var(X) = E[(X - \mu)^2] = \sigma^2$$

3. The shape of the probability density function is a symmetric bell-shaped curve centered on the mean, μ, as shown in Figure 6.8.
4. If we know the mean and variance, we can define the normal distribution by using the notation

$$X \sim N(\mu, \sigma^2)$$

For our applied statistical analyses the normal distribution has a number of important characteristics. It is symmetric. Different central tendencies are indicated by differences in μ. In contrast, differences in σ^2 result in density functions of different widths. By selecting values for μ and σ^2 we can define a large family of normal probability density functions. Differences in the mean result in shifts of entire distributions. In contrast, differences in the variance result in distributions with different widths.

The distribution mean provides a measure of central location, and the variance gives a measure of dispersion about the mean. Thus, the parameters μ and σ^2 have different effects on the probability density function of a normal random variable. Figure 6.9(a) shows probability density functions for two normal distributions with a common variance and different means. We see that increases in the mean shift the distribution without changing its shape. In Figure 6.9(b) the two density functions have the same mean but different variances. Each is symmetric about the common mean, but the larger variance results in a wider distribution.

Our next task is to learn how to obtain probabilities for a specified normal distribution. First, we introduce the *cumulative distribution function*.

Figure 6.9 Effects of μ and σ^2 on the Probability Density Function of a Normal Random Variable:

a. Two Normal Distributions with Different Means
b. Two Normal Distributions with Different Variances and Mean = 5

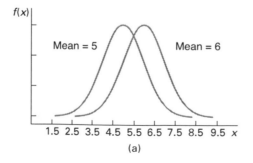

(a)

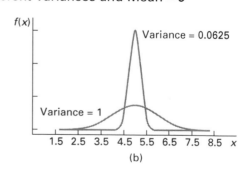

(b)

Cumulative Distribution Function of the Normal Distribution

Suppose that X is a normal random variable with mean μ and variance σ^2; that is, $X \sim N(\mu, \sigma^2)$. Then the cumulative distribution function is

$$F(x_0) = P(X \le x_0)$$

This is the area under the normal probability density function to the left of x_0, as illustrated in Figure 6.10. As for any proper density function, the total area under the curve is 1; that is,

$$F(\infty) = 1$$

Figure 6.10 The Shaded Area Is the Probability That X Does Not Exceed x_0 for a Normal Random Variable

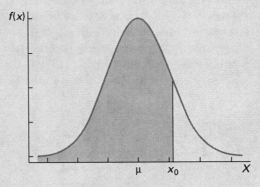

We do not have a simple algebraic expression for calculating the cumulative distribution function for a normally distributed random variable (see the chapter Appendix). The general shape of the cumulative distribution function is shown in Figure 6.11. Equation 6.12 is used to compute normal probabilities using the cumulative distribution function.

Figure 6.11 Cumulative Distribution for a Normal Random Variable

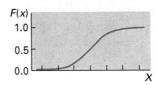

Range Probabilities for Normal Random Variables

Let X be a normal random variable with cumulative distribution function $F(x)$, and let a and b be two possible values of X, with $a < b$. Then

$$P(a < X < b) = F(b) - F(a) \tag{6.12}$$

The probability is the area under the corresponding probability density function between a and b, as shown in Figure 6.12.

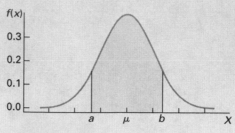

Figure 6.12   Normal Density Function with the Shaded Area Indicating the Probability That *X* Is Between *a* and *b*

Any probability can be obtained from the cumulative distribution function. However, we do not have a convenient way to directly compute the probability for any normal distribution with a specific mean and variance. We could use numerical integration procedures with a computer, but that approach would be tedious and cumbersome. Fortunately, we can convert any normal distribution to a *standard normal distribution* with mean 0 and variance 1.

The Standard Normal Distribution

Let *Z* be a normal random variable with mean 0 and variance 1; that is,

$$Z \sim N(0,1)$$

We say that *Z* follows the **standard normal distribution.**

Denote the cumulative distribution function as *F(z)* and *a* and *b* as two numbers with *a < b*; then

$$P(a < Z < b) = F(b) - F(a) \tag{6.13}$$

We can obtain probabilities for any normally distributed random variable by first converting the random variable to the standard normally distributed random variable, Z. There is always a direct relationship between any normally distributed random variable and Z. That relationship uses the transformation

$$Z = \frac{X - \mu}{\sigma}$$

where X is a normally distributed random variable:

$$X \sim N(\mu, \sigma^2)$$

This important result allows us to use the standard normal table to compute probabilities associated with any normally distributed random variable. Now let us see how probabilities can be computed for the standard normal Z.

The cumulative distribution function of the standard normal distribution is tabulated in Table 1 in the Appendix. This table gives values of

$$F(z) = P(Z \leq z)$$

Figure 6.13 Standard Normal Distribution with Probability for $Z = 1.25$

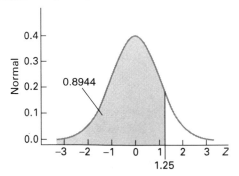

Figure 6.14 Standard Normal Distribution for Negative Z Equal to -1

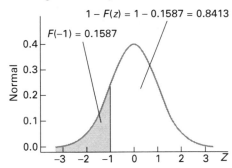

for non-negative values of z. For example, the cumulative probability for a Z value of 1.25 from Table 1 is

$$F(1.25) = 0.8944$$

This is the area, designated in Figure 6.13, for Z less than 1.25. Because of the symmetry of the normal distribution, the probability that $Z > -1.25$ is also equal to 0.8944. In general, values of the cumulative distribution function for negative values of Z can be inferred using the symmetry of the probability density function.

To find the cumulative probability for a negative Z (for example, $Z = -1.0$) defined as

$$F(-Z_0) = P(Z \le -z_0) = F(-1.0)$$

we use the complement of the probability for $Z = +1$, as shown in Figure 6.14.

From the symmetry we can state that

$$F(-Z) = 1 - P(Z \le +Z) = 1 - F(Z)$$
$$F(-1) = 1 - P(Z \le +1) = 1 - F(1)$$

Figure 6.15 indicates the symmetry for the corresponding positive values of Z.

In Figure 6.16 we can see that the area under the curve to the left of $Z = -1$ is equal to the area to the right of $Z = +1$ because of the symmetry of the normal distribution. The area substantially below $-Z$ is often called the "lower tail," and the area substantially above $+Z$ is called the "upper tail."

Figure 6.15 Standard Normal Distribution for Positive Z Equal to $+1$

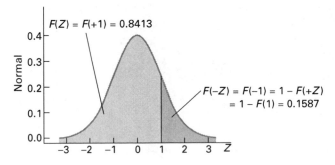

Figure 6.16 Normal Density Function with Symmetric Upper and Lower Values

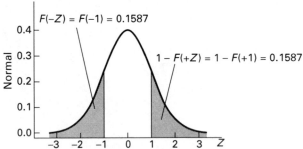

We can also use normal tables that provide probabilities for just the upper half or positive Z values from the normal distribution. An example of this type of table is shown inside the front cover of this textbook. This form of the normal table is used to find probabilities the same as those above. With positive Z values we add 0.50 to the values given in the table inside the front cover of the textbook. With negative values of Z we utilize the symmetry of the normal to obtain the desired probabilities.

Example 6.3   Investment Portfolio Value Probabilities (Normal Probabilities)

A client has an investment portfolio whose mean value is equal to $500,000, with a standard deviation of $15,000. She has asked you to determine the probability that the value of her portfolio is between $485,000 and $530,000.

Solution   The problem is illustrated in Figure 6.17. To solve the problem, we must first determine the corresponding Z values for the portfolio limits. For $485,000 the corresponding Z value is

$$z_{485} = \frac{485,000 - 500,000}{15,000} = -1.0$$

And for the upper value, $530,000, the Z value is

$$z_{530} = \frac{530,000 - 500,000}{15,000} = +2.0$$

As shown in Figure 6.17, the probability that the portfolio value, X, is between $485,000 and $530,000 is equal to the probability that Z is between -1 and $+2$. To obtain the probability, we first compute the probabilities for the lower and the upper tails and subtract these probabilities from 1. Algebraically, the result is

$$P(485,000 \leq X \leq 530,000) = P(-1 \leq Z \leq +2) = 1 - P(Z \leq -1) - P(Z \geq +2)$$
$$= 1 - 0.1587 - 0.0228 = 0.8185$$

The probability for the indicated range is thus 0.8185.

Figure 6.17   Normal Distribution for Example 6.3

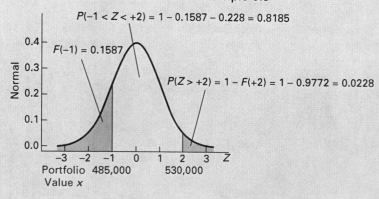

Recall from Chapter 2 that we presented the empirical rule, which states as a rough guide that $\mu \pm \sigma$ covers about 68% of the range, while $\mu \pm 2\sigma$ covers about 95% of the range. For all practical purposes almost none of the range is outside $\mu \pm 3\sigma$. This useful approximation tool for interpretations based on descriptive statistics is based on the normal distribution.

Probabilities can also be computed by using Equation 6.14.

Finding Probabilities for Normally Distributed Random Variables

Let X be a normally distributed random variable with mean μ and variance σ^2. Then random variable $Z = (X - \mu)/\sigma$ has a standard normal distribution: $Z \sim N(0, 1)$.

It follows that, if a and b are any numbers with $a < b$, then

$$P(a < X < b) = P\left(\frac{a - \mu}{\sigma} < Z < \frac{b - \mu}{\sigma}\right)$$

$$= F\left(\frac{b - \mu}{\sigma}\right) - F\left(\frac{a - \mu}{\sigma}\right) \tag{6.14}$$

where Z is the standard normal random variable and F denotes its cumulative distribution function.

Example 6.4 Normal Probability Distribution (Normal Probabilities)

If $X \sim N(15, 16)$, find the probability that X is larger than 18.

Solution This probability can be computed as follows:

$$P(x > 18) = P\left(Z > \frac{18 - \mu}{\sigma}\right)$$
$$= P\left(Z > \frac{18 - 15}{4}\right)$$
$$= P(Z > 0.75)$$
$$= 1 - P(Z < 0.75)$$
$$= 1 - F(0.75)$$

From Table 1 in the Appendix, $F(0.75)$ is 0.7734, and, therefore,

$$P(X > 18) = 1 - 0.7734 = 0.2266$$

Example 6.5 Lightbulb Life (Normal Probabilities)

A company produces lightbulbs whose life follows a normal distribution, with mean 1,200 hours and standard deviation 250 hours. If we choose a lightbulb at random, what is the probability that its lifetime will be between 900 and 1,300 hours?

Solution   Let X represent lifetime in hours. Then

$$P(900 < X < 1{,}300) = P\left(\frac{900 - 1{,}200}{250} < Z < \frac{1{,}300 - 1{,}200}{250}\right)$$
$$= P(-1.2 < Z < 0.4)$$
$$= F(0.4) - F(-1.2)$$
$$= 0.6554 - (1 - 0.8849) = 0.5403$$

Hence, the probability is approximately 0.54 that a lightbulb will last between 900 and 1,300 hours.

Example 6.6   Student Test Scores (Normal Probabilities)

A very large group of students obtains test scores that are normally distributed, with mean 60 and standard deviation 15. What proportion of the students obtained scores between 85 and 95?

Solution   Let X denote the test score. Then the probability can be computed as follows:

$$P(85 < X < 95) = P\left(\frac{85 - 60}{15} < Z < \frac{95 - 60}{15}\right)$$
$$= P(1.67 < Z < 2.33)$$
$$= F(2.33) - F(1.67)$$
$$= 0.9901 - 0.9525 = 0.0376$$

That is, 3.76% of the students obtained scores in the range 85 to 95.

Example 6.7   Cutoff Points for Student Test Scores (Normal Random Variables)

For the test scores of Example 6.6 find the cutoff point for the top 10% of all students.

Solution   Define b as the cutoff point. To determine the numerical value of the cutoff point, we first note that the probability of exceeding b is 0.10, and, thus, the probability of being less than b is 0.90. The upper tail value of 0.10 is shown in Figure 6.18. We can now state the probability from the cumulative distribution as

$$0.90 = P\left(Z < \frac{b - 60}{15}\right)$$
$$= F\left(\frac{b - 60}{15}\right)$$

From Table 1 of the Appendix, we find that $Z = 1.28$ when $F(Z) = 0.90$. Therefore, solving for b, we have

$$\frac{b - 60}{15} = 1.28$$
$$b = 79.2$$

Thus, we conclude that 10% of the students obtain scores above 79.2 as shown in Figure 6.18.

Figure 6.18   Normal Distribution with Mean 60 and Standard Deviation 15 Showing Upper Tail Probability Equal to 0.10

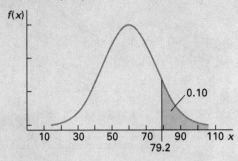

We note that test scores, such as those in Examples 6.6 and 6.7, are typically given as integer values, and, thus, the distribution of test scores is discrete. However, because of the large number of possible outcomes, the normal distribution provides a very good approximation for the discrete distribution. In most applied business and economic problems we are, in fact, using the normal distribution to approximate a discrete distribution that has many different outcomes.

Normal Probability Plots

The normal probability model is the most used probability model for the reasons previously noted. In applied problems we would like to know if the data have come from a distribution that approximates a normal distribution closely enough to ensure a valid result. Thus, we are seeking evidence to support the assumption that the normal distribution is a close approximation to the actual unknown distribution. Normal probability plots provide a good way to test this assumption and determine if the normal model can be used. Usage is simple. If the data follow a normal distribution, the plot will be a straight line.

Figure 6.19 is a normal probability plot for a random sample of $n = 1,000$ observations from a normal distribution with $\mu = 100$ and $\sigma = 25$. The plot was generated using Minitab. The horizontal axis indicates the data points ranked in order from the smallest to the largest. The vertical axis indicates the cumulative normal probabilities of the ranked data values if the sample data were obtained from a population whose random variables follow a normal distribution. We see that the vertical axis has a transformed normal scale. The data plots in Figure 6.19 are close to a straight line even at the upper and lower limits, and that result provides solid evidence that the data have a normal distribution. The dotted lines provide an interval within which data points from a normally distributed random variable would occur in most cases. Thus, if the plotted points are within the boundaries established by the dotted lines, we can conclude that the data points represent a normally distributed random variable.

Figure 6.19
Normal
Probability Plot
for a Normal
Distribution
(Minitab Output)

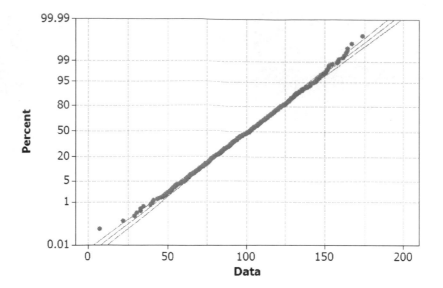

Figure 6.20
Normal
Probability Plot for
a Uniform
Distribution
(Minitab Output)

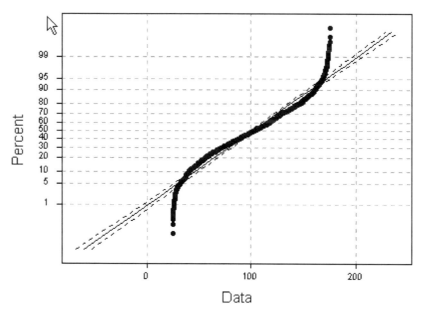

Next, consider a random sample of $n = 1,000$ observations drawn from a *uniform distribution* with limits 25 to 175. Figure 6.20 shows the normal probability plot. In this case the data plot has an **S** shape that clearly deviates from a straight line, and the sample data do not follow a normal distribution. Large deviations at the extreme high and low values are a major concern because statistical inference is often based on small probabilities of extreme values.

Next, let us consider a highly skewed discrete distribution, as shown in Figure 6.21. In Figure 6.22 we see the normal probability plot for this highly skewed distribution. Again, we see that the data plot is not a straight line but has considerable deviation at the extreme high and low values. This plot clearly indicates that the data do not come from a normal distribution.

The previous examples provide us with an indication of possible results from a normal probability plot. If the plot from your problem is similar to Figure 6.19, then

Figure 6.21
Skewed Discrete
Probability
Distribution
Function

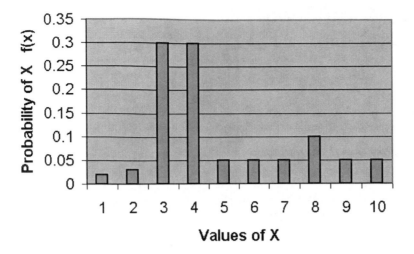

Figure 6.22
Normal
Probability Plot
for a Highly
Skewed
Distribution
(Minitab
Output)

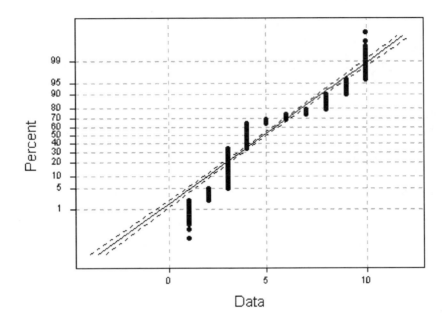

you are safe in assuming that the normal model is a good approximation. Note, however, that if your plot deviates from a straight line, as do those in Figures 6.20 and 6.22, then the normal probability distribution should not be used.

EXERCISES

Basic Exercises

6.17 Let the random variable Z follow a standard normal distribution.

  a. Find $P(Z < 1.20)$.
  b. Find $P(Z > 1.33)$.
  c. Find $P(Z < -1.70)$.
  d. Find $P(Z > -1.00)$.
  e. Find $P(1.20 < Z < 1.33)$.
  f. Find $P(-1.70 < Z < 1.20)$.
  g. Find $P(-1.70 < Z < -1.00)$.

6.18 Let the random variable Z follow a standard normal distribution.

  a. The probability is 0.70 that Z is less than what number?
  b. The probability is 0.25 that Z is less than what number?

c. The probability is 0.2 that Z is greater than what number?

d. The probability is 0.6 that Z is greater than what number?

6.19 Let the random variable X follow a normal distribution with $\mu = 50$ and $\sigma^2 = 64$.

a. Find the probability that X is greater than 60.

b. Find the probability that X is greater than 35 and less than 62.

c. Find the probability that X is less than 55.

d. The probability is 0.2 that X is greater than what number?

e. The probability is 0.05 that X is in the symmetric interval about the mean between which two numbers?

6.20 Let the random variable X follow a normal distribution with $\mu = 80$ and $\sigma^2 = 100$.

a. Find the probability that X is greater than 60.

b. Find the probability that X is greater than 72 and less than 82.

c. Find the probability that X is less than 55.

d. The probability is 0.1 that X is greater than what number?

e. The probability is 0.08 that X is in the symmetric interval about the mean between which two numbers?

6.21 Let the random variable X follow a normal distribution with $\mu = 0.2$ and $\sigma^2 = .0025$.

a. Find the probability that X is greater than 0.4.

b. Find the probability that X is greater than 0.15 and less than 0.28.

c. Find the probability that X is less than 0.10.

d. The probability is 0.2 that X is greater than what number?

e. The probability is 0.05 that X is in the symmetric interval about the mean between which two numbers?

Application Exercises

6.22 It is known that amounts of money spent on textbooks in a year by students on a particular campus follow a normal distribution with mean $380 and standard deviation $50.

a. What is the probability that a randomly chosen student will spend less than $400 on textbooks in a year?

b. What is the probability that a randomly chosen student will spend more than $360 on textbooks in a year?

c. Draw a graph to illustrate why the answers to parts (a) and (b) are the same.

d. What is the probability that a randomly chosen student will spend between $300 and $400 on textbooks in a year?

e. You want to find a range of dollar spending on textbooks in a year that includes 80% of all students on this campus. Explain why any number of such ranges could be found, and find the shortest one.

6.23 Anticipated consumer demand for a product next month can be represented by a normal random variable with mean 1,200 units and standard deviation 100 units.

a. What is the probability that sales will exceed 1,000 units?

b. What is the probability that sales will be between 1,100 and 1,300 units?

c. The probability is 0.10 that sales will be more than how many units?

6.24 The tread life of a particular brand of tire has a normal distribution with mean 35,000 miles and standard deviation 4,000 miles.

a. What proportion of these tires has a tread life of more than 38,000 miles?

b. What proportion of these tires has a tread life of less than 32,000 miles?

c. What proportion of these tires has a tread life of between 32,000 and 38,000 miles?

d. Draw a graph of the probability density function of tread lives, illustrating:

i. Why the answers to parts (a) and (b) are the same

ii. Why the answers to parts (a), (b), and (c) sum to 1

6.25 An investment portfolio contains stocks of a large number of corporations. Over the last year the rates of return on these corporate stocks followed a normal distribution with mean 12.2% and standard deviation 7.2%.

a. For what proportion of these corporations was the rate of return higher than 20%?

b. For what proportion of these corporations was the rate of return negative?

c. For what proportion of these corporations was the rate of return between 5% and 15%?

6.26 A company produces bags of a chemical, and it is concerned about impurity content. It is believed that the weights of impurities per bag are normally distributed with mean 12.2 grams and standard deviation 2.8 grams. A bag is chosen at random.

a. What is the probability that it contains less than 10 grams of impurities?

b. What is the probability that it contains more than 15 grams of impurities?

c. What is the probability that it contains between 12 and 15 grams of impurities?

d. It is possible, without doing the detailed calculations, to deduce which of the answers to parts (a) and (b) will be the larger. How?

6.27 A contractor regards the cost of fulfilling a particular contract as a normally distributed random variable with mean $500,000 and standard deviation $50,000.

   a. What is the probability that the cost of fulfilling the contract will be between $460,000 and $540,000?

   b. The probability is 0.2 that the contract will cost less than how much to fulfill?

   c. Find the shortest range such that the probability is 0.95 that the cost of fulfilling the contract will fall in this range.

6.28 Scores on a test follow a normal distribution. What is the probability that a randomly selected student will achieve a score that exceeds the mean score by more than 1.5 standard deviations?

6.29 A new television series is to be shown. A broadcasting executive feels that his uncertainty about the rating which the show will receive in its first month can be represented by a normal distribution with mean 18.2 and standard deviation 1.6. According to this executive, the probability is 0.1 that the rating will be less than what number?

6.30 A broadcasting executive is reviewing the prospects for a new television series. According to her judgment, the probability is 0.25 that the show will achieve a rating higher than 17.8, and the probability is 0.15 that it will achieve a rating higher than 19.2. If the executive's uncertainty about the rating can be represented by a normal distribution, what are the mean and variance of that distribution?

6.31 Scores on an examination taken by a very large group of students are normally distributed with mean 700 and standard deviation 120.

   a. An A is awarded for a score higher than 820. What proportion of all students obtain an A?

   b. A B is awarded for scores between 730 and 820. An instructor has a section of 100 students who can be viewed as a random sample of all students in the large group. Find the expected number of students in this section who will obtain a B.

   c. It is decided to give a failing grade to 5% of students with the lowest scores. What is the minimum score needed to avoid a failing grade?

6.32 I am considering two alternative investments. In both cases I am unsure about the percentage return but believe that my uncertainty can be represented by normal distributions with the means and standard deviations shown in the accompanying table. I want to make the investment that is more likely to produce a return of at least 10%. Which should I choose?

	Mean	Standard Deviation
Investment A	10.4	1.2
Investment B	11.0	4.0

6.33 A company can purchase raw material from either of two suppliers and is concerned about the amounts of impurity the material contains. A review of the records for each supplier indicates that the percentage impurity levels in consignments of the raw material follow normal distributions with the means and standard deviations given in the following table. The company is particularly anxious that the impurity level in a consignment not exceed 5% and wants to purchase from the supplier more likely to meet that specification. Which supplier should be chosen?

	Mean	Standard Deviation
Supplier A	4.4	0.4
Supplier B	4.2	0.6

6.34 An instructor has found that the time spent by students on a particular homework assignment follows a normal distribution with mean 150 minutes and standard deviation 40 minutes.

   a. The probability is 0.9 that a randomly chosen student spends more than how many minutes on this assignment?

   b. The probability is 0.8 that a randomly chosen student spends less than how many minutes on this assignment?

   c. Two students are chosen at random. What is the probability that at least one of them spends at least 2 hours on this assignment?

6.35 A company services copiers. A review of its records shows that the time taken for a service call can be represented by a normal random variable with mean 75 minutes and standard deviation 20 minutes.

   a. What proportion of service calls takes less than 1 hour?

   b. What proportion of service calls takes more than 90 minutes?

   c. Sketch a graph to show why the answers to parts (a) and (b) are the same.

   d. The probability is 0.1 that a service call takes more than how many minutes?

6.36 Scores on an achievement test are known to be normally distributed with mean 420 and standard deviation 80.

   a. For a randomly chosen person taking this test, what is the probability of a score between 400 and 480?

   b. What is the minimum test score needed in order to be in the top 10% of all people taking the test?

c. For a randomly chosen individual, state, without doing the calculations, in which of the following ranges his or her score is most likely to be: 400–439, 440–479, 480–519, or 520–559.

d. In which of the ranges listed in part (c) is the individual's score least likely to be?

e. Two people taking the test are chosen at random. What is the probability that at least one of them scores more than 500 points?

6.37 It is estimated that the time that a well-known rock band, the Living Ingrates, spends on stage at their concerts follows a normal distribution with mean 200 minutes and standard deviation 20 minutes.

a. What proportion of concerts played by this band lasts between 180 and 200 minutes?

b. An audience member smuggles a tape recorder with reel-to-reel tapes with a capacity of 245 minutes into a Living Ingrates concert. What is

the probability that this capacity will be insufficient to record the entire concert?

c. If the standard deviation of concert time was only 15 minutes, state, without doing the calculations, whether the probability that a concert would last more than 245 minutes would be larger than, smaller than, or the same as that found in part (b). Sketch a graph to illustrate your answer.

d. The probability is 0.1 that a Living Ingrates concert will last less than how many minutes? (Assume, as originally, that the population standard deviation is 20 minutes.)

6.38 An economics test is taken by a large group of students. The test scores are normally distributed with mean 70, and the probability that a randomly chosen student receives a score less than 85 is 0.9332. Four students are chosen at random. What is the probability that at least one of them scores more than 80 points on this test?

6.4 NORMAL DISTRIBUTION APPROXIMATION FOR BINOMIAL DISTRIBUTION

In this section we show how the normal distribution can be used to approximate the discrete binomial and proportion random variables that are used extensively in business and economics. This approximation can be used to compute probabilities for larger sample sizes when tables are not readily available. The normal distribution approximation of the binomial distribution also provides a benefit for applied problem solving. We learn that procedures based on the normal distribution can also be applied in problems involving binomial and proportion random variables. Thus, you can reduce the number of different statistical procedures that you need to know to solve business problems.

Let us consider a problem with n independent trials, each with probability of success P. In Section 5.4 we saw that the binomial random variable X could be written as the sum of n independent Bernoulli random variables:

$$X = X_1 + X_2 + \cdots + X_n$$

where the random variable X_i takes the value 1 if the outcome of the ith trial is "success" and 0 otherwise, with respective probabilities P and $1 - P$. The number X of successes that result has a binomial distribution with mean and variance

$$E(X) = \mu = nP$$
$$\text{Var}(X) = \sigma^2 = nP(1 - P)$$

The plot of a binomial distribution with $P = 0.5$ and $n = 100$, in Figure 6.23, shows us that the binomial has the same shape as the normal. This visual evidence that the binomial can be approximated by a normal distribution with the same mean and variance is also established in work done by mathematical statisticians. A good rule

Figure 6.23
Binomial
Distribution
with *n* = 100 and
P = 0.50

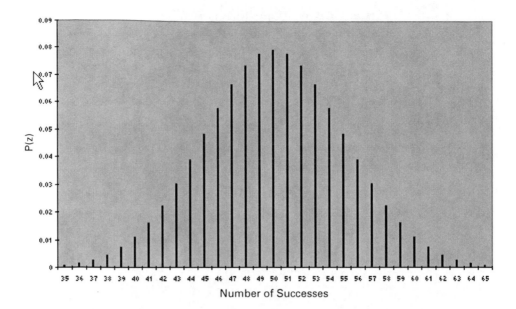

for us is that the normal distribution provides a good approximation for the binomial distribution when $nP(1 - P) > 9$.

In order to better understand the normal distribution approximation for the binomial distribution, consider Figure 6.24(a) and (b). In both (a) and (b) we have shown points from a normal probability density function compared to the corresponding probabilities from a binomial distribution using graphs prepared using Minitab. In part (a) we note that the approximation rule value is

$$nP(1 - P) = 100(0.5)(1 - 0.5) = 25 > 9$$

and that the normal distribution provides a very close approximation to the binomial distribution. In contrast, the example in part (b) has an approximation rule value of

$$nP(1 - P) = 25(0.2)(1 - 0.2) = 4 < 9$$

and the normal distribution does not provide a good approximation for the binomial distribution. Evidence such as that contained in Figure 6.24 has provided the rationale for widespread application of the normal approximation for the binomial. We will now proceed to develop the procedure for its application.

By using the mean and the variance from the binomial distribution, we find that, if the number of trials *n* is large—such that $nP(1 - P) > 9$—then the distribution of the random variable

$$Z = \frac{X - E(X)}{\sqrt{\text{Var}(X)}} = \frac{X - nP}{\sqrt{nP(1 - P)}}$$

is approximately standard normal.

This result is very important because it allows us to find, for large *n*, the probability that the number of successes lies in a given range. If we want to determine

Figure 6.24   Comparison of Binomial and Normal Approximations (Minitab Output):

a. Binomial with $P = 0.50$ and $n = 100$, and Normal with $\mu = 50$ and $\sigma = 5$
b. Binomial with $P = 0.20$ and $n = 25$, and Normal with $\mu = 5$ and $\sigma = 2$

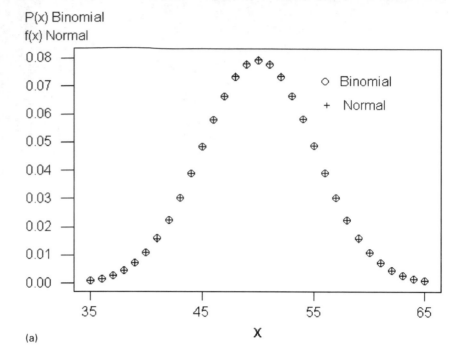

(a)

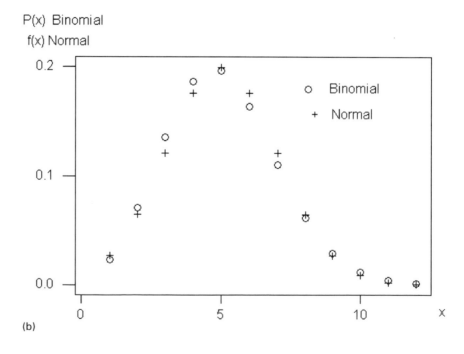

(b)

the probability that the number of successes will be between a and b, inclusive, we have

$$P(a \leq X \leq b) = P\left(\frac{a - nP}{\sqrt{nP(1 - P)}} \leq \frac{X - nP}{\sqrt{nP(1 - P)}} \leq \frac{b - nP}{\sqrt{nP(1 - P)}}\right)$$

$$= P\left(\frac{a - nP}{\sqrt{nP(1 - P)}} \leq Z \leq \frac{b - nP}{\sqrt{nP(1 - P)}}\right)$$

With n large, Z is well approximated by the standard normal, and we can find the probability using the methods from Section 6.3.

Example 6.8 Customer Sales (Normal Probabilities)

A saleswoman makes initial telephone contact with potential customers in an effort to assess whether a follow-up visit to their homes is likely to be worthwhile. Her experience suggests that 40% of the initial contacts lead to follow-up visits. If she contacts 100 people by telephone, what is the probability that between 45 and 50 home visits will result?

Solution   Let X be the number of follow-up visits. Then X has a binomial distribution with $n = 100$ and $P = 0.40$. Approximating the required probability gives

$$P(45 \leq X \leq 50) \cong P\left(\frac{45 - (100)(0.4)}{\sqrt{(100)(0.4)(0.6)}} \leq Z \leq \frac{50 - (100)(0.4)}{\sqrt{(100)(0.4)(0.6)}}\right)$$

$$= P(1.02 \leq Z \leq 2.04)$$

$$= F(2.04) - F(1.02)$$

$$= 0.9793 - 0.8461 = 0.1332$$

This probability is shown as an area under the standard normal curve in Figure 6.25.

Figure 6.25   **Probability of 45 to 50 Successes for a Binomial Distribution with $n = 100$ and $P = 0.4$**

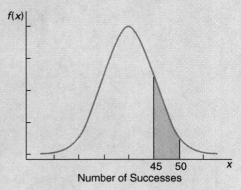

Proportion Random Variable

In a number of applied problems we have a need to compute probabilities for proportion or percentage intervals. We can do this by using a direct extension of the normal distribution approximation for the binomial distribution. A proportion random variable, P, can be computed by dividing the number of successes, X, by the sample size, n.

$$P = \frac{X}{n}$$

Then, using the linear transformation of random variables, the mean and the variance of P can be computed as

$$\mu = P$$
$$\sigma^2 = \frac{P(1 - P)}{n}$$

We can use the resulting mean and variance with the normal distribution to compute the desired probability.

Example 6.9   Election Forecasting (Proportion Probabilities)

We have often observed the success of television networks in forecasting elections. This is a good example of the successful use of probability methods in applied problems. Consider how elections can be predicted by using relatively small samples in a simplified example. An election forecaster has obtained a random sample of 900 voters, in which 500 indicate that they will vote for Susan Chung. Should Susan anticipate winning the election?

Solution   In this problem we assume only two candidates, and, thus, if more than 50% of the population supports Susan, she will win the election. We compute the probability that 500 or more voters out of a sample of 900 support Susan under the assumption that exactly 50%, $P = 0.50$, of the entire population supports Susan.

$$P(X \geq 500 \mid n = 900, P = 0.50) \approx P(X \geq 500 \mid \mu = 450, \sigma^2 = 225)$$
$$= P\left(Z \geq \frac{500 - 450}{\sqrt{225}}\right)$$
$$= P(Z \geq 3.33)$$
$$= 0.000$$

The probability of 500 successes out of 900 trials if $P = 0.50$ is very small, and, therefore, we conclude that P must be greater than 0.50. Hence, we predict that Susan Chung will win the election.

    We could also compute the probability that more than 55.6% (500/900) of the sample indicates support for Susan if the population proportion is $P = 0.50$. Using the mean and variance for proportion random variables,

$$\mu = P = 0.50$$

$$\sigma^2 = \frac{P(1-P)}{n} = \frac{.50(1-0.50)}{900}$$

$$\sigma = 0.0167$$

$$P(P \geq 0.556 \mid n = 900, P = 0.50) \approx P(P \geq 0.556 \mid \mu = 0.50, \sigma = 0.0167)$$

$$= P\left(Z \geq \frac{0.556 - 0.50}{0.0167}\right)$$

$$= P(Z \geq 3.33)$$

$$= 0.000$$

Note that the probability is exactly the same as that for the corresponding binomial random variable. This is always the case because each proportion or percentage value is directly related to a specific number of successes. Because percent is a more common term than proportion in business and economic language, we will tend to use percent more often than proportion in exercises and discussion in this textbook.

EXERCISES

Basic Exercises

6.39 Given a random sample of size $n = 900$ from a binomial probability distribution with $P = 0.50$:

a. Find the probability that the number of successes is greater than 500.

b. Find the probability that the number of successes is less than 430.

c. Find the probability that the number of successes is between 440 and 480.

d. With probability 0.10 the number of successes is less than how many?

e. With probability 0.08 the number of successes is greater than how many?

6.40 Given a random sample of size $n = 1,600$ from a binomial probability distribution with $P = 0.40$:

a. Find the probability that the number of successes is greater than 1,650.

b. Find the probability that the number of successes is less than 1,530.

c. Find the probability that the number of successes is between 1,550 and 1,650.

d. With probability 0.09 the number of successes is less than how many?

e. With probability 0.20 the number of successes is greater than how many?

6.41 Given a random sample of size $n = 900$ from a binomial probability distribution with $P = 0.10$:

a. Find the probability that the number of successes is greater than 110.

b. Find the probability that the number of successes is less than 53.

c. Find the probability that the number of successes is between 55 and 120.

d. With probability 0.10 the number of successes is less than how many?

e. With probability 0.08 the number of successes is greater than how many?

6.42 Given a random sample of size $n = 1,600$ from a binomial probability distribution with $P = 0.40$:

a. Find the probability that the percentage of successes is greater than 0.45.

b. Find the probability that the percentage of successes is less than 0.36.

c. Find the probability that the percentage of successes is between 0.37 and 0.44.

d. With probability 0.20 the percentage of successes is less than what percent?

e. With probability 0.09 the percentage of successes is greater than what percent?

6.43 Given a random sample of size $n = 400$ from a binomial probability distribution with $P = 0.20$:

a. Find the probability that the percentage of successes is greater than 0.25.

b. Find the probability that the percentage of successes is less than 0.16.

c. Find the probability that the percentage of successes is between 0.17 and 0.24.

d. With probability 0.15 the percentage of successes is less than what percent?

e. With probability 0.11 the percentage of successes is greater than what percent?

Application Exercises

6.44 A car rental company has determined that the probability a car will need service work in any given month is 0.2. The company has 900 cars.

   a. What is the probability that more than 200 cars will require service work in a particular month?
   b. What is the probability that fewer than 175 cars will need service work in a given month?

6.45 It is known that 10% of all the items produced by a particular manufacturing process are defective. From the very large output of a single day, 400 items are selected at random.

   a. What is the probability that at least 35 of the selected items are defective?
   b. What is the probability that between 40 and 50 of the selected items are defective?
   c. What is the probability that between 34 and 48 of the selected items are defective?
   d. Without doing the calculations, state which of the following ranges of defectives has the highest probability: 38–39, 40–41, 42–43, 44–45, 46–47.

6.46 A sample of 100 blue-collar employees at a large corporation are surveyed to assess their attitudes toward a proposed new work schedule. If 60% of all blue-collar employees at this corporation favor the new schedule, what is the probability that less than 50 of the sample members will be in favor?

6.47 A hospital finds that 25% of its bills are at least 1 month in arrears. A random sample of 450 bills was taken.

   a. What is the probability that less than 100 bills in the sample were at least 1 month in arrears?
   b. What is the probability that the number of bills in the sample at least 1 month in arrears was between 120 and 150 (inclusive)?

6.48 The tread life of a brand of tire can be represented (as in Exercise 6.24) by a normal distribution with mean 35,000 miles and standard deviation 4,000 miles. A sample of 100 of these tires is taken. What is the probability that more than 25 of them have tread lives of more than 38,000 miles?

6.49 Bags of a chemical produced by a company have impurity weights that can be represented by a normal distribution with mean 12.2 grams and standard deviation 2.8 grams. A random sample of 400 of these bags is taken. What is the probability that at least 100 of them contain less than 10 grams of impurities?

6.5 THE EXPONENTIAL DISTRIBUTION

We now introduce a continuous distribution, the *exponential distribution*, that has been found to be particularly useful for waiting line, or queuing, problems. In many service-time problems the service times can be modeled using the exponential distribution. We should note that the exponential distribution differs from the normal in two important ways: It is restricted to random variables with positive values, and its distribution is not symmetric.

The Exponential Distribution

The exponential random variable $T(t > 0)$ has a probability density function

$$f(t) = \lambda e^{-\lambda t} \quad \text{for } t > 0 \tag{6.15}$$

where λ is the mean number of occurrences per time unit, t is the number of time units until the next occurrence, and $e = 2.71828. \ldots$ Then T is said to follow an **exponential probability distribution**. It can be shown that λ is the same parameter used for the Poisson distribution in Section 5.6 and that the mean time between occurrences is $1/\lambda$.

The cumulative distribution function is

$$F(t) = 1 - e^{-\lambda t} \quad \text{for } t > 0 \tag{6.16}$$

The distribution has mean $1/\lambda$ and variance $1/\lambda^2$.

Figure 6.26
Probability
Density Function
for an Exponential
Distribution
with $\lambda = 0.2$

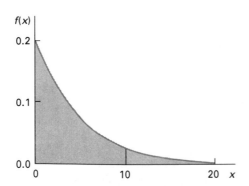

The random variable T can be used to represent the length of time until the end of a service time or until the next arrival to a queuing process, beginning at an arbitrary time 0. The model assumptions are the same as those for the Poisson distribution. Note that the Poisson distribution provides the probability of X successes or arrivals during a time unit. In contrast, the exponential distribution provides the probability that a success or arrival will occur during an interval of time t. Figure 6.26 shows the probability density function for an exponential distribution with $\lambda = 0.2$. The area to the left of 10 gives the probability that a task will be completed before time 10. This area can be obtained by evaluating the function $1 - e^{-\lambda t}$ for the given value of $t = 10$. The function can be computed by using your electronic calculator. Now let us consider an example problem to demonstrate the application of the exponential distribution.

Example 6.10   Service Time at Library Information Desk (Exponential Probabilities)

Service times for customers at a library information desk can be modeled by an exponential distribution with a mean service time of 5 minutes. What is the probability that a customer service time will take longer than 10 minutes?

Solution   Let t denote the service time in minutes. The service rate is $\lambda = 1/5 = 0.2$ per minute, and the probability density function is

$$f(t) = \lambda e^{-\lambda t}$$

which is shown in Figure 6.26. The required probability can be computed as follows:

$$
\begin{aligned}
P(T > 10) &= 1 - P(T < 10) \\
&= 1 - F(10) \\
&= 1 - (1 - e^{-(0.20)(10)}) \\
&= e^{-2.0} = 0.1353
\end{aligned}
$$

Thus, the probability that a service time exceeds 10 minutes is 0.1353.

Example 6.11   Time Between Accidents in Typical British Industrial Plants (Exponential Probabilities)

An industrial plant in Britain with 2,000 employees has a mean number of lost-time accidents per week equal to $\lambda = 0.4$, and the number of accidents follows a Poisson distribution. What is the probability that the time between accidents is less than 2 weeks?

Solution   In this problem we note that the time interval is measured in weeks and our rate is $\lambda = 0.4$ per week, giving a mean time between accidents of $\mu = 1/(0.4) = 2.5$ weeks. Then the probability that the time between accidents is less than 2 weeks is

$$
\begin{aligned}
P(T < 2) = F(2) &= 1 - e^{-(0.4)(2)} \\
&= 1 - e^{-0.8} \\
&= 1 - 0.4493 = 0.5507
\end{aligned}
$$

Thus, the probability of less than 2 weeks between accidents is about 55%.

EXERCISES

Basic Exercises

6.50 Given an arrival process with $\lambda = 1.0$, what is the probability that an arrival occurs in the first $t = 2$ time units?

6.51 Given an arrival process with $\lambda = 8.0$, what is the probability that an arrival occurs in the first $t = 7$ time units?

6.52 Given an arrival process with $\lambda = 5.0$, what is the probability that an arrival occurs after $t = 7$ time units?

6.53 Given an arrival process with $\lambda = 6.0$, what is the probability that an arrival occurs after $t = 5$ time units?

6.54 Given an arrival process with $\lambda = 3.0$, what is the probability that an arrival occurs in the first $t = 2$ time units?

Application Exercises

6.55 A professor sees students during regular office hours. Times spent with students follow an exponential distribution with mean 10 minutes.

  a. Find the probability that a given student spends less than 20 minutes with the professor.

  b. Find the probability that a given student spends more than 5 minutes with the professor.

  c. Find the probability that a given student spends between 10 and 15 minutes with the professor.

6.56 Times to gather preliminary information from arrivals at an outpatient clinic follow an exponential distribution with mean 15 minutes. Find the probability, for a randomly chosen arrival, that more than 18 minutes will be required.

6.57 It is known that for a laboratory computing system the number of system failures during a month has a Poisson distribution with mean 0.8. The system has just failed. Find the probability that at least 2 months will elapse before a further failure.

6.58 Suppose that the time between successive occurrences of an event follows an exponential distribution with mean $1/\lambda$ minutes. Assume that an event occurs.

  a. Show that the probability that more than 3 minutes elapses before the occurrence of the next event is $e^{-3\lambda}$.

  b. Show that the probability that more than 6 minutes elapses before the occurrence of the next event is $e^{-6\lambda}$.

  c. Using the results of parts (a) and (b), show that, if 3 minutes have already elapsed, the probability that a further 3 minutes will elapse before the next occurrence is $e^{-3\lambda}$. Explain your answer in words.

6.6 JOINTLY DISTRIBUTED CONTINUOUS RANDOM VARIABLES

In Section 5.7 we introduced joint distributions for discrete random variables. Here, we show that many of the concepts and results from discrete random variables also apply for continuous random variables. Many continuous random variables can be modeled using jointly distributed random variables. The market values of various stock prices are regularly modeled as joint random variables. Studies of the production and sales patterns for various companies and industries use jointly distributed continuous random variables. The number of units sold by a large retail store during a particular week and the price per unit can be modeled by joint random variables. Studies of import and export behavior for various countries regularly use joint random variables as part of the analysis.

After we have developed some basic concepts, we present a number of application examples to show the importance of the procedures and how to analyze jointly distributed continuous random variables.

Joint Cumulative Distribution Function

Let $X_1, X_2, \ldots, X_k$ be continuous random variables.

1. Their **joint cumulative distribution function**, $F(x_1, x_2, \ldots, x_k)$, defines the probability that simultaneously X_1 is less than x_1, X_2 is less than x_2, and so on; that is,

$$F(x_1, x_2, \ldots, x_k) = P(X_1 < x_1 \cap X_2 < x_2 \cap \cdots \cap X_k < x_k) \qquad (6.17)$$

2. The cumulative distribution functions—$F(x_1), F(x_2), \ldots, F(x_k)$—of the individual random variables are called their **marginal distribution functions**. For any i, $F(x_i)$ is the probability that the random variable X_i does not exceed the specific value x_i.
3. The random variables are *independent* if and only if

$$F(x_1, x_2, \ldots, x_k) = F(x_1)F(x_2) \cdots F(x_k) \qquad (6.18)$$

We note that the notion of independence here is precisely the same as in the discrete case. Independence of a set of random variables implies that the probability distribution of any one of them is unaffected by the values taken by the others. Thus, for example, the assertion that consecutive daily changes in the price of a share of common stock are independent of one another implies that information about the past price changes is of no value in assessing what is likely to happen tomorrow.

The notion of expectation extends to functions of jointly distributed continuous random variables. As in the case of discrete random variables, we have the concept of *covariance*, which is used in assessing linear relationships between pairs of random variables.

Covariance

Let X and Y be a pair of continuous random variables with respective means μ_x and μ_y. The expected value of $(X - \mu_x)(Y - \mu_y)$ is called the **covariance** (Cov) between X and Y. That is,

$$\text{Cov}(X, Y) = E[(X - \mu_X)(Y - \mu_Y)] \tag{6.19}$$

An alternative, but equivalent, expression can be derived as

$$\text{Cov}(X, Y) = E(XY) - \mu_X \mu_Y \tag{6.20}$$

If the random variables X and Y are independent, then the covariance between them is 0. However, the converse is not necessarily true.

In Section 5.7 we also presented the *correlation* as a standardized measure of the relationship between two discrete random variables. The same results hold for continuous random variables.

Correlation

Let X and Y be jointly distributed random variables. The **correlation** (Corr) between X and Y is

$$\rho = \text{Corr}(X, Y) = \frac{\text{Cov}(X, Y)}{\sigma_X \sigma_Y} \tag{6.21}$$

In Section 5.7 we presented the means and variances for sums and differences of discrete random variables. The same results apply for continuous random variables because the results are established using expectations and thus are not affected by the condition of discrete or continuous random variables.

Sums of Random Variables

Let $X_1, X_2, \ldots, X_K$ be K random variables with means $\mu_1, \mu_2, \ldots, \mu_K$ and variances $\sigma_1^2, \sigma_2^2, \ldots, \sigma_k^2$. The following properties hold:

1. The mean of their sum is the sum of their means; that is,

$$E(X_1 + X_2 + \cdots + X_K) = \mu_1 + \mu_2 + \cdots + \mu_K \tag{6.22}$$

2. If the covariance between every pair of these random variables is 0, then the variance of their sum is the sum of their variances; that is,

$$\text{Var}(X_1 + X_2 + \cdots + X_K) = \sigma_1^2 + \sigma_2^2 + \cdots + \sigma_K^2 \tag{6.23}$$

However, if the covariances between pairs of random variables are not 0, the variance of their sum is

$$\text{Var}(X_1 + X_2 + \cdots + X_K) = \sigma_1^2 + \sigma_2^2 + \cdots + \sigma_K^2 + 2 \sum_{i=1}^{K-1} \sum_{j=i+1}^{K} \text{Cov}(X_i, X_j) \tag{6.24}$$

Differences Between a Pair of Random Variables

Let X and Y be a pair of random variables with means μ_X and μ_Y and variances σ_X^2 and σ_Y^2. The following properties hold:

1. The mean of their difference is the difference of their means; that is,

$$E(X - Y) = \mu_X - \mu_Y \qquad (6.25)$$

2. If the covariance between X and Y is 0, then the variance of their difference is

$$\text{Var}(X - Y) = \sigma_X^2 + \sigma_Y^2 \qquad (6.26)$$

3. If the covariance between X and Y is not 0, then the variance of their difference is

$$\text{Var}(X - Y) = \sigma_X^2 + \sigma_Y^2 - 2\,\text{Cov}(X, Y) \qquad (6.27)$$

Example 6.12 Total Project Costs (Mean and Standard Deviation)

A contractor is uncertain of the precise total costs for either materials or labor for a project. In addition, the total line of credit for financing the project is $260,000, and the contractor wants to know the probability that total costs exceed $260,000. It is believed that material costs can be represented by a normally distributed random variable with mean $100,000 and standard deviation $10,000. Labor costs are $1,500 a day, and the number of days needed to complete the project can be represented by a normally distributed random variable with mean 80 and standard deviation 12. Assuming that material and labor costs are independent, what are the mean and standard deviation of the total project cost (materials plus labor)? In addition, what is the probability that the total project cost is greater than $260,000?

Solution Let the random variables X_1 and X_2 denote, respectively, materials and labor costs. Then X_1 has mean $\mu_1 = 100{,}000$ and standard deviation $\sigma_1 = 10{,}000$. For the random variable X_2

$$\mu_2 = (1{,}500)(80) = 120{,}000 \quad \text{and} \quad \sigma_2 = (1{,}500)(12) = 18{,}000$$

The total project cost is $W = X_1 + X_2$, and we have mean cost

$$\mu_W = \mu_1 + \mu_2 = 100{,}000 + 120{,}000 = \$220{,}000$$

and since X_1 and X_2 are independent, the variance of their sum is

$$\sigma_W^2 = \sigma_1^2 + \sigma_2^2 = (10{,}000)^2 + (18{,}000)^2 = 424{,}000{,}000$$

Taking the square root, we find that the standard deviation is $20,591.

Since X_1 and X_2 are normally distributed, it can be shown that their sum, W, is also normally distributed. Thus, the mean and variance of W can be used to compute a standard normal random variable, Z, and then the probability that W is greater than \$260,000.

$$Z = \frac{260,000 - 220,000}{20,591} = 1.94$$

Using the cumulative normal probability table, we find that the probability that the total cost exceeds \$260,000 is 0.0262. Since this probability is small, the contractor has some confidence that the project can be completed within the available line of credit.

Example 6.13 Investment Portfolio Risk (Linear Function Mean and Variance)

Henry Chang has asked for your assistance in establishing a portfolio containing two stocks. Henry has \$1,000, which can be allocated in any proportion to two alternative stocks. The returns per dollar from these investments will be designated as random variables X and Y. Both of these random variables are independent and have the same mean and variance. Henry wishes to know the risk for various allocation options. You point out that risk is directly related to variance and thus that his question would be answered if he knew the variance of various allocation options.

Solution The amount of money allocated to the first investment will be designated as α, and, hence, the remaining $1,000 - \alpha$ will be allocated to the second investment. The total return on the investment is

$$R = \alpha X + (1,000 - \alpha)Y$$

This random variable has expected value

$$E(R) = \alpha E(X) + (1,000 - \alpha)\, E(Y)$$
$$= \alpha\mu + (1,000 - \alpha)\, \mu = \$1,000\mu$$

Thus, we see that the expected return is the same for any allocation. However, the risk or variance is a different story.

$$Var(R) = \alpha^2\, Var(X) + (1,000 - \alpha)^2\, Var(Y)$$
$$= \alpha^2\sigma^2 + (1,000 - \alpha)^2\sigma^2$$
$$= (2\alpha^2 - 2,000\,\alpha + 1,000,000)\sigma^2$$

If α is equal to either 0 or 1,000, so that the entire portfolio is allocated to just one of the stocks, the variance of the total return is $1,000,000\, \sigma^2$. However, if \$500 is allocated to each investment, the variance of the total return is $500,000\, \sigma^2$, which is the smallest possible variance. By spreading his investment over two stocks, Henry is able to mitigate the effect of either high or low returns from one of the shares. Thus, it is possible to obtain the same expected return with a variety of risk levels.

Linear Combinations of Random Variables

In Chapter 5 we developed the mean and variance for linear combinations of discrete random variables. These results also apply for continuous random variables because their development is based on operations with expected values and does not depend on the particular probability distributions. Equations 6.28 through 6.31 indicate the important properties of linear combinations.

Linear Combinations of Random Variables

The linear combination of two random variables, X and Y, is

$$W = aX + bY \tag{6.28}$$

where a and b are constant numbers.

The mean value for W is

$$\mu_W = E[W] = E[aX + bY]$$
$$= a\mu_X + b\mu_Y \tag{6.29}$$

The variance for W is

$$\sigma_W^2 = a^2\sigma_X^2 + b^2\sigma_Y^2 + 2ab\,\text{Cov}(X, Y) \tag{6.30}$$

or, using the correlation,

$$\sigma_W^2 = a^2\sigma_X^2 + b^2\sigma_Y^2 + 2ab\,\text{Corr}(X, Y)\sigma_X\sigma_Y \tag{6.31}$$

If the linear combination in Equation 6.28 is a difference—that is, if

$$W = aX - bY \tag{6.32}$$

then the mean and the variance are

$$\mu_w = E[W] = E[aX - bY]$$
$$= a\mu_X - b\mu_Y \tag{6.33}$$

$$\sigma_W^2 = a^2\sigma_X^2 + b^2\sigma_Y^2 - 2ab\,\text{Cov}(X, Y) \tag{6.34}$$

or using the correlation

$$\sigma_W^2 = a^2\sigma_X^2 + b^2\sigma_Y^2 - 2ab\,\text{Corr}(X, Y)\sigma_X\sigma_Y \tag{6.35}$$

These results come directly from Equations 6.28 through 6.31 by merely substituting a negative value for the coefficient b in the equations.

If both X and Y are joint normally distributed random variables, then the resulting random variable, W, is also normally distributed with mean and variance derived as shown. This result enables us to determine the probability that the linear combination, W, is within a specific interval.

Example 6.14 Portfolio Analysis (Probability of a Portfolio)

Kirsten Judge, the account manager for Northern Securities, has a portfolio that includes 20 shares of Albertine Information Systems and 30 shares of Beta Cyber Analytics. Both firms provide Web access devices that compete in the consumer market. The price of Albertine stock is normally distributed with mean $\mu_X = 25$ and variance $\sigma_X^2 = 81$. The price of Beta stock is also normally distributed with mean $\mu_Y = 40$ and variance $\sigma_Y^2 = 121$. The stock prices have a negative correlation, $\rho_{XY} = -0.40$. Kirsten has asked you to determine the probability that the portfolio value exceeds 2,000.

Solution The value of Kirsten's portfolio, W, is defined by the linear combination

$$W = 20X + 30Y$$

and W is normally distributed. The mean value for her stock portfolio is

$$\mu_W = 20\mu_X + 30\mu_Y$$
$$= 20 \times 25 + 30 \times 40 = 1{,}700$$

The variance for the portfolio value is

$$\sigma_W^2 = 20^2\sigma_X^2 + 30^2\sigma_Y^2 + 2 \times 20 \times 30\,\text{Corr}(X, Y)\sigma_X\sigma_Y$$
$$= 20^2 \times 81 + 30^2 \times 121 + 2 \times 20 \times 30 \times (-0.40) \times 9 \times 11 = 93{,}780$$

and the standard deviation of the portfolio value is

$$\sigma_W = 306.24$$

The standard normal Z for 2,000 is

$$Z_W = \frac{2{,}000 - 1{,}700}{306.24} = 0.980$$

And the probability that the portfolio value exceeds 2,000 is 0.1635. From the symmetry of the normal distribution, it follows that the probability that the portfolio value is less than 1,400 is also 0.1635.

If the two stock prices had a positive correlation, $\rho = +0.40$, the mean would be the same, but the variance and standard deviation would be

$$\sigma_W^2 = 20^2\sigma_X^2 + 30^2\sigma_Y^2 + 2 \times 20 \times 30\,\text{Corr}(X, Y)\sigma_X\sigma_Y$$
$$= 20^2 \times 81 + 30^2 \times 121 + 2 \times 20 \times 30 \times (+0.40) \times 9 \times 11 = 188{,}820$$
$$\sigma_W = 434.53$$

The standard normal Z for 2,000 is

$$Z_W = \frac{2{,}000 - 1{,}700}{434.53} = 0.690$$

The probability that her portfolio value exceeds 2,000 is 0.2451, and the probability that it is less than 1,400 is also 0.2451.

Thus, we see that a positive correlation between stock prices leads to a higher variance and higher risk. The risk in this example increases the probability that the portfolio exceeds 2,000, from 0.1635 to 0.2451. This also implies a similar change in the probability that the portfolio value is less than 1,400. The higher risk implies that there is a higher probability that the portfolio has higher or lower values compared to the lower risk option.

INTERPRETATION The example above illustrates a very important fundamental principle in the design of investment portfolios. Recall that the risk of an investment is directly related to the variance of the investment value. In the above example it was shown that, if the values of the two stock prices are positively correlated, then the resulting portfolio will have a larger variance and hence a higher risk. And if the two stock prices are negatively correlated, then the resulting portfolio will have a smaller variance and hence a lower risk. The term *hedging* is often used by fund managers to describe this phenomenon. This important principle for a two-stock portfolio extends directly to a portfolio with a large number of different stocks, but in that case the algebra is more complex and is typically computed using a sophisticated computer program. Investment fund managers use this principle to select combinations of many different stocks in order to obtain the desired portfolio value and risk characteristics that are the objectives for a particular investment fund.

EXERCISES

Basic Exercises

6.59 A random variable X is normally distributed with mean 100 and variance 100, and a random variable Y is normally distributed with mean 200 and variance 400. The random variables have a correlation coefficient equal to 0.5. Find the mean and variance of the random variable

$$W = 5X + 4Y$$

6.60 A random variable X is normally distributed with mean 100 and variance 100, and a random variable Y is normally distributed with mean 200 and variance 400. The random variables have a correlation coefficient equal to -0.5. Find the mean and variance of the random variable

$$W = 5X + 4Y$$

6.61 A random variable X is normally distributed with mean 100 and variance 100, and a random variable Y is normally distributed with mean 200 and variance 400. The random variables have a correlation coefficient equal to 0.5. Find the mean and variance of the random variable

$$W = 5X - 4Y$$

6.62 A random variable X is normally distributed with mean 500 and variance 100, and a random variable Y is normally distributed with mean 200 and variance 400. The random variables have a correlation coefficient equal to 0.5. Find the mean and variance of the random variable

$$W = 5X - 4Y$$

6.63 A random variable X is normally distributed with mean 100 and variance 500, and a random variable Y is normally distributed with mean 200 and variance 400. The random variables have a correlation coefficient equal to -0.5. Find the mean and variance of the random variable

$$W = 5X - 4Y$$

Application Exercises

6.64 An investor plans to divide $200,000 between two investments. The first yields a certain profit of 10%, while the second yields a profit with expected value 18% and standard deviation 6%. If the investor divides the money equally between these two investments, find the mean and standard deviation of the total profit.

6.65 A homeowner has installed a new energy-efficient furnace. It is estimated that over a year the new furnace will reduce energy costs by an amount that can be regarded as a random variable with mean $200 and standard deviation $60. Stating any assumptions you need to make, find the mean and standard deviation of the total energy cost reductions over a period of 5 years.

6.66 A consultant is beginning work on three projects. The expected profits from these projects are $50,000, $72,000, and $40,000. The associated standard deviations are $10,000, $12,000, and $9,000. Assuming independence of outcomes, find the mean and standard deviation of the consultant's total profit from these three projects.

6.67 A consultant has three sources of income—from teaching short courses, from selling computer software, and from advising on projects. His expected annual incomes from these sources are $20,000, $25,000, and $15,000, and the respective standard deviations are $2,000, $5,000, and $4,000. Assuming independence, find the mean and standard deviation of his total annual income.

6.68 Five inspectors are employed to check the quality of components produced on an assembly line. For each inspector the number of components that can be checked in a shift can be represented by a random variable with mean 120 and standard deviation 16. Let X represent the number of components checked by an inspector in a shift. Then the total number checked is $5X$, which has mean 600 and standard deviation 80. What is wrong with this argument? Assuming that inspectors' performances are independent of one another, find the mean and standard deviation of the total number of components checked in a shift.

6.69 It is estimated that in normal highway driving the number of miles that can be covered by automobiles of a particular model on 1 gallon of gasoline can be represented by a random variable with mean 28 and standard deviation 2.4. Sixteen of these cars, each with 1 gallon of gasoline, are driven independently under highway conditions. Find the mean and standard deviation of the average number of miles that will be achieved by these cars.

6.70 Shirley Johnson, portfolio manager, has asked you to analyze a newly acquired portfolio to determine its mean value and variability. The portfolio consists of 50 shares of Xylophone Music and 40 shares of Yankee Workshop. Analysis of past history indicates that the share price of Xylophone Music has a mean of 25 and a variance of 121. A similar analysis indicates that Yankee has a mean share price of 40 with a variance of 225. Your best evidence indicates that the share prices have a correlation of +0.5.

a. Compute the mean and variance of the portfolio.
b. Suppose that the correlation between share prices was actually −0.5. Now what are the mean and variance of the portfolio?

6.71 Prairie Flower Cereal has an annual sales revenue of $400,000,000. George Severn, a 58-year-old senior vice president, is responsible for production and sales of Nougy 93 Fruity cereal. Daily production in cases is normally distributed with a mean of 100 and a variance of 625. Daily sales in cases are also normally distributed with a mean of 100 and a standard deviation of 8. Sales and production have a correlation of 0.60. The selling price per case is $10. The variable production cost per case is $7. The fixed production costs per day are $250.

a. What is the probability that total revenue is greater than total costs on any day?
b. Construct a 95% acceptance interval for total sales revenue minus total costs.

6.72 The nation of Olecarl, located in the South Pacific, has asked you to analyze international trade patterns. You first discover that each year it exports 10

units and imports 10 units of wonderful stuff. The price of exports is a random variable with a mean of 100 and a variance of 100. The price of imports is a random variable with a mean of 90 and a variance of 400. In addition, you discover that the prices of imports and exports have a correlation of $\rho = -0.40$. The prices of both exports and imports follow a normal probability density function. Define the balance of trade as the difference between the total revenue from exports and the total cost of imports.

a. What are the mean and variance of the balance of trade?
b. What is the probability that the balance of trade is negative?

6.73 You have been asked to determine the probability that the contribution margin for a particular product line exceeds the fixed cost of $2,000. The total number of units sold is a normally distributed random variable with a mean of 400 and a variance of 900 $X \sim N(400,900)$. The selling price per unit is $10. The total number of units produced is a normally distributed random variable with a mean of 400 and a variance of 1600 $Y \sim N(400,1600)$. The variable production cost is $4 per unit. Production and sales have a positive correlation of 0.50.

6.74 The nation of Waipo has recently created an economic development plan that includes expanded exports and imports. It has completed a series of extensive studies of the world economy and Waipo's economic capability, following Waipo's extensive 10-year educational enhancement program. The resulting model indicates that in the next year exports will be normally distributed with a mean of 100 and a variance of 900 (in billions of Waipo yuan). In addition, imports are expected to be normally distributed with a mean of 105 and a variance of 625 in the same units. The correlation between exports and imports is expected to be +0.70. Define the trade balance as exports minus imports.

a. Determine the mean and variance of the trade balance (exports minus imports) if the model parameters given above are true.
b. What is the probability that the trade balance will be positive?

SUMMARY

In Chapter 6 we have developed continuous random variable probability models following a pattern similar to that used for discrete random variable probability models in Chapter 5. We developed two parametric probability distribution models, the normal and the exponential. In addition, we showed how the normal can be used as an approximation for the binomial when the sample size is large. Finally, we developed

joint distributions for continuous random variables. We extended the linear combinations of random variable models to show how we can use the mean and variance to compute the probability that the total portfolio is in a specific range, based on the normal probability model. These and other extensive applications provide a solid foundation for using continuous random variables.

KEY WORDS

- approximating binomial probabilities using the normal distribution
- areas under continuous probability density functions
- correlation
- covariance
- cumulative distribution function
- cumulative distribution function for the normal distribution
- differences between pairs of random variables
- expected value for continuous random variables

- exponential probability distribution
- finding range probabilities for normal random variables
- joint cumulative distribution function
- linear combinations of random variables
- linear functions of random variables
- marginal distribution functions
- mean of a continuous random variable
- probability density function

- probability density function of the normal distribution
- properties of the normal distribution
- range probabilities for normal random variables
- range probabilities using a cumulative distribution function
- standard deviation for a continuous random variable
- standard normal distribution
- sums of random variables
- uniform probability distribution
- variance

CHAPTER EXERCISES AND APPLICATIONS

6.75 A consultant knows that it will cost her $10,000 to fulfill a particular contract. The contract is to be put out for bids, and she believes that the lowest bid, excluding her own, can be represented by a distribution that is uniform between $8,000 and $20,000. Therefore, if the random variable X denotes the lowest of all other bids (in thousands of dollars), its probability density function is

$$f_X(x) = \begin{cases} 1/12 & \text{for } 8 < x < 20 \\ 0 & \text{for all other values of } x \end{cases}$$

a. What is the probability that the lowest of the other bids will be less than the consultant's cost estimate of $10,000?

b. If the consultant submits a bid of $12,000, what is the probability that she will secure the contract?

c. The consultant decides to submit a bid of $12,000. What is her expected profit from this strategy?

d. If the consultant wants to submit a bid so that her expected profit is as high as possible, discuss how she should go about making this choice.

6.76 The ages of a group of executives attending a convention are uniformly distributed between 35 and 65 years. If the random variable X denotes ages in years, the probability density function is

$$f_X(x) = \begin{cases} 1/30 & \text{for } 35 < x < 65 \\ 0 & \text{for all other values of } x \end{cases}$$

a. Draw the probability density function for X.

b. Find and draw the cumulative distribution function for X.

c. Find the probability that the age of a randomly chosen executive in this group is between 40 and 50 years.

d. Find the mean age of the executives in the group.

6.77 The random variable X has probability density function

$$f_X(x) = \begin{cases} x & \text{for } 0 < x < 1 \\ 2 - x & \text{for } 1 < x < 2 \\ 0 & \text{for all other values of } x \end{cases}$$

a. Draw the probability density function for X.

b. Show that the density has the properties of a proper probability density function.

c. Find the probability that X takes a value between 0.5 and 1.5.

6.78 An investor puts $2,000 into a deposit account with a fixed rate of return of 10% per annum. A second sum of $1,000 is invested in a fund with an expected rate of return of 16% and a standard deviation of 8% per annum.

a. Find the expected value of the total amount of money this investor will have after a year.

b. Find the standard deviation of the total amount after a year.

6.79 A hamburger stand sells burgers for $1.45 each. Daily sales have a distribution with mean 530 and standard deviation 69.

a. Find the mean daily total revenues from the sale of hamburgers.
b. Find the standard deviation of total revenues from the sale of hamburgers.
c. Daily costs (in dollars) are given by

$$C = 100 + 0.95X$$

where X is the number of hamburgers sold. Find the mean and standard deviation of daily profits from sales.

6.80 An analyst forecasts corporate earnings, and her record is evaluated by comparing actual earnings with predicted earnings. Define

Actual Earnings = Predicted Earnings +
Forecast Error

If the predicted earnings and forecast error are independent of each other, show that the variance of predicted earnings is less than the variance of actual earnings.

6.81 Let X_1 and X_2 be a pair of random variables. Show that the covariance between the random variables $(X_1 + X_2)$ and $(X_1 - X_2)$ is 0 if and only if X_1 and X_2 have the same variance.

6.82 Grade point averages of students on a large campus follow a normal distribution with mean 2.6 and standard deviation 0.5.

a. One student is chosen at random from this campus. What is the probability that this student has a grade point average higher than 3.0?
b. One student is chosen at random from this campus. What is the probability that this student has a grade point average between 2.25 and 2.75?
c. What is the minimum grade point average needed for a student's grade point average to be among the highest 10% on this campus?
d. A random sample of 400 students is chosen from this campus. What is the probability that at least 80 of these students have grade point averages higher than 3.0?
e. Two students are chosen at random from this campus. What is the probability that at least one of them has a grade point average higher than 3.0?

6.83 A company services home air conditioners. It is known that times for service calls follow a normal distribution with mean 60 minutes and standard deviation 10 minutes.

a. What is the probability that a single service call takes more than 65 minutes?
b. What is the probability that a single service call takes between 50 and 70 minutes?
c. The probability is 0.025 that a single service call takes more than how many minutes?

d. Find the shortest range of times that includes 50% of all service calls.
e. A random sample of four service calls is taken. What is the probability that exactly two of them take more than 65 minutes?

6.84 It has been found that times taken by people to complete a particular tax form follow a normal distribution with mean 100 minutes and standard deviation 30 minutes.

a. What is the probability that a randomly chosen person takes less than 85 minutes to complete this form?
b. What is the probability that a randomly chosen person takes between 70 and 130 minutes to complete this form?
c. Five percent of all people take more than how many minutes to complete this form?
d. Two people are chosen at random. What is the probability that at least one of them takes more than an hour to complete this form?
e. Four people are chosen at random. What is the probability that exactly two of them take longer than an hour to complete this form?
f. For a randomly chosen person, state in which of the following ranges (expressed in minutes) time to complete the form is most likely to lie.

    70–89   90–109   110–129   130–149

g. For a randomly chosen person, state in which of the following ranges (expressed in minutes) time to complete the form is least likely to lie.

    70–89   90–109   110–129   130–149

6.85 A pizza delivery service delivers to a campus dormitory. Delivery times follow a normal distribution with mean 20 minutes and standard deviation 4 minutes.

a. What is the probability that a delivery will take between 15 and 25 minutes?
b. The service does not charge for the pizza if delivery takes more than 30 minutes. What is the probability of getting a free pizza from a single order?
c. During final exams, a student plans to order pizza five consecutive evenings. Assume that these delivery times are independent of each other. What is the probability that the student will get at least one free pizza?
d. Find the shortest range of times that includes 40% of all deliveries from this service.
e. For a single delivery, state in which of the following ranges (expressed in minutes) delivery time is most likely to lie.

    18–20   19–21   20–22   21–23

f. For a single delivery, state in which of the following ranges (expressed in minutes) delivery time is least likely to lie.

      18–20   19–21   20–22   21–23

6.86 A video rental chain estimates that annual expenditures of members on rentals follow a normal distribution with mean $100. It was also found that 10% of all members spend more than $130 in a year. What percentage of members spend more than $140 in a year?

6.87 It is estimated that amounts of money spent on gasoline by customers at a gas station follow a normal distribution with standard deviation $2.50. It is also found that 10% of all customers spent more than $25. What percentage of customers spent less than $20?

6.88 A market research organization has found that 40% of all supermarket shoppers refuse to cooperate when questioned by its pollsters. If 1,000 shoppers are approached, what is the probability that less than 500 will refuse to cooperate?

6.89 An organization that gives regular seminars on sales motivation methods determines that 60% of its clients have attended previous seminars. From a sample of 400 clients what is the probability that more than half have attended previous seminars?

6.90 An emergency towing service receives an average of 70 calls per day for assistance. For any given day what is the probability that fewer than 50 calls will be received?

6.91 In a large department store a customer complaints office handles an average of six complaints per hour about quality of service. The distribution is Poisson.

a. What is the probability that in any hour exactly six complaints will be received?

b. What is the probability that more than 20 minutes will elapse between successive complaints?

c. What is the probability that less than 5 minutes will elapse between successive complaints?

d. The store manager observes the complaints office for a 30-minute period, during which no complaints are received. She concludes that a talk she gave to her staff on the theme "The Customer Is Always Right" has obviously had a beneficial effect. Suppose that, in fact, the talk had no effect. What is the probability of the manager's observing a period of 30 minutes or longer with no complaints?

6.92 A Chicago radio station believes that 40% of its listeners are younger than 25 years of age. Six hundred listeners are chosen at random.

a. If the station's belief is correct, what is the probability that more than 260 of these listeners are younger than 25?

b. If the station's belief is correct, the probability is 0.6 that more than how many of these 600 listeners are younger than 25?

6.93 It is estimated that major league baseball game times-to-completion follow a normal distribution with mean 132 minutes and standard deviation 12 minutes.

a. What proportion of all games last between 120 minutes and 150 minutes?

b. Thirty-three percent of all games last longer than how many minutes?

c. What proportion of games last less than 120 minutes?

d. If 100 games are chosen at random, what is the probability that at least 25 of these games last less than 120 minutes?

6.94 A management consultant found that the amount of time per day spent by executives performing tasks that could equally well be done by subordinates followed a normal distribution with mean 2.4 hours. It was also found that 10% of executives spent over 3.5 hours per day on tasks of this type. For a random sample of 400 executives find the probability that more than 80 spend more than 3 hours per day on tasks of this type.

6.95 Financial Managers Inc. buys and sells a large number of stocks routinely for the various accounts that it manages. Portfolio manager Andrea Colson has asked for your assistance in the analysis of the Johnson Fund. A portion of this portfolio consists of 10 shares of stock A and 8 shares of stock B. The price of A has a mean of 10 and a variance of 16, while the price of B has a mean of 12 and a variance of 9. The correlation between prices is 0.3.

a. What are the mean and variance of the portfolio value?

b. Andrea has been asked to reduce the variance (risk) of the portfolio. She offers to trade the 10 shares of stock A and receives two offers from which she can select one: 10 shares of stock 1 with a mean price of 10, a variance of 25, and a correlation with the price of stock B equal to −0.2; or 10 shares of stock 2 with a mean price of 10, a variance of 9, and a correlation with the price of stock B equal to +0.6. Which offer should she select?

6.96 Financial Managers Inc. buys and sells a large number of stocks routinely for the various accounts that it manages. Portfolio manager Sarah Bloom has asked for your assistance in the analysis of the Burde Fund. A portion of this portfolio consists of 10 shares of stock A and 8 shares of stock B. The price of A has a mean of 12 and a variance of 14, while the price of B has a mean of 10 and a variance of 12. The correlation between prices is 0.5.

a. What are the mean and variance of the portfolio value?

b. Sarah has been asked to reduce the variance (risk) of the portfolio. She offers to trade the 10 shares of stock A and receives two offers from which she can select one: 10 shares of stock 1 with a mean price of 12, a variance of 25, and a correlation with the price of stock B equal to −0.2; or 10 shares of stock 2 with a mean price of 10, a variance of 9, and a correlation with the price of stock B, equal to 0.6. Which offer should she select?

6.97 Big Nail Construction Inc. is building a large new student center for a famous midwestern liberal arts college. During the project Christine Buildumbig, the project manager, requests that a pile of sand weighing betweeen 138,000 pounds and 141,000 pounds be placed on the newly constructed driveway. You have been asked to determine the probability that the delivered sand satisfies Christine's request. You have ordered that one big truck and one small truck be used to deliver the sand. Sand loads in the big truck are normally distributed with a mean of 80,000 and a variance of 1,000,000, and

sand loads in the small truck are also normally distributed with a mean weight of 60,000 pounds and a variance of 810,000. From past experience with the sand-loading facility, you know that the weight of sand in the two trucks has a correlation of 0.40. What is the probability that the resulting pile of sand has a weight that is between 138,000 and 141,000 pounds?

6.98 Flybynite Airlines has a regularly scheduled flight from Minneapolis to Frankfurt every weekday evening at 6:30. Based on a complex relationship between Flybynite and Bigrain Airlines, a local line that flys to a number of small towns, 100 seats are reserved for passengers from two of Bigrain's flights that arrive at 5:00 P.M. each weekday. The number of passengers on the flight from Tri-mountain, Montana, has a normal distribution with a mean of 40 passengers and a variance of 100. The number of passengers on the other flight, from Bighog, Iowa, is also normally distributed with a mean of 35 passengers and a variance of 144. The numbers of passengers on these two flights have a correlation of 0.6.

a. What is the probability that all 100 seats on the Frankfurt flight will be filled?

b. What is the probability that between 75 and 90 seats will be filled?

Appendix

1. Readers with a knowledge of calculus will recognize that the probability that a random variable lies in a given range is the integral of the probability density function between the endpoints of the range; that is,

$$P(a < X < b) = \int_a^b f(x)\,dx$$

2. Formally, in integral calculus notation

$$\int_{-\infty}^{\infty} f(x)\,dx = 1$$

The cumulative distribution function is thus the integral

$$F(x_0) = \int_{-\infty}^{x_0} f(x)\,dx$$

It, therefore, follows that the probability density function is the derivative of the cumulative distribution function; that is,

$$f(x) = \frac{dF(x)}{dx}$$

3. Formally using integral calculus we express the expected value of the random variable X by

$$E(X) = \int_{-\infty}^{\infty} x f(x) \, dx$$

and the expected value of the function $g(X)$ by

$$E[g(X)] = \int_{-\infty}^{\infty} g(x)f(x) \, dx$$

Notice that in forming these expectations the integral plays the same role as the summation operator in the discrete case.

4. The integral

$$F(x_0) = \int_{-\infty}^{x_0} \frac{1}{\sqrt{2\pi\sigma^2}} e^{-(x-\mu)^2/2\sigma^2} \, dx$$

does not have a simple algebraic form.

5. Using integral calculus we see that

$$P(t \leq T) = \int_{0}^{T} \lambda e^{-\lambda t} \, dt$$
$$= 1 - e^{-\lambda T}$$

Topic 8

Data Collection and Sampling Methods

Data collection and sampling methods

Learning outcomes

By the end of this chapter you should be able to:

- recognise the distinction between primary and secondary data sources
- avoid a variety of common pitfalls when using secondary data
- make use of electronic sources to gather data
- recognise the main types of random sample and understand their relative merits
- appreciate how such data are collected
- conduct a small sample survey yourself

Introduction

It may seem a little odd to look at data collection now, after several chapters covering the analysis of data. Collection of data logically comes first, but the fact is that most people's experience is as a user of data, which determines their priorities. Also, it is difficult to have the motivation for learning about data collection when one does not know what it is subsequently used for. Having spent considerable time learning how to analyse data, it is now time to look at its collection and preparation.

There are two reasons why you might find this chapter useful. First, it will help if you have to carry out some kind of survey yourself. Second, it will help you in your data analysis, even if you are using someone else's data. Knowing the issues involved in data collection can help your judgement about the quality of the data you are using.

When conducting statistical research, there are two ways of obtaining data:

1 use secondary data sources, such as the UN Yearbook, or
2 collect sample data personally, a primary data source.

The first category should nowadays be divided into two sub-sections: printed and electronic sources. The latter is obviously becoming more important as time progresses, but printed documentation still has its uses. Using secondary data sources sounds simple, but it is easy to waste valuable time by making elementary errors. The first part of this chapter provides some simple advice to help you avoid such mistakes.

Much of this text has been concerned with the analysis of sample evidence and the inferences that can be drawn from it. It has been stressed that this evidence must come from randomly drawn samples and, although the notion of randomness was discussed in Chapter 2, the precise details of random sampling have not been set out.

The second part of this chapter is therefore concerned with the problems of collecting sample survey data prior to its analysis. The decision to collect the data personally depends upon the type of problem faced, the current availability of data relating to the problem and the time and cost needed to conduct a survey. It should not be forgotten that the first question that needs answering is whether the answer obtained is worth the cost of finding it. It is probably not worthwhile for the government to spend £50 000 to find out how many biscuits people eat, on average (though it may be worth biscuit manufacturers doing this). The sampling procedure is always subject to some limit on cost, therefore, and the researcher is trying to obtain the best value for money.

Using secondary data sources

Much of the research in economics is based on secondary data sources, i.e. data which the researcher did not collect herself. The data may be in the form of official statistics such as those published in *Economic Trends* or they may come from unofficial surveys. In either case one has to use the data as presented; there is no control over sampling procedures.

It may seem easy enough to look up some figures in a publication, but there are a number of pitfalls for the unwary. The following advice comes from experience, some of it painful, and it may help you to avoid wasting time and effort. I have also learned much from the experiences of my students, whom I have also watched suffer.

A lot of data is now available online, so the advice given here covers both printed and electronic sources, with a separate section for the latter.

Make sure you collect the right data

This may seem obvious, but most variables can be measured in a variety of different ways. Suppose you want to measure the cost of labour (over time) to firms. Should you use the wage rate or earnings? The latter includes payment for extra hours such as overtime payments and reflects general changes in the length of the working week. Is the wage measured per hour or per week? Does it include part-time workers? If so, a trend in the proportion of part-timers will bias the wage series. Does the series cover all workers, men only, or women only? Again, changes in the composition will influence the wage series. What about tax and social security costs? Are they included? There are many questions one could ask.

One needs to have a clear idea therefore of the precise variable one needs to collect. This will presumably depend upon the issue in question. Economic theory might provide some guidance: for instance, theory suggests that firms care about *real* wage rates (i.e. after taking account of inflation, so related to the price of the goods the firm sells) so this is what one should measure. Check the definition of any series you collect (this is often at the back of the printed publication, or in a separate supplement giving explanatory notes and definitions). Make sure that the definition has not changed over the time period you require: the definition of unemployment used in the UK changed about twenty times in the 1980s, generally with the effect of reducing *measured* unemployment, even if actual unemployment was unaffected. In the UK the geographical coverage of data may vary: one series may relate to the UK, another to Great Britain and yet another to England and Wales. Care should obviously be taken if one is trying to compare such series.

Try to get the most up-to-date figures

Many macroeconomic series are revised as more information becomes available. The balance of payments serves as a good example. The first edition of this book showed the balance of payments (current balance, in £m for the UK) for 1970, as published in successive years, as follows:

1971	1972	1973	1974	1975	1976	1977	1978	. . .	1986
579	681	692	707	735	733	695	731	. . .	795

The difference between the largest and smallest figures is of the order of 37%, a wide range. In the third edition of this book the figure was (from the 1999 edition of *Economic Trends Annual Supplement*) £911m which is 57% higher than the initial estimate. The latest figure at the time of writing is £819m. Most series are better than this. The balance of payments is hard to measure because it is the small difference between two large numbers, exports and imports. A

5% increase in measured exports and a 5% decrease in measured imports could thus change the measured balance by 100% or more.

One should always try to get the most up-to-date figures, therefore, which often means working *backwards* through data publications, i.e. use the current issue first and get data back as far as is available, then get the previous issue to go back a little further, etc. This can be tedious but it will also give some idea of the reliability of the data from the size of data revisions.

Keep a record of your data sources

You should always keep *precise* details of where you obtained each item of data. If you need to go back to the original publication (to check on the definition of a series, for example) you will then be able to find it easily. It is easy to spend hours (if not *days*) trying to find the source of some interesting numbers that you wish to update. 'Precise details' means the name of the publication, issue number or date, and table or page number. It also helps to keep the library reference number of the publication if it is obscure. It is best to take a photo-copy of the data (but check copyright restrictions) rather than just copy it down, if possible.

Keeping data in *Excel* or another spreadsheet

Spreadsheets are ideal for keeping your data. It is often a good idea to keep the data all together in one worksheet and extract portions of them as necessary and analyse them in another worksheet. Alternatively, it is usually quite easy to transfer data from the spreadsheet to another program (e.g. *Minitab* or *SPSS*) for more sophisticated analysis. In most spreadsheets you can attach a comment to any cell, so you can use this to keep a record of the source of each observation, changes of definition, etc. Thus you can retain all the information about your data together in one place.

Check your data

Once you have collected your data you must check it. Once you have done this, it is probably worth checking it again. Better, get someone else to do the second check. Note that if your data are wrong then all your subsequent calculations could be incorrect and you will have wasted much time.

A useful way to check the data is first to graph it (e.g. a time-series plot). Obvious outliers will show up and you can investigate them for possible errors. Do not just rely on the graphs, however, look through your data and check it against the original source. Don't forget that the original source could be wrong too, so be wary of 'unusual' observations.

Using electronic sources of data

A vast amount of data is now available electronically, usually online, and this is becoming increasingly the norm. Sometimes the data are available free but sometimes they have to be paid for, especially if they have a commercial value. My experience suggests that many students nowadays only consider online resources, which I feel is a mistake. Not everything is online and sometimes, even if it is, it is extremely hard to find. It can sometimes take less time to go to the library, find the appropriate journal and type in the numbers. As an estimate, one hundred observations should take no longer than about ten minutes to type into a computer, which is probably quicker than finding them electronically, converting to the right format, etc. Hence the advantage of online data lies principally with large datasets.

Obtaining data electronically should avoid input errors and provide consistent, up-to-date figures. However, this is not always guaranteed. For example, the UK Office for National Statistics (ONS) online databank provides plenty of information, but some of the series clearly have breaks in them and there is little warning of this in the on-screen documentation. The series for revenue per admission to cinemas (roughly the price of admission) goes:

1963	1964	1965	1966	1967
37.00	40.30	45.30	20.60	21.80

which strongly suggests a break in the series in 1966 (especially as admissions *fell* by 12% between 1965 and 1966!). Later in the series, the observations appear to be divided by 100. The lesson is that even with electronic data you should check the numbers to ensure they are correct.

You need to follow the same advice with electronic sources as with printed ones: make sure you collect the right variables and keep a note of your source. Online sources seem to be less good than many printed sources about providing definitions of the variables. It is often unclear if the data are in real terms, seasonally adjusted, etc. Sometimes you may need to go to the printed document to find the definitions, even if the data themselves come from the internet. Keeping a note of your source means taking down the URL of the site you visit. Remember that some sites generate the page 'on demand' so the web address is not a permanent one and typing it in later on will not take you back to the same source. In these circumstances is may be better to note the 'root' part of the address (e.g. www.imf.org/data/) rather than the complete detail. You should also take a note of the date you accessed the site, this may be needed if you put the source into a bibliography.

Tips on downloading data

- If you are downloading a spreadsheet, save it to your hard disk then include the URL of the source within the spreadsheet itself. You will always know where it came from. You can do the same with Word documents.
- You cannot do this with PDF files, which are read-only. You could save the file to your disk, including the URL within the file name (but avoid putting extra full stops in the file name, that confuses the operating system. Replace them with hyphens.)
- You can use the 'Text select tool' within Acrobat to copy items of data from a PDF file and then paste them into a spreadsheet.
- Often, when pasting several columns of data into Excel, all the numbers go into a single column. You can fix this using the Data, Text to Columns menu. Experimentation is required, but it works well.

Since there are now so many online sources (and they are constantly changing) a list of useful data sites rapidly becomes out of date. The following sites seem to have withstood the test of time so far and have a good chance of surviving throughout the life of this edition.

- The UK Office for National Statistics is at http://www.statistics.gov.uk/ and their Statbase service supplies over 1000 datasets online for free. This is tied to information on 13 'themes', such as education, agriculture, etc.
- The Data and Story Library at http://lib.stat.cmu.edu/DASL/ is just that: datasets with accompanying statistical analyses which are useful for learning.
- The IMF's World Economic Database is at http://www.imf.org/ (follow the links to publications, World Economic Outlook, then the database). It has macroeconomic series for most countries for several years. It is easy to download in csv (text) format, for use in spreadsheets.
- The Biz/Ed site at http://www.bized.ac.uk/ contains useful material on business (including financial case studies of companies) as well as economic data. There is a link from here to the Penn World Tables, which contain national accounts data for many countries (on a useful, comparable basis) from 1960 onwards. Alternatively, visit the Penn home page at http://pwt.econ.upenn.edu/.
- The World Bank provides a lot of information, particularly relating to developing countries, at http://www.worldbank.org/data/. Much of the data appears to be in .pdf format so, although it is easy to view on-screen, it cannot be easily transferred into a spreadsheet or similar software.
- Bill Goffe's Resources for Economists site (www.rfe.wustl.edu/EconFAQ) contains a data section which is a good starting-off point for data sources.
- Google. Possibly the most useful website of all. Intelligent use of this search tool is often the best way to find what you want.
- http://davidmlane.com/hyperstat/index.html has an online textbook and glossary. This is useful if you have a computer handy but not a textbook.

Collecting primary data

Primary data are data that you have collected yourself from original sources, often by means of a sample survey. This has the advantage that you can design the questionnaire to include the questions of interest to you and you have total control over all aspects of data collection. You can also choose the size of the sample (as long as you have sufficient funds available) so as to achieve the desired width of any confidence intervals.

Almost all surveys rely upon some method of sampling, whether random or not. The probability distributions which have been used in previous chapters as the basis of the techniques of estimation and hypothesis testing rely upon the samples having been drawn at random from the population. If this is not the case, then the formulae for confidence intervals, hypothesis tests, etc. are incorrect and not strictly applicable (they may be reasonable approximations but it is difficult to know how reasonable). In addition, the results about the bias and precision of estimators will be incorrect. For example, suppose an estimate of the average expenditure on repairs and maintenance by car owners is obtained from a sample survey. A poor estimate would arise if only Rolls-Royce owners were sampled, since they are not representative of the population as a whole. The precision of the estimator (the sample mean, $\bar{x}$) is likely to be poor because the mean of the sample could either be very low (Rolls-Royce cars are very reliable so rarely need repairs) or very high (if they do break down the high quality of the car necessitates a costly repair). This means the confidence interval estimate will be very wide and thus imprecise. It is not immediately obvious if the estimator would be biased upwards or downwards.

Thus some form of random sampling method is needed to be able to use the theory of the probability distributions of random variables. Nor should it be believed that the theory of random sampling can be ignored if a very large sample is taken, as the following cautionary tale shows. In 1936 the *Literary Digest* tried to predict the result of the forthcoming US election by sending out 10 million mail questionnaires. Two million were returned, but even with this enormous sample size Roosevelt's vote was incorrectly estimated by a margin of 19 percentage points. The problem is that those who respond to questionnaires are not a random sample of those who receive them.

The meaning of random sampling

The definition of random sampling is that every element of the population should have a known, non-zero probability of being included in the sample. The problem with the sample of cars used above was that Ford cars (for example) had a zero probability of being included. Many sampling procedures give an equal probability of being selected to each member of the population but this is not an essential requirement. It is possible to adjust the sample data to take account of unequal probabilities of selection. If, for example, Rolls-Royce had a much greater chance of being included than Ford, then the estimate of the population mean would be calculated as a weighted average of the sample observations, with greater weight being given to the few 'Ford' observations than to relatively abundant 'Rolls-Royce' observations. A very simple illustration of this is given below. Suppose that for the population we have the following data:

	Rolls-Royce	Ford
Number in population	20 000	2 000 000
Annual repair bill	£1000	£200

Then the average repair bill is

$$\mu = \frac{20\ 000 \times 1000 + 2\ 000\ 000 \times 200}{2\ 020\ 000} = 207.92$$

Suppose the sample data are as follows:

	Rolls-Royce	Ford
Number in sample	20	40
Probability of selection	1/1000	1/50 000
Repair bill	£990	£205

To calculate the average repair bill from the sample data we use a weighted average, using the relative population sizes as weights, not the sample sizes:

$$\bar{x} = \frac{20\ 000 \times 990 + 2\ 000\ 000 \times 205}{2\ 020\ 000} = 212.77$$

If the sample sizes were used as weights the average would come out at £466.67, which is substantially incorrect.

As long as the probability of being in the sample is known (and hence the relative population sizes known), the weight can be derived; but if the probability is zero this procedure breaks down.

Other theoretical assumptions necessary for deriving the probability distribution of the sample mean or proportion are that the population is of infinite size and that each observation is independently drawn. In practice the former condition is never satisfied since no population is of infinite size, but most populations are large enough that it does not matter. For each observation to be independently drawn (i.e. the fact of one observation being drawn does not alter the probability of others in the sample being drawn) strictly requires that sampling be done with replacement, i.e. each observation drawn is returned to the population before the next observation is drawn. Again in practice this is often not the case, sampling being done without replacement, but again this is of negligible practical importance.

On occasion the population is quite small and the sample constitutes a substantial fraction of it. In these circumstances the finite population correction (fpc) should be applied to the formula for the variance of $\bar{x}$, the fpc being given by

(9.1) $\text{fpc} = (1 - n/N)$

where N is the population size and n the sample size. The table below illustrates its usage:

Variance of $\bar{x}$ from infinite population	Variance of $\bar{x}$ from finite population	Example values of fpc			
		$n = 20$	25	50	100
		$N = 50$	100	1000	10 000
σ^2/n	$\sigma^2/n \times (1 - n/N)$	0.60	0.75	0.95	0.99

The finite population correction serves to narrow the confidence interval because a sample size of (say) 25 reveals more about a population of 100 than about a population of 100 000, so there is less uncertainty about population parameters. When the sample size constitutes only a small fraction of the population (e.g. 5% or less) the finite population correction can be ignored in practice. If the whole population is sampled ($n = N$) then the variance becomes zero and there is no uncertainty about the population mean.

A further important aspect of random sampling occurs when there are two samples to be analysed, when it is important that the two samples are independently drawn. This means that the drawing of the first sample does not influence the drawing of the second sample. This is a necessary condition for the derivation of the probability distribution of the difference between the sample means (or proportions).

Types of random sample

The meaning and importance of randomness in the context of sampling has been explained. However, there are various different types of sampling, all of them random, but which have different statistical properties. Some methods lead to greater precision of the estimates, while others can lead to considerable cost savings in the collection of the sample data, but at the cost of lower precision. The aim of sampling is usually to obtain the most precise estimates of the parameter in question, but the best method of sampling will depend on the circumstances of each case. If it is costly to sample individuals, a sampling method which lowers cost may allow a much larger sample size to be drawn and thus good (precise) estimates to be obtained, even if the method is inherently not very precise. These issues are investigated in more detail below, as a number of different sampling methods are examined.

Simple random sampling

This type of sampling has the property that every possible sample that could be obtained from the population has an equal chance of being selected. This implies that each element of the population has an equal probability of being included in the sample, but this is not the defining characteristic of simple random sampling. As will be shown below, there are sampling methods where every member of the population has an equal chance of being selected, but some samples (i.e. certain combinations of population members) can never be selected.

The statistical methods in this book are based upon the assumption of simple random sampling from the population. It leads to the most straightforward formulae for estimation of the population parameters. Although many statistical surveys are not based upon simple random sampling, the use of statistical tests based on simple random sampling is justified since the sampling process is often hypothetical. For example, if one were to compare annual growth rates of two countries over a 30-year period, a z test on the difference of two sample means (i.e. the average annual growth rate in each country) would be conducted. In a sense the data are not a sample since they are the only possible data for those two countries over that time period. Why not just regard the data as constituting the whole population, therefore? Then it would just be a case of finding which country had the higher growth rate; there would be no uncertainty about it.

The alternative way of looking at the data would be to suppose that there exists some hypothetical population of annual growth rates and that the data for the two countries were drawn by (simple) random sampling from this population. Is this story consistent with the data available? In other words, could the data we have simply arise by chance? If the answer to this is no (i.e. the z score exceeds the critical value) then there is something causing a difference between the two countries (it may not be clear what that something is). In this case it is reasonable to assume that all possible samples have an equal chance of selection, i.e. that simple random sampling takes place. Since the population is hypothetical one might as well suppose it to have an infinite number of members, again required by sampling theory.

Stratified sampling

Returning to the practical business of sampling, one problem with simple random sampling is that it is possible to collect 'bad' samples, i.e. those which are unrepresentative of the population. An example of this is the 'basketball player' problem, i.e. in trying to estimate the average height of the population, the sample (by sheer bad luck) contains a lot of basketball players. One way round this problem is to ensure that the proportion of basketball players in the sample accurately reflects the proportion of basketball players in the population (i.e. very small!). The way to do this is to divide up the population into 'strata' and then to ensure that each stratum is properly represented in the sample. This is best illustrated by means of an example.

A survey of newspaper readership, which is thought to be associated with social class, is to be carried out. People higher up the social scale are more likely to read a newspaper and to read different newspapers from those at the bottom of the social scale. Suppose the population is made up of three social classes, A (highest), B and C as follows:

Percentage of population in social class		
A	B	C
20%	50%	30%

Suppose a sample of size 100 is taken. With luck it would contain 20 people from class A, 50 from B and 30 from C and thus would be representative of the population as a whole. But if, by bad luck (or bad sample design), all 100 people in the sample were from class A, poor results would be obtained since newspaper readership differs between social classes.

To avoid this type of problem a stratified sample is taken, which ensures that all social classes are represented in the sample. This means that the survey would have to ask people about their social class as well as their reading habits. The simplest form of stratified sampling is equiproportionate sampling, whereby a stratum which constitutes (say) 20% of the population also makes up 20% of the sample. For the example above the sample would be made up as follows:

Class	A	B	C	Total
Number in sample	20	50	30	100

It should be clear why stratified sampling constitutes an improvement over simple random sampling, since it rules out 'bad' samples, i.e. those not representative of the population. It is simply impossible to get a sample consisting completely of social class A, or B, or C. In fact, it is impossible to get a sample in anything but the proportions 20:50:30, as in the population; this is ensured by the method of collecting the sample.

It is easy to see when stratification leads to large improvements over simple random sampling. If there were no difference between strata (social classes) in reading habits then there would be no gain from stratification. If reading habits were the same regardless of social class there would be no point in dividing up the population by social class. On the other hand, if there were large differences between strata, but within strata reading habits were similar, then the gains from stratification would be large.

Stratification is beneficial therefore when

- the between-strata differences are large and
- the within-strata differences are small.

These benefits take the form of greater precision of the estimates, i.e. narrower confidence intervals.[1] The greater precision arises because stratified sampling makes use of supplementary information – i.e. the proportion of the population in each social class. Simple random sampling does not make use of this. Obviously, therefore, if those proportions of the population are unknown, stratified sampling cannot be carried out. However, even if the proportions are only known approximately there could be a gain in precision.

In this example social class is a stratification factor, i.e. a variable which is used to divide the population into strata. Other factors could, of course, be used, such as income or even height. A good stratification factor is one which is related to the subject of investigation. Income would probably be a good stratification factor, therefore, since it is related to reading habits, but height is not since there is probably little difference between tall and short people in the newspaper they read. What is a good stratification factor obviously depends upon the subject of study. A bed manufacturer might well find height to be a good stratification factor if conducting an enquiry into preferences about the size of beds. Although good stratification factors improve the precision of estimates, bad factors do not make them worse; there will simply be no gain over simple random sampling. It would be as if there were no differences between the social classes in reading habits, so that ensuring the right proportions in the sample is irrelevant, but it has no detrimental effects.

Proportional allocation of sample observations to the different strata (as done above) is the simplest method but is not necessarily the best. For the optimal allocation there should generally be a divergence from proportional allocation, and the sample should have more observations in a particular stratum (relative to proportional allocation):

- the more diverse the stratum, and
- the cheaper it is to sample the stratum.

Starting from the 20:50:30 proportional allocation derived earlier, suppose that members of class A all read the same newspaper, but those of class C read a variety of titles. Then the representation of class C in the sample should be increased, and that of A reduced. If it really were true that everyone in class A read the same paper then one observation from that class would be sufficient to yield all there is to know about it. Furthermore, if it is cheaper to sample class C, perhaps because they are geographically more concentrated than class A, then again the representation of class C in the sample should be increased. This is because, for a given budget, it will allow a larger total sample size.

---

[1] The formulae for calculating confidence intervals with stratified sampling are not given here, since they merit a whole book to themselves. The interested reader should consult C.A. Moser and G. Kalton, *Survey Methods in Social Investigation*, Heinemann, 1971.

Surveying concert-goers

A colleague and I carried out a survey of people attending a concert in Brighton (by Jamiroquai – hope they're still popular by the time you read this) to find out who they were, how much they spent in the town and how they got to the concert. The spreadsheet gives some of the results.

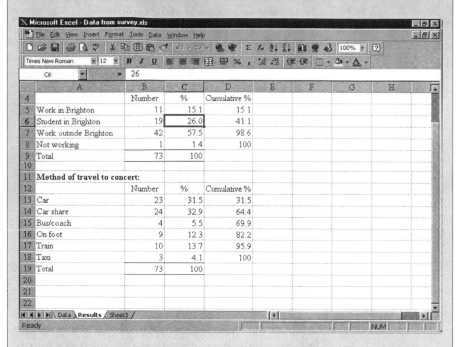

Note that the data are kept on one sheet and results on another, which are named appropriately.

The data were collected by face-to-face interviews before the concert. We did not have a sampling frame, so the (student) interviewers simply had to choose the sample themselves on the night. The one important instruction about sampling we gave them was that they should not interview more than one person in any group. People in the same group are likely to be influenced by each other (e.g. travel together) so we would not get independent observations, reducing the effective sample size.

From the results you can see that 41.1% either worked or studied in Brighton and that only one person in the sample was neither working nor studying. The second half of the table shows that 64.4% travelled to the show in a car (obviously adding to congestion in the town), about half of whom shared a car ride. Perhaps surprisingly, Brighton residents were just as likely to use their car to travel as were those from out of town.

The average level of spending was £24.20, predominantly on food (£7.38), drink (£5.97) and shopping (£5.37). The last category had a high variance associated with it – many people spent nothing, one person spent £200 in the local shops.

Cluster sampling   A third form of sampling is cluster sampling which, although intrinsically inefficient, can be much cheaper than other forms of sampling, allowing a larger sample size to be collected. Drawing a simple, or stratified, random sample of size 100 from the whole of Britain would be very expensive to collect since the sample observations would be geographically very spread out. Interviewers would have to make many long and expensive journeys simply to collect one or two observations. To avoid this, the population can be divided into 'clusters' (for example, regions or local authorities) and one or more of these clusters are then randomly chosen. Sampling takes place only within the selected clusters, and is therefore geographically concentrated, and the cost of sampling falls, allowing a larger sample to be collected.

Within each cluster one can have either a 100% sample or a lower sampling fraction, which is called multi-stage sampling (this is explained further below). Cluster sampling gives unbiased estimates of population parameters but, for a given sample size, these are less precise than the results from simple or stratified sampling. This arises in particular when the clusters are very different from each other, but fairly homogeneous within themselves. In this case, once a cluster is chosen, if it is unrepresentative of the population, a poor (inaccurate) estimate of the population parameter is inevitable. The ideal circumstances for cluster sampling are when all clusters are identical, since in that case examining one cluster is as good as examining the whole population.

Dividing up the population into clusters and dividing it into strata are similar procedures, but the difference is that sampling is from one or at most a few clusters, but from all strata. This is reflected in the characteristics which make for good sampling. In the case of stratified sampling, it is beneficial if the between-strata differences are large and the within-strata differences small. For cluster sampling this is reversed: it is desirable to have small between-cluster differences but heterogeneity within clusters. Cluster sampling is less efficient (precise) for a given sample size, but is cheaper and so can offset this disadvantage with a larger sample size. In general, cluster sampling needs a much larger sample to be effective, so is only worthwhile where there are significant gains in cost.

Multi-stage sampling

Multi-stage sampling was briefly referred to in the previous section and is commonly found in practice. It may consist of a mixture of simple, stratified and cluster sampling at the various stages of sampling. Consider the problem of selecting a random sample of 1000 people from a population of 25 million to find out about voting intentions. A simple random sample would be extremely expensive to collect, for the reasons given above, so an alternative method must be found. Suppose further that it is suspected that voting intentions differ according to whether one lives in the north or south of the country and whether one is a home owner or renter. How is the sample to be selected? The following would be one appropriate method.

First the country is divided up into clusters of counties or regions, and a random sample of these taken, say one in five. This would be the first way of reducing the cost of selection, since only one-fifth of all counties now need to be visited. This one-in-five sample would be stratified to ensure that north and south were both appropriately represented. To ensure that each voter has an equal chance of being in the sample, the probability of a county being drawn should be proportional to its adult population. Thus a county with twice the population of another should have twice the probability of being in the sample.

Having selected the counties, the second stage would be to select a random sample of local authorities within each selected county. This might be a one-in-ten sample from each county and would be a simple random sample within each cluster. Finally a selection of voters from within each local authority would be taken, stratified according to tenure. This might be a one in 500 sample. The sampling fractions would therefore be

$$\frac{1}{5} \times \frac{1}{10} \times \frac{1}{500} = \frac{1}{25\ 000}$$

So from the population of 25 million voters a sample of 1000 would be collected. For different population sizes the sampling fractions could be adjusted so as to achieve the goal of a sample size of 1000.

The sampling procedure is a mixture of simple, stratified and cluster sampling. The two stages of cluster sampling allow the selection of 50 local authorities for study and so costs are reduced. The north and south of the country are both adequately represented and housing tenures are also correctly represented in the sample by the stratification at the final stage. The resulting confidence intervals will be difficult to calculate but should give an improvement over the method of simple random sampling.

Quota sampling

Quota sampling is a non-random method of sampling and therefore it is impossible to use sampling theory to calculate confidence intervals from the sample data, or to find whether or not the sample will give biased results. Quota sampling simply means obtaining the sample information as best one can, for example, by asking people in the street. However, it is by far the cheapest method of sampling and so allows much larger sample sizes. As shown above, large sample sizes can still give biased results if sampling is non-random; but in some cases the budget is too small to afford even the smallest properly conducted random sample, so a quota sample is the only alternative.

Even with quota sampling, where the interviewer is simply told to go out and obtain (say) 1000 observations, it is worth making some crude attempt at stratification. The problem with human interviewers is that they are notoriously non-random, so that when they are instructed to interview every tenth person they see (a reasonably random method), if that person turns out to be a shabbily dressed tramp slightly the worse for drink, they are quite likely to select the eleventh person instead. Shabbily dressed tramps, slightly the worse for drink, are therefore under-represented in the sample. To combat this sort of problem the interviewers are given quotas to fulfil, for example, 20 men and 20 women, ten old-age pensioners, one shabbily dressed tramp, etc., so that the sample will at least broadly reflect the population under study and give reasonable results.

It is difficult to know how accurate quota samples are, since it is rare for their results to be checked against proper random samples or against the population itself. Probably the most common quota samples relate to voting intentions and so can be checked against actual election results. The 1992 UK general election provides an interesting illustration. The opinion polls predicted a fairly substantial Labour victory but the outcome was a narrow Conservative majority. An enquiry concluded that the erroneous forecast occurred because a substantial number of voters changed their minds at the last moment and that there was 'differential turn-out', i.e. Conservative supporters were more likely to vote than Labour ones. Presumably, future opinion polls will try to take this into account.

Calculating the required sample size

Before collecting sample data it is obviously necessary to know how large the sample size has to be. The required sample size will depend upon two factors:

- the desired level of precision of the estimate, and
- the funds available to carry out the survey.

The greater the precision required the larger the sample size needs to be, other things being equal. But a larger sample will obviously cost more to collect and this might conflict with a limited amount of funds being available. There is a trade-off therefore between the two desirable objectives of high precision and low cost. The following example shows how these two objectives conflict.

A firm producing sweets wishes to find out the average amount of pocket money children receive per week. It wants to be 99% confident that the estimate is within 20 pence of the correct value. How large a sample is needed?

The problem is one of estimating a confidence interval, turned on its head. Instead of having the sample information $\bar{x}$, s and n, and calculating the confidence interval for μ, the desired width of the confidence interval is given and it is necessary to find the sample size n which will ensure this. The formula for the 99% confidence interval, assuming a Normal rather than t distribution (i.e. it is assumed that the required sample size will be large), is

(9.2) $[\bar{x} - 2.58 \times \sqrt{s^2/n}, \bar{x} + 2.58 \times \sqrt{s^2/n}]$

Diagrammatically this can be represented as in Figure 9.1.

The firm wants the distance between $\bar{x}$ and μ to be no more than 20 pence in either direction, which means that the confidence interval must be 40 pence wide. The value of n which makes the confidence interval 40 pence wide has to be found. This can be done by solving the equation

$20 = 2.58 \times \sqrt{s^2/n}$

and hence by rearranging:

(9.3) $n = \dfrac{2.58^2 \times s^2}{20^2}$

Figure 9.1
The desired width of the confidence interval

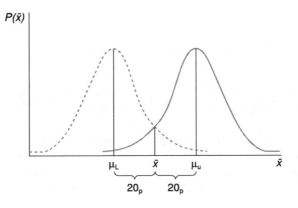

All that is now required to solve the problem is the value of s^2, the sample variance; but since the sample hasn't yet been taken this is not available. There are a number of ways of trying to get round this problem:

- using the results of existing surveys if available,
- conducting a small, preliminary, survey,
- guessing.

These may not seem very satisfactory (particularly the last), but something has to be done and some intelligent guesswork should give a reasonable estimate of s^2. Suppose, for example, that a survey of children's *spending* taken five years previously showed a standard deviation of 30p. It might be reasonable to expect that the standard deviation of spending would be similar to the standard deviation of income, so 30p (updated for inflation) can be used as an estimate of the standard deviation. Suppose that five years' inflation turns the 30p into 50p. Using $s = 50$ we obtain

$$n = \frac{2.58^2 \times 50^2}{20^2} = 41.6$$

giving a required sample size of 42 (the sample size has to be an integer). This is a large ($n \geq 25$) sample size so the use of the Normal distribution was justified.

Is the firm willing to pay for such a large sample? Suppose it was willing to pay out £1000 in total for the survey, which costs £600 to set up and then £6 per person sampled. The total cost would be £600 + 42 × 6 = £852 which is within the firm's budget. If the firm wished to spend less than this, it would have to accept a smaller sample size and thus a lower precision or a lower level of confidence. For example, if only a 95% confidence level were required, the appropriate z score would be 1.96, yielding

$$n = \frac{1.96^2 \times 50^2}{20^2} = 24.01$$

A sample size of 24 would only cost £600 + 6 × 24 = £804. (At this sample size the assumption that $\bar{x}$ follows a Normal distribution becomes less tenable, so the results should be treated with caution. Use of the t distribution is tricky, because the appropriate t value depends upon the number of degrees of freedom which in turn depends on sample size, which is what is being looked for!)

The general formula for finding the required sample size is

(9.4) $$n = \frac{z_\alpha^2 \times s^2}{p^2}$$

where z_α is the z score appropriate for the $(100 - \alpha)\%$ confidence level and p is the desired accuracy (20 pence in this case).

Collecting the sample

The sampling frame

We now move on to the fine detail of how to select the individual observations which make up the sample. In order to do this it is necessary to have some sort of sampling frame, i.e. a list of all the members of the population from which the sample is to be drawn. This can be a problem if the population is extremely large, for example the population of a country, since it is difficult to manipulate so much information (cutting up 50 million pieces of paper to put into a hat for a random draw is a tedious business). Alternatively the list might not even exist or, if it does, not be in one place convenient for consultation and use. In this case there is often an advantage to multi-stage sampling, for the selection of regions or even local authorities is fairly straightforward and not too time-consuming. Once at this lower level the sampling frame is more manageable (each local authority has an electoral register, for example) and individual observations can be relatively easily chosen. Thus it is not always necessary to have a complete sampling frame for the entire population in one place.

Choosing from the sampling frame

There is a variety of methods available for selecting a sample of (say) 1000 observations from a sampling frame of (say) 25 000 names, varying from the manual to the electronic. The oldest method is to cut up 25 000 pieces of paper, put them in a (large) hat, shake it (to randomise) and pick out 1000. This is fairly time-consuming, however, and has some pitfalls – if the pieces are not all cut to the same size is the probability of selection the same? It is much better if the population in the sampling frame is numbered in some way, for then one only has to select random numbers. This can be done by using a table of random numbers (see Table A1 on page **364**, for example), or a computer. The use of random number tables for such purposes is an important feature of statistics and in 1955 the Rand Corporation produced a book entitled *A Million Random Digits with 100 000 Normal Deviates*. This book, as the title suggests, contained nothing but pages of random numbers which allowed researchers to collect random samples. Interestingly, the authors did not bother to fully proofread the text, since a few (random) errors here and there wouldn't matter! These numbers were calculated electronically and nowadays every computer has a facility for rapidly choosing a set of random numbers. (It is an interesting question how a computer, which follows rigid rules of behaviour, can select random numbers which, by definition, are unpredictable by any rule.)

A further alternative, if a 1 in 25 sample is required, is to select a random starting point between 1 and 25 and then select every subsequent 25th observation (e.g. the 3rd, 28th, 53rd, etc.). This is a satisfactory procedure if the sampling frame is randomly sorted to start with, but otherwise there can be problems. For example, if the list is sorted by income (poorest first), a low starting value will almost certainly give an underestimate of the population mean. If all the numbers were randomly selected, this 'error' in the starting value will not be important.

Interviewing techniques

Good training of interviewers is vitally important to the results of a survey. It is very easy to lead an interviewee into a particular answer to a question. Consider the following two sets of questions:

A

1 Do you know how many people were killed by the atomic bomb at Hiroshima?
2 Do you think nuclear weapons should be banned?

B

1 Do you believe in nuclear deterrence?
2 Do you think nuclear weapons should be banned?

$A2$ is almost certain to get a higher 'yes' response than $B2$. Even a different ordering of the questions can have an effect upon the answers (consider asking $A2$ before $A1$). The construction of the questionnaire has to be done with care, therefore. The manner in which the questions are asked is also important, since it can often suggest the answer. Good interviewers are trained to avoid these problems by sticking precisely to the wording of the question and not to suggest an expected answer.

Telephone surveys

An article by M. Collins in the *Journal of the Royal Statistical Society* reveals some of the difficulties in conducting surveys by telephone. First, the sampling frame is incomplete since, although most people have a telephone, some are not listed in the directory. In the late 1980s this was believed to be around 12% of all numbers, but it has been growing since, to around 40%. (Part of this trend, of course, may be due to people getting fed up with being pestered by salespersons and 'market researchers'.) Researchers have responded with 'random digit dialling' which is presumably made easier by modern computerised equipment.

Matters are unlikely to improve for researchers in the future. The answering machine is often used as a barrier to unwanted calls and many residential lines connect to fax machines. Increasing deregulation and mobile phone use mean it will probably become more and more difficult to obtain a decent sampling frame for a proper survey.

Source: M. Collins, Sampling for UK telephone surveys, *J. Royal Statistical Society*, Series A, 162 (1), 1999.

Even when these procedures are adhered to there can be various types of response bias. The first problem is of non-response, due to the subject not being at home when the interviewer calls. There might be a temptation to remove that person from the sample and call on someone else, but this should be resisted. There could well be important differences between those who are at home all day and those who are not, especially if the survey concerns employment or spending patterns, for example. Continued efforts should be made to contact the subject. One should be wary of surveys which have low response rates, particularly where it is suspected that the non-response is in some way systematic and related to the goal of the survey.

A second problem is that subjects may not answer the question truthfully for one reason or another, sometimes inadvertently. An interesting example of this occurred in the survey into sexual behaviour carried out in Britain in 1992 (see *Nature*, 3 December 1992). Amongst other things, this found the following:

- The average number of heterosexual partners during a woman's lifetime is 3.4.
- The average number of heterosexual partners during a man's lifetime is 9.9.

This may be in line with one's beliefs about behaviour, but, in fact, the figures must be wrong. The *total* number of partners of all women must by definition equal the *total* number for all men. Since there are approximately equal numbers of males and females in the UK the averages must therefore be about the same. So how do the above figures come about?

It is too much to believe that international trade holds the answer. It seems unlikely that British men are so much more attractive to foreign women than British women are to foreign men. Nor is an unrepresentative sample likely. It was carefully chosen and quite large (around 20 000). The answer would appear to be that some people are lying. Either women are being excessively modest or (more likely?) men are boasting. Perhaps the answer is to divide by three whenever a man talks about his sexual exploits!

For an update on this story, see the article by J. Wadsworth *et al.*, What is a mean? An examination of the inconsistency between men and women in reporting sexual partnerships, *J. Royal Statistical Society*, 1996, Series A. 159 (1).

Case study: the UK Expenditure and Food Survey

Introduction

The Expenditure and Food Survey (EFS) is an example of a large government survey which examines households' expenditure patterns (with a particular focus on food expenditures) and income receipts. It is worth having a brief look at it, therefore, to see how the principles of sampling techniques outlined in this chapter are put into practice. The EFS succeeded the Family Expenditure in 2001 and uses a similar design. The EFS is used for many different purposes, including the calculation of weights to be used in the UK Retail Price Index, and the assessment of the effects of changes in taxes and state benefits upon different households.

Choosing the sample

The sample design is known as a three-stage, rotating, stratified, random sample. This is obviously quite complex so will be examined stage by stage.

Stage 1

The country is first divided into 168 strata, each stratum made up of a number of local authorities sharing similar characteristics. The characteristics used as stratification factors are

- geographic area,
- urban or rural character (based on a measure of population density),
- prosperity (based on a measure of property values).

A stratum might therefore be made up of local authorities in the South West region, of medium population density and high prosperity.

In each quarter of the year, one local authority from each stratum is chosen at random, the probability of selection being proportional to population. Once an authority has been chosen, it remains in the sample for one year (four quarters) before being replaced. Only a quarter of the authorities in the sample are replaced in any quarter, which gives the sample its 'rotating' characteristic. Each quarter some authorities are discarded, some kept and some new ones brought in.

Stage 2

From each local authority selected, four wards (smaller administrative units) are selected, one to be used in each of the four quarters for which the local authority appears in the sample.

Stage 3

Finally, within each ward, 16 addresses are chosen at random, and these constitute the sample.

Altogether this means that 10 752 ($168 \times 4 \times 16$) households are chosen each year to make up the sample.

The sampling frame

The Postcode Address File, a list of all postal delivery addresses, is used as the sampling frame. Previously the register of electors in each ward was used but had some drawbacks: it was under-representative of those who have no permanent home or who move frequently (e.g. tramps, students, etc.). The fact that many people took themselves off the register in the early 1990s in order to avoid paying the Community Charge could also have affected the sample. The addresses are chosen from the register by interval sampling from a random starting point.

About 12 000 addresses are targeted each year, but around 11% prove to be business addresses, leaving approximately the 10 752 households mentioned above. The response rate is about 63% (from the 12 000), meaning that the actual sample consists of about 7500 households each year. Given the complexity of the information gathered, this is a remarkably good figure.

Collection of information

The data are collected by interview, and by asking participants to keep a diary in which they record everything they purchase over a two-week period. Highly skilled interviewers are required to ensure accuracy and compliance with the survey, and each participating family is visited serveral times. As a small inducement to cooperate, each member of the family is paid a small sum of money (it is to be hoped that the anticipation of this does not distort their expenditure patterns!).

Sampling errors

Given the complicated survey design it is difficult to calculate sampling errors exactly. The multi-stage design of the sample actually tends to increase the sampling error relative to a simple random sample, but, of course, this is offset by cost savings which allow a greatly increased sample size. Overall, the results of the survey are of good quality, and can be verified by comparison with other statistics, such as retail sales, for example.

Summary

- A primary data source is one where you obtain the data yourself or have access to all the original observations.

- A secondary data source contains a summary of the original data, usually in the form of tables.

- When collecting data always keep detailed notes of the sources of all information, how it was collected, precise definitions of the variables, etc.

- Some data can be obtained electronically, which saves having to type it into a computer, but the data still need to be checked for errors.

- There are various types of random sample, including simple, stratified and clustered random samples. The methods are sometimes combined in multi-stage samples.

- The type of sampling affects the size of the standard errors of the sample statistics. The most precise sampling method is not necessarily the best if it costs more to collect (since the overall sample size that can be afforded will be smaller).

- Quota sampling is a non-random method of sampling which has the advantage of being extremely cheap. It is often used for opinion polls and surveys.

- The sampling frame is the list (or lists) from which the sample is drawn. If it omits important elements of the population its use could lead to biased results.

- Careful interviewing techniques are needed to ensure reliable answers are obtained from participants in a survey.

Key terms and concepts		
primary and secondary data	quota sampling	spreadsheet
online data sources	sampling methods	finite population correction
simple random sampling	random sample	cluster sampling
	stratified sampling	sampling frame
	multi-stage sampling	

Problems

Some of the more challenging problems are indicated by highlighting the problem number in colour.

Problem 9.1 What issues of definition arise in trying to measure 'output'?

Problem 9.2 What issues of definition arise in trying to measure 'unemployment'?

Problem 9.3 Find the gross domestic product for both the UK and the US for the period 1995–2003. Obtain both series in constant prices.

Problem 9.4 Find figures for the monetary aggregate M0 for the years 1995–2003 in the UK, in nominal terms.

Problem 9.5 A firm wishes to know the average weekly expenditure on food by households to within £2, with 95% confidence. If the variance of food expenditure is thought to be about 400, what sample size does the firm need to achieve its aim?

Problem 9.6 A firm has £10 000 to spend on a survey. It wishes to know the average expenditure on gas by businesses to within £30 with 99% confidence. The variance of expenditure is believed to be about 40 000. The survey costs £7000 to set up and then £15 to survey each firm. Can the firm achieve its aim with the budget available?

Problem 9.7
(Project)
Visit your college library to collect data to answer the following question. Has females' remuneration risen relative to men's over the past ten years? You should write a short report on your findings. This should include a section describing the data collection process, including any problems encountered and decisions you had to make. Compare your results with those of other students.

Problem 9.8
(Project)
Do a survey to find the average age of cars parked on your college campus. (A letter or digit denoting the registration year can be found on the number plate – precise details can be obtained in various guides to used-car prices.) You might need stratified sampling (e.g. if administrators have newer cars than faculty and students, for example). You could extend the analysis by comparing the results with a public car park. You should write a brief report outlining your survey methods and the results you obtain. If several students do such a survey you could compare results.

References   C.A. Moset and G. Kalton, *Survey Methods in Social Investigations*, Heinemann, 1971.

Rand Corporation, *A Million Random Digits with 100 000 Normal Deviates*, The Glencoe Press, 1955.

Topic 9

Sampling and Sampling Distributions

Chapter 7

Sampling and Sampling Distributions

Chapter Outline

Introduction

In Chapters 4, 5, and 6 we developed probability models that can be used to represent the underlying variability of various business and economic processes. In Chapter 3 we presented descriptive statistics that can be used to summarize samples of data obtained from these various processes. In this chapter we link these concepts. This combination enables us to construct probability models for various statistics computed from sample data. These probability models are called *sampling distributions* and will be used to develop various procedures for statistical inference throughout the remainder of this book.

Statistical procedures focus on drawing inferences about large populations of items by using a small sample of the items. Typical examples of populations include:

1. *All* families living in the city of Chicago
2. *All* stocks traded on the New York Stock Exchange
3. The set of *all* claims for automobile accident insurance coverage received during a year
4. *All* cars of a particular model
5. *All* accounts receivable for a large automobile parts supplier

We might be interested in learning about specific measured characteristics for individuals in these populations. For example, we might want to make an inference about the mean and variance of the population distribution of family incomes in Chicago or about the proportion of all families in the city with annual incomes below $20,000.

7.1 SAMPLING FROM A POPULATION

We often use samples instead of the entire population because the cost and time of measuring every item in the population would be prohibitive. Also, in some cases measurement requires destruction of individual items. In general, we achieve greater accuracy by carefully obtaining a random sample of the population instead of spending the resources to measure every item. There are two important reasons for this result. First, it is often very difficult to obtain and measure every item in a population, and even if possible, the cost would be very high for a large population. For example, it is well known among statistical professionals that the census conducted every 10 years produces an undercount in which certain groups are seriously underrepresented (Reference 2). Second, as we learn in this chapter, properly selected samples can be used to obtain measured estimates of population characteristics that are quite close to the actual population values. The ideal sample for this purpose is a *simple random sample*.

> ### Simple Random Sample
> Suppose that we want to select a sample of *n* objects from a population of *N* objects. A **simple random sample** is selected such that every object has an equal probability of being selected and the objects are selected independently—the selection of one object does not change the probability of selecting any other objects.
>
> Simple random samples are the ideal. In a number of real-world sampling studies analysts develop alternative sampling procedures to lower the costs of sampling. But the basis for determining if these alternative sampling strategies are acceptable is how closely the results approximate those of a simple random sample.

It is important that a sample represent the population as a whole. If a marketing manager wants to assess reactions to a new food product, she does not sample only her friends and neighbors. Those groups are unlikely to have views that represent those of the entire population and are likely to be concentrated over a narrower range. To avoid these problems, we select a simple random sample. Random sampling is our insurance policy against allowing personal biases to influence the selection.

Simple random sampling can be implemented in many ways. We can place the *N population* items—for example, colored balls—in a large barrel and mix them thoroughly. Then from this well-mixed barrel we can select individual balls from different parts of the barrel. In practice, we often use random numbers to select objects that can be assigned some numerical value. For example, market research groups may use random numbers to select telephone numbers to call and ask about preferences for a product. Various statistical computer packages and spreadsheets have routines for obtaining random numbers, and these are generally used for most sampling studies. These computer-generated random numbers have the required properties to develop random samples. Organizations that require random samples from large human populations—for example, political candidates seeking to determine voter preference—will use professional sampling firms, which are organized to select and manage the sampling process. Good sampling requires considerable work and has a high cost.

We focus here on methods for analyzing results from simple random samples to gain information about the population. This process, our coverage of which will extend over the next five chapters, is known as classical inference. These methods generally assume that simple random samples are being used. However, there are other sampling procedures, and in some applied circumstances alternative sampling schemes may be preferred.

Random samples provide protection against the sample's being unrepresentative of the population. If a population is repeatedly sampled using random sampling procedures, no particular subgroup is overrepresented or underrepresented in the samples. Moreover, the concept of a sampling distribution allows us to determine the probability of obtaining a particular sample.

We use sample information to make inferences about the parent population. The distribution of all values of interest in this population can be represented by a random variable. It would be too ambitious to attempt to describe the entire population distribution based on a small random sample of observations. However, we may well be able to make quite firm inferences about important characteristics of the population distribution, such as the population mean and variance. For example, given a random sample of the fuel consumption for 20 cars of a particular model, we can use the sample mean and variance to make inferential statements about the population mean and variance of fuel consumption. This inference will be based on the sample information. We can ask questions such as this: "If the fuel consumption, in miles per gallon, of the population of all cars of a particular model has a mean of 25 and a standard deviation of 2, what is the probability that for a random sample of 20 such cars the sample mean fuel consumption will be less than 24 miles per gallon?" We can then use the sampling distribution of the sample mean to answer that question.

We need to distinguish between the population attributes and the random sample attributes. In the preceding paragraph the population of fuel consumption measurements for all automobiles of a particular model has a distribution with a specific mean. This mean, an attribute of the population, is a fixed (but unknown) number. We make inferences about this attribute by drawing a random sample from the population and computing the sample mean. For each sample we draw, there will be a different sample mean, and the sample mean can be regarded as a random variable with a probability distribution. The distribution of possible sample means provides a basis for inferential statements about the sample. In this chapter we examine the properties of *sampling distributions*.

Sampling Distributions

Consider a random sample selected from a population that is used to make an inference about some population characteristic, such as the population mean, μ, using a sample statistic, such as the sample mean, $\bar{x}$. The inference is based on the realization that every random sample has a different number for $\bar{x}$, and, thus, $\bar{x}$ is a random variable. The **sampling distribution** of this statistic is the probability distribution of the sample means obtained from all possible samples of the same number of observations drawn from the population.

We illustrate the concept of a sampling distribution by considering the position of a supervisor with six employees, whose years of experience are

$$2 \quad 4 \quad 6 \quad 6 \quad 7 \quad 8$$

Two of these employees are to be chosen randomly for a particular work group. The mean of the years of experience for this population of six employees is

$$\mu = \frac{2 + 4 + 6 + 6 + 7 + 8}{6} = 5.5$$

Now, let us consider the mean number of years of experience of the two employees chosen randomly from the population of six. Fifteen possible different random samples could be selected. Table 7.1 shows all of the possible samples and associated sample means. Note that some samples (such as 2, 6) occur twice because there are two employees with six years of experience in the population.

Each of the 15 samples in Table 7.1 has the same probability, 1/15, of being selected. Note that there are several occurrences of the same sample mean. For example, the sample mean 5.0 occurs three times, and, thus, the probability of obtaining a sample mean of 5.0 is 3/15. Table 7.2 presents the sampling distribution for the various sample means from the population, and the probability function is graphed in Figure 7.1.

We see that, while the number of years of experience for the six workers ranges from 2 to 8, the possible values of the sample mean have a range from only 3.0 to 7.5. In addition, more of the values lie in the central portion of the range.

Table 7.3 presents similar results for a sample size of $n = 5$, and Figure 7.2 presents the graph for the sampling distribution. Notice that the means are concentrated over a narrower range. These sample means are all closer to the population mean,

Table 7.1 Samples and Sample Means from the Worker Population Sample Size $n = 2$

Sample	Sample Mean	Sample	Sample Mean
2, 4	3.0	4, 8	6.0
2, 6	4.0	6, 6	6.0
2, 6	4.0	6, 7	6.5
2, 7	4.5	6, 8	7.0
2, 8	5.0	6, 7	6.5
4, 6	5.0	6, 8	7.0
4, 6	5.0	7, 8	7.5
4, 7	5.5		

Table 7.2   Sampling Distribution of the Sample Means from the Worker
Population Sample Size $n = 2$

SAMPLE MEAN $\bar{X}$	PROBABILITY OF $\bar{X}$
3.0	1/15
4.0	2/15
4.5	1/15
5.0	3/15
5.5	1/15
6.0	2/15
6.5	2/15
7.0	2/15
7.5	1/15

$\mu = 5.5$. We will always find this to be true—the sampling distribution be-comes concentrated closer to the population mean as the sample size increases. This important result provides an important foundation for statistical inference. In the fol-lowing sections and chapters we will build a set of rigorous analysis tools on this foundation.

INTERPRETATION

In this section we have developed the basic concept of sampling distributions. Here, the examples have come from a simple discrete distribution where it is possible to define all possible samples of a given sample size. From each possible sample the sample mean was computed, and the probability distribution of all possible sample means was constructed. From this simple process we discovered that, as the sample size increases, the distribution of the sample means—the sam-pling distribution—becomes more concentrated around the population mean. In most applied statistical work the populations are very large, and it is not practical or rational to construct the distribution of all possible samples of a given sample size. But by using what we have learned about random variables, we will be able to show that the sampling distributions for samples from all populations have the same characteristics as those shown for our simple discrete population. That result pro-vides the basis for the many useful applications that will be developed in subsequent chapters.

Figure 7.1
Probability
Function for
the Sampling
Distribution of
the Sample Means
for the Worker
Population
Sample Size $n = 2$

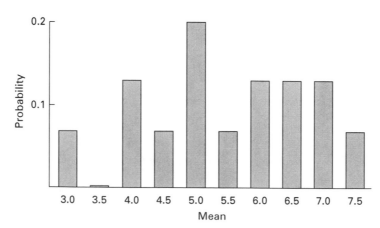

Table 7.3 Sampling Distribution of the Sample Means from the Worker Population Sample Size $n = 5$

Sample	$\bar{x}$	Probability
2, 4, 6, 6, 7	5.0	1/6
2, 4, 6, 6, 8	5.2	1/6
2, 4, 6, 7, 8	5.4	1/3
2, 6, 6, 7, 8	5.8	1/6
4, 6, 6, 7, 8	6.2	1/6

Figure 7.2
Probability
Function for
the Sampling
Distribution of
the Sample Means
for the Worker
Population
Sample Size
$n = 5$

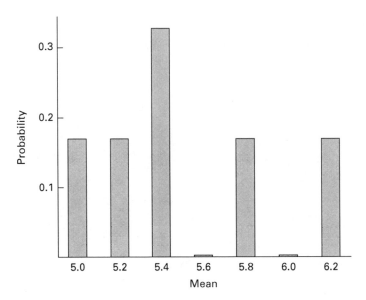

EXERCISES

Basic Exercises

7.1 Suppose that you toss a pair of dice and write down the value of the faces from each die.

   a. What is the population distribution for one die?

   b. Determine the sampling distribution of the sample means obtained by tossing two dice.

7.2 Suppose that you have a fair coin and you label the head side as 1 and the tail side as 0.

   a. Now, you are asked to flip the coin 2 times and write down the numerical value that results from each toss. Without actually flipping the coin write down the sampling distribution of the sample means.

   b. Repeat part (a) with the coin flipped 4 times.

   c. Repeat part (a) with the coin flipped 10 times.

Application Exercises

7.3 A population contains 6 million 0's and 4 million 1's. What is the approximate sampling distribution of the sample mean when

   a. The sample size is $n = 5$.

   b. The sample size is $n = 100$.

Note: There is a hard way and an easy way to answer this question. We recommend the latter.

7.4   Suppose that a mathematician said that it is impossible to obtain a simple random sample from a real-world population. Therefore, the whole basis for applying statistical procedures to real problems is useless. How would you respond?

7.2 SAMPLING DISTRIBUTIONS OF SAMPLE MEANS

We now develop important properties of the sampling distribution of the sample means. Our analysis begins with a random sample of n observations from a very large population with mean μ and variance σ^2; the sample observations are denoted $X_1, X_2, \ldots, X_n$. Before the sample is observed, there is uncertainty about the outcomes. This uncertainty is modeled by viewing the individual observations as random variables with the population mean μ and variance σ^2. Our primary interest is in making inferences about the population mean μ. An obvious starting point is the *sample mean*.

> **Sample Mean**
> Let the random variables $X_1, X_2, \ldots, X_n$ denote a random sample from a population. The **sample mean** value of these random variables is defined as
>
> $$\overline{X} = \frac{1}{n}\sum_{i=1}^{n} X_i$$

Consider the sampling distribution of the random variable $\overline{X}$. At this point we cannot determine the shape of the sampling distribution, but we can determine the mean and variance of the sampling distribution from basic definitions we have learned in Chapters 5 and 6. First, determine the mean of the distribution. In Chapters 5 and 6 we saw that the expectation of a linear combination of random variables is the linear combination of the expectations:

$$E(\overline{X}) = E\left(\frac{1}{n}(X_1 + X_2 + \cdots + X_n)\right) = \frac{n\mu}{n} = \mu$$

Thus, the mean of the sampling distribution of the sample means is the population mean. If samples of n random and independent observations are repeatedly and independently drawn from a population, then as the number of samples becomes very large, the mean of the sample means approaches the true population mean. This is an important result of random sampling and indicates the protection that random samples provide against unrepresentative samples. A single sample mean could be larger or smaller than the population mean. However, on average, there is no reason for us to expect a sample mean that is either higher or lower than the population mean. Later in this section this result is demonstrated using computer-generated random samples.

Example 7.1 Expected Value of the Sample Mean (Expected Value)

Compute the expected value of the sample mean for the employee group example previously discussed.

Solution The sampling distribution of the sample means is shown in Table 7.2 and Figure 7.1. From this distribution we can compute the expected value of the sample mean as

$$E(\overline{X}) = \sum \overline{x} P(\overline{x}) = (3.0)\left(\frac{1}{15}\right) + (4.0)\left(\frac{2}{15}\right) + \cdots + (7.5)\left(\frac{1}{15}\right) = 5.5$$

which is the population mean, μ. A similar calculation can be made to obtain the same result using the sampling distribution in Table 7.3.

Now that we have established that the distribution of sample means is centered about the population mean, we need to determine the variance of the distribution of sample means. Suppose that a random sample of 20 cars yields an average fuel consumption of 24 miles per gallon. The sample mean can be used as an estimate of the population mean. But we also wish to know how good $\overline{x} = 24$ is as the approximation of the population mean. We use the variance of the sampling distribution of the sample means to provide the answer.

If the population is very large compared to the sample size, then the distributions of the individual sample members from random samples are approximately independent of each other. In Chapters 5 and 6 we saw that the variance of a linear combination of independent random variables is the sum of the linear coefficients squared times the variance of the random variables. It follows that

$$\text{Var}(\overline{X}) = \text{Var}\left(\frac{1}{n}X_1 + \frac{1}{n}X_2 + \cdots + \frac{1}{n}X_n\right) = \sum_{i=1}^{n}\left(\frac{1}{n}\right)^2 \sigma_i^2 = \frac{n\sigma^2}{n^2} = \frac{\sigma^2}{n}$$

The variance of the sampling distribution of $\overline{X}$ decreases as the sample size n increases. In effect, this says that larger sample sizes result in more concentrated sampling distributions. The simple example in the previous section demonstrated this result. Thus, larger samples result in greater certainty about our inference of the population mean. This is to be expected. As we obtain more information from a population—from a larger sample—we are able to learn more about population characteristics such as the population mean. The variance of the sample mean is denoted as $\sigma_{\overline{x}}^2$ and the corresponding standard deviation, called the standard error of $\overline{X}$, is given by

$$\sigma_{\overline{X}} = \frac{\sigma}{\sqrt{n}}$$

If the sample size, n, is not a small fraction of the population size, N, then the individual sample members are not distributed independently of one another. Since a population member cannot be included more than once in a sample, the probability of a specific sample member being the second observation depends on the sample member chosen as the first observation. Thus, the observations are not selected independently. It can be shown in this case that the variance of the sample mean is

$$\mathrm{Var}\,(\overline{X}) = \frac{\sigma^2}{n} \cdot \frac{N-n}{N-1}$$

INTERPRETATION

The term $(N-n)/(N-1)$ is often called a *finite population correction factor*.

We have now developed expressions for the mean and variance of the sampling distribution of $\overline{X}$. For most applications the mean and variance will define the sampling distribution. These results for the mean and variance of the sampling distribution apply for any probability distribution that defines the pattern of the values in the population. If it were impossible to extend these results any further, then these results might be interesting theoretically but would have little value for applied applications. Fortunately, we will see that with some additional analysis these results can become very powerful for many practical applications. First, we examine these results under the assumption that the underlying population has a normal probability distribution. Next, we explore the sampling distributions of the sample mean as the sample size increases. This second case will provide some very powerful results for many practical applications in business and economics.

First, we consider the results if the parent population has a normal distribution. The parent population is the population of interest from which the random sample is obtained. If the parent population has a normal distribution, then the sampling distribution of the sample means also has a normal distribution. This intuitive conclusion comes from the well-established result that linear functions of normally distributed random variables are also normally distributed. We saw applications of this in the portfolio problems in Chapter 6. With the sampling distribution as a normal probability distribution, we can compute the standard normal Z for the sample mean. In Chapter 6 we saw that we can use the standard normal Z to compute probabilities for any normally distributed random variable. That result also applies for the sample mean.

Standard Normal Distribution for the Sample Means

Whenever the sampling distribution of the sample means is a normal distribution, we can compute a **standardized normal random variable, Z,** that has mean 0 and variance 1:

$$Z = \frac{\overline{X} - \mu}{\sigma_{\overline{X}}} = \frac{\overline{X} - \mu}{\dfrac{\sigma}{\sqrt{n}}} \tag{7.1}$$

Finally, the results of this section are summarized.

Results for the Sampling Distribution of the Sample Means

Let $\overline{X}$ denote the sample mean of a random sample of n observations from a population with mean μ_X and variance σ^2. Then

1. The sampling distribution of $\overline{X}$ has mean

$$E(\overline{X}) = \mu \qquad\qquad (7.2)$$

2. The sampling distribution of $\overline{X}$ has standard deviation

$$\sigma_{\overline{X}} = \frac{\sigma}{\sqrt{n}} \qquad\qquad (7.3)$$

This is called the standard error of $\overline{X}$.

3. If the sample size, n, is not small compared to the population size, N, then the standard error of $\overline{X}$ is

$$\sigma_{\overline{X}} = \frac{\sigma}{\sqrt{n}} \cdot \sqrt{\frac{N-n}{N-1}} \qquad\qquad (7.4)$$

4. If the parent population distribution is normal and thus the sampling distribution of the sample means is normal, then the random variable

$$Z = \frac{\overline{X} - \mu}{\sigma_{\overline{X}}} \qquad\qquad (7.5)$$

has a standard normal distribution with mean 0 and variance 1.

Figure 7.3 shows the sampling distribution of the sample means for sample sizes $n = 25$ and $n = 100$ from a normal distribution. Each distribution is centered on the mean, but as the sample size increases, the distribution becomes concentrated more closely around the population mean because the standard error of the sample mean decreases as the sample size increases. Thus, the probability that a sample mean is a fixed distance from the population mean decreases with increased sample size.

Figure 7.3
Probability
Density Functions
for Sample Means
from a Population
with $\mu = 100$ and
$\sigma = 5$

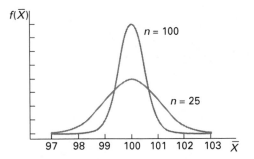

Example 7.2 Executive Salary Distributions (Normal Probability)

Suppose that the annual percentage salary increases for the chief executive officers of all midsize corporations are normally distributed with mean 12.2% and standard deviation 3.6%. A random sample of nine observations is obtained from this population and the sample mean computed. What is the probability that the sample mean will be less than 10%?

Solution   We know that

$$\mu = 12.2 \qquad \sigma = 3.6 \qquad n = 9$$

Let $\bar{x}$ denote the sample mean, and compute the standard error of the sample mean

$$\sigma_{\bar{x}} = \frac{\sigma}{\sqrt{n}} = \frac{3.6}{\sqrt{9}} = 1.2$$

Then we can compute

$$P(\bar{x} < 10) = P\left(\frac{\bar{x} - \mu}{\sigma_{\bar{x}}} < \frac{10 - 12.2}{1.2}\right) = P(Z < -1.83) = 0.0336$$

where Z has a standard normal distribution and the resulting probability is obtained from Table 1 of the Appendix using the procedures developed in Chapter 6.

From this analysis we conclude that the probability that the sample mean will be less than 10% is only 0.0336. If a sample mean of less than 10% actually occurred, we might begin to suspect that the population mean is less than 12.2%.

Example 7.3   Spark Plug Life (Normal Probability)

A spark plug manufacturer claims that the lives of its plugs are normally distributed with mean 36,000 miles and standard deviation 4,000 miles. A random sample of 16 plugs had an average life of 34,500 miles. If the manufacturer's claim is correct, what is the probability of finding a sample mean of 34,500 or less?

Solution   To compute the probability, we need to first obtain the standard error of the sample mean

$$\sigma_{\bar{x}} = \frac{\sigma}{\sqrt{n}} = \frac{4,000}{\sqrt{16}} = 1,000$$

The desired probability is

$$P(\bar{x} < 34,500) = P\left(\frac{\bar{x} - \mu}{\sigma_{\bar{x}}} < \frac{34,500 - 36,000}{1,000}\right) = P(Z < -1.50) = 0.0668$$

Figure 7.4a shows the probability density function of $\bar{X}$, with the shaded portion indicating the probability that the sample mean is less than 34,500. In Figure 7.4b we see the standard normal density function, and the shaded area indicates the probability that Z is less than −1.5. Note that in comparing these figures we see that every value of $\bar{X}$ has a corresponding value of Z and the comparable probability statements provide the same result.

Using the standard normal Z, the normal probability values from Table 1 of the Appendix, and the procedures from Chapter 6, we find that the probability

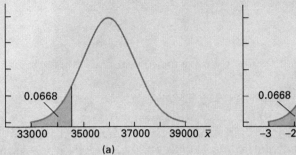
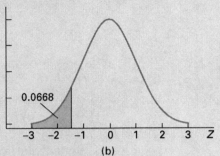

Figure 7.4 (a) Probability That Sample Mean Is Less than 34,500; (b) Probability That Standard Normal Random Variable Is Less than −1.5

that $\bar{X}$ is less than 34,500 is 0.0668. This probability suggests that, if the manufacturer's claims—$\mu = 36{,}000$ and $\sigma = 4{,}000$—are true, then a sample mean of 34,500 or less has a small probability. As a result we are skeptical about the manufacturer's claims. This important concept—using the probability of sample statistics to question the original assumption—will be developed more fully in Chapter 10.

Central Limit Theorem

In the previous section we learned that the sample mean, $\bar{x}$ for a random sample of size n drawn from a population with a normal distribution with mean μ and variance σ^2, is also normally distributed with mean μ and variance σ^2/n. In this section we present the *central limit theorem*, which states that the mean of a random sample, drawn from a population with any probability distribution, will be approximately normally distributed with mean μ and variance σ^2/n, given a large enough sample size.

This important result enables us to use the normal distribution to compute probabilities for sample means obtained from many different populations. In applied statistics the probability distribution for the population being sampled is often not known, and in particular there is no way to conclude that the underlying distribution is normal.

In applied statistical analysis many of the random variables used can be characterized as the sum or mean of a large number of random variables. For example, total daily sales in a store are the result of a number of sales to individual customers—each of which can be modeled as a random variable. Total national investment spending in a month is the sum of many individual investment decisions by specific firms. Thus, if $X_1, X_2, \ldots, X_n$ represents the result of individual random events, the observed random variable

$$X = X_1 + X_2 + \cdots + X_n$$

and from Chapter 5

$$E(X) = n\mu \qquad \mathrm{Var}(X) = n\sigma^2$$

The central limit theorem states that the resulting sum, X, is normally distributed and can be used to compute a random variable, Z, with mean 0 and variance 1:

$$Z = \frac{X - E(X)}{\sqrt{\mathrm{Var}(X)}} = \frac{X - n\mu}{\sqrt{n\sigma^2}}$$

In addition, if X is divided by n to obtain a mean $\overline{X}$, then a corresponding Z with mean 0 and variance 1 can also be computed:

$$Z = \frac{\overline{X} - \mu_X}{\sigma_{\overline{X}}} = \frac{\overline{X} - \mu_X}{\frac{\sigma_X}{\sqrt{n}}}$$

Using these results, we have the central limit theorem.

Statement of the Central Limit Theorem

Let $X_1, X_2, \ldots, X_n$ be a set of n independent random variables having identical distributions with mean μ and variance σ^2, and with X as the sum and $\overline{X}$ as the mean of these random variables. As n becomes large, the **central limit theorem** states that the distribution of

$$Z = \frac{\overline{X} - \mu_{\overline{X}}}{\sigma_{\overline{X}}} = \frac{X - n\mu_X}{\sqrt{n\sigma^2}} \tag{7.6}$$

approaches the standard normal distribution.

The central limit theorem provides the basis for considerable work in applied statistical analysis. As indicated, many random variables can be modeled as sums or means of independent random variables. By this theorem the normal distribution very often provides a good approximation of the true distribution. Thus, the standard normal distribution can be used to obtain probability values for many observed sample means or sums.

The central limit theorem can be applied to both discrete and continuous random variables. In Section 7.3 we use this theorem with discrete random variables when we develop probabilities for proportion random variables, using procedures similar to those used for sample means.

The central limit theorem results from a formal mathematical proof that is beyond the scope of this book. This theorem is a key result that supports many statistical applications. Results from random sample simulations can also be used to demonstrate the central limit theorem. In addition, there are homework problems that enable you to conduct further experimental analysis. We now present some results using Monte Carlo sample simulations to obtain sampling distributions. To obtain each of these results, we selected 1,000 random samples of size n and displayed the sampling distributions in histograms and normal probability plots. The chapter Appendix presents the procedure for obtaining sampling distributions for the sample means from any probability distribution. In this Appendix and on the data disk we include a Minitab Computer Macro for easily obtaining your own sampling distributions.

First, let us consider a uniform probability distribution over the range 1 to 10. The probability distribution is shown in Figure 7.5. Clearly, the values of the random variable are not normally distributed, since the values are uniform over the range from 1 to 10. Next, we show the results from computer simulations that generated random samples of various sizes from this probability distribution, computed the mean for each sample, and prepared the sampling distribution of those sample means in a histogram. This process constructs empirical sampling distributions of

Figure 7.5
Probability
Distribution for a
Uniform Random
Variable

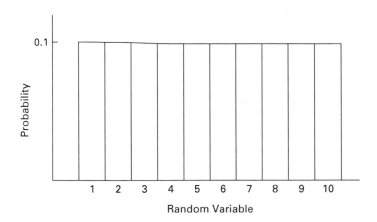

Figure 7.6
Sampling
Distribution of the
Sample Means
from a Uniform
Distribution with
$n = 2$

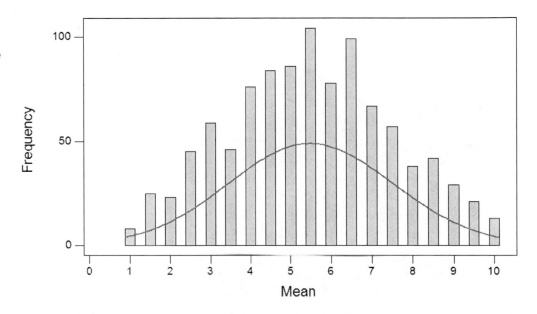

the sample means. Look at the histograms in Figures 7.6 and 7.7, using 1,000 samples first with sample size $n = 2$ and then with sample size $n = 25$. A normal probability density function with the same mean and variance is sketched over each histogram to provide a comparison.

We can see from the histograms that the means from samples of size 2 tend toward central values. However, with samples of size 25 the histogram is symmetric and is similar to sample histograms that would be obtained from a normal distribution. Generally, the distribution of sample means from uniform or symmetric distributions can be closely approximated by the normal distribution, with samples of size 25 or more.

Next, let us consider a population with a probability distribution that is skewed to the right. In Chapter 2 we saw that the distributions of observations for many business and economic processes are skewed. For example, family incomes and housing prices in a city, state, or country are often skewed to the right. There is typically a small percentage of families with very high incomes, and these families tend to live in expensive houses. Consider the discrete probability distribution shown in Figure 7.8. This could be a distribution of family incomes for a developing country.

Figure 7.7
Sampling
Distribution of the
Sample Means
from a Uniform
Distribution
with $n = 25$

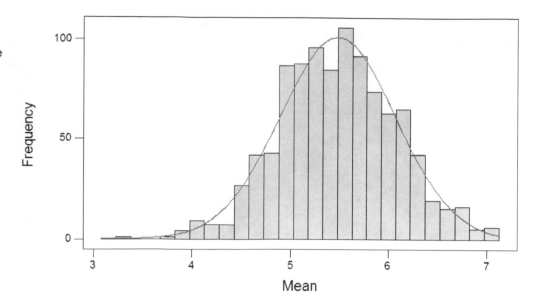

Figure 7.8
Probability
Distribution for a
Skewed
Distribution

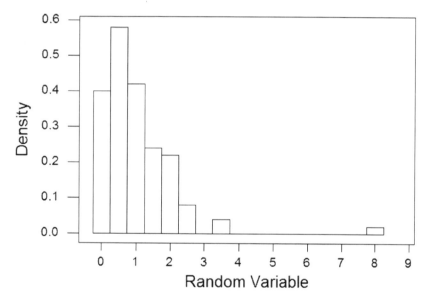

Suppose that you wanted to compare the mean income for that country with the means for a larger set of countries with similar educational levels.

The sampling distributions of mean incomes are compared using a random sample from the probability distribution. Figure 7.9 shows a histogram for 1,000 samples of size $n = 10$, and Figure 7.10 shows a histogram for 1,000 samples of size $n = 25$. If you use a random sample of size $n = 10$ and assume that the sample mean is normally distributed, the chances for estimating incorrect probabilities are great. These mistakes in probability estimates are particularly large for sample means in the upper tail of the distribution. Note that the histogram is different from one that would be obtained from a normal distribution. But if you use a random sample of size $n = 25$, your results are much better. Note that the second histogram—$n = 25$—is much closer to a normal distribution. If we obtained sampling distributions for larger samples, the results would be even better. Thus, even when the distribution of individual

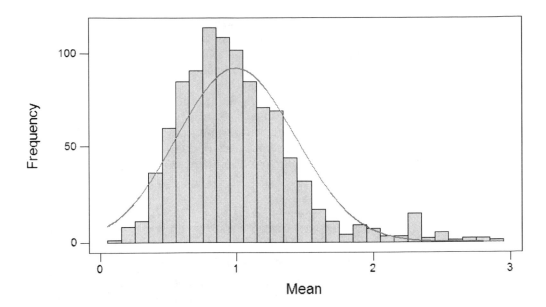

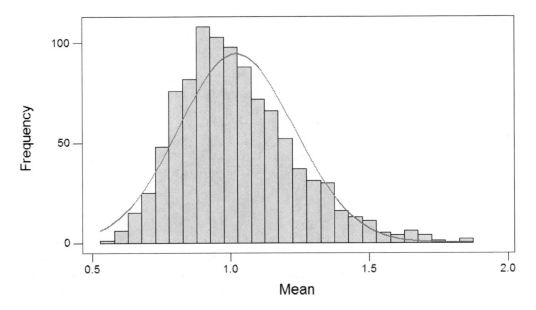

observations is highly skewed, the sampling distribution of sample means closely approximates a normal distribution when $A \geq 25$.

In Chapter 6 we learned that the binomial random variable has an approximate normal distribution as the sample size becomes large. From the random sampling studies in this chapter and our previous study of the binomial distribution, we have additional evidence to demonstrate the central limit theorem. Similar demonstrations have been produced numerous times by many statisticians. As a result, a large body of empirical evidence supports the application of the central limit theorem to realistic statistical applications, in addition to theoretical results.

The question for applied analysis concerns the sample size required to ensure that sample means have a normal distribution. Based on considerable research and experience, we know that, if the distributions are symmetric, then the means from

330 Quantitative Analysis for Management

samples of $n = 20$ to 25 are well approximated by the normal distribution. For skewed distributions the required sample sizes are generally somewhat larger. But note that in the previous examples using a skewed distribution a sample size of $n = 25$ produced a sampling distribution of sample means that closely followed a normal distribution.

In this chapter we have begun our discussion of the important statistical problem when making inferences about a population based on results from a sample. The sample mean or sample proportion is often computed to make inferences about population means or proportions. By using the central limit theorem we have a rationale for applying the techniques we will develop in future chapters to a wide range of problems. The following examples show important applications of the central limit theorem.

Example 7.4   Marketing Study for Antelope Coffee (Normal Probability)

Antelope Coffee Inc. is considering the possibility of opening a gourmet coffee shop in Big Rock, Montana. Previous research has indicated that its shops will be successful in cities of this size if the per capita annual income is above $60,000. It is also known that the standard deviation of income is $5,000.

A random sample of 36 people was obtained and the mean income was $62,300. Does this sample provide evidence to conclude that a shop should be opened?

Solution   The distribution of incomes is known to be skewed, but the central limit theorem enables us to conclude that the sample mean is approximately normally distributed. To answer the question, we need to determine the probability of obtaining a sample mean at least as high as $\bar{x} = 62{,}300$ if the population mean is $\mu = 60{,}000$.

First, compute the standardized normal Z statistic:

$$Z = \frac{\bar{x} - \mu}{\frac{\sigma}{\sqrt{n}}} = \frac{62{,}300 - 60{,}000}{\frac{5{,}000}{\sqrt{36}}} = 2.76$$

From the standard normal table we find that the probability of obtaining a Z value of 2.76 or larger is 0.0029. Because this probability is very small, we can conclude that it is likely that the population mean income is not 60,000 but is a larger value. This result provides strong evidence that the population mean income is higher than $60,000 and that the coffee shop is likely to be a success. In this example we can see the importance of sampling distributions and the central limit theorem for problem solving.

Acceptance Intervals

In many statistical applications we would like to determine the range within which sample means are likely to occur. Determining such ranges is a direct application of the sampling distribution concepts we have developed. An **acceptance interval** is an interval within which a sample mean has a high probability of occurring, given that we know the population mean and variance. If the sample mean is within that interval, then we can accept the conclusion that the random sample came from the population with the known population mean and variance. The probability that the sample mean is within a particular interval can be computed if the sample means have a distribution that is close to normal.

Acceptance intervals based on the normal distribution are defined by the distribution mean and variance. From the central limit theorem we know that the sampling distribution of sample means is often approximately normal, and, thus, acceptance intervals based on the normal distribution have wide applications. Assuming that we know the population mean μ, and variance σ^2, then we can construct a symmetric acceptance interval:

$$\mu \pm Z_{\alpha/2}\,\sigma_{\bar{x}}$$

provided that $\bar{x}$ has a normal distribution and $z_{\alpha/2}$ is the standard normal when the upper tail probability is $\alpha/2$. The probability that the sample mean $\bar{x}$ is included in the interval is $1 - \alpha$.

Acceptance intervals are widely used for quality control monitoring of various production and service processes. The interval

$$\mu \pm Z_{\alpha/2}\,\sigma_{\bar{x}}$$

is plotted over time (the result is called an X-bar chart) and provides limits for the sample mean $\bar{x}$, given that the population mean is μ. Typically, α is very small ($\alpha < .01$), and standard practice in U.S. industries is to use $z = 3$. If the sample mean is outside the acceptance interval, then we suspect that the population mean is not μ. In a typical example engineers will take various steps to achieve a small variance for important product measurements that are directly related to product quality. Once the process has been adjusted so that the variance is small, an acceptance interval for a sample mean—called a *control interval*—is established in the form of a control chart. Then periodic random samples are obtained and compared to the control interval. If the sample mean is within the control interval, it is concluded that the process is operating properly and no action is taken. But if the sample mean is outside of the control interval, it is concluded that the process is not operating properly and steps are taken to correct the process. In Chapter 18 we will develop control charts much more extensively.

Example 7.5   Monitoring Health Insurance Claims (Acceptance Interval)

Charlotte King, vice president of financial underwriting for a large health insurance company, wishes to monitor daily insurance claim payments to determine if the average number of claims per subscriber is stable, increasing, or decreasing. The number of individual claims varies up and down from one day to the next, and it would be naive to draw conclusions or change operations based on these daily variations. But at some point the changes become substantial and should be noted. She has asked you to develop a procedure for monitoring the level of claims.

Solution   Your initial investigation indicates that health insurance claims are highly skewed, with a small number of very large claims for major medical procedures. To determine changes, you first need to determine the historical mean and variance for individual claims. After some investigation you also find that the mean for random samples of $n = 100$ claims is normally distributed. Based on past history the mean, μ, level for individual claims is \$4,000 with a standard deviation of $\sigma = 2,000$.

Using this information you proceed to develop a claims monitoring system that obtains a random sample of 100 claims each day and computes the sample mean. The company has established a 95% acceptance interval for monitoring claims. An interval defined for the standard normal using $Z = \pm 1.96$ includes 95% of the values. From this you compute the 95% acceptance interval for insurance claims as

$$4,000 \pm 1.96 \frac{2,000}{\sqrt{100}} = 4,000 \pm 392$$

Each day the sample mean for 100 randomly selected claims is computed and compared to the acceptance interval. If the sample mean is outside the interval 3,608 to 4,392, Ms. King can conclude that claims are deviating from the historical standard. You explain to her that this conclusion will be correct 95% of the time. The sample mean could be outside the interval even with a population mean of 4,000 with probability 0.05. In those cases Ms. King's conclusion that the mean claim level has changed from the historical standard would be wrong. To simplify the analysis, you instruct the analysts to plot the daily claims mean on a control chart, shown in Figure 7.11. Using this control chart Charlotte King and her staff can study the patterns of the sample means and determine if there are trends and if means are outside of the boundaries that indicate standard claims behavior.

Figure 7.11   Ninety-Five Percent Acceptance Interval for Health Insurance Claims

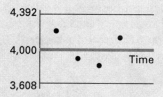

Example 7.6   Prairie View Cereal Package Weights (Acceptance Intervals)

Prairie View Cereals, Inc., is concerned about maintaining correct package weights at its cereal packaging facility. The package label weight is 440 grams, and company officials are interested in monitoring the process to ensure that package weights are stable.

Solution   A random sample of five packages is collected every 30 minutes and each package is weighed electronically. The mean weight is then plotted on an X-bar control chart such as the one in Figure 7.12. When an X-bar chart is used for

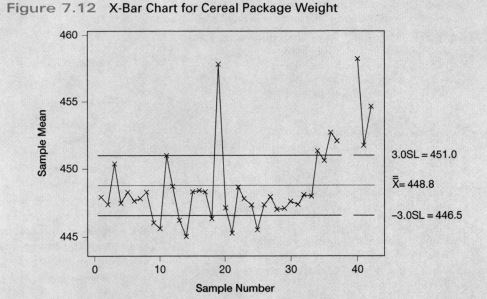

Figure 7.12   X-Bar Chart for Cereal Package Weight

3.0SL = 451.0

$\bar{\bar{X}}$ = 448.8

–3.0SL = 446.5

monitoring limits on product quality—and numerous highly successful firms do—the central limit theorem provides the rationale for using the normal distribution to establish limits for the small sample means. Thus, a fundamentally important statistical theory drives a key management process.

INTERPRETATION

In this chart SL is the standard deviation for the sample mean. The upper and lower limits are set at $\pm 3\sigma_{\bar{x}}$ instead of $\pm 1.96\sigma_{\bar{X}}$, or 95%, the acceptance interval used in the previous example. The interval $\bar{X} \pm 3\sigma_{\bar{x}}$ (Minitab labels the mean for the entire population as $\bar{\bar{X}}$) includes almost all of the sample means under the normal distribution, given a stable mean and variance. Thus, a sample mean outside of the control limits indicates that something has changed and corrections should be made. Given the number of points outside the acceptance interval, we recommend that the process be stopped and adjusted.

EXERCISES

Basic Exercises

7.5   Given a population with mean $\mu = 100$ and variance $\sigma^2 = 81$, the central limit applies when the sample size $n \geq 25$. A random sample of size $n = 25$ is obtained.

   a. What are the mean and variance of the sampling distribution for the sample means?
   b. What is the probability that $\bar{x} > 102$?
   c. What is the probability that $98 \leq \bar{x} \leq 101$?
   d. What is the probability that $\bar{x} \leq 101.5$?

7.6   Given a population with mean $\mu = 100$ and variance $\sigma^2 = 900$, the central limit applies when the sample size $n \geq 25$. A random sample of size $n = 30$ is obtained.

   a. What are the mean and variance of the sampling distribution for the sample means?
   b. What is the probability that $\bar{x} > 109$?
   c. What is the probability that $96 \leq \bar{x} \leq 110$?
   d. What is the probability that $\bar{x} \leq 107$?

7.7   Given a population with mean $\mu = 200$ and variance $\sigma^2 = 625$, the central limit applies when the sample size $n \geq 25$. A random sample of size $n = 25$ is obtained.

   a. What are the mean and variance of the sampling distribution for the sample mean?
   b. What is the probability that $\bar{x} > 209$?
   c. What is the probability that $198 \leq \bar{x} \leq 211$?
   d. What is the probability that $\bar{x} \leq 202$?

7.8 Given a population with mean $\mu = 400$ and variance $\sigma^2 = 1,600$, the central limit applies when the sample size $n \geq 25$. A random sample of size $n = 35$ is obtained.

a. What are the mean and variance of the sampling distribution for the sample means?
b. What is the probability that $\bar{x} > 412$?
c. What is the probability that $393 \leq \bar{x} \leq 407$?
d. What is the probability that $\bar{x} \leq 389$?

Application Exercises

7.9 When a production process is operating correctly, the number of units produced per hour has a normal distribution with mean 92.0 and standard deviation 3.6. A random sample of four different hours was taken.

a. Find the mean of the sampling distribution of the sample means.
b. Find the variance of the sample mean.
c. Find the standard error of the sample mean.
d. What is the probability that the sample mean exceeds 93.0 units?

7.10 The lifetimes of light bulbs produced by a particular manufacturer have a mean of 1,200 hours and a standard deviation of 400 hours. The population distribution is normal. Suppose that you purchase nine bulbs, which can be regarded as a random sample from the manufacturer's output.

a. What is the mean of the sample mean lifetime?
b. What is the variance of the sample mean?
c. What is the standard error of the sample mean?
d. What is the probability that, on average, those nine lightbulbs have lives of less than 1,050 hours?

7.11 The fuel consumption, in miles per gallon, of all cars of a particular model has mean 25 and standard deviation 2. The population distribution can be assumed to be normal. A random sample of these cars is taken.

a. Find the probability that sample mean fuel consumption will be less than 24 miles per gallon if

  i. A sample of 1 observation is taken.
  ii. A sample of 4 observations is taken.
  iii. A sample of 16 observations is taken.

b. Explain why the three answers in part (a) differ in the way they do. Draw a graph to illustrate your reasoning.

7.12 The mean selling price of new homes in a city over a year was $115,000. The population standard deviation was $25,000. A random sample of 100 new home sales from this city was taken.

a. What is the probability that the sample mean selling price was more than $110,000?
b. What is the probability that the sample mean selling price was between $113,000 and $117,000?

c. What is the probability that the sample mean selling price was between $114,000 and $116,000?
d. Without doing the calculations, state in which of the following ranges the sample mean selling price is most likely to lie:

$113,000 to $115,000 $114,000 to $116,000

$115,000 to $117,000 $116,000 to $118,000

e. Suppose that, after you had done these calculations, a friend asserted that the population distribution of selling prices of new homes in this city was almost certainly not normal. How would you respond?

7.13 Candidates for employment at a city fire department are required to take a written aptitude test. Scores on this test are normally distributed with mean 280 and standard deviation 60. A random sample of nine test scores was taken.

a. What is the standard error of the sample mean score?
b. What is the probability that the sample mean score is less than 270?
c. What is the probability that the sample mean score is more than 250?
d. Suppose that the population standard deviation is, in fact, 40, rather than 60. Without doing the calculations, state how this would change your answers to parts (a), (b), and (c). Illustrate your conclusions with appropriate graphs.

7.14 A random sample of 16 junior managers in the offices of corporations in a large city center was taken to estimate average daily commuting time for all such managers. Suppose that the population times have a normal distribution with mean 87 minutes and standard deviation 22 minutes.

a. What is the standard error of the sample mean commuting time?
b. What is the probability that the sample mean is less than 100 minutes?
c. What is the probability that the sample mean is more than 80 minutes?
d. What is the probability that the sample mean is outside the range 85 to 95 minutes?
e. Suppose that a second (independent) random sample of 50 junior managers is taken. Without doing the calculations, state whether the probabilities in parts (b), (c), and (d) would be higher, lower, or the same for the second sample. Sketch graphs to illustrate your answers.

7.15 A company produces breakfast cereal. The true mean weight of the contents of its cereal boxes is 20 ounces, and the standard deviation is 0.6 ounce. The population distribution of weights is normal.

Suppose that you purchase four boxes, which can be regarded as a random sample of all those produced.

a. What is the standard error of the sample mean weight?
b. What is the probability that, on average, the contents of these four boxes will weigh less than 19.7 ounces?
c. What is the probability that, on average, the contents of these four boxes will weigh more than 20.6 ounces?
d. What is the probability that, on average, the contents of these four boxes will weigh between 19.5 and 20.5 ounces?
e. Two of the four boxes are chosen at random. What is the probability that, the average, contents of these two boxes will weigh between 19.5 and 20.5 ounces?

7.16 Assume that the standard deviation of monthly rents paid by students in a particular town is $40. A random sample of 100 students was taken to estimate the mean monthly rent paid by the whole student population.

a. What is the standard error of the sample mean monthly rent?
b. What is the probability that the sample mean exceeds the population mean by more than $5?
c. What is the probability that the sample mean is more than $4 below the population mean?
d. What is the probability that the sample mean differs from the population mean by more than $3?

7.17 Times spent studying by students in the week before final exams follow a normal distribution with standard deviation 8 hours. A random sample of 4 students was taken in order to estimate the mean study time for the population of all students.

a. What is the probability that the sample mean exceeds the population mean by more than 2 hours?
b. What is the probability that the sample mean is more than 3 hours below the population mean?
c. What is the probability that the sample mean differs from the population mean by more than 4 hours?
d. Suppose that a second (independent) random sample of 10 students was taken. Without doing the calculations, state whether the probabilities in parts (a), (b), and (c) would be higher, lower, or the same for the second sample.

7.18 An industrial process produces batches of a chemical whose impurity levels follow a normal distribution with standard deviation 1.6 grams per 100 grams of chemical. A random sample of 100 batches is selected in order to estimate the population mean impurity level.

a. The probability is 0.05 that the sample mean impurity level exceeds the population mean by how much?
b. The probability is 0.10 that the sample mean impurity level is below the population mean by how much?
c. The probability is 0.15 that the sample mean impurity level differs from the population mean by how much?

7.19 The price-earnings ratios for all companies whose shares are traded on the New York Stock Exchange follow a normal distribution with a standard deviation 3.8. A random sample of these companies is selected in order to estimate the population mean price-earnings ratio.

a. How large a sample is necessary in order to ensure that the probability that the sample mean differs from the population mean by more than 1.0 is less than 0.10?
b. Without doing the calculations, state whether a larger or smaller sample than that in part (a) would be required to guarantee that the probability that the sample mean differs from the population mean by more than 1.0 is less than 0.05.
c. Without doing the calculations, state whether a larger or smaller sample than that in part (a) would be required to guarantee that the probability that the sample mean differs from the population mean by more than 1.5 hours is less than 0.05.

7.20 The number of hours spent studying by students on a large campus in the week before final exams follows a normal distribution with standard deviation 8.4 hours. A random sample of these students is taken to estimate the population mean number of hours studying.

a. How large a sample is needed to ensure that the probability that the sample mean differs from the population mean by more than 2.0 hours is less than 0.05?
b. Without doing the calculations, state whether a larger or smaller sample than that in part (a) would be required to guarantee that the probability that the sample mean differs from the population mean by more than 2.0 hours is less than 0.10.
c. Without doing the calculations, state whether a larger or smaller sample than that in part (a) would be required to guarantee that the probability that the sample mean differs from the population mean by more than 1.5 hours is less than 0.05.

7.21 In Table 7.1 and Example 7.1, we considered samples of $n = 2$ observations from a population of $N = 6$ values of years on the job for employees. The population mean is $\mu = 5.5$ years.

a. Confirm from the six population values that the population variance is

$$\sigma^2 = 3.92$$

b. Confirm, following the approach of Example 7.1, that the variance of the sampling distribution of the sample mean is

$$\sigma_{\bar{x}}^2 = \sum_{i=1}^{15} (\bar{x}_i - \mu)^2 P(x_i) = 1.57$$

c. Verify for this example that

$$\sigma_{\bar{x}}^2 = \frac{\sigma^2}{n} \cdot \frac{N-n}{N-1}$$

7.22 In taking a sample of n observations from a population of N members, the variance of the sampling distribution of the sample means is

$$\sigma_{\bar{x}}^2 = \frac{\sigma^2}{n} \cdot \frac{N-n}{N-1}$$

The quantity $\frac{(N-n)}{(N-1)}$ is called the *finite population correction factor*.

a. To get some feeling for possible magnitudes of the finite population correction factor, calculate it for samples of $n = 20$ observations from populations of $N = 20, 40, 100, 1,000$, and $10,000$ members.

b. Explain why the result for $N = 20$, found in part (a), is precisely what one should expect on intuitive grounds.

c. Given the results in part (a), discuss the practical significance of using the finite population correction factor for samples of 20 observations from populations of different sizes.

7.23 A town has 500 real estate agents. The mean value of the properties sold in a year by these agents is $800,000, and the standard deviation is $300,000. A random sample of 100 agents is selected, and the value of the properties they sold in a year is recorded.

a. What is the standard error of the sample mean?

b. What is the probability that the sample mean exceeds $825,000?

c. What is the probability that the sample mean exceeds $780,000?

d. What is the probability that the sample mean is between $790,000 and $820,000?

7.24 An economics course was taken by 250 students. Each member of a random sample of 50 of these students was asked to estimate the amount of time he or she spent on the previous week's assignment. Suppose that the population standard deviation is 30 minutes.

a. What is the probability that the sample mean exceeds the population mean by more than 2.5 minutes?

b. What is the probability that the sample mean is more than 5 minutes below the population mean?

c. What is the probability that the sample mean differs from the population mean by more than 10 minutes?

7.25 For an audience of 600 people attending a concert, the average time on the journey to the concert was 32 minutes, and the standard deviation was 10 minutes. A random sample of 150 audience members was taken.

a. What is the probability that the sample mean journey time was more than 31 minutes?

b. What is the probability that the sample mean journey time was less than 33 minutes?

c. Draw a graph to illustrate why the answers to parts (a) and (b) are the same.

d. What is the probability that the sample mean journey time was not between 31 and 33 minutes?

7.3 SAMPLING DISTRIBUTIONS OF SAMPLE PROPORTIONS

In Section 5.4 we developed the binomial distribution as the sum of n independent Bernoulli random variables, each with probability of success P. To characterize the distribution, we need a value for P. Here, we indicate how we can use the sample proportion to obtain inferences about the population proportion. The proportion random variable has many applications, including percent market share, percent successful business investments, and outcomes of elections.

Sample Proportion

Let X be the number of successes in a binomial sample of n observations with parameter P. The parameter is the proportion of the population members that have a characteristic of interest. We define the **sample proportion** as

$$\hat{P} = \frac{X}{n} \qquad (7.7)$$

X is the sum of a set of n independent Bernoulli random variables, each with probability of success P. As a result, $\hat{P}$ is the mean of a set of independent random variables, and the results we developed in the previous sections for sample means apply. In addition, the central limit theorem can be used to argue that the probability distribution for $\hat{P}$ can be modeled as a normally distributed random variable.

In Section 6.4 it was shown that the number of successes in a binomial distribution and the proportion of successes have a distribution that is closely approximated by a normal distribution (see Figures 6.23 and 6.24). This provides a very close approximation when $nP(1 - P) > 9$.

The mean and variance of the sampling distribution of the sample proportion $\hat{P}$ can be obtained from the mean and variance of the number of successes, X.

$$E(X) = nP \qquad \text{Var}(X) = nP(1-P)$$

and, thus,

$$E(\hat{P}) = E\left(\frac{X}{n}\right) = \frac{1}{n} E(X) = P$$

We see that the mean of the distribution of $\hat{P}$ is the population proportion, P.

The variance of $\hat{P}$ is the variance of the population distribution of the Bernoulli random variables divided by n.

$$\sigma_{\hat{P}}^2 = \text{Var}\left(\frac{X}{n}\right) = \frac{1}{n^2} \text{Var}(X) = \frac{P(1 - P)}{n}$$

The standard deviation of $\hat{P}$, which is the square root of the variance, is called its standard error.

Since the distribution of the sample proportion is approximately normal for large sample sizes, we can obtain a standard normal random variable by subtracting P from $\hat{P}$ and dividing by the standard error.

Sampling Distribution of the Sample Proportion

Let $\hat{P}$ be the sample proportion of successes in a random sample from a population with proportion of success P. Then

1. The sampling distribution of $\hat{P}$ has mean P:

$$E(\hat{P}) = P \qquad (7.8)$$

2. The sampling distribution of p has standard deviation

$$\sigma_{\hat{P}} = \sqrt{\frac{P(1-P)}{n}}$$ (7.9)

3. If the sample size is large, the random variable

$$Z = \frac{\hat{P} - P}{\sigma_{\hat{P}}}$$ (7.10)

is approximately distributed as a standard normal. This approximation is good if

$$nP(1-P) > 9$$

Similar to the results from the previous section, we see that the standard error of the sample proportion, $\hat{P}$, decreases as the sample size increases and the distribution becomes more concentrated, as seen in Figure 7.13. This is expected because the sample proportion is a sample mean. With larger sample sizes our inferences about the population proportion improve. From the central limit theorem we know that the binomial distribution can be approximated by the normal distribution with corresponding mean and variance. We see this result in the following examples.

Figure 7.13
Probability Density Functions for the Sample Proportions

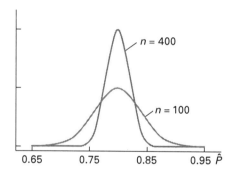

Example 7.7   Evaluation of Home Electric Wiring (Probability of Sample Proportion)

A random sample of 250 homes was taken from a large population of older homes to estimate the proportion of homes with unsafe wiring. If, in fact, 30% of the homes have unsafe wiring, what is the probability that the sample proportion will be between 25% and 35% of homes with unsafe wiring?

Solution   For this problem we have

$$P = 0.30 \qquad n = 250$$

We can compute the standard deviation of the sample proportion, $\hat{P}$, as

$$\sigma_{\hat{P}} = \sqrt{\frac{P(1-P)}{n}} = \sqrt{\frac{0.30(1-0.30)}{250}} = 0.029$$

The required probability is

$$P(0.25 < \hat{P} < 0.35) = P\left(\frac{0.25 - P}{\sigma_{\hat{P}}} < \frac{\hat{P} - P}{\sigma_{\hat{P}}} < \frac{0.35 - P}{\sigma_{\hat{P}}}\right)$$

$$= P\left(\frac{0.25 - 0.30}{0.029} < Z < \frac{0.35 - 0.30}{0.029}\right)$$

$$= P(-1.72 < Z < 1.72)$$

$$= 0.9146$$

where the probability for the Z interval is obtained using Table 1 in the Appendix.

Thus, we see that the probability that the sample proportion is within the interval 0.25 to 0.35, given $P = 0.30$, is 0.9146. This interval can be called a 91.46% acceptance interval. We can also note that, if the sample proportion was actually outside this interval, we might begin to suspect that the population proportion, P, is not 0.30.

Example 7.8 Business Course Selection (Probability of Sample Proportion)

It has been estimated that 43% of business graduates believe that a course in business ethics is very important for imparting ethical values to students (Reference 1). Find the probability that more than one-half of a random sample of 80 business graduates have this belief.

Solution We are given that

$$P = 0.43 \qquad n = 80$$

We will first compute the standard deviation of the sample proportion:

$$\sigma_{\hat{P}} = \sqrt{\frac{P(1 - P)}{n}} = \sqrt{\frac{0.43(1 - 0.43)}{80}} = 0.055$$

Then the required probability can be computed as

$$P(\hat{P} > 0.50) = P\left(\frac{\hat{P} - P}{\sigma_{\hat{P}}} > \frac{0.50 - P}{\sigma_{\hat{P}}}\right)$$

$$= P\left(Z > \frac{0.50 - 0.43}{0.055}\right)$$

$$= P(Z > 1.27)$$

$$= 0.1020$$

This probability, as shown in Figure 7.14, was obtained from Table 1 in the Appendix. The probability of having one-half of the sample believing in the value of business ethics courses is approximately 0.1.

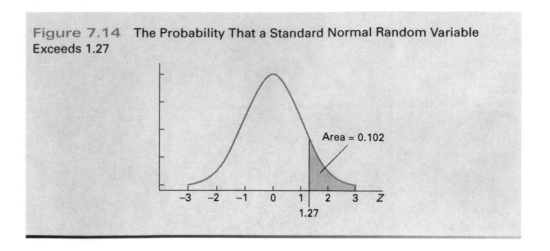

Figure 7.14   **The Probability That a Standard Normal Random Variable Exceeds 1.27**

EXERCISES

Basic Exercises

7.26 Suppose that we have a population with proportion $P = 0.40$ and a random sample of size $n = 100$ drawn from the population.

  a. What is the probability that the sample proportion is greater than 0.45?
  b. What is the probability that the sample proportion is less than 0.29?
  c. What is the probability that the sample proportion is between 0.35 and 0.51?

7.27 Suppose that we have a population with proportion $P = 0.25$ and a random sample of size $n = 200$ drawn from the population.

  a. What is the probability that the sample proportion is greater than 0.31?
  b. What is the probability that the sample proportion is less than 0.14?
  c. What is the probability that the sample proportion is between 0.24 and 0.40?

7.28 Suppose that we have a population with proportion $P = 0.60$ and a random sample of size $n = 100$ drawn from the population.

  a. What is the probability that the sample proportion is greater than 0.66?
  b. What is the probability that the sample proportion is less than 0.48?
  c. What is the probability that the sample proportion is between 0.52 and 0.66?

7.29 Suppose that we have a population with proportion $P = 0.50$ and a random sample of size $n = 900$ drawn from the population.

  a. What is the probability that the sample proportion is greater than 0.52?
  b. What is the probability that the sample proportion is less than 0.46?
  c. What is the probability that the sample proportion is between 0.47 and 0.53?

Application Exercises

7.30 In 1992, Canadians voted in a referendum on a new constitution. In the province of Quebec, 42.4% of those who voted were in favor of the new constitution. A random sample of 100 voters from the province was taken.

  a. What is the mean of the distribution of the sample proportion in favor of a new constitution?
  b. What is the variance of the sample proportion?
  c. What is the standard error of the sample proportion?
  d. What is the probability that the sample proportion is bigger than 0.5?

7.31 According to the Internal Revenue Service, 75% of all tax returns lead to a refund. A random sample of 100 tax returns is taken.

  a. What is the mean of the distribution of the sample proportion of returns leading to refunds?
  b. What is the variance of the sample proportion?
  c. What is the standard error of the sample proportion?
  d. What is the probability that the sample proportion exceeds 0.8?

7.32 A record store owner finds that 20% of customers entering her store make a purchase. One morning 180 people, who can be regarded as a random sample of all customers, enter the store.

  a. What is the mean of the distribution of the sample proportion of customers making a purchase?

b. What is the variance of the sample proportion?

c. What is the standard error of the sample proportion?

d. What is the probability that the sample proportion is less than 0.15?

7.33 An administrator for a large group of hospitals believes that of all patients 30% will generate bills that become at least 2 months overdue. A random sample of 200 patients is taken.

a. What is the standard error of the sample proportion that will generate bills that become at least 2 months overdue?

b. What is the probability that the sample proportion is less than 0.25?

c. What is the probability that the sample proportion is more than 0.33?

d. What is the probability that the sample proportion is between 0.27 and 0.33?

7.34 A corporation receives 120 applications for positions from recent college graduates in business. Assuming that these applicants can be viewed as a random sample of all such graduates, what is the probability that between 35% and 45% of them are women if 40% of all recent college graduates in business are women?

7.35 A charity has found that 42% of all donors from last year will donate again this year. A random sample of 300 donors from last year was taken.

a. What is the standard error of the sample proportion who will donate again this year?

b. What is the probability that more than half of these sample members will donate again this year?

c. What is the probability that the sample proportion is between 0.40 and 0.45?

d. Without doing the calculations, state in which of the following ranges the sample proportion is more likely to lie: 0.39 to 0.41, 0.41 to 0.43, 0.43 to 0.45, 0.45 to 0.47.

7.36 A corporation is considering a new issue of convertible bonds. Management believes that the offer terms will be found attractive by 20% of all its current stockholders. Suppose that this belief is correct. A random sample of 130 current stockholders is taken.

a. What is the standard error of the sample proportion who find this offer attractive?

b. What is the probability that the sample proportion is more than 0.15?

c. What is the probability that the sample proportion is between 0.18 and 0.22?

d. Suppose that a sample of 500 current stockholders had been taken. Without doing the calculations, state whether the probabilities in parts (b) and (c) would have been higher, lower, or the same as those found.

7.37 A store has determined that 30% of all lawn mower purchasers will also purchase a service agreement. In 1 month 280 lawn mowers are sold to customers who can be regarded as a random sample of all purchasers.

a. What is the standard error of the sample proportion of those who will purchase a service agreement?

b. What is the probability that the sample proportion will be less than 0.32?

c. Without doing the calculations, state in which of the following ranges the sample proportion is most likely to be: 0.29 to 0.31, 0.30 to 0.32, 0.31 to 0.33, 0.32 to 0.34.

7.38 A random sample of 100 voters is taken to estimate the proportion of a state's electorate in favor of increasing the gasoline tax to provide additional revenue for highway repairs. What is the largest value that the standard error of the sample proportion in favor of this measure can take?

7.39 In Exercise 7.38 above, suppose that it is decided that a sample of 100 voters is too small to provide a sufficiently reliable estimate of the population proportion. It is required instead that the probability that the sample proportion differs from the population proportion (whatever its value) by more than 0.03 should not exceed 0.05. How large a sample is needed to guarantee that this requirement is met?

7.40 A company wants to estimate the proportion of people who are likely to purchase electric shavers and who watch the nationally telecast baseball playoffs. A random sample obtained information from 120 people who were identified as likely to purchase electric shavers. Suppose that the proportion of those likely to purchase electric shavers in the population who watch the telecast is 0.25.

a. The probability is 0.10 that the sample proportion watching the telecast exceeds the population proportion by how much?

b. The probability is 0.05 that the sample proportion is lower than the population proportion by how much?

c. The probability is 0.30 that the sample proportion differs from the population proportion by how much?

7.41 Suppose that 50% of all adult Americans believe that a major overhaul of the nation's health care delivery system is essential. What is the probability that more than 56% of a random sample of 150 adult Americans would hold this belief?

7.42 Suppose that 50% of all adult Americans believe that federal budget deficits at recent levels cause long-term harm to the nation's economy. What is the probability that more than 58% of a random sample of 250 adult Americans would hold this belief.

7.43 A journalist wanted to learn the views of the chief executive officers of the 500 largest U.S. corporations on program trading of stocks. In the time available, it was only possible to contact a random sample of 81 of these chief executive officers. If 55% of all the population members believe that program trading should be banned, what is the probability that less than half the sample members hold this view?

7.44 A small college has an entering freshman class of 528 students. Of these, 211 have brought their own personal computers to campus. A random sample of 120 entering freshmen was taken.

a. What is the standard error of the sample proportion bringing their own personal computers to campus?

b. What is the probability that the sample proportion is less than 0.33?

c. What is the probability that the sample proportion is between 0.5 and 0.6?

7.45 A manufacturing plant has 438 blue-collar employees. Of this group, 239 are concerned about future health care benefits. A random sample of 80 of these employees was questioned to estimate the population proportion concerned about future health care benefits.

a. What is the standard error of the sample proportion who are concerned?

b. What is the probability that the sample proportion is less than 0.5?

c. What is the probability that the sample proportion is between 0.5 and 0.6?

7.46 The annual percentage salary increases for the chief executive officers of all midsize corporations are normally distributed with mean 12.2% and standard deviation 3.6%. A random sample of 81 of these chief executive officers was taken. What is the probability that more than half the sample members had salary increases of less than 10%?

7.4 SAMPLING DISTRIBUTIONS OF SAMPLE VARIANCES

Now that sampling distributions for sample means and proportions have been developed, we will consider sampling distributions of sample variances. As business and industry increase their emphasis on producing products that satisfy customer quality standards, there is an increased need to measure and reduce population variance. High variance for a process implies a wider range of possible values for important product characteristics. This wider range of outcomes will result in more individual products that perform below an acceptable standard. After all, a customer does not care if a product performs well "on average." She is concerned that the particular item that she purchased works. High-quality products can be obtained from a manufacturing process if the process has a low population variance, so that fewer units are below the desired quality standard. By understanding the sampling distribution of sample variances, we can make inferences about the population variance. Thus, processes that have high variance can be identified and corrected. In addition, a smaller population variance improves our ability to make inferences about population means using sample means.

We begin by considering a random sample of n observations drawn from a population with unknown mean μ and unknown variance σ^2. Denote the sample members as $x_1, x_2, \ldots, x_n$. The population variance is the expectation

$$\sigma^2 = E[(X - \mu)^2]$$

which suggests that we consider the mean of $(x_i - \bar{x})^2$ over n observations. Since μ is unknown, we will use the sample mean $\bar{x}$ to compute a sample variance.

Sample Variance

Let $x_1, x_2, \ldots, x_n$ be a random sample of observations from a population. The quantity

$$s^2 = \frac{1}{n-1} \sum_{i=1}^{n} (x_i - \bar{x})^2$$

is called the **sample variance**, and its square root, s, is called the *sample standard deviation*. Given a specific random sample, we could compute the sample variance, and the sample variance would be different for each random sample because of differences in sample observations.

We might be initially surprised by the use of $(n-1)$ as the divisor in the above definition. One simple explanation is that in a random sample of n observations we have n different independent values or degrees of freedom. But after we know the computed sample mean, there are only $n-1$ different values that can be uniquely defined. In addition, it can be shown that the expected value of the sample variance computed in this way is the population variance. This result is established in the chapter Appendix and holds when the actual sample size, n, is a small proportion of the population size N:

$$E(s^2) = \sigma^2$$

The conclusion that the expected value of the sample variance is the population variance is quite general. But for statistical inference we would like to know more about the sampling distribution. If we can assume that the underlying population distribution is normal, then it can be shown that the sample variance and the population variance are related through a probability distribution known as the *chi-square distribution*.

Chi-Square Distribution of Sample and Population Variances

Given a random sample of n observations from a normally distributed population whose population variance is σ^2 and whose resulting sample variance is s^2, it can be shown that

$$\frac{(n-1)s^2}{\sigma^2} = \frac{\sum_{i=1}^{n} (x_i - \bar{x})^2}{\sigma^2}$$

has a distribution known as the χ^2 **(chi-square) distribution** with $n-1$ degrees of freedom.

The chi-square family of distributions is used in applied statistical analysis because it provides a link between the sample and the population variances. The chi-square distribution with $n-1$ degrees of freedom is the distribution of the sum of squares of $n-1$ independent standard normal random variables. The above

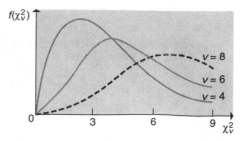

chi-square distribution and the resulting computed probabilities for various values of s^2 require that the population distribution be normal. Thus, the assumption of an underlying normal distribution is more important for determining probabilities of sample variances than it is for determining probabilities of sample means.

The distribution is defined for only positive values, since variances are all positive values. An example of the probability density function is shown in Figure 7.15. The density function is asymmetric with a long positive tail. We can characterize a particular member of the family of chi-square distributions by a single parameter referred to as the degrees of freedom, denoted as v. A χ^2 distribution with v degrees of freedom will be denoted as χ_v^2. The mean and variance of this distribution are equal to the number of degrees of freedom and twice the number of degrees of freedom.

$$E\left(\chi_v^2\right) = v \quad \text{and} \quad \text{Var}\left(\chi_v^2\right) = 2v$$

Using these results for the mean and variance of the chi-square distribution, we find that

$$E\left[\frac{(n-1)s^2}{\sigma^2}\right] = (n-1)$$

$$\frac{(n-1)}{\sigma^2} E(s^2) = (n-1)$$

$$E(s^2) = \sigma^2$$

To obtain the variance of s^2, we have

$$\text{Var}\left[\frac{(n-1)s^2}{\sigma^2}\right] = 2(n-1)$$

$$\frac{(n-1)^2}{\sigma^4} \text{Var}(s^2) = 2(n-1)$$

$$\text{Var}(s^2) = \frac{2\sigma^4}{(n-1)}$$

We can use the properties of the χ^2 distribution to find the variance of the sampling distribution of the sample variance when the parent population is normal.

The parameter v of the χ^2 distribution is called the *degrees of freedom*. To help understand the degrees of freedom concept, consider first that the sample variance is the sum of squares for n values of the form $(x_i - \bar{x})$. These n values are not independent because their sum is zero (as we can show using the definition of the mean). Thus, if we know any $n - 1$ of the values $(x_i - \bar{x})$,

$$\sum_{i=1}^{n} (x_i - \bar{x}) = 0$$

$$x_n - \bar{x} = \sum_{i=1}^{n-1} (x_i - \bar{x})$$

Since we can determine the nth quantity if we know the remaining $n - 1$ quantities, we say that there are $n - 1$ degrees of freedom—independent values—for computing s^2. In contrast, if μ were known, we could compute an estimate of σ^2 by using the quantities

$$(x_1 - \mu), (x_2 - \mu), \ldots, (x_n - \mu)$$

each of which is independent. In that case we would have n degrees of freedom from the n independent sample observations, x_i. However, μ is not known, and we must use its estimate $\bar{x}$ to compute the estimate of σ^2. As a result, one degree of freedom is lost in computing the sample mean, and we have $n - 1$ degrees of freedom for s^2.

For many applications involving the population variance we need to find values for the cumulative distribution of χ^2, especially the upper and lower tails of the distribution; for example,

$$P(\chi_{10}^2 < K) = 0.05$$
$$P(\chi_{10}^2 > K) = 0.05$$

For this purpose we have the distribution of the chi-square random variable tabulated in Table 7 in the Appendix. In Table 7 the degrees of freedom are noted in the left column and the critical values of K for various probability levels are indicated in the other columns. Thus, for 10 degrees of freedom the value of K for the lower interval is 3.94. This result is found by going to the row with 10 degrees of freedom in the left column and then reading over to the column headed by the probability 0.950 to the right of these column entries. The chi-square value is 3.94. Similarly, for the upper 0.05 interval the value of K is 18.31. This result is found by going to the row with 10 degrees of freedom in the left column and then reading over to the column headed by the probability 0.050 to the right of these column entries. The chi-square value is 18.31. These probabilities are shown schematically in Figure 7.16.

$$P(\chi_{10}^2 < 3.94) = 0.05$$
$$P(\chi_{10}^2 > 18.31) = 0.05$$

The sampling distribution results are summarized in the following box.

Figure 7.16
Upper and Lower χ_{10}^2 Probabilities with 10 Degrees of Freedom

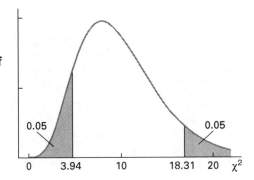

Sampling Distribution of the Sample Variances

Let s^2 denote the sample variance for a random sample of n observations from a population with a variance σ^2. Then

1. The sampling distribution of s^2 has mean σ^2:

$$E(s^2) = \sigma^2 \tag{7.11}$$

2. The variance of the sampling distribution of s^2 depends on the underlying population distribution. If that distribution is normal, then

$$\text{Var}(s^2) = \frac{2\sigma^4}{n-1} \tag{7.12}$$

3. If the population distribution is normal, then $\frac{(n-1)s^2}{\sigma^2}$ is distributed as $\chi^2_{(n-1)}$.

Thus, if we have a random sample from a population with a normal distribution, we can make inferences about the sample variance σ^2 by using s^2 and the chi-square distribution. This process is illustrated in the following examples.

Example 7.9 Process Monitoring for Integrated Electronics (Probability of Sample Variance)

George Samson is responsible for quality assurance at Integrated Electronics. He has asked you to establish a quality monitoring process for the manufacture of control device A. The variability of the electrical resistance, measured in ohms, is critical for this device. Manufacturing standards specify a standard deviation of 3.6, and the population distribution of resistance measures is normal. The monitoring process requires that a random sample of $n = 6$ observations be obtained from the population of devices and the sample variance be computed. Determine an upper limit for the sample variance such that the probability of exceeding this limit, given a population standard deviation of 3.6, is less than 0.05.

Solution   For this problem we have $n = 6$ and $\sigma^2 = (3.6)^2 = 12.96$. Using the chi-square distribution, we can state that

$$P(s^2 > K) = P\left(\frac{(n-1)s^2}{12.96} > \chi^2_5\right) = 0.05$$

where K is the desired upper limit and $\chi^2_5 = 11.07$ is the upper 0.05 critical value of the chi-square distribution with 5 degrees of freedom, from row 5 of Table 7. The required upper limit for s^2—labeled as K—can be obtained by solving

$$\frac{(n-1)K}{12.96} = 11.07$$

$$K = \frac{(11.07)(12.96)}{(6-1)} = 28.69$$

If the sample variance, s^2, from a random sample of size $n = 6$ exceeds 28.69, there is strong evidence to suspect that the population variance exceeds 12.96 and that the manufacturing process should be halted and appropriate adjustments performed.

Example 7.10 Process Analysis for Green Valley Foods (Probability of Sample Variance)

Shirley Mendez is the manager of quality assurance for Green Valley Foods, Inc., a packer of frozen vegetable products. Shirley wants to be sure that the variation of package weights is small so that the company does not produce a large proportion of packages that are under the stated package weight. She has asked you to obtain upper and lower limits for the ratio of the sample variance divided by the population variance for a random sample of $n = 20$ observations. The limits are such that the probability that the ratio is below the lower limit is 0.025 and the probability that the ratio is above the upper limit is 0.025. Thus, 95% of the ratios will be between these limits. The population distribution can be assumed to be normal.

Solution   We are asked to obtain values K_L and K_U such that

$$P\left(\frac{s^2}{\sigma^2} < K_L\right) = 0.025 \qquad \text{and} \qquad P\left(\frac{s^2}{\sigma^2} > K_U\right) = 0.025$$

given that a random sample of size $n = 20$ is used to compute the sample variance. For the lower limit we can state

$$0.025 = P\left[\frac{(n-1)s^2}{\sigma^2} < (n-1)K_L\right] = P\left[\chi_{19}^2 < (n-1)K_L\right]$$

For the upper limit we can state

$$0.975 = P\left[\frac{(n-1)s^2}{\sigma^2} > (n-1)K_U\right] = P\left[\chi_{19}^2 > (n-1)K_U\right]$$

These upper and lower limits of chi-square define an interval such that, if the sample computed chi-square is within that interval, we accept the assumption that the process variance is at the assumed value. This interval is defined as an *acceptance interval*.

Using the lower and upper bounds for the chi-square acceptance interval, we can compute the acceptance interval limits, K_L and K_U, for the ratio of sample variance to population variance. The upper and lower values for the chi-square distribution can be found in Table 7 as

$$\chi_{19L}^2 = 8.91$$
$$\chi_{19U}^2 = 32.85$$
$$0.025 = P\left[\chi_{19L}^2 < (n-1)K_L\right] = P[8.91 < (19)K_L]$$

and thus

$$K_L = 0.469$$

For the upper limit we have

$$0.975 = P\left[\chi^2_{19U} > (n-1)K_U\right] = P\left[32.85 > (19)K_U\right]$$

and thus

$$K_U = 1.729$$

The 95% acceptance interval for the ratio of sample variance divided by population variance is

$$P\left(0.469 \leq \frac{s^2}{\sigma^2} \leq 1.729\right) = 0.95$$

Thus, the sample variance is between 46.9% and 172.9% of the population variance with probability 0.95.

INTERPRETATION

At this point it is important that we emphasize that the procedures used to make inferences about the population variance are substantially influenced by the assumption of a normal population distribution. Inferences concerning the population mean based on the sample mean are not substantially affected by departures from a normal distribution. In addition, inferences based on the sample mean can make use of the central limit theorem, which states that sample means will typically be normally distributed if the sample size is reasonably large. Thus, we state that inferences based on the sample mean are robust with respect to the assumption of normality. Unfortunately, inferences based on sample variances are not robust with respect to the assumption of normality.

We know that in many applications the population variance is of direct interest to an investigator. But when using the procedures we have demonstrated, we must keep in mind that, if only a moderate number of sample observations are available, serious departures from normality in the parent population can severely invalidate the conclusions of analyses. The cautious analyst will therefore be rather tentative in making inferences in these circumstances.

EXERCISES

Basic Exercises

7.47   A random sample of size $n = 16$ is obtained from a normally distributed population with population mean $\mu = 100$ and $\sigma^2 = 25$.

   a. What is the probability that $\bar{x} > 101$?
   b. What is the probability that the sample variance is greater than 45?
   c. What is the probability that the sample variance is greater than 60?

7.48   A random sample of size $n = 25$ is obtained from a normally distributed population with population mean $\mu = 198$ and variance $\sigma^2 = 100$.

   a. What is the probability that the sample mean is greater than 200?
   b. What is the value of the sample variance such that 5% of the sample variances would be less than this value?

c. What is the value of the sample variance such that 5% of the sample variances would be greater than this value?

7.49 A random sample of size $n = 18$ is obtained from a normally distributed population with population mean $\mu = 46$ and variance $\sigma^2 = 50$.

a. What is the probability that the sample mean is greater than 50?

b. What is the value of the sample variance such that 5% of the sample variances would be less than this value?

c. What is the value of the sample variance such that 5% of the sample variances would be greater than this value?

7.50 A process produces batches of a chemical whose impurity concentrations follow a normal distribution with variance 1.75. A random sample of 20 of these batches is chosen. Find the probability that the sample variance exceeds 3.10.

7.51 Monthly rates of return on the shares of a particular common stock are independent of one another and normally distributed with a standard deviation of 1.7. A sample of 12 months is taken.

a. Find the probability that the sample standard deviation is less than 2.5.

b. Find the probability that the sample standard deviation is more than 1.0.

7.52 It is believed that first-year salaries for newly qualified accountants follow a normal distribution with standard deviation $2,500. A random sample of 16 observations was taken.

a. Find the probability that the sample standard deviation is more than $3,000.

b. Find the probability that the sample standard deviation is less than $1,500.

Application Exercises

7.53 A mathematics test of 100 multiple-choice questions is to be given to all freshmen entering a large university. Initially, in a pilot study the test was given to a random sample of 20 freshmen. Suppose that, for the population of all entering freshmen, the distribution of number of correct answers would be normal with variance 250.

a. What is the probability that the sample variance would be less than 100?

b. What is the probability that the sample variance would be more than 500?

7.54 In a large city it was found that summer electricity bills for single-family homes followed a normal distribution with standard deviation $100. A random sample of 25 bills was taken.

a. Find the probability that the sample standard deviation is less than $75.

b. Find the probability that the sample standard deviation is more than $150.

7.55 Numbers of hours spent watching television by students in the week before final exams have a normal distribution with standard deviation 4.5 hours. A random sample of 30 students was taken.

a. Is the probability more than 0.95 that the sample standard deviation exceeds 3.5 hours?

b. Is the probability more than 0.95 that the sample standard deviation is less than 6 hours?

7.56 In Table 7.1 we considered the 15 possible samples of two observations from a population of $N = 6$ values of years on the job for employees. The population variance for these six values is

$$\sigma^2 = \frac{47}{12}$$

For each of the 15 possible samples, calculate the sample variance. Find the average of these 15 sample variances, thus confirming that the expected value of the sample variance is not equal to the population variance when the number of sample members is not a small proportion of the number of population members. [In fact, as you can verify here, $E(s^2) = N\sigma^2/(N-1)$.]

7.57 A production process manufactures electronic components with timing signals whose duration follows a normal distribution. A random sample of six components was taken, and the durations of their timing signals were measured.

a. The probability is 0.05 that the sample variance is bigger than what percentage of the population variance?

b. The probability is 0.10 that the sample variance is less than what percentage of the population variance?

7.58 A random sample of 10 stock market mutual funds was taken. Suppose that rates of returns on the population of all stock market mutual funds follow a normal distribution.

a. The probability is 0.10 that sample variance is bigger than what percentage of the population variance?

b. Find any pair of numbers, a and b, to complete the following sentence: The probability is 0.95 that the sample variance is between a% and b% of the population variance.

c. Suppose that a sample of 20 mutual funds had been taken. Without doing the calculations, indicate how this would change your answer to part (b).

7.59 Each member of a random sample of 15 business economists was asked to predict the rate of inflation for the coming year. Assume that the predictions for the whole population of business economists follow a normal distribution with standard deviation 1.8%.

a. The probability is 0.01 that the sample standard deviation is bigger than what number?
b. The probability is 0.025 that the sample standard deviation is smaller than what number?
c. Find any pair of numbers such that the probability that the sample standard deviation lies between these numbers is 0.90.

7.60 A precision instrument is checked by making 12 readings on the same quantity. The population distribution of readings is normal.

a. The probability is 0.95 that the sample variance is more than what percentage of the population variance?
b. The probability is 0.90 that the sample variance is more than what percentage of the population variance?
c. Determine any pair of appropriate numbers, *a* and *b*, to complete the following sentence: The probability is 0.95 that the sample variance is between *a*% and *b*% of the population variance.

7.61 A drug company produces pills containing an active ingredient. The company is concerned about the mean weight of this ingredient per pill, but it also requires that the variance (in squared milligrams) be no more than 1.5. A random sample of 20 pills is selected, and the sample variance is found to be 2.05. How likely is it that a sample variance this high or higher would be found if the population variance is, in fact, 1.5? Assume that the population distribution is normal.

7.62 A manufacturer has been purchasing raw materials from a supplier whose consignments have a variance of 15.4 (in squared pounds) in impurity levels. A rival supplier claims that he can supply consignments of this raw material with the same mean impurity level but with lower variance. For a random sample of 25 consignments from the second supplier, the variance in impurity levels was found to be 12.2. What is the probability of observing a value this low or lower for the sample variance if, in fact, the true population variance is 15.4? Assume that the population distribution is normal.

SUMMARY

In Chapter 7 we presented the concept of sampling distributions, defined as the probability distributions for sample statistics. Sampling distributions enable us to determine the probability of a particular sample statistic, given a specific probability distribution model for the sampling distribution. We are thus linking the sample statistics developed in Chapter 3 with the probability distributions developed in Chapters 5 and 6. We will see in future chapters how this link allows us to use our sample statistics to draw certain conclusions or inferences about the system and process that develop a population of data from which our sample was obtained. This is the basis for objective decisions based on sample data. In our discussion we included the important concept of acceptance intervals. Acceptance intervals define a range, with a given probability, for sample statistics based on an assumed probability distribution function. If the sample statistic is within that range, then we "accept" the assumed probability model as being correct.

KEY WORDS

- acceptance interval
- central limit theorem
- chi-square distribution
- finite population correction factor
- sample mean
- sample proportion
- sample variance
- sampling distribution of the sample means
- sampling distribution of the sample proportion
- sampling distribution of the sample variances
- sampling distributions
- simple random sample
- standard normal distribution for sample means
- standardized normal random variable

CHAPTER EXERCISES AND APPLICATIONS

7.63 What is meant by the statement that the sample mean has a sampling distribution?

7.64 An investor is considering six different money market funds. The average number of days to maturity for each of these funds is

41	39	35	35	33	38

Two of these funds are to be chosen at random.

a. How many possible samples of two funds are there?
b. List all possible samples.
c. Find the probability function of the sampling distribution of the sample means.
d. Verify directly that the mean of the sampling distribution of the sample means is equal to the population mean.

7.65 Of what relevance is the central limit theorem to the sampling distribution of the sample means?

7.66 The scores of all applicants taking an aptitude test required by a law school have a normal distribution with mean 420 and standard deviation 100. A random sample of 25 scores is taken.

a. Find the probability that the sample mean score is higher than 450.
b. Find the probability that the sample mean score is between 400 and 450.
c. The probability is 0.10 that the sample mean score is higher than what number?
d. The probability is 0.10 that the sample mean score is lower than what number?
e. The probability is 0.05 that the sample standard deviation of the scores is higher than what number?
f. The probability is 0.05 that the sample standard deviation of the scores is lower than what number?
g. If a sample of 50 test scores had been taken, would the probability of a sample mean score higher than 450 be smaller than, larger than, or the same as the correct answer to part (a)? It is not necessary to do the detailed calculations here. Sketch a graph to illustrate your reasoning.

7.67 A company services home air conditioners. It has been found that times for service calls follow a normal distribution with mean 60 minutes and standard deviation 10 minutes. A random sample of four service calls was taken.

a. What is the probability that the sample mean service time is more than 65 minutes?

b. The probability is 0.10 that the sample mean service time is less than how many minutes?
c. The probability is 0.10 that the sample standard deviation of service times is more than how many minutes?
d. The probability is 0.10 that the sample standard deviation of service times is less than how many minutes?
e. What is the probability that more than two of these calls take more than 65 minutes?

7.68 In a particular year, the percentage rates of return of U.S. common stock mutual funds had a normal distribution with mean 14.8 and standard deviation 6.3. A random sample of nine of these mutual funds was taken.

a. What is the probability that the sample mean percentage rate of return is more than 19.0?
b. What is the probability that the sample mean percentage rate of return is between 10.6 and 19.0?
c. The probability is 0.25 that the sample mean percentage return is less than what number?
d. The probability is 0.10 that the sample standard deviation of percentage return is more than what number?
e. If a sample of 20 of these funds was taken, state whether the probability of a sample mean percentage rate of return of more than 19.0 would be smaller than, larger than, or the same as the correct answer to part (a). Sketch a graph to illustrate your reasoning.

7.69 The lifetimes of a certain electronic component are known to be normally distributed with a mean of 1,600 hours and a standard deviation of 400 hours.

a. For a random sample of 16 components find the probability that the sample mean is more than 1,500 hours.
b. For a random sample of 16 components the probability is 0.15 that the sample mean lifetime is more than how many hours?
c. For a random sample of 16 components the probability is 0.10 that the sample standard deviation lifetime is more than how many hours?

7.70 Refer to the chapter Appendix in order to derive the mean of the sampling distribution of the sample variances for a sample of n observations from a population of N members when the population variance is σ^2. By appropriately modifying the argument regarding variances in the chapter Appendix, show that

$$E(s^2) = N\sigma^2/(N-1)$$

Note the intuitive plausibility of this result when $n = N$.

7.71   It has been found that times taken by people to complete a particular tax form follow a normal distribution with mean 100 minutes and standard deviation 30 minutes. A random sample of nine people who have completed this tax form was taken.

   a. What is the probability that the sample mean time taken is more than 120 minutes?
   b. The probability is 0.20 that the sample mean time taken is less than how many minutes?
   c. The probability is 0.05 that the sample standard deviation of time taken is less than how many minutes?

7.72   It was found that 80% of seniors at a particular college had accepted a job offer before graduation. For those accepting offers, salary distribution was normal with mean $29,000 and standard deviation $4,000.

   a. For a random sample of 60 seniors what is the probability that less than 70% have accepted job offers?
   b. For a random sample of 6 seniors what is the probability that less than 70% have accepted job offers?
   c. For a random sample of 6 seniors who have accepted job offers what is the probability that the average salary is more than $30,000?
   d. A senior is chosen at random. What is the probability that he or she has accepted a job offer with a salary of more than $30,000?

7.73   Plastic bags used for packaging produce are manufactured so that the breaking strengths of the bags are normally distributed with a standard deviation of 1.8 pounds per square inch. A random sample of 16 bags is selected.

   a. The probability is 0.01 that the sample standard deviation of breaking strengths exceeds what number?
   b. The probability is 0.15 that the sample mean exceeds the population mean by how much?
   c. The probability is 0.05 that the sample mean differs from the population mean by how much?

7.74   A quality control manager was concerned about variability in the amount of active ingredient in pills produced by a particular process. A random sample of 21 pills was taken. What is the probability that the sample variance of the amount of active ingredient was more than twice the population variance?

7.75   A sample of 100 students is to be taken to determine which of two brands of beer is preferred in a blind taste test. Suppose that, in the whole population of students, 50% would prefer brand A.

   a. What is the probability that more than 60% of the sample members prefer brand A?
   b. What is the probability that between 45% and 55% of the sample members prefer brand A?
   c. Suppose that a sample of only 10 students was available. Indicate how the method of calculation of probabilities would differ, compared with your solutions to parts (a) and (b)?

7.76   Scores on a particular test, taken by a large group of students, follow a normal distribution with standard deviation 40 points. A random sample of 16 scores was taken to estimate the population mean score. Let $\bar{X}$ denote the sample mean. What is the probability that the interval $(\bar{X} - 10)$ to $(\bar{X} + 10)$ contains the true population mean?

7.77   A manufacturer of liquid detergent claims that the mean weight of liquid in containers sold is at least 30 ounces. It is known that the population distribution of weights is normal with standard deviation 1.3 ounces. In order to check the manufacturer's claim, a random sample of 16 containers of detergent is examined. The claim will be questioned if the sample mean weight is less than 29.5 ounces. What is the probability that the claim will be questioned if, in fact, the population mean weight is 30 ounces?

7.78   In a particular year 40% of home sales were partially financed by the seller. A random sample of 250 sales is examined.

   a. The probability is 0.8 that the sample proportion is bigger than what amount?
   b. The probability is 0.9 that the sample proportion is smaller than what amount?
   c. The probability is 0.7 that the sample proportion differs from the population proportion by how much?

7.79   A candidate for office intends to campaign in a state if her initial support level exceeds 30% of the voters. A random sample of 300 voters is taken, and it is decided to campaign if the sample proportion supporting the candidate exceeds 0.28.

   a. What is the probability of a decision not to campaign if, in fact, the initial support level is 20%?
   b. What is the probability of a decision not to campaign if, in fact, the initial support level is 40%?

7.80   It is known that the incomes of subscribers to a particular magazine have a normal distribution with standard deviation $6,600. A random sample of 25 subscribers is taken.

   a. What is the probability that the sample standard deviation of their incomes is bigger than $4,000?
   b. What is the probability that the sample standard deviation of their incomes is less than $8,000?

7.81 Batches of chemical are manufactured by a production process. Samples of 20 batches from a production run are selected for testing. If the standard deviation of the percentage impurity contents in the sample batches exceeds 2.5%, the production process is thoroughly checked. Assume that the population distribution of percentage impurity concentrations is normal. What is the probability that the production process will be thoroughly checked if the population standard deviation of percentage impurity concentrations is 2%.

Appendix

1. MONTE CARLO SAMPLE SIMULATIONS USING MINITAB

In Section 7.2 we presented results from Monte Carlo sampling simulations to demonstrate the central limit theorem. In this appendix we will indicate how you can construct similar simulations for a probability distribution. The simulation can be performed using a Minitab macro named Centlimit.mac, which is contained on the disk supplied with the textbook. To use this macro, copy it to the directory

```
MTBWIN\MACROS\
```

using the Windows Explorer. This macro will then be stored with other macros supplied with the Minitab package. When the macro is stored in this directory, it can be run directly in Minitab. Alternatively, the macro can be stored in another directory, and the entire path is supplied to run the macro. To run the sampling simulation, use the following steps:

1. In column 1 store a set of values that have the frequency indicated by the probability distribution that you are interested in simulating. Typically, we store 100 values, but any number could be stored. For example, to store a binomial distribution with $P = 0.40$, you would store 40 1's and 60 0's in column 1. You could also store an empirical distribution of numbers from a population being studied. Another procedure for obtaining the sample values is to use the command

```
CALC>RANDOM DATA>"SELECT PROBABILITY DISTRIBUTION"
```

This would provide you with a random sample from one of a number of common probability distributions.

2. In the Minitab Session Window type the command

```
MTB>%CENTLIMIT N1 N2 C1-C3
```

where N1 is the sample size for the individual samples being simulated and N2 is the number of samples whose means are to be obtained from the simulation. Generally, 500 to 1,000 samples will provide a good sampling distribution, but you can select any reasonable value. Recognize that the greater the number of samples, the longer it will take to run the simulation. C1 to C3 are the columns used by Minitab for the simulation, with your probability distribution of interest in column 1. You could use any columns as long as your probability distribution is in column 1.

Figure 7.17 shows a run of the sampling simulation.

The simulation will generate samples in column 2 and compute the sample mean. The mean for each sample will be stored in column 3, titled "Mean." Descriptive statistics and histograms will be computed for the "random variable" values in column 1 and for the sample means in column 3. By clicking on the menu command

```
WINDOWS>TILE
```

you can obtain the screen in Figure 7.18, which is useful for comparing the original distribution and the sampling distribution with a comparable normal.

Figure 7.17
Monte Carlo
Sampling
Simulation in
Minitab

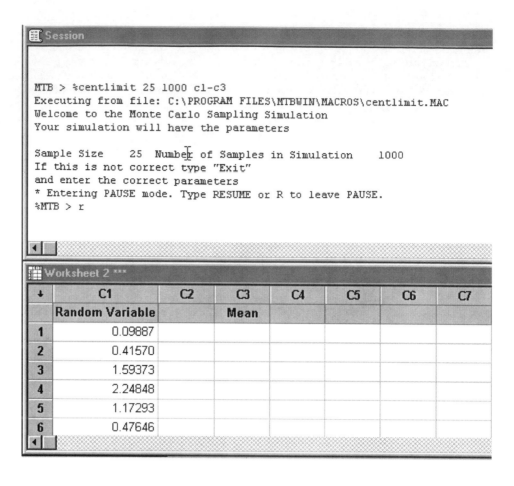

Figure 7.18
Results of the
Monte Carlo
Sampling
Simulation

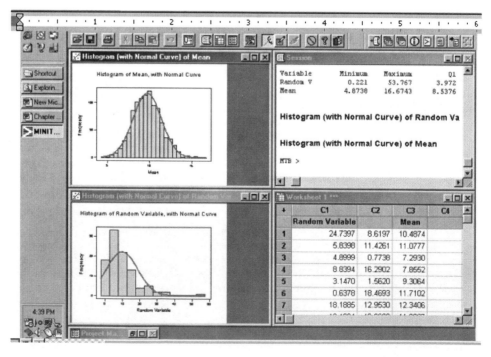

Figure 7.19
Copy of the
Minitab Macro
Centlimit.mac

```
Macro
Centlimit n1,n2,Dist,Samp,Xbar
#  Dr.William L. Carlson
#  Professor of Economics
#  St Olaf College
#  Northfield MN   55057
#  Carlson@Stolaf.edu
#  To Execute this Macro in Minitab  Type
#  %Centlimit "sample size"  "Number of Samples"  C1 C2 C3
#
#The output includes a histogram and a normal probability plot for the
original #distribution and a histogram and normal probability plot for the
sampling #distribution of sample means
#Macro is Stored as a text file in C:\program
files\mtbwin\macros\centlimit.mac
#
#Definition of Variables
#
# n1  Sample size obtained from probability distribution
# n2  Number of samples of size n1 obtained in this simulation
# Dist      Column that contains an empirical distribution from which the
random #          sample is obtained.
# Xbar      Column that contains the sample means from each of the n2 samples
#           obtained in the simulation
# Samp      Column that will be used to generate each of the samples.
#
#
Mconstant  n1 n2 k1 k2
Mcolumn Dist Xbar Samp c11 c12 c13 c14
Name Dist 'Random Variable' Xbar 'Mean'
Let c11="Sample Size"
Let c12= n1
Let c13="Number of Samples in Simulation"
Let c14=n2
Note Welcome to the Monte Carlo Sampling Simulation
Note Your simulation will have the parameters
Write 'Terminal' c11-c14
Note If this is not correct type "exit"
Note and enter the correct parameters
Pause
Brief 0
Do k1=1:n2
Sample n1 Dist Samp;
Replace.
Mean Samp k2
Let xbar(k1)=k2
Enddo
Brief
Describe Dist Xbar;
GNHist.
Endmacro
```

In Figure 7.18 we see that the distribution of the random variable is definitely not normal; rather, it is highly skewed to the right. In contrast, the sampling distribution of the means closely approximates a normal distribution. Figure 7.19 presents a copy of the Centlimit.mac Minitab macro, which is also stored on the data disk for the textbook. Users familiar with Minitab macros could modify this macro to obtain different outputs.

2. MEAN OF THE SAMPLING DISTRIBUTION OF THE SAMPLE VARIANCES

In this appendix, we show that the mean of the sampling distribution of the sample variances is the population variance. We begin by finding the expectation of the sum of squares of the sample members about their mean; that is, the expectation of

$$\sum_{i=1}^{n} \left(X_i - \overline{X}\right)^2 = \sum_{i=1}^{n} \left[\left(X_i - \mu\right) - \left(\overline{X} - \mu\right)\right]^2$$

$$= \sum_{i=1}^{n} \left[\left(X_i - \mu\right)^2 - 2\left(\overline{X} - \mu\right)\left(X_i - \mu\right) + \left(\overline{X} - \mu\right)^2\right]$$

$$= \sum_{i=1}^{n} (X_i - \mu)^2 - 2(\overline{X} - \mu) \sum_{i=1}^{n} (X_i - \mu) + \sum_{i=1}^{n} (\overline{X} - \mu)^2$$

$$= \sum_{i=1}^{n} (X_i - \mu)^2 - 2n(\overline{X} - \mu)^2 + n(\overline{X} - \mu)^2$$

$$= \sum_{i=1}^{n} (X_i - \mu)^2 - n(\overline{X} - \mu)^2$$

Taking expectations then gives

$$E\left[\sum_{i=1}^{n} (X_i - \overline{X})^2\right] = E\left[\sum_{i=1}^{n} (X_i - \mu)^2\right] - nE\left[(\overline{X} - \mu)^2\right]$$

$$= \sum_{i=1}^{n} E\left[(X_i - \mu)^2\right] - nE\left[(\overline{X} - \mu)^2\right]$$

Now, the expectation of each $(X_i - \mu)^2$ is the population variance, σ^2, and the expectation of $(\overline{X} - \mu)^2$ is the variance of the sample mean, σ^2/n. Hence, we have

$$E\left[\sum_{i=1}^{n} (X_i - \overline{X})^2\right] = n\sigma^2 - \frac{n\sigma^2}{n} = (n - 1)\sigma^2$$

Finally, for the expected value of the sample variance we have

$$E(s^2) = E\left[\frac{1}{n-1} \sum_{i=1}^{n} (X_i - \overline{X})^2\right]$$

$$= \frac{1}{n-1} E\left[\sum_{i=1}^{n} (X_i - \overline{X})^2\right]$$

$$= \frac{1}{n-1} (n-1)\sigma^2 = \sigma^2$$

This is the result we set out to establish.

REFERENCES

1. David, F. R., L. M. Anderson, and K. W. Lawrimore. "Perspectives on Business Ethics in Management Education." *S. A. M. Advanced Management Journal* 55, no. 4 (1990): 26–32.
2. Hogan, H. "The 1990 Post-enumeration Survey: An Overview." *American Statistician* 46 (1992): 261–269.

Topic 10

Estimation: Single Population

Chapter 8

Estimation: Single Population

Introduction

This chapter emphasizes inferential statements concerning estimation of a single population parameter, based on information contained in a random sample. We focus on procedures to estimate a population mean or a proportion of population members that possess some specific characteristic. For example, we may want an estimate of average weekly demand for a particular brand of orange juice or an estimate of the proportion of a corporation's employees favoring the introduction of a modified bonus plan.

We present two estimation procedures in this chapter. First, we estimate an unknown population parameter by a single number called a point estimate. Properties of this point estimate are considered in Section 8.1. For most practical problems a point estimate alone is not adequate. A more complete understanding of the process that generated the population also requires a measure of variability. The remainder of the chapter discusses a second procedure, which takes into account this variation by establishing a range of values in which the quantity to be estimated appears likely to lie.

Estimation of the difference between the means or proportions of two populations and estimation of variance will be considered in Chapter 9.

8.1 PROPERTIES OF POINT ESTIMATORS

Any inference drawn about the population will be based on sample statistics. The choice of appropriate statistics will depend on which population parameter is of interest. The value of the population parameter will be unknown, and one objective of sampling is to estimate its value. A distinction must be made between the terms *estimator* and *estimate*.

> ### Estimator and Estimate
> An **estimator** of a population parameter is a random variable that depends on the sample information; its value provides approximations to this unknown parameter. A specific value of that random variable is called an **estimate.**

Hildebrand and Ott (Reference 4) point out that there is "a technical distinction between an *estimator* as a function of random variables and an *estimate* as a single number. It is the distinction between a process (the estimator) and the result of that process (the estimate)." To clarify this distinction between estimator and estimate, consider the estimation of the mean weekly sales of a particular brand of orange juice. One possible *estimator* of the population mean is the sample mean. If the mean of a random sample of weekly sales is found to be 3,280 gallons, then 3,280 is an *estimate* of the population mean weekly sales. Another possible *estimator* of the mean weekly sales could be the sample median.

In Chapter 3 we studied other estimators, such as sample variance, s^2, and sample correlation coefficient, r. If the value of the sample variance for the weekly demand of orange juice is 300 gallons, then s^2 is the estimator and 300 is the estimate.

In discussing the estimation of an unknown parameter, two possibilities must be considered. First, a *single number* could be computed from the sample as most representative of the unknown population parameter. This is called a *point estimate*. The estimate of 3,280 gallons of orange juice is an example of a point estimate. Alternatively, it might be possible to find an interval or range that most likely contains the value of the population parameter. For example, the mean weekly demand in this store for this particular brand of orange juice is, with some specified degree of confidence, between 2,500 and 3,500 gallons. This interval estimate is an example of one type of *confidence interval* that we will discuss in this chapter.

> ### Point Estimator and Point Estimate
> Consider a population parameter such as the population mean μ or the population proportion P. A **point estimator** of a population parameter is a function of the sample information that produces a single number called a **point estimate.** For example, the sample mean $\bar{X}$ is a point estimator of the population mean, μ, and the value that $\bar{X}$ assumes for a given set of data is called the point estimate, $\bar{x}$.

At the outset it must be pointed out that no single mechanism exists for the determination of a uniquely "best" point estimator in all circumstances. What is available instead is a set of criteria under which particular estimators can be evaluated. The sample median also gives a point estimate of the population mean, μ. However, we show later in this chapter that the median is not the best estimator for the mean of some distributions.

We will evaluate estimators based on three important properties: unbiasedness, consistency, and efficiency.

Unbiased Estimator

In searching for an estimator of a population parameter, the first property an estimator should possess is *unbiasedness*.

> ## Unbiased Estimator
> A point estimator is said to be an **unbiased estimator** of a population parameter if its expected value is equal to that parameter; that is, if
>
> $$E(\hat{\theta}) = \theta$$
>
> then $\hat{\theta}$ is an unbiased estimator of θ.

Notice that unbiasedness does not mean that a *particular* value of $\hat{\theta}$ must be exactly the correct value of θ. Rather, an unbiased estimator has "the capability of estimating the population parameter correctly on the average. . . . An unbiased estimator is correct on the average. We can think of the expected value of $\hat{\theta}$ as the average of $\hat{\theta}$ values for all possible samples, or alternatively, as the long-run average of $\hat{\theta}$ values for repeated samples. The condition that the estimator $\hat{\theta}$ should be unbiased says that the *average* $\hat{\theta}$ value is exactly correct. It does not state that a particular $\hat{\theta}$ value is exactly correct" (Reference 4).

Sometimes $\hat{\theta}$ will overestimate and other times underestimate the parameter, but it follows from the notion of expectation that, if the sampling procedure is repeated many times, then, on the average, the value obtained for an unbiased estimator will be equal to the population parameter. It seems reasonable to assert that, all other things being equal, unbiasedness is a desirable property in a point estimator. Figure 8.1 illustrates the probability density functions for two estimators, $\hat{\theta}_1$ and $\hat{\theta}_2$, of the parameter θ. It should be obvious that $\hat{\theta}_1$ is an unbiased estimator of θ and $\hat{\theta}_2$ is not an unbiased estimator.

The sample mean, sample variance, and sample proportion are unbiased estimators of their corresponding population parameters:

1. The sample mean is an unbiased estimator of μ, $[E(\overline{x}) = \mu]$
2. The sample variance is an unbiased estimator of σ^2, $[E(s^2) = \sigma^2]$
3. The sample proportion is an unbiased estimator of P, $[E(\hat{p}) = P]$

An estimator that is not unbiased is *biased*. The extent of the bias is the difference between the mean of the estimator and the true parameter.

Figure 8.1
Probability
Density Functions
for Estimators $\hat{\theta}_1$
(Unbiased) and
$\hat{\theta}_2$ (Biased)

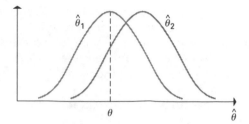

Bias
Let $\hat{\theta}$ be an estimator of θ. The **bias** in $\hat{\theta}$ is defined as the difference between its mean and θ; that is,

$$\text{Bias}(\hat{\theta}) = E(\hat{\theta}) - \theta$$

It follows that the bias of an unbiased estimator is 0.

Unbiasedness alone is not the only desirable characteristic of an estimator. There may be several unbiased estimators for a population parameter. For example, if the population is normally distributed, both the sample mean and the median are unbiased estimators of the population mean.

Consistent Estimator

We consider now a second property called *consistency*.

Consistent Estimator
A point estimator $\hat{\theta}$ is said to be a **consistent estimator** of the parameter θ if the difference between the expected value of the estimator and the parameter decreases as the sample size increases. This is the same as stating that the bias becomes smaller with increased sample size.

Consistent estimators are used in cases where it is difficult or impossible to obtain unbiased estimators, which occurs in some advanced econometric work. Not all unbiased estimators are consistent, and by no means are all consistent estimators unbiased. If the sample variance were calculated as

$$s^2 = \frac{\sum (x_i - \bar{x})^2}{n},$$

then it would be a biased estimator of the population variance. However, it is consistent, since it approaches the unbiased estimator

$$s^2 = \frac{\sum (x_i - \bar{x})^2}{n - 1}$$

as the sample size increases.

Loosely speaking, the use of a consistent estimator with an infinite amount of sample information gives the correct result. Conversely, the use of an inconsistent estimator does not yield the correct result even with an infinite amount of sample information. For this reason, inconsistency in a point estimator is regarded as undesirable.

Efficient Estimator

In many practical problems, different unbiased estimators can be obtained, and some method of choosing among them needs to be found. In this situation it is natural to prefer the estimator whose distribution is most closely concentrated about the population parameter being estimated. Values of such an estimator are less likely to differ, by any fixed amount, from the parameter being estimated than are those of its competitors. Using variance as a measure of concentration, the *efficiency* of an estimator as a criterion for preferring one estimator to another estimator is introduced.

Most Efficient Estimator and Relative Efficiency

If there are several unbiased estimators of a parameter, then the unbiased estimator with the smallest variance is called the **most efficient estimator** or the **minimum variance unbiased estimator**. Let $\hat{\theta}_1$ and $\hat{\theta}_2$ be two unbiased estimators of θ, based on the same number of sample observations. Then

1. $\hat{\theta}_1$ is said to be more efficient than $\hat{\theta}_2$ if $Var(\hat{\theta}_1) < Var(\hat{\theta}_2)$.
2. The **relative efficiency** of $\hat{\theta}_1$ with respect to $\hat{\theta}_2$ is the ratio of their variances; that is,

$$\text{Relative Efficiency} = \frac{Var(\hat{\theta}_2)}{Var(\hat{\theta}_1)}$$

Example 8.1   Selection from Competing Unbiased Estimators (Relative Efficiency)

Let $x_1, x_2, \ldots, x_n$ be a random sample from a normally distributed population with mean μ and variance σ^2. Should the sample mean or the sample median be used to estimate the population mean?

Solution   Assuming a population that is normally distributed with a very large population size compared to the sample size, the sample mean, $\overline{X}$, is an unbiased estimator of the population mean with variance:

$$Var(\overline{X}) = \frac{\sigma^2}{n}$$

As an alternative estimator, the median of the sample observations could be used. It can be shown that this estimator is also unbiased for μ and that, when n is large, its variance is

$$Var(\text{Median}) = \frac{\pi}{2} \times \frac{\sigma^2}{n} = \frac{1.57\sigma^2}{n}$$

The sample mean is more efficient than the median, the relative efficiency of the mean with respect to the median being

$$\text{Relative Efficiency} = \frac{\text{Var(Median)}}{\text{Var}(\overline{X})} = 1.57$$

The variance of the sample median is 57% higher than that of the sample mean. Here, in order for the sample median to have as small a variance as the sample mean, it would have to be based on 57% more observations. One advantage of the median over the mean is that it gives less weight to extreme observations. A potential disadvantage of using the sample median as a measure of central location lies in its relative efficiency.

We emphasize the importance of using a normal probability plot to determine if there is any evidence of non-normality. If the population is not normally distributed, the sample mean may not be the most efficient estimator of the population mean. In particular, if outliers heavily affect the population distribution, the sample mean is less efficient than other estimators (such as the median). Table 8.1 is a summary of some properties for selected point estimators. It is neither an exhaustive list of estimators nor an exhaustive list of properties that an estimator possesses.

Table 8.1   Properties of Selected Point Estimators

POPULATION PARAMETER	POINT ESTIMATOR	PROPERTIES
Mean, μ	$\overline{X}$	Unbiased, consistent, most efficient (assuming normality)
Mean, μ	Median	Unbiased (assuming normality), but not most efficient
Proportion, P	$\hat{p}$	Unbiased, consistent, most efficient
Variance, σ^2	s^2	Unbiased, consistent, most efficient (assuming normality)

Example 8.2   Price-Earnings Ratios (Estimators)

Suppose that we randomly sampled stocks traded on the New York Stock Exchange on a particular day and found the price-earnings ratios of these stocks to be

10	16	13	11	12	14	12
15	14	14	13	13	13	

Does the normal probability plot suggest non-normality? Find point estimates of the mean and variance. Discuss the properties of these estimators.

Solution   From the normal probability plot in Figure 8.2 there appears to be no evidence of non-normality. Assuming a normal distribution, an estimate of the mean price-earnings ratios is the sample mean, 13.1, and an estimate of the variance is $s^2 = 2.58$. Both $\overline{x}$ and s^2 are unbiased, consistent, and efficient point estimators of μ and σ^2, respectively.

Figure 8.2 Price-Earnings Ratios Example (Minitab)

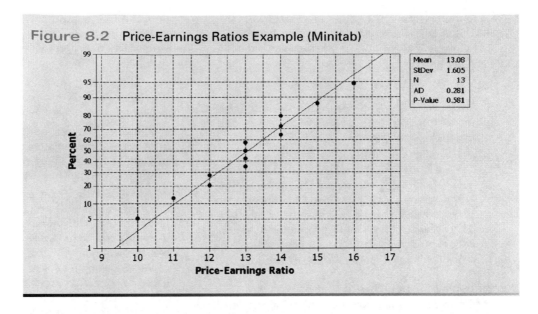

Mean	13.08
StDev	1.605
N	13
AD	0.281
P-Value	0.581

A problem that often arises in practice is how to choose an appropriate point estimator for a population parameter. An attractive possibility is to choose the most efficient of all unbiased estimators. However, sometimes there are estimation problems for which no unbiased estimator is very satisfactory, or there may be situations in which it is not always possible to find a minimum variance unbiased estimator. It is also possible that data may not be normally distributed. In these situations selecting the best point estimator is not straightforward and involves considerable mathematical intricacy beyond the scope of this book.

EXERCISES

Basic Exercises

8.1 Consider the following data:

6   8   7   10   3   5   9   8

a. Check for evidence of non-normality.
b. Find a point estimate of the population mean that is unbiased, efficient, and consistent.
c. Use an unbiased estimation procedure to find a point estimate of the variance of the sample mean.

8.2 A random sample of eight homes in a particular suburb had the following selling prices (in thousands of dollars):

92   83   112   127   109   96   102   90

a. Check for evidence of non-normality
b. Find a point estimate of the population mean that is unbiased and efficient.
c. Use an unbiased estimation procedure to find a point estimate of the variance of the sample mean.

d. Use an unbiased estimator to estimate the proportion of homes in this suburb selling for less than $92,500.

8.3 A random sample of 10 economists produced the following forecasts for percentage growth in real gross domestic product in the next year:

2.2   2.8   3.0   2.5   2.4   2.6   2.5   2.4   2.7   2.6

Use unbiased estimation procedures to find point estimates for:

a. The population mean
b. The population variance
c. The variance of the sample mean
d. The population proportion of economists predicting growth of at least 2.5% in real gross domestic product
e. The variance of the sample proportion of economists predicting growth of at least 2.5% in real gross domestic product

8.4   A random sample of 12 blue-collar employees in a large manufacturing plant found the following figures for number of hours of overtime worked in the last month:

22   16   28   12   18   36   23   11   41   29   26   31

Use unbiased estimation procedures to find point estimates for:

a. The population mean
b. The population variance
c. The variance of the sample mean
d. The population proportion of blue-collar employees working more than 30 hours of overtime in this plant in the last month
e. The variance of the sample proportion of blue-collar employees working more than 30 hours of overtime in this plant in the last month

Application Exercises

8.5   ● Project Romanian Rescue (PRR) is a registered Romanian foundation ministering to the needs of the tragically disadvantaged children in Constanta, Romania (Reference 7). As an interdenominational Christian mission, PRR's services include street outreach, a day center, a boys' group home (Casa Charis), a girls' group home (Casa Chara), and individualized educational assistance for children from poor families. PRR intends to open a village center in nearby Kogalniceanu to house additional street children. Suppose that Daniel Mercado, the project founder, and Camelia Vilcoci, the managing director of the project, maintain records such as the number of meals delivered daily to street children, the number of children who attend the day center, and the ages of the children, and suppose that a random sample of such records is contained in the data file **PRR**.

a. Check each variable to determine if the data are normally distributed.
b. Find unbiased estimates of the population mean and population variance.

8.6   Suppose that x_1 and x_2 are random samples of observations from a population with mean μ and variance σ^2. Consider the following three point estimators, X, Y, Z, of μ:

$$X = \frac{1}{2}x_1 + \frac{1}{2}x_2 \qquad Y = \frac{1}{4}x_1 + \frac{3}{4}x_2 \qquad Z = \frac{1}{3}x_1 + \frac{2}{3}x$$

a. Show that all three estimators are unbiased.
b. Which of the estimators is the most efficient?
c. Find the relative efficiency of X with respect to each of the other two estimators.

8.7   ● Al Fiedler, the plant manager at LDS Vacuum Products, Altamonte Springs, Florida, applies statistical thinking in his workplace. As a major supplier to automobile manufacturers, LDS wants to be sure that the leak rate (in cubic centimeters per second) of transmission oil coolers (TOCs) meets the established specification limits. A random sample of 50 TOCs is tested, and the leak rates are recorded in the file named **TOC** (Reference 3).

a. Is there evidence that the data are not normally distributed?
b. Find a minimum variance unbiased point estimate of the population mean.
c. Use an unbiased estimation procedure to find a point estimate of the variance of the sample mean.

8.8   ● The demand for bottled water increases during the hurricane season in Florida. The operations manager at a plant that bottles drinking water wants to be sure that the filling process for 1-gallon bottles is operating properly. Currently, the company is testing the volumes of 1-gallon bottles. Suppose that a random sample of 75 bottles is tested, and the measurements are recorded in the data file **Water**.

a. Is there evidence that the data are not normally distributed?
b. Find a minimum variance unbiased point estimate of the population mean.
c. Find a minimum variance unbiased point estimate of the population variance.

8.2 CONFIDENCE INTERVALS FOR THE MEAN: POPULATION VARIANCE KNOWN

We first assume that a random sample is taken from a population that is normally distributed with unknown mean and *known* variance. Our objective is to find a range of values, rather than a single number, to estimate a population mean. *This problem is somewhat unrealistic, since rarely will a population variance be precisely known and yet the mean be unknown.* It does sometimes happen, however, that similar populations have been sampled so often in the past that the variance of the population of interest can be assumed known to a very close approximation on the basis of past experience. When the sample size *n* is large enough, the procedures developed for the case where the population variance is known can be used if that variance has to be estimated from the sample. Nevertheless, the chief virtue in beginning with this problem is that it allows a fairly straightforward exposition of the procedures involved in finding confidence intervals.

The average number of cars produced per day in a factory is an important measure. Wide variation above and below the mean might result in excessive inventory costs or lost sales. An estimator and an estimate that take into account this variation are needed, giving a range of values in which the quantity to be estimated appears likely to lie. In this section the general format for such estimators is established.

In sampling from a population, with all other things being equal, a more secure *knowledge* about that population is obtained with a relatively large sample than would be obtained from a smaller sample. However, this factor is not reflected in point estimates. For example, a point estimate of the proportion of defective parts in a shipment would be the same if 1 defective part in a sample of 10 parts is observed or if 100 defective parts in a sample of 1,000 parts are observed. Increased precision in our information about population parameters is reflected in *confidence interval estimates*; specifically, the larger the sample size, the shorter, all other things being equal, the interval estimates that reflect our uncertainty about a parameter's true value.

Confidence Interval Estimator

A **confidence interval estimator** for a population parameter is a rule for determining (based on sample information) a range or an interval that is likely to include the parameter. The corresponding estimate is called a **confidence interval estimate.**

So far, interval estimators have been described as being "likely" or "very likely" to include the true, but unknown, value of the population parameter. To make our discussion more precise, it is necessary to phrase such terms as probability statements. Suppose that a random sample has been taken and that, based on the sample information, it is possible to find two random variables, *A* and *B*, with *A* less than *B*. If the specific sample values of the random variables *A* and *B* are *a* and *b*, then the interval extending from *a* to *b* either includes the parameter or it doesn't. We really don't know for sure.

However, suppose that random samples are repeatedly taken from the population and in this same fashion similar intervals are found. In the long run a certain percentage of these intervals (say, 95% or 98%) will contain the unknown value. According to the relative frequency concept of probability, an interpretation of such intervals follows: *If the population is repeatedly sampled and intervals calculated in this fashion, then in the long run 95% (or some other percentage) of the intervals would contain the true value of the unknown parameter.* The interval from *A* to *B* is then said to be a 95% confidence interval estimator for the population proportion. The general case follows.

Confidence Interval and Confidence Level

Let θ be an unknown parameter. Suppose that on the basis of sample information random variables *A* and *B* are found such that $P(A < \theta < B) = 1 - \alpha$, where α is any number between 0 and 1. If the specific sample values of *A* and *B* are *a* and *b*, then the interval from *a* to *b* is called a

> $100(1 - \alpha)\%$ **confidence interval** of θ. The quantity $100(1 - \alpha)\%$ is called the **confidence level** of the interval.
>
> If the population is repeatedly sampled a very large number of times, the true value of the parameter θ will be contained in $100(1 - \alpha)\%$ of intervals calculated this way. The confidence interval calculated in this manner is written as $a < \theta < b$ with $100(1 - \alpha)\%$ confidence.

Keep in mind that any time sampling occurs, one expects the possibility of a difference between the particular value of an estimator and the parameter's true value. The true value of an unknown parameter might be somewhat greater or somewhat less than the value determined by even the best point estimator. It is not surprising that for many estimation problems a confidence interval estimate of the unknown parameter takes on this form: best point estimate ± an error factor.

Intervals Based on the Normal Distribution

Let $x_1, x_2, \ldots, x_n$ be a random sample of n observations from a normally distributed population with unknown mean μ and known variance σ^2. Suppose that we want a $100(1-\alpha)\%$ confidence interval of the population mean. In Chapter 7 we saw that

$$Z = \frac{\bar{x} - \mu}{\sigma/\sqrt{n}}$$

has a standard normal distribution and $z_{\alpha/2}$ is the value from the standard normal distribution such that the upper tail probability is $\alpha/2$. We use basic algebra to find

$$
\begin{aligned}
1 - \alpha &= P(-z_{\alpha/2} < Z < z_{\alpha/2}) \\
&= P\left(-z_{\alpha/2} < \frac{\bar{x} - \mu}{\sigma/\sqrt{n}} < z_{\alpha/2}\right) \\
&= P\left(-z_{\alpha/2}\frac{\sigma}{\sqrt{n}} < \bar{x} - \mu < z_{\alpha/2}\frac{\sigma}{\sqrt{n}}\right) \\
&= P\left(\bar{x} - z_{\alpha/2}\frac{\sigma}{\sqrt{n}} < \mu < \bar{x} + z_{\alpha/2}\frac{\sigma}{\sqrt{n}}\right)
\end{aligned}
$$

For a 95% confidence level it follows that

$$P\left(\bar{x} - 1.96\frac{\sigma}{\sqrt{n}} < \mu < \bar{x} + 1.96\frac{\sigma}{\sqrt{n}}\right) = 0.95$$

Figure 8.3 shows that the probability is 0.95 that a standard normal random variable falls between the numbers -1.96 and 1.96.

Figure 8.3
$P(-1.96 < z < 1.96) = 0.95$, Where z Is a Standard Normal Random Variable

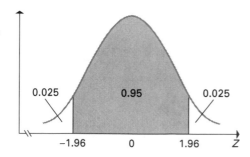

0.025   0.95   0.025

-1.96 0   1.96 Z

Confidence Intervals for the Mean of a Population that is Normally Distributed: Population Variance Known

Consider a random sample of n observations from a normal distribution with mean μ and variance σ^2. If the sample mean is $\bar{x}$, then a $100(1 - \alpha)\%$ **confidence interval for the population mean with known variance** is given by

$$\bar{x} - z_{\alpha/2}\frac{\sigma}{\sqrt{n}} < \mu < \bar{x} + z_{\alpha/2}\frac{\sigma}{\sqrt{n}} \tag{8.1}$$

or equivalently

$$\bar{x} \pm ME$$

where ME, the **margin of error** (also called the **sampling error**), is given by

$$ME = z_{\alpha/2}\frac{\sigma}{\sqrt{n}} \tag{8.2}$$

The **width**, w, is equal to twice the margin of error:

$$w = 2(ME) \tag{8.3}$$

The **upper confidence limit, UCL**, is given by

$$UCL = \bar{x} + z_{\alpha/2}\frac{\sigma}{\sqrt{n}} \tag{8.4}$$

The **lower confidence limit, LCL**, is given by

$$LCL = \bar{x} - z_{\alpha/2}\frac{\sigma}{\sqrt{n}} \tag{8.5}$$

We need to interpret accurately confidence intervals. If random samples of n observations are drawn repeatedly and independently from the population and $100(1 - \alpha)\%$ confidence intervals are calculated by Equation 8.1, then over a very large number of repeated trials, $100(1 - \alpha)\%$ of these intervals will contain the true value of the population mean.

For selected confidence levels, Table 8.2 lists corresponding values of $Z_{\alpha/2}$, sometimes called the **reliability factor**. For a 90% confidence interval Equation 8.1 becomes

$$\bar{x} - 1.645\frac{\sigma}{\sqrt{n}} < \mu < \bar{x} + 1.645\frac{\sigma}{\sqrt{n}}$$

For a 95% confidence interval Equation 8.1 becomes

$$\bar{x} - 1.96\frac{\sigma}{\sqrt{n}} < \mu < \bar{x} + 1.96\frac{\sigma}{\sqrt{n}}$$

Table 8.2 Selected Confidence Levels and Corresponding Values of $Z_{\alpha/2}$

CONFIDENCE LEVEL	90%	95%	98%	99%
α	0.10	0.05	0.02	0.01
$z_{\alpha/2}$	1.645	1.96	2.33	2.58

Example 8.3   Time at the Grocery Store (Confidence Interval)

Suppose that shopping times for customers at a local grocery store are normally distributed. A random sample of 16 shoppers in the local grocery store had a mean time of 25 minutes. Assume $\sigma = 6$ minutes. Find the standard error, margin of error, and width for a 95% confidence interval for the population mean, μ.

Solution   The standard error and the margin of error are

$$\frac{\sigma}{\sqrt{n}} = \frac{6}{\sqrt{16}} = 1.5$$

$$ME = z_{\alpha/2}\frac{\sigma}{\sqrt{n}} = 1.96(1.5) = 2.94$$

It follows that the width = 2(2.94) = 5.88 and the 95% confidence interval is 22.06 < μ < 27.94.

How should such a confidence interval be interpreted? Based on a sample of 16 observations, a 95% confidence interval for the unknown population mean ranges from approximately 22 minutes to approximately 28 minutes. Now, this particular sample is just one of many that might have been drawn from the population. If we start over again and take a second sample of 16 shoppers, it is virtually certain that the mean of the second sample will differ from that of the first. Accordingly, if a 95% confidence interval is calculated from the results of the second sample, it probably will differ from the interval just found. Imagine taking a very large number of independent random samples of 16 observations from this population and, from each sample result, calculating a 95% confidence interval. *The confidence level of the interval implies that in the long run 95% of intervals found in this manner contain the true value of the population mean.* It is in this sense that it is reported that there is 95% confidence in our interval estimate. However, it is not known whether our interval is one of the good 95% or bad 5% without knowing μ.

Figure 8.4 shows the sampling distribution of the sample mean of n observations from a population that is normally distributed with mean μ and standard deviation σ. This sampling distribution is normally distributed with mean μ and standard deviation $\sigma/\sqrt{n}$. A confidence interval for the population mean will be based on the observed value of the sample mean—that is, on an observation drawn from our sampling distribution.

Figure 8.5 shows a schematic description of a sequence of 95% confidence intervals, obtained from independent samples taken from the population. The centers of these intervals, which are just the observed sample means, will often be quite close to the population mean, μ. However, some may differ quite substantially from μ. It follows that 95% of a large number of these intervals will contain the population mean.

Figure 8.4 Sampling Distribution of Sample Mean of n Observations from a Normal Distribution with Mean μ, Variance σ^2, and 95% Confidence Level

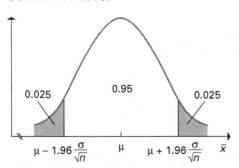

Figure 8.5 Schematic Description of 95% Confidence Intervals

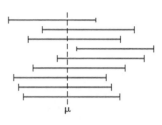

Example 8.4 Refined Sugar (Confidence Interval)

A process produces bags of refined sugar. The weights of the contents of these bags are normally distributed with standard deviation 1.2 ounces. The contents of a random sample of 25 bags had a mean weight of 19.8 ounces. Find the upper and lower confidence limits of a 99% confidence interval for the true mean weight for all bags of sugar produced by the process.

Solution For a 99% confidence interval the reliability factor is

$$z_{0.005} = 2.58$$

and with a sample mean of 19.8, $n = 25$, and a standard deviation of 1.2, the confidence limits are

$$UCL = \bar{x} + z_{\alpha/2}\frac{\sigma}{\sqrt{n}} = 19.8 + 2.58\frac{1.2}{\sqrt{25}} = 20.42$$

$$LCL = \bar{x} - z_{\alpha/2}\frac{\sigma}{\sqrt{n}} = 19.8 - 2.58\frac{1.2}{\sqrt{25}} = 19.18$$

Reducing Margin of Error

Can the margin of error (and, consequently, the width) of a confidence interval be reduced? Consider the factors that affect the margin of error: the population standard deviation, the sample size n, and the confidence level.

Keeping all other factors constant, the more that the population standard deviation, σ, can be reduced, the smaller the margin of error will be. Corporations strive to reduce variability in product measurements (Chapter 18). When possible, this should be the first step to decrease width. However, sometimes the population standard deviation cannot be reduced.

Another way to reduce the margin of error is to increase the sample size. This will reduce the standard deviation of the sampling distribution of the sample mean and hence the margin of error. That is, keeping all other factors constant, an increase in the sample size n will decrease the margin of error. The more information obtained from a population, the more precise our inference about its mean should be. When

INTERPRETATION

Figure 8.6
Effects of Sample
Size, Population
Standard
Deviation, and
Confidence Level
on Confidence
Intervals

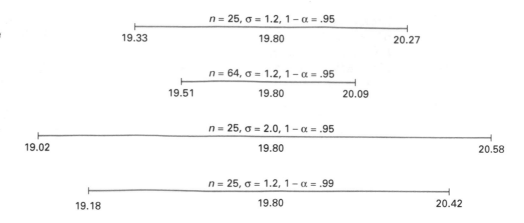

looking at the equation for the margin of error, notice that the interval width is directly proportional to $1/\sqrt{n}$. For example, if the sample size is increased by a factor of 4, the interval width will be reduced by half. If the original sample size were 100, an increase to a sample size of 400 would lead to an interval half the width of the original confidence interval (keeping all other factors constant). The disadvantage to an increased sample size is increased costs.

Finally, keeping all other factors constant, if the confidence level $(1 - \alpha)$ is decreased, the margin of error will be reduced. For example, a 95% confidence interval will be shorter than a 99% confidence interval based on the same information. *Caution*: The reduction of the confidence level reduces the probability that the interval includes the value of the true population parameter. Figure 8.6 illustrates some of the effects of sample size n, population standard deviation σ, and confidence level $(1 - \alpha)$ on confidence intervals for the mean of a population that has a normal distribution; in each case the sample mean is 19.80.

EXERCISES

Basic Exercises

8.9 Find the reliability factor, $z_{\alpha/2}$, for each of the following:

  a. 96% confidence level
  b. 88% confidence level
  c. 85% confidence level
  d. $\alpha = 0.07$
  e. $\alpha/2 = 0.07$

8.10 Calculate the margin of error to estimate the population mean, μ, for:

  a. 98% confidence level; $n = 64$; $\sigma^2 = 144$
  b. 99% confidence level, $n = 120$; $\sigma = 100$

8.11 Calculate the width to estimate the population mean, μ, for:

  a. 90% confidence level; $n = 100$; $\sigma^2 = 169$
  b. 95% confidence level; $n = 120$; $\sigma = 25$

8.12 Calculate the LCL and UCL for each of the following:

  a. $\bar{x} = 50$; $n = 64$; $\sigma = 40$; $\alpha = 0.05$
  b. $\bar{x} = 85$; $n = 225$; $\sigma^2 = 400$; $\alpha = 0.01$
  c. $\bar{x} = 510$; $n = 485$; $\sigma = 50$; $\alpha = 0.10$

Application Exercises

8.13 A personnel manager has found that historically the scores on aptitude tests given to applicants for entry-level positions follow a normal distribution with a standard deviation of 32.4 points. A random sample of nine test scores from the current group of applicants had a mean score of 187.9 points.

  a. Find an 80% confidence interval for the population mean score of the current group of applicants.
  b. Based on these sample results, a statistician found for the population mean a confidence interval extending from 165.8 to 210.0 points. Find the confidence level of this interval.

8.14 It is known that the standard deviation in the volumes of 24-ounce (710-mL) bottles of natural spring water bottled by a particular company is 6 mL. Ninety bottles are randomly sampled and measured.

  a. Find the reliability factor for a 92% confidence interval for the population mean volume.

b. Calculate the standard error of the mean.

c. Calculate the width for a 92% confidence interval for the population mean volume.

8.15 A college admissions officer for an M.B.A. program has determined that historically applicants have undergraduate grade point averages that are normally distributed with standard deviation 0.45. From a random sample of 25 applications from the current year, the sample mean grade point average is 2.90.

a. Find a 95% confidence interval for the population mean.

b. Based on these sample results, a statistician computes for the population mean a confidence interval extending from 2.81 to 2.99. Find the confidence level associated with this interval.

8.16 A process producing bricks is known to give output whose weights are normally distributed with standard deviation of 0.12 lb. A random sample of 16 bricks from today's output had a mean weight of 4.07 lb.

a. Find a 99% confidence interval for the mean weight of all bricks produced this day.

b. Without doing the calculations, explain whether a 95% confidence interval for the population mean would be wider than, narrower than, or the same width as that found in part (a).

c. It is decided that tomorrow a sample of 20 bricks will be taken. Without doing the calculations, explain whether a correctly calculated 99% confidence interval for the mean weight of tomorrow's output would be wider than, narrower than, or the same width as that found in part (a).

d. Suppose that the population standard deviation for today's output is 0.15 pound (not 0.12 pound). Without doing the calculations, explain whether a correctly calculated 99% confidence interval for the mean weight of today's output would be wider than, narrower than, or the same width as that found in part (a).

8.3 CONFIDENCE INTERVALS FOR THE MEAN: POPULATION VARIANCE UNKNOWN

In the preceding section confidence intervals for the mean of a normal population when the population variance was known were derived. Now, we study the case of considerable practical importance where the value of the population variance is unknown. For example,

1. Corporate executives employed by retail distributors may want to estimate mean daily sales for their retail stores.
2. Manufacturers may want to estimate the average productivity, in units per hour, for workers using a particular manufacturing process.
3. Automobile/truck manufacturers may want to estimate the average fuel consumption, measured in miles per gallon, for a particular vehicle model.

In these types of situations, there probably is no historical information concerning either the population mean or the population variance. To proceed further, it is necessary to introduce a new class of probability distributions that were developed by William Sealy Gosset, an Irish statistician, who was employed by the Guinness Brewery in Dublin in the early 1900s (Reference 5).

Student's t Distribution

Gosset sought to develop a probability distribution, when the population variance σ^2 is not known, for a normally distributed random variable. At this time laboratory tests and the scientific method were beginning to be applied to the brewing industry. Gosset, whose works appeared under the pseudonym "Student," was influential in the development of modern statistical thinking and process variation. "The circumstances of brewing work, with its variable materials and susceptibility to temperature change . . . emphasize the necessity for a correct method of treating small samples. It was thus no accident, but the circumstances of his work, that directed Student's attention to this problem, and led to his discovery of the distribution of the sample standard deviation . . . " (Reference 6). Gosset showed the connection between statistical research and practical problems. The distribution is still known as the "Student's t distribution." The t distribution developed by Gosset is the ratio of two distributions, the standard normal distribution and the square root of the chi-square distribution divided by its degrees of freedom, v (see chapter Appendix).

The development of Section 8.2 was based on the fact that the random variable, Z, given by

$$Z = \frac{\bar{x} - \mu}{\sigma/\sqrt{n}}$$

has a standard normal distribution. In the case where the population standard deviation is unknown, this result cannot be used directly. It is natural in such circumstances to consider the random variable obtained by replacing the unknown σ by the sample standard deviation, s, giving

$$t = \frac{\bar{x} - \mu}{s/\sqrt{n}}$$

This random variable does not follow a standard normal distribution. However, its distribution is known and is, in fact, a member of a family of distributions called Student's t.

Student's t Distribution

Given a random sample of n observations, with mean $\bar{x}$ and standard deviation s, from a normally distributed population with mean μ, the random variable t follows the **Student's t distribution** with $(n-1)$ degrees of freedom and is given by

$$t = \frac{\bar{x} - \mu}{s/\sqrt{n}}$$

A specific member of the family of Student's t distributions is characterized by the number of degrees of freedom. We will use the parameter v to represent the degrees of freedom and a Student's t random variable with v degrees of freedom will be denoted t_v. The shape of the Student's t distribution is rather similar to that of the standard normal distribution. Both distributions have mean 0, and the probability density functions of both are symmetric about their means. However, the density function of the Student's t distribution has a larger dispersion (reflected in a larger variance) than the standard normal distribution. This can be seen in Figure 8.7, which shows density functions for the standard normal distribution and the Student's t distribution with 3 degrees of freedom.

The additional dispersion in the Student's t distribution arises as a result of the extra uncertainty caused by replacing the known population standard deviation with its sample estimator. As the number of degrees of freedom increases, the Student's t distribution becomes increasingly similar to the standard normal distribution. For large degrees of freedom the two distributions are virtually identical. That

Figure 8.7 Probability Density Functions of the Standard Normal and the Student's *t* Distribution with 3 Degrees of Freedom

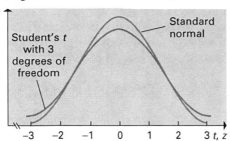

Figure 8.8 $P(t_v > t_{v,\alpha/2}) = \alpha/2$, Where t_v is a Student's *t* Random Variable with *v* Degrees of Freedom

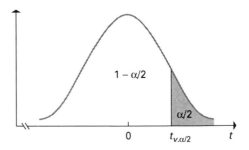

is, the Student's *t* distribution converges to $N(0,1)$, which is quite close to the *t* as long as *n* is large. This is intuitively reasonable and follows from the fact that for a large sample the sample standard deviation is a very precise estimator of the population standard deviation.

In order to base inferences about a population mean on the Student's *t* distribution, critical values analogous to $z_{\alpha/2}$ are needed. Just as $z_{\alpha/2}$ is the value from the standard normal distribution such that the upper tail probability is $\alpha/2$, so $t_{v,\alpha/2}$ is the value from the Student's *t* distribution for *v* (degrees of freedom) such that the upper tail probability is $\alpha/2$ as shown in Figure 8.8.

> ### Notation
> A random variable having the Student's *t* distribution with *v* degrees of freedom will be denoted t_v. Then $t_{v,\alpha/2}$ is the reliability factor, defined as the number for which
>
> $$P(t_v > t_{v,\alpha/2}) = \alpha/2$$

Suppose that the number that is exceeded with probability 0.05 by a Student's *t* random variable with 15 degrees of freedom is required. That is,

$$P(t_{15} > t_{15,0.05}) = 0.05$$

Reading directly from the Student's *t* distribution table,

$$t_{15,0.05} = 1.753$$

Many computer programs can be used to obtain these values as well.

Intervals Based on the Student's t Distribution

We will encounter many situations in which the population variance is not known. Finding the $100(1 - \alpha)\%$ confidence interval for this type of problem follows precisely the same line of reasoning as in Section 8.2. Terminology is analogous.

Confidence Intervals for the Mean of a Normal Population: Population Variance Unknown

Suppose there is a random sample of n observations from a *normal distribution* with mean μ and unknown variance. If the sample mean and standard deviation are, respectively, $\bar{x}$ and s, then the degrees of freedom $v = n - 1$ and a $100(1 - \alpha)\%$ **confidence interval for the population mean, variance unknown,** is given by

$$\bar{x} - t_{n-1,\alpha/2} \frac{s}{\sqrt{n}} < \mu < \bar{x} + t_{n-1,\alpha/2} \frac{s}{\sqrt{n}} \tag{8.6}$$

or equivalently

$$\bar{x} \pm ME$$

where *ME*, the **margin of error,** is given by

$$ME = t_{n-1,\alpha/2} \frac{s}{\sqrt{n}} \tag{8.7}$$

Assume that a random sample of n observations is available from a normal population with mean μ and unknown variance and that confidence intervals for the population mean are required. The normal probability plot is one method to test if the data are not normally distributed. We assume normality throughout this chapter. In applications to business, government, and medical or other research, we should check first to determine if the data indicate non-normality. Confidence interval terminology for a population mean with unknown variance is similar to the situation with variance known.

Example 8.5 Trucks: Gasoline Consumption (Confidence Interval)

Gasoline prices rose drastically during the early years of this century. Suppose that a recent study was conducted using truck drivers with equivalent years of experience to test run 24 trucks of a particular model over the same highway. Estimate the population mean fuel consumption for this truck model with 90% confidence if the fuel consumption, in miles per gallon, for these 24 trucks was

15.5	21.0	18.5	19.3	19.7	16.9	20.2	14.5
16.5	19.2	18.7	18.2	18.0	17.5	18.5	20.5
18.6	19.1	19.8	18.0	19.8	18.2	20.3	21.8

Trucks

The data is stored in the data file **TRUCKS**.

Solution The normal probability plot in Figure 8.9 does not provide evidence of non-normality. Calculating the mean and standard deviation, we find

$$\bar{x} = 18.68 \qquad s = 1.69526 \qquad t_{n-1,\alpha/2} = t_{23,0.05} = 1.714$$

By Equation 8.6 the 90% confidence interval is

$$\bar{x} \pm t_{n-1,\alpha/2} \frac{s}{\sqrt{n}} = 18.68 \pm t_{23,0.05} \frac{1.69526}{\sqrt{24}} = 18.68 \pm (1.714) \times (0.3460)$$

$$= 18.68 \pm 0.5930$$

Figure 8.9   Normal Probability Plot

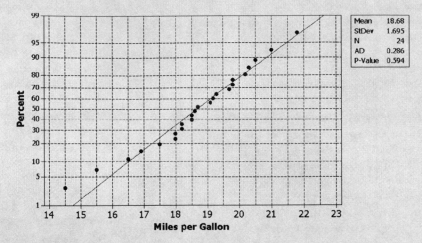

The confidence interval then is 18.1 < μ < 19.3. For larger data sets we will want to use the computer. Figure 8.10 is the Minitab output and Figure 8.11 is the Excel output generated for Example 8.5.

The interpretation of the confidence interval is important. If independent random samples of 24 trucks are repeatedly selected from the population and confidence intervals for each of these samples are determined, then over a very large number of repeated trials 90% of these intervals will contain the value of the true mean fuel consumption for this model truck. In practice, however, one does not repeatedly draw such independent samples.

Figure 8.10   Output for Data File **Trucks** in Example 8.5 (Minitab Output)

```
Variable   N      Mean     StDev    SE Mean        90% cr
MPG        24   18.6792   1.6953    0.3460    (18.0861, 19.2722)
```

Figure 8.11   Output for Data File **Trucks** in Example 8.5 (Excel Output)

Mean	18.67917
Standard Error	0.346043
Median	18.65
Mode	18.5
Standard Deviation	1.695257
Sample Variance	2.873895
Kurtosis	0.624798
Skewness	−0.60902
Range	7.3
Minimum	14.5
Maximum	21.8
Sum	448.3
Count	24
Confidence Level (90.0%)	0.593073

EXERCISES

Basic Exercises

8.17 Find the reliability factor, $t_{v,\alpha/2}$, to estimate population mean, μ, for the following:

    a. $n = 20$; 90% confidence level

    b. $n = 7$; 98% confidence level

    c. $n = 16$; 95% confidence level

    d. $n = 23$; 99% confidence level

8.18 Find the margin of error for each of the following:

    a. $n = 20$, 90% confidence level; $s = 36$

    b. $n = 7$; 98% confidence level; $s = 16$

    c. $n = 16$; 95% confidence level; $s^2 = 43$

    d. 99% confidence level; $x_1 = 15$; $x_2 = 17$; $x_3 = 13$; $x_4 = 11$

8.19 Times (in minutes) that a random sample of five people spend driving to work are

    30   42   35   40   45

    a. Calculate the standard error.

    b. Find $t_{v,\alpha/2}$ for a 95% confidence interval for the true population mean.

    c. Calculate width for a 95% confidence interval for the population mean time spent driving to work.

8.20 Find the *LCL* and *UCL* for each of the following:

    a. $\alpha = 0.05$; $n = 25$; $\bar{x} = 560$; $s = 45$

    b. $\alpha/2 = 0.05$; $n = 9$; $\bar{x} = 160$; $s^2 = 36$

    c. $1 - \alpha = 0.98$; $n = 22$; $\bar{x} = 58$; $s = 15$

8.21 Calculate the margin of error to estimate the population mean, μ, for each of the following:

    a. 98% confidence level; $n = 64$; $s^2 = 144$

    b. 99% confidence level; $n = 120$; $s = 100$

    c. 95% confidence level; $n = 200$; $s = 40$

8.22 Calculate the width for each of the following:

    a. $n = 6$; $s = 40$; $\alpha = 0.05$

    b. $n = 22$; $s^2 = 400$; $\alpha = 0.01$

    c. $n = 25$; $s = 50$; $\alpha = 0.10$

Application Exercises

8.23 Al Fiedler, plant manager at LDS Vacuum Products, Altamonte Springs, Florida, applies statistical thinking in his workplace. As a major supplier to automobile manufacturers, LDS wants to be sure that the leak rate (in cubic centimeters per second) of transmission oil coolers (TOCs) meets the established specification limits. A random sample of 50 TOCs is tested, and the leak rates are recorded in the data file named **TOC** (Reference 3).

    a. Estimate with 95% confidence the mean leak rate for this particular product.

    b. Estimate with 98% confidence the mean leak rate for this particular product.

8.24 A machine that packages 18-ounce (510-gram) boxes of sugar-coated wheat cereal is being studied. The weights for a random sample of 100 boxes of cereal packaged by this machine are contained in the data file **Sugar**.

    a. Find a 90% confidence interval for the population mean cereal weight.

    b. Without doing the calculations, state whether an 80% confidence interval for the population mean would be wider than, narrower than, or the same as the answer to part (a).

8.25 A clothing store is interested in how much college students spend on clothing during the first month of the school year. For a random sample of nine students the mean expenditure was $157.82, and the sample standard deviation was $38.89. Assuming that the population is normally distributed, find the margin of error of a 95% confidence interval for the population mean.

8.26 There is concern about the speed of automobiles traveling over a particular stretch of highway. For a random sample of seven automobiles radar indicated the following speeds, in miles per hour:

    79   73   68   77   86   71   69

Assuming a normal population distribution, find the margin of error of a 95% confidence interval for the mean speed of all automobiles traveling over this stretch of highway.

8.27 A clinic offers a weight-reduction program. A review of its records found the following weight losses, in pounds, for a random sample of 10 of its clients at the conclusion of the program:

    18 25 6 11 15 20 16 19 12 17

    a. Find a 99% confidence interval for the population mean.

    b. Without doing the calculations, explain whether a 90% confidence interval for the population mean would be wider than, narrower than, or the same as that found in part (a).

8.28 A business school placement director wants to estimate the mean annual salaries five years after students graduate. A random sample of 25 such graduates found a sample mean of $42,740 and a sample standard deviation of $4,780. Find a 90% confidence interval for the population mean, assuming that the population distribution is normal.

8.29 A car rental company is interested in the amount of time its vehicles are out of operation for repair work. State all assumptions and find a 90% confidence interval for the mean number of days in a year that all vehicles in the company's fleet are out of operation if a random sample of nine cars showed the following number of days that each had been inoperative:

16   10   21   22   8   17   19   14   19

8.4 CONFIDENCE INTERVALS FOR POPULATION PROPORTION (LARGE SAMPLES)

What percent of Romanians favor their nation's possible entrance into the European Union? Do the majority of college admission personnel think that SAT scores are a good indicator of academic success in college? What proportion of the students at a particular university would like classes to be offered on Saturdays? In each of these scenarios the proportion of population members possessing some specific characteristic is of interest. If a random sample is taken from the population, the sample proportion provides a natural point estimator of the population proportion. In this section confidence intervals for the population proportion are established.

Using the binomial setup, let $\hat{p}$ denote the proportion of "successes" in n independent trials, each with probability of success P. It was seen earlier in this book that, if the number n of sample members is large, then the random variable

$$Z = \frac{\hat{p} - P}{\sqrt{\dfrac{P(1-P)}{n}}}$$

has, to a close approximation, a standard normal distribution. If the sample size is large enough that $(n)(P)(1-P) > 9$, then a good approximation is obtained if P is replaced by the point estimator $\hat{p}$ in the denominator; that is

$$\sqrt{\frac{P(1-P)}{n}} \approx \sqrt{\frac{\hat{p}(1-\hat{p})}{n}}$$

Hence, for large sample sizes the distribution of the random variable

$$Z = \frac{\hat{p} - P}{\sqrt{\hat{p}(1-\hat{p})/n}}$$

is approximately standard normal. This result can now be used to obtain confidence intervals for the population proportion. The derivation is similar to the preceding examples.

$$1 - \alpha = P(-z_{\alpha/2} < Z < z_{\alpha/2})$$

$$= P\left(-z_{\alpha/2} < \frac{\hat{p} - P}{\sqrt{\dfrac{\hat{p}(1-\hat{p})}{n}}} < z_{\alpha/2}\right)$$

$$= P\left(-z_{\alpha/2}\sqrt{\frac{\hat{p}(1-\hat{p})}{n}} < \hat{p} - P < z_{\alpha/2}\sqrt{\frac{\hat{p}(1-\hat{p})}{n}}\right)$$

$$= P\left(\hat{p} - z_{\alpha/2}\sqrt{\frac{\hat{p}(1-\hat{p})}{n}} < P < \hat{p} + z_{\alpha/2}\sqrt{\frac{\hat{p}(1-\hat{p})}{n}}\right)$$

Therefore, if the observed sample proportion is $\hat{p}$, an approximate $100(1-\alpha)\%$ confidence interval for the population proportion is given, as seen in Equation 8.8, which follows.

Confidence Intervals for Population Proportion (Large Samples)

Let $\hat{p}$ denote the observed proportion of "successes" in a random sample of n observations from a population with a proportion of successes P. Then, if n is large enough that $(n)(P)(1-P) > 9$, a $100(1-\alpha)\%$ **confidence interval for the population proportion** is given by

$$\hat{p} - z_{\alpha/2}\sqrt{\frac{\hat{p}(1-\hat{p})}{n}} < P < \hat{p} + z_{\alpha/2}\sqrt{\frac{\hat{p}(1-\hat{p})}{n}} \tag{8.8}$$

or equivalently

$$\hat{p} \pm ME$$

where *ME*, **the margin of error**, is given by

$$ME = z_{\alpha/2}\sqrt{\frac{\hat{p}(1-\hat{p})}{n}} \tag{8.9}$$

Recent research suggests the possibility of other intervals as alternatives to the confidence interval stated in Equation 8.8. Such adjusted intervals are useful with both large and small samples (References 1 and 2). These readings are recommended for more advanced studies.

Confidence intervals for the population proportion are centered on the sample proportion. Also, it can be seen that, all other things being equal, the larger the sample size, n, the narrower the confidence interval. This reflects the increasing precision of the information about the population proportion obtained as the sample size becomes larger.

Example 8.6 Modified Bonus Plan (Confidence Interval)

Management wants an estimate of the proportion of the corporation's employees who favor a modified bonus plan. From a random sample of 344 employees it was found that 261 were in favor of this particular plan. Find a 90% confidence interval estimate of the true population proportion that favors this modified bonus plan.

Solution If P denotes the true population proportion and $\hat{p}$ the sample proportion, then confidence intervals for the population proportion are obtained from Equation 8.8 as

$$\hat{p} - z_{\alpha/2}\sqrt{\frac{\hat{p}(1-\hat{p})}{n}} < P < \hat{p} + z_{\alpha/2}\sqrt{\frac{\hat{p}(1-\hat{p})}{n}}$$

where, for a 90% confidence interval, $\alpha = 0.10$, so that from the standard normal distribution

$$\alpha/2 = 0.05 \quad \text{and} \quad z_{\alpha/2} = z_{0.05} = 1.645$$

It follows that

$$n = 344 \qquad \hat{p} = 261/344 = 0.759$$

and

$$z_{\alpha/2} = 1.645$$

Therefore, a 90% confidence interval for the population proportion is

$$0.759 - 1.645\sqrt{\frac{(0.759)(0.241)}{344}} < P < 0.759 + 1.645\sqrt{\frac{(0.759)(0.241)}{344}}$$

or $0.721 < P < 0.797$. Strictly speaking, what do these numbers imply? We could say that, in the long run, approximately 76% (with a 4% margin of error at the 90% confidence level) of the population of all employees in this corporation favor a modified bonus plan.

We compare the 90% and the 99% confidence intervals in Figures 8.12 and 8.13, respectively.

Figure 8.12 Modified Bonus Plan from Example 8.6: 90% (Minitab Output)

Confidence Interval for Proportion

Sample	X	N	Sample p	90.0% CI	Z-Value	P-Value
1	261	344	0.758721	**(0.720776, 0.796665)**	9.60	0.000

Figure 8.13 Modified Bonus Plan from Example 8.6: 99% (Minitab Output)

Confidence Interval for Proportion

Sample	X	N	Sample p	99% CI	Z-Value	P-Value
1	261	344	0.758721	**(0.699300, 0.818142)**	9.60	0.000

We see that, by increasing the confidence level from 90% to 99%, the margin of error (and the width) also increased. For the 90% confidence interval the range was from approximately 72.1% to 79.7%, giving a 3.8% margin of error, whereas for the 99% confidence interval the range was from approximately 69.9% to 81.8%, giving a 5.95% margin of error. Wide intervals for a given α reflect imprecision in our knowledge about the population proportion. Narrower confidence intervals can be obtained by taking larger samples.

EXERCISES

Basic Exercises

8.30 Find the standard error of the proportion for:
   a. $n = 250; \hat{p} = 0.3$
   b. $n = 175; \hat{p} = 0.45$
   c. $n = 400; \hat{p} = 0.05$

8.31 Find the margin of error for:
   a. $n = 250; \hat{p} = 0.3; \alpha = 0.05$
   b. $n = 175; \hat{p} = 0.45; \alpha = 0.08$
   c. $n = 400; \hat{p} = 0.05; \alpha = 0.04$

8.32 Find the confidence interval for estimating the population proportion for:
   a. 92.5% confidence level; $n = 650; \hat{p} = 0.10$
   b. 99% confidence level; $n = 140; \hat{p} = 0.01$
   c. $\alpha = 0.09; n = 365; \hat{p} = 0.50$

Application Exercises

8.33 Suppose that a random sample of 142 graduate admissions personnel was asked what role scores on standardized tests (such as the GMAT or GRE) play in the consideration of a candidate for graduate school. Of these sample members 87 answered "very important." Find a 95% confidence interval for the population proportion of graduate admissions personnel with this view.

8.34 In a random sample of 95 manufacturing firms 67 indicated that their company attained ISO certification within the last two years. Find a 99% confidence interval for the population proportion of companies that have been certified within the last 2 years.

8.35 ⊙ In a recent study of a university library, students were asked if they thought that the school's library had an adequate collection of books. The survey results are stored in a data file called **Library**.

   a. Find an unbiased point estimate of the proportion of students who think that the collection is adequate (coded as 1-yes, 2-no).
   b. Find a 90% confidence interval for the proportion of students who think that the school's library collection is adequate.

8.36 The University of Michigan School of Business publishes the American Customer Satisfaction Index (ACSI) four times a year (Reference 1). Started in 1994 and based on thousands of customer interviews, customer satisfaction ratings based on a scale from 0 to 100 are gathered for retailers, supermarkets, financial services, parcel-delivery services, airlines, and so forth. "Understaffed stores, clueless sales clerks, automated phone lines that lead you in circles" are a few reasons why the scores for most companies declined between 1995 and 2000 (Reference 8). Concerned about this report, the manager of a national retail store in one community surveyed a random sample of 320 customers. The survey indicated that 80 customers thought that customer service in this store was also on the decline. What conclusions can we draw from this data? State the level of confidence.

8.37 From a random sample of 400 registered voters in one city, 320 indicated that they would vote in favor of a proposed policy in an upcoming election.

   a. Calculate the *LCL* for a 98% confidence interval estimate for the population proportion in favor of this policy.
   b. Calculate the width of a 90% confidence interval estimate for the population proportion in favor of this policy.

8.38 Of a random sample of 198 marketing students 98 rated a case of résumé inflation as unethical. Based on this information (Reference 2), a statistician computed for the population proportion a confidence interval extending from 0.445 to 0.545. What is the confidence level of this interval?

8.39 In a presidential election year, candidates want to know how voters in various parts of the country will vote. Suppose that 420 registered voters in the Northeast are asked if they would vote for a particular candidate if the election were held today. From this sample 223 indicated that they would vote for this particular candidate. What is the margin of error? Determine the 95% confidence interval estimate of this candidate's support in the Northeast.

8.40 Suppose that the U.S. Centers for Disease Control and Prevention (CDC) believe that influenza activity will be lower than the same period last year. Residents in the Atlanta metropolitan area were asked if this news by the CDC would persuade them to not take the flu vaccine. If only 40 people from a random sample of 246 stated that they now would not take the flu vaccine, estimate with 98% confidence the proportion of all residents in the Atlanta metro area who now consider the flu vaccine unnecessary.

8.41 It is important for airlines to follow the published scheduled departure times of flights. Suppose that one airline that recently sampled the records of 246 flights originating in Orlando found that 10 flights were delayed for severe weather, 4 flights were delayed for maintenance concerns, and all the other flights were on time.

   a. Estimate the percentage of on-time departures using a 98% confidence level.
   b. Estimate the percentage of flights delayed for severe weather using a 98% confidence level.

SUMMARY

This chapter emphasized estimators and confidence intervals. Three properties of estimators were discussed—namely, unbiasedness, consistency, and efficiency. Both the sample mean and the sample variance are unbiased, consistent, and efficient estimators of the population mean and the population variance, respectively. We developed confidence interval estimates for such parameters as (1) the population mean of a normally distributed population when the population variance is either known or unknown and (2) the population proportion for large samples. Generally, adding and subtracting the sampling error from the point estimator forms confidence intervals. However, in Chapter 9 we will see that this will not be the case for the population variance. Two tables, the standard normal Z table and the Student's *t* table, were used in the development of the confidence intervals in this chapter.

KEY WORDS

- bias
- confidence interval
  - estimate
  - estimator
  - for mean, with known variance
  - for mean, with unknown variance
  - for proportion
- confidence level

- consistent estimator
- efficient estimator
  - estimate
  - estimator
- lower confidence limit, LCL
- margin of error
- minimum variance unbiased estimator
- most efficient estimator

- point estimate
- point estimator
- relative efficiency
- reliability factor
- sampling error
- Student's t
- unbiased estimator
- upper confidence limit, UCL
- width

CHAPTER EXERCISES AND APPLICATIONS

8.42 Several drugs are used to treat diabetes. A sales specialist for a leading pharmaceutical company needs an estimate of the number of new prescriptions that were written during a particular month for his company's new diabetes drug. The numbers of new prescriptions in a sample of 10 sales districts are

210	240	190	275	290
265	312	284	261	243

   a. Find a 90% confidence interval for the average number of new prescriptions written for this new drug among all the sales districts. State the assumptions.

   b. Calculate the widths for 95% and 98% confidence intervals.

8.43 Suppose that Brent Matthews, manager of a Sam's Club in Chattanooga, Tennessee, wants to estimate the mean number of gallons of milk that are sold during a typical weekday. Brent checked the sales records for a random sample of 16 days and found the mean number of gallons sold is 150 gallons per day; the sample standard deviation is 12 gallons. With 95% confidence estimate the number of gallons that Brent should stock daily.

8.44 Everyone knows that exercise is important. Recently, residents in one community were surveyed and asked, "How many minutes do you spend daily on some form of rigorous exercise?" From a random sample of 50 residents the mean time spent on vigorous daily exercise was half an hour. The standard deviation was found to be 4.2 minutes. Find a 90% interval estimate of the time spent daily on rigorous exercise by these residents.

8.45 The following data represent the number of passengers per flight for a random sample of 50 flights from Jacksonville, Florida, to Baltimore, Maryland, on one particular airline:

163	165	094	137	123	095	170	096	117	129
152	138	147	119	166	125	148	180	152	149
167	120	129	159	150	119	113	147	169	151
116	150	110	110	143	090	134	145	156	165
174	133	128	100	086	148	139	150	145	100

Estimate the average number of passengers per flight with a 95% interval estimate.

8.46 ⚫ The supervisor of a bottle-filling plant randomly sampled bottles to determine if any of the following defects were present: dents, missing labels, incorrect labels, and a wrong color. The types of defects are in the data file **Defects**.

   a. Estimate the proportion of defects due to an incorrect label. Use a 5% risk.

   b. Estimate the percentage of defects due to a missing label. Use a 90% confidence level.

8.47 Eight randomly selected batches of a chemical were tested for impurity concentration. The percentage impurity levels found in this sample were

3.2	4.3	2.1	2.8	3.2	3.6	4.0	3.8

   a. Find the most efficient estimates of the population mean and variance.

   b. Estimate the proportion of batches with impurity levels greater than 3.75%.

8.48 A marketing research assistant for a veterinary hospital surveyed a random sample of 457 pet owners. Respondents were asked to indicate the number of times that they visit their veterinarian each year. The sample mean response was 3.59 and the sample standard deviation was 1.045. Based on these results a confidence interval from 3.49 to 3.69 was calculated for the population mean. Find the probability content for this interval.

8.49 A random sample of 174 college students was asked to indicate the number of hours per week that they surf the Internet for either personal information or material for a class assignment. The sample mean response was 6.06 hours and the sample standard deviation was 1.43 hours. Based on these results, a confidence interval extending from 5.96 to 6.16 was calculated for the population mean. Find the confidence level of this interval.

8.50   A sample of 33 accounting students recorded the number of hours that they spent studying for a final exam. The data are stored in the data file **Study**.

   a. Give an example of an unbiased, consistent, and efficient estimator of the population mean.
   b. Find the sampling error for a 95% confidence interval estimate of the mean number of hours students studied for this exam.

8.51   Dr. Mihaela Sabou wants to estimate the average length of a hospital stay (number of days) for patients with a certain infectious disease. From a random sample of 25 patient records she finds that the average number of days in the hospital for such patients is 6 days with a standard deviation of 1.8 days.

   a. Find the reliability factor for a 95% confidence interval estimate of the population mean length of stay.
   b. Find the *LCL* for a 99% confidence interval estimate of the population mean length of stay.

8.52   Suppose that a survey of race fans at this week's Daytona 500 NASCAR race were asked, "Is this your first time to attend the Daytona 500?" From a random sample of 250 race fans 100 answered in the affirmative.

   a. Find the standard error to estimate population proportion of first timers.
   b. Find the sampling error to estimate population proportion of first timers.
   c. Estimate the proportion of repeat fans with 92% confidence level.

8.53   The following data represent the number of passengers per flight in a random sample of 20 flights from Vienna, Austria, to Cluj-Napoca, Romania, with a new airline:

63   65   94   37   83   95   70   96   47   29
52   38   47   79   66   25   48   80   52   49

   a. What is the reliability factor for a 90% confidence interval estimate of the mean number of passengers per flight?
   b. Find the *LCL* for a 99% confidence interval estimate of the mean number of passengers per flight?

8.54   A group of business students conducted a survey on their university campus to determine student demand for a particular product, a protein supplement for Smoothies. As part of their initial steps they randomly sampled 113 students and obtained data that could be helpful in developing their marketing strategy. The responses to this survey are contained in the data file **Smoothies**.

   a. Find a 95% confidence interval estimate for the population proportion of students who would like supplements such as protein, creatine, or energy boosters in their Smoothies.
   b. Estimate the population proportion of students who consider that they are very health conscious with a 98% confidence level.
   c. Of the 113 respondents 77 indicated that they drank Smoothies in the afternoon. Determine with 90% confidence an estimate of the population proportion who drink Smoothies in the afternoon.

8.55   A random sample of 100 students at a small university were asked a series of questions such as their status as an American or International student, major, gender, age, year in school, and current GPA. Other questions were asked about levels of satisfaction with campus parking, campus housing, and campus dining. Finally, students were asked if they planned to attend graduate school within five years of their college graduation. These data is contained in the data file **Finstad and Lie Study**.

   a. Estimate the population grade point average with 95% confidence level.
   b. Estimate the population proportion of students who were very dissatisfied (code 1) or moderately dissatisfied (code 2) with parking facilities on campus. Use a 90% confidence level.
   c. Estimate the population proportion of students who were at least moderately satisfied (codes 4 and 5) with on-campus food service.

8.56   In Chapter 1 we proposed several questions that might be of interest to the manager of Florin's Flower Mart. Use the data stored in the data file **Florin** to provide answers to each of the following questions proposed in Chapter 1.

   a. Estimate the mean age of the store's customers.
   b. Estimate the population proportion of customers that are dissatisifed with the store's delivery system.
   c. Estimate the population mean amount charged to a Visa credit card.

8.57   What is the most common method to renew vehicle registration? In checking a random sample of 500 motor vehicle renewal registrations in one county, the finance department found that 200 were mailed, 160 were paid in person at the county finance department office, and the remainder were paid on-line at the county's Web site. Phone registration renewals were not available.

a. Estimate the population proportion to pay for vehicle registration renewals in person at the county finance department office. Use a 90% confidence level.

b. Estimate the population proportion of on-line renewals. Use a 95% confidence level.

8.58 Consider the data in Exercise 8.57. Suppose that we computed for the population proportion who pay for vehicle registration by mail a confidence interval extending from 0.34 to 0.46. What is the confidence level of this interval?

8.59 Consider the data in Exercise 8.57. It was reported in the local paper that less than one-third (from 23.7% to 32.3%) of the population prefers the on-line renewal process. What is the confidence level of this interval estimate?

8.60 The county finance department also wants information about renewals of disabled parking placards. Suppose that in a sample of 350 transactions for dis-

abled parking placards it was found that 250 were paid electronically.

a. What is the margin of error for a 99% confidence interval estimate of the population proportion of disabled renewal transactions paid electronically?

b. Without calculating, is the margin of error for a 95% confidence interval estimate of the population proportion of disabled renewal transactions paid electronically larger, smaller, or the same as that found in part (a) for a 99% confidence interval?

8.61 What is the typical age of a person who renews his or her driver's license on-line? From a random sample of 460 driver's license renewal transactions the mean age was 42.6 and the standard deviation was 5.4. Compute the 98% confidence interval estimate of the mean age of on-line renewal users in this county.

Appendix

STUDENT'S t DISTRIBUTION

Gosset sought to develop a probability distribution for normally distributed random variables that did not include the population variance σ^2. As a result, he took the ratio of Z, a standard normal random variable, and the square root of χ^2 divided by its degrees of freedom, v. In mathematical notation

$$t = \frac{Z}{\sqrt{\chi^2/v}}$$

$$t = \frac{(x-\mu)/\sigma}{\sqrt{s^2(n-1)/\sigma^2(n-1)}} = \frac{(x-\mu)}{s}$$

The resulting t statistic has $n-1$ degrees of freedom. Notice that the t probability distribution is based on normally distributed random variables. For applications, the normal Z is used when the population variance σ^2 is available, and the Student's t is used when only the sample variance s^2 is available. Statistical research using computer-generated random samples has shown that t can be used to study the distribution of sample means even if the distribution of the individual random variables is not normal.

REFERENCES

1. *American Customer Satisfaction Index.* (Ann Arbor: University of Michigan Business School, 2000).

2. Dabholkar, P. A., and J. J. Kellaris. "Toward Understanding Marketing Students' Ethical Judgment of Controversial Personal Selling Practices." *Journal of Business Research* 24 (1992): 313–329.

3. Fiedler, Alfred W., Plant Manager. "Machine Reading Leak Rate Repeatability Studies Conducted at LDS Vacuum Products." (Altamonte Springs, FL, February 1999).

4. Hildebrand, David, and A. L. Ott. *Statistical Thinking for Managers*. (New York: Brooks/Cole, 1998).

5. Pearson, Egon Sharpe, and R. L. Plackett (eds.). *Student: A Statistical Biography of William Sealy Gosset*. (Oxford, England: Clarendon Press, 1990).

6. Pearson, Egon Sharpe, and John Wishart (eds.). *Development of Statistics: Student's Collected Papers*. (Cambridge: 1958). Foreword by Launce McMullen. Materials provided to the authors by Teresa O'Donnell, Guinness (GIG) Archivist, September 13, 2000.

7. "Project Romanian Rescue: Headline News," October 2000.

8. Wessel, Harry. "Lousy Service? Get Used to It." *Orlando Sentinel*, November 24, 2000, p. A1.

Topic 11

Goodness-of-Fit Tests and Contingency Tables

Chapter

16

Goodness-of-Fit Tests and Contingency Tables

Introduction

In this chapter certain tests that are based on the chi-square distribution are discussed. A test of the hypothesis that data are generated by a *fully specified* probability distribution is considered first. This technique is often used by market researchers to determine if products are equally preferred by potential customers or to check if the market shares for several brands of a product have changed over a given period of time.

Next, we test the hypothesis that data are generated by some distribution, such as the binomial, the Poisson, or the normal, without assuming the parameters of that distribution to be known. In these circumstances the available data can be used to estimate the unknown population parameters. A goodness-of-fit test is used when population parameters are estimated.

The chi-square test can be extended to deal with a problem in which a sample is taken from a population, each of whose members can be uniquely cross-classified according to a pair of attributes. The hypothesis to be tested is of no association in the population between possessions of these attributes. Business professionals use this procedure frequently. For larger contingency tables it is convenient to use a software package to determine the test statistic and *p*-value.

16.1 GOODNESS-OF-FIT TESTS: SPECIFIED PROBABILITIES

The most straightforward test of this type is illustrated with a study that observed a random sample of 33 subjects purchasing a soft drink. Of these subjects, 8 selected brand A, 10 selected brand B, and the remainder selected brand C. This information is displayed in Table 16.1.

More generally, consider a random sample of n observations that can be classified according to K categories. If the number of observations falling into each category is $O_1, O_2, \ldots, O_K$, the setup is as shown in Table 16.2.

The sample data are to be used to test a null hypothesis specifying the probabilities that an observation falls in each of the categories. In the example of 33 subjects purchasing a soft drink, the null hypothesis (H_0) might be that a randomly chosen subject is equally likely to select any of the three different varieties. This null hypothesis, then, specifies that the probability is one-third that a sample observation falls into each of the three categories. To test this hypothesis, it is natural to compare the sample numbers *observed* with what would be *expected* if the null hypothesis was true. Given a total of 33 sample observations, the expected number of subjects in each category under the null hypothesis would be $(33)(1/3) = 11$. This information is summarized in Table 16.3.

In the general case of K categories, suppose that the null hypothesis specifies $P_1, P_2, \ldots, P_K$ for the probabilities that an observation falls into the categories. Assume that these possibilities are mutually exclusive and collectively exhaustive—that is, each sample observation must belong to one of the categories and cannot belong to more than one. In this case, the hypothesized probabilities must sum to 1; that is,

$$P_1 + P_2 + \cdots + P_K = 1$$

Table 16.1 Brand Selection

CATEGORY (BRAND)	A	B	C	TOTAL
Number of subjects	8	10	15	33

Table 16.2 Classification of *n* Observations into *K* Categories

CATEGORY	1	2	...	K	TOTAL
Number of observations	O_1	O_2	...	O_K	n

Table 16.3 Observed and Expected Number of Purchases for Three Brands of Soft Drink

CATEGORY (BRAND)	A	B	C	TOTAL
Observed number of subjects	8	10	15	33
Probability (under H_0)	1/3	1/3	1/3	1
Expected number of subjects (under H_0)	11	11	11	33

Table 16.4   Observed and Expected Numbers for n Observations and K Categories

CATEGORY	1	2	...	K	TOTAL
Observed number	O_1	O_2	...	O_K	n
Probability (under H_0)	P_1	P_2	...	P_K	1
Expected number (under H_0)	$E_1 = nP_1$	$E_2 = nP_2$	...	$E_K = nP_K$	n

Then, if there are n sample observations, the expected numbers in each category, under the null hypothesis, will be

$$E_i = nP_i \quad (i = 1, 2, \ldots, K)$$

This is shown in Table 16.4.

The null hypothesis about the population specifies the probabilities that a sample observation will fall into each possible category. The sample observations are to be used to check this hypothesis. If the sample values observed in each category are very close to those expected if the null hypothesis was true, this fact would lend support to that hypothesis. In such circumstances the data provide a close *fit* to the assumed population distribution of probabilities. Tests of the null hypothesis are based on an assessment of the closeness of this fit and are generally referred to as **goodness-of-fit-tests**.

Now, in order to test the null hypothesis, it is natural to look at the magnitudes of the discrepancies between what is observed and what is expected. The larger these discrepancies are in absolute value, the more suspicious we are of the null hypothesis. The random variable in Equation 16.1 is known as the chi-square random variable.

Chi-Square Random Variable

A random sample of n observations, each of which can be classified into exactly one of K categories, is selected. Suppose the observed numbers in each category are $O_1, O_2, \ldots, O_K$. If a null hypothesis (H_0) specifies probabilities $P_1, P_2, \ldots, P_K$ for an observation falling into each of these categories, the expected numbers in the categories, under H_0, would be

$$E_i = nP_i \quad (i = 1, 2, \ldots, K)$$

If the null hypothesis is true and the sample size is large enough that the expected values are at least 5, then the random variable associated with

$$\chi^2 = \sum_{i=1}^{K} \frac{(O_i - E_i)^2}{E_i} \tag{16.1}$$

has, to a good approximation, a chi-square distribution with $(K - 1)$ degrees of freedom.

Intuitively, the number of degrees of freedom follows from the fact that the O_i must sum to n. Hence, if the number of sample members, n, and the numbers of observations falling in any $(K-1)$ of the categories are known, then the number in the

*K*th category is also known. The null hypothesis will be rejected when the observed numbers differ substantially from the expected numbers—that is, for unusually large values of the statistic in Equation 16.1. The appropriate goodness-of-fit test follows.

A Goodness-of-Fit Test: Specified Probabilities

A goodness-of-fit test, of significance level α, of H_0 against the alternative that the specified probabilities are not correct is based on the decision rule

$$\text{Reject } H_0 \text{ if } \quad \sum_{i=1}^{k} \frac{(O_i - E_i)^2}{E_i} > \chi^2_{K-1,\alpha}$$

where $\chi^2_{K-1,\alpha}$ is the number for which

$$P(\chi^2_{K-1} > \chi^2_{K-1,\alpha}) = \alpha$$

and the random variable χ^2_{K-1} follows a chi-square distribution with $(K-1)$ degrees of freedom.

To illustrate this test, consider again the data of Table 16.3 on brand selection. The null hypothesis is that the probabilities are the same for the three categories. The test of this hypothesis is based on

$$\chi^2 = \sum_{i-1}^{3} \frac{(O_i - E_i)^2}{E_i} = \frac{(8-11)^2}{11} + \frac{(10-11)^2}{11} + \frac{(15-11)^2}{11} = 2.36$$

There are $K = 3$ categories, so $K - 1 = 2$ degrees of freedom are associated with the chi-square distribution. From Table 7 in the Appendix,

$$\chi^2_{2,0.10} = 4.61$$

Therefore, according to our decision rule, the null hypothesis cannot be rejected at the 10% significance level. These data do not contain strong evidence against the hypothesis that a randomly chosen subject is equally likely to select any of the three soft drink brands.

Example 16.1   Gas Company (Chi-Square)

A gas company has determined from past experience that at the end of winter 80% of its accounts are fully paid, 10% are 1 month in arrears, 6% are 2 months in arrears, and 4% are more than 2 months in arrears. At the end of this winter the company checked a random sample of 400 of its accounts, finding 287 to be fully paid, 49 to be 1 month in arrears, 30 to be 2 months in arrears, and 34 to be more than 2 months in arrears. Do these data suggest that the pattern of previous years is not being followed this winter?

Solution   Under the null hypothesis that the proportions in the present winter conform to the historical record, the respective probabilities for the four categories are 0.8, 0.1, 0.06, and 0.04. Under that hypothesis the expected numbers of accounts in each category, for a random sample of 400 accounts, would be

$$400(0.8) = 320 \qquad 400(0.1) = 40 \quad 400(0.06) = 24 \qquad 400(0.04) = 16$$

The observed and expected numbers are

Number of Months in Arrears	0	1	2	More than 2	Total
Observed number	287	49	30	34	400
Probability (under H_0)	0.80	0.10	0.06	0.04	1
Expected number (under H_0)	320	40	24	16	400

The test of the null hypothesis (H_0) is based on

$$\chi^2 = \sum_{i-1}^{4} \frac{(O_i - E_i)^2}{E_i} = \frac{(287 - 320)^2}{320} + \frac{(49 - 40)^2}{40} + \frac{(30 - 24)^2}{24} + \frac{(34 - 16)^2}{16} = 27.17$$

Here there are $K = 4$ categories, so there are $K - 1 = 3$ degrees of freedom. From Table 7 in the Appendix

$$\chi^2_{3,0.005} = 12.84$$

Since 27.178 is much bigger than 12.84, the null hypothesis is very clearly rejected, even at the 0.5% significance level. Certainly, these data provide considerable evidence to suspect that the pattern of payments of gas bills this year differs from the historical norm. Inspection of the numbers in the table shows that more accounts are in arrears over a longer time period than is usually the case.

A word of caution is in order. The figures used in calculating the test statistic in Equation 16.1 must be the *observed* and *expected numbers* in each category. It is not correct, for example, to use instead the percentages of sample members in each category.

EXERCISES

Application Exercises

16.1 A professor is planning to use a new book for a financial accounting course and is considering three possibilities: *Financial Accounting Made Easy, Financial Accounting Without Tears,* and *Financial Accounting for Profit and Pleasure.* He contacted a random sample of 60 students who had already taken his course and asked each to review the three books, indicating a first preference. The results obtained are shown in the table. Test the null hypothesis that for this population their first preferences are evenly distributed over the three books.

Book	Made Easy	Without Tears	Profit and Pleasure
Number of first preferences	17	25	18

16.2 A random sample of 75 mutual funds whose performance ranked in the top 20% of all funds in 1998–2000 was selected. Their performance was observed over the next 3 years. In this later period suppose that 13 of the sample funds ranked in the top 20% of all funds, 20 in the second 20%, 18 in the third 20%, 11 in the fourth 20%, and the remainder in the bottom 20%. Test the null hypothesis that a randomly chosen top 20% fund from 1998–2000 is equally likely to fall into each of the five possible performance categories over the following 3 years.

16.3 An insurance company in Chattanooga, Tennessee, wanted to determine the importance of price as a factor in choosing a hospital in that region. A random sample of 450 consumers was asked to select "not important," "important," or "very important" as an answer. Respective numbers selecting these answers were 142, 175, and 133. Test the null hypothesis that a randomly chosen consumer is equally likely to select each of these three answers.

16.4 Production records indicate that in normal operation for a certain electronic component 93% have no faults, 5% have one fault, and 2% have more than one fault. For a random sample of 500 of these components from a week's output, 458 were found to have no faults, 30 to have one fault, and 12 to have more than one fault. Test at the 5% level the null hypothesis that the quality of the output from this week conforms to the usual pattern.

16.5 A charity solicits donations by telephone. It has been found that 60% of all calls result in a refusal to donate; 30% result in a request for more information through the mail, with a promise to at least consider donating; and 10% generate an immediate credit card donation. For a random sample of 100 calls made in the current week, 65 resulted in a refusal to donate, 31 in a request for more information through the mail, and 4 in an immediate credit card donation. Test at the 10% level the null hypothesis that the usual pattern of outcomes is being followed in the current week.

16.6 A campus administrator has found that 60% of all students view courses as very useful, 20% as somewhat useful, and 20% as worthless. Of a random sample of 100 students taking business courses, 68 found the course in question very useful, 18 somewhat useful, and 14 worthless. Test the null hypothesis that the population distribution for business courses is the same as that for all courses.

16.7 Several types of yogurt are sold in a small general store in New England. From a past study of customer selections the owner knows that 20% of the customers ordered flavor A, 35% flavor B, 18% flavor C, 12% flavor D, and the remainder flavor E. Now the owner, who thinks that the customer

preferences have changed, randomly samples 80 customers and finds that 12 prefer A, 16 prefer B, 30 prefer C, 7 prefer E, and the remainder prefer D. Determine if the customers' preferences have changed from the last study.

16.8 In a recent market survey five different soft drinks were tested to determine if consumers have a preference for any of the soft drinks. Each person was asked to indicate his or her favorite drink. The results were as follows: drink A, 20; drink B, 25; drink C, 28; drink D, 15; and drink E, 27. Is there a preference for any of these soft drinks?

16.9 A team of marketing research students was asked to determine the pizza best liked by students enrolled in their college. Two years ago a similar study was conducted, and it was found that 40% of all students at this college preferred Bellini's pizza, 25% chose Anthony's pizza as the best, 20% selected Ferrara's pizza, and the rest selected Marie's pizza. To see if preferences have changed, 180 students were randomly selected and asked to indicate their pizza preferences. The results were as follows: 40 selected Ferrara's as their favorite, 32 students chose Marie's, 80 students preferred Bellini's, and the remainder selected Anthony's. Do the data indicate that the preferences today differ from those from the last study?

16.10 A random sample of statistics professors was asked to complete a survey including questions on curriculum content, computer integration, and software preferences. Of the 250 responses, 100 professors indicated that they preferred software package M and 80 preferred software package E, while the remainder were evenly split between preference for software package S and software package P. Do the data indicate that professors have a preference for any of these software packages?

16.2 GOODNESS-OF-FIT TESTS: POPULATION PARAMETERS UNKNOWN

In Section 16.1 the hypothesis concerned data that are generated by a *fully specified* probability distribution. The null hypothesis in this test specifies the probability that a sample observation will fall in any category. However, it often is required to test the hypothesis that data are generated by some distribution, such as the binomial, the Poisson, or the normal, without assuming the parameters of that distribution to be known. In these circumstances Section 16.1 is not applicable, but the available data can be used to estimate the unknown population parameters. The goodness-of-fit test used when population parameters are estimated is stated next.

Goodness-of-Fit Tests When Population Parameters Are Estimated

Suppose that a null hypothesis specifies category probabilities that depend on the estimation (from the data) of m unknown population parameters. The appropriate **goodness-of-fit test when population parameters are estimated** is precisely as in Section 16.1, except that the number of degrees of freedom for the chi-square random variable is

$$\text{Degrees of Freedom} = (K - m - 1) \tag{16.2}$$

where K is the number of categories.

Consider a test to determine if data are generated by the Poisson distribution. One procedure for attempting to resolve questions of disputed authorship is to count the number of occurrences of particular words in blocks of text. These can be compared with results from passages whose authorship is known; often this comparison can be achieved through the assumption that the number of occurrences follows a Poisson distribution. An example of this type of research involves the study of *The Federalist Papers* (Reference 10).

Example 16.2   Federalist Papers (Chi-Square)

For a sample of 262 blocks of text (each approximately 200 words in length) from *The Federalist Papers* (Reference 10), the mean number of occurrences of the word *may* was 0.66. Table 16.5 shows the observed frequencies of occurrence of this word in the 262 sampled blocks of text. Test the null hypothesis that the population distribution of occurrences is Poisson, without assuming prior knowledge of the mean of this distribution.

Solution   Recall that, if the Poisson distribution is appropriate, the probability of x occurrences is

$$P(x) = \frac{e^{-\lambda}\lambda^x}{x!}$$

where λ is the mean number of occurrences. Although this population mean is unknown, it can be estimated by the sample mean 0.66. It is then possible, by substituting 0.66 for λ, to estimate the probability for any number of occurrences

Table 16.5   Occurrences of the Word *may* in 262 Blocks of Text in *The Federalist Papers*

NUMBER OF OCCURRENCES	0	1	2	3 OR MORE
Observed frequency	156	63	29	14

Table 16.6   Observed and Expected Frequencies for *The Federalist Papers*

NUMBER OF OCCURRENCES	0	1	2	3 OR MORE	TOTAL
Observed frequencies	156	63	29	14	262
Probabilities	0.5169	0.3412	0.1126	0.0293	1
Expected frequencies under H_0	135.4	89.4	29.5	7.7	262

under the null hypothesis that the population distribution is Poisson. For example, the probability of two occurrences is

$$P(2) = \frac{e^{-0.66}(0.66)^2}{2!}$$
$$= \frac{(0.5169)(0.66)^2}{2} = 0.1126$$

Similarly, the probabilities for zero and one occurrence can be found, so the probability of three or more occurrences is

$$P(X \geq 3) = 1 - P(0) - P(1) - P(2)$$

These probabilities are shown in the second row of Table 16.6.

Then, exactly as before, the expected frequencies under the null hypothesis are obtained from

$$E_i = nP_i \quad (i = 1, 2, \ldots, K)$$

Thus, for example, the expected frequency of two occurrences of the word *may* in 262 blocks of text is $(262)(0.1126) = 29.5$. Since the variable itself is an integer, it is best not to round these expected values to integer values. The bottom row of Table 16.6 shows these expected frequencies. The test-statistic is then

$$\chi^2 = \sum_{i=1}^{4} \frac{(O_i - E_i)^2}{E_i} = \frac{(156 - 135.4)^2}{135.4} + \frac{(63 - 89.4)^2}{89.4} + \frac{(29 - 29.5)^2}{29.5} + \frac{(14 - 7.7)^2}{7.7} = 16.0$$

Since there are four categories and one parameter has been estimated, the approximate number of degrees of freedom for the test is 2. From Table 7 in the Appendix

$$\chi^2_{2,0.005} = 10.60$$

Thus, the null hypothesis that the population distribution is Poisson can be rejected at the 0.5% significance level. The evidence in the data against that hypothesis are, then, very strong indeed.

To solve Example 16.2 using Excel, see the Appendix to this chapter.

A Test of Normality

The normal distribution plays an important role in statistics, and many practical procedures rely for their validity, or for particular optimality properties, on an assumption that sample data are from a normal distribution. In Chapter 6 we discussed the normal probability plot to check for evidence of non-normality. Also, in Chapter 8 (Figure 8.2 and Figure 8.9) we visually tested for evidence of non-normality by determining if the dots in the normal quantile plots were "close" to the straight line. Next, consider a test of the normality assumption through an adaptation of the chi-square procedure. This test is both easy to carry out and likely to be more powerful.

Suppose that we have a sample $X_1, X_2, \ldots, X_n$ of n observations from a population. Our approach is based on checking whether these data reflect two characteristics of the normal distribution. The first characteristic is symmetry about the mean. Using sample information, **skewness** of a population is estimated by

$$\text{Skewness} = \frac{\sum_{i=1}^{n}(x_i - \bar{x})^3}{ns^3}$$

where $\bar{x}$ and s are the sample mean and sample standard deviation, respectively. The important part of this expression is the numerator; the denominator serves the purpose of standardization, making units of measurement irrelevant. Positive skewness will result if a distribution is skewed to the right, since average cubed discrepancies about the mean are positive. Skewness will be negative for distributions skewed to the left and 0 for distributions, such as the normal, that are symmetric about their mean.

Since there are different symmetric distributions, a further characteristic is required to distinguish a normal distribution. In computing the sample variance, squared discrepancies about the mean are used, while skewness is based on cubed discrepancies about the mean. The next logical step is to look at the fourth powers of these discrepancies, leading to the sample **kurtosis**:

$$\text{Kurtosis} = \frac{\sum_{i=1}^{n}(x_i - \bar{x})^4}{ns^4}$$

Kurtosis provides a measure of the weight in the tails of a probability density function. It is known that for the normal distribution the population kurtosis is 3.

Sample skewness and kurtosis can be computed from data using these formulas. Skewness and kurtosis are also included in the standard output of most statistical software packages. However, alternative formulas may be used in the software packages to find these values. A test that takes into account both skewness and kurtosis is called the *Bowman–Shelton test statistic* for normality and is given in Equation 6.3.

Bowman–Shelton Test for Normality

The **Bowman–Shelton test for normality** is based on the closeness to 0 of the sample skewness and the closeness to 3 of the sample kurtosis. The test-statistic is

$$B = n\left[\frac{(\text{Skewness})^2}{6} + \frac{(\text{Kurtosis} - 3)^2}{24}\right] \tag{16.3}$$

It is known that, as the number of sample observations becomes very large, this statistic has, under the null hypothesis that the population distribution is normal, a chi-square distribution with 2 degrees of freedom. The null hypothesis is, of course, rejected for large values of the test statistic.

Unfortunately, the chi-square approximation to the distribution of the Bowman–Shelton test-statistic, B, is close only for very large sample sizes. Table 16.7 shows significance points appropriate for a range of sample sizes for tests at the 5% and 10% levels. The recommended procedure, then, is to calculate the statistic, B, in Equation 16.3 and reject the null hypothesis of normality if the test statistic exceeds the appropriate value tabulated in Table 16.7.

Table 16.7   Significance Points of the Bowman–Shelton Statistic (Reference 1)

SAMPLE SIZE n	10% POINT	5% POINT	SAMPLE SIZE n	10% POINT	5% POINT
20	2.13	3.26	200	3.48	4.43
30	2.49	3.71	250	3.54	4.51
40	2.70	3.99	300	3.68	4.60
50	2.90	4.26	400	3.76	4.74
75	3.09	4.27	500	3.91	4.82
100	3.14	4.29	800	4.32	5.46
125	3.31	4.34	∞	4.61	5.99
150	3.43	4.39			

Example 16.3   Rates of Return (Normality Test)

Suppose that a random sample of 300 daily rates of return on a citrus futures contract had skewness 0.0305 and kurtosis 3.08. Test the null hypothesis that the true distribution for these rates of return is normal.

Solution   We find the Bowman–Shelton statistic, B:

$$B = 300 \left[\frac{(0.0305)^2}{6} + \frac{(0.08)^2}{24} \right] = 0.1265$$

Comparison of this result with the significance points in Table 16.7 certainly provides little ground to think that population distribution is not normal.

Numerous other tests for normality exist, including the Kolmogorov–Smirnov test, the Anderson–Darling test, and the Ryan–Joiner test. These procedures, which are not included here, are available using software such as Minitab.

EXERCISES

Application Exercises

16.11 The number of times a machine broke down each week was observed over a period of 100 weeks and recorded in the accompanying table. It was found that the average number of breakdowns per week over this period was 2.1. Test the null hypothesis that the population distribution of breakdown is Poisson.

Number of Breakdowns	0	1	2	3	4	5 or More
Number of weeks	10	24	32	23	6	5

16.12 In a period of 100 minutes there were a total of 190 arrivals at a highway toll booth. The accompanying table shows the frequency of arrivals per minute over this period. Test the null hypothesis that the population distribution is Poisson.

Number of Arrivals in Minutes	0	1	2	3	4 or More
Observed Frequency	10	26	35	24	5

16.13 A random sample of 50 students was asked to estimate how much money they spent on textbooks in a year. The sample skewness of these amounts was found to be 0.83 and the sample kurtosis was 3.98. Test at the 10% level the null hypothesis that the population distribution of amounts spent is normal.

16.14 A random sample of 100 measurements of the resistance of electronic components produced in a period of 1 week was taken. The sample skewness was 0.63 and the sample kurtosis was 3.85. Test the null hypothesis that the population distribution is normal.

16.15 ● Use the Bowman–Shelton test to determine if the amounts spent on groceries for a random sample of customers at Bishop's Supermarket follows a normal distribution. Use the data file **Bishop**.

16.16 A random sample of 125 monthly balances for holders of a particular credit card indicated that the sample skewness was 0.55 and the sample kurtosis was 2.77. Test the null hypothesis that the population distribution is normal.

16.3 CONTINGENCY TABLES

Suppose that a sample is taken from a population, each of whose members can be uniquely cross-classified according to a pair of attributes, A and B. The hypothesis to be tested is of no association or dependence in the population between possession of attribute A and attribute B. For example, a travel agency may want to know if there is any relationship between clients' gender and the method clients use to make an airline reservation. An accounting firm may want to examine the relationship between the age of people and the type of income tax return filed by these individuals. Or perhaps, in a medical study, a pharmaceutical company may want to know if the success of a drug used to control cholesterol is dependent on a person's weight. A marketing research company may test if a customer's choice of cereal is in some way dependent on the color of the cereal box. Perhaps there is an association between political affiliation and support for a particular amendment that is to appear on the next election's ballot.

Assume that there are r categories for A and c categories for B, so a total of rc cross-classifications is possible. The number of sample observations belonging to both the ith category of A and the jth category of B will be denoted O_{ij}, where $i = 1, 2, \ldots, r$ and $j = 1, 2, \ldots, c$. Table 16.8 is called an $r \times c$ contingency table. For convenience, row and column totals were added to Table 16.8, denoted respectively $R_1, R_2, \ldots, R_r$ and $C_1, C_2, \ldots, C_c$.

To test the null hypothesis of no association between attributes A and B, we ask how many observations we would expect to find in each cross-classification if that hypothesis was true. This question becomes meaningful when the row and column totals are *fixed*. Consider, then, the joint classification corresponding to the ith row and jth column of the table. There are a total of C_j observations in the jth column, and,

Table 16.8 Cross-Classification of n Observations in an $r \times c$ Contingency Table

Attribute A	Attribute B 1	2	...	c	Total
1	O_{11}	O_{12}	...	O_{1c}	R_1
2	O_{21}	O_{22}	...	O_{2c}	R_2
⋮	⋮	⋮	...	⋮	⋮
r	O_{r1}	O_{r2}	...	O_{rc}	R_r
Total	C_1	C_2	...	C_c	n

given no association, we would expect each of these column totals to be distributed among the rows in proportion to the total number of observations in each ith row. Thus, we would expect a proportion R_i/n of these C_j observations to be in the ith row. Hence, the estimated expected number of observations in the cross-classifications is

$$E_{ij} = \frac{R_i C_j}{n} \quad \text{for } (i = 1, 2, \dots, r; \; j = 1, 2, \dots, c)$$

where R_i and C_j are the corresponding row and column totals.

Our test of the null hypothesis of no association is based on the magnitudes of the discrepancies between the observed numbers and those that would be expected if that hypothesis was true. The random variable given in Equation 16.4 is a generalized version of that introduced in Section 16.1.

Chi-Square Random Variable for Contingency Tables

It can be shown that under the null hypothesis the random variable associated with

$$\chi^2 = \sum_{i=1}^{r} \sum_{j=1}^{c} \frac{(O_{ij} - E_{ij})^2}{E_{ij}} \qquad (16.4)$$

has, to a good approximation, a chi-square distribution with $(r - 1)(c - 1)$ degrees of freedom. The approximation works well if no more than 20% of the estimated expected numbers E_{ij} is less than 5. Sometimes adjacent classes can be combined in order to meet this assumption.

The double summation in Equation 16.4 implies that summation extends over all rc cells of the table. The number of degrees of freedom follows from regarding the row and column totals as fixed. If these are known and the $(r - 1)(c - 1)$ entries corresponding to the first $(r - 1)$ rows and $(c - 1)$ columns are also known, the remaining entries in the table can be deduced. Clearly, the null hypothesis of no association will be rejected for large absolute discrepancies between observed and expected numbers—that is, for high values of the statistic in Equation 16.4. The test procedure is summarized as follows.

A Test of Association in Contingency Tables

Suppose that a sample of n observations is cross-classified according to two attributes in an $r \times c$ contingency table. Denote by O_{ij} the number of observations in the cell that is in the ith row and jth column. If the null hypothesis is

H_0: No association exists between the two attributes in the population

then the estimated expected number of observations in each cell, under H_0, is

$$E_{ij} = \frac{R_i C_j}{n} \qquad (16.5)$$

where R_i and C_j are the corresponding row and column totals. **A test of association** at a significance level α is based on the following decision rule:

$$\text{Reject } H_0 \text{ if } \sum_{i=1}^{r} \sum_{j=1}^{c} \frac{(O_{ij} - E_{ij})^2}{E_{ij}} > \chi^2_{(r-1)(c-1),\alpha}$$

Example 16.4   American Traveler Survey (Test of Association)

The 1999 American Traveler Survey conducted by Plog Research Inc. provides information based on a random sample of 10,536 U.S. adults (18 years or older) concerning their business and leisure travel habits, use of technology, and travel spending patterns and a comparison of the travel habits of travel agent users with those who do not use agents (Reference 6). Suppose that in a similar study a travel agent randomly sampled individuals in her target market to determine if there is any association between the respondents' gender and the methods used by respondents to make airline reservations for their last leisure trip, whether domestic or international. Table 16.9 shows the numbers of observations in each of the six possible cross-classifications. For convenience, row and column totals are also given in the table. Test the null hypothesis of no association between these attributes—in this case, that there is no association between subjects' gender and method used to make airline reservations.

Solution   The null hypothesis to be tested implies that, in the population, the proportion of airline reservations made by the client using a travel agent, booked by the client on the Internet, or made by the client calling an airline's toll-free number would be the same for male as for female subjects. To test the null hypothesis of no association between the attributes, we again ask how many observations we would *expect* to find in each cross-classification if that hypothesis were true.

For example, if there was no association between gender and method used to make an airline reservation in Table 16.9, we would expect, since 363 of 513 reservations were made by women, a proportion of 363/513 of the 330 reservations made by use of a travel agent to be made by females; that is,

$$E_{11} = \frac{(330)(363)}{513} = 233.5$$

Table 16.9 Air Flight Reservations by Gender and Booking Method

RESERVATION METHOD	FEMALE	MALE	TOTAL
Used a travel agent	256	74	330
Booked on the Internet	41	42	83
Called the airline's toll-free number	66	34	100
Total	**363**	**150**	**513**

The other expected numbers are calculated in the same way and are shown in Table 16.10 alongside the corresponding observed numbers.

The test of the null hypothesis of no association is based on the magnitudes of the discrepancies between the observed numbers and those that would be expected if that hypothesis was true. Extending Equation 16.1 to include each of the six cross-classifications gives the following value of the chi-square test statistic:

$$\chi^2 = \frac{(256-233.5)^2}{233.5} + \frac{(74-96.5)^2}{96.5} + \frac{(41-58.7)^2}{58.7} + \frac{(42-24.3)^2}{24.3}$$
$$+ \frac{(66-70.8)^2}{70.8} + \frac{(34-29.2)^2}{29.2} = 26.8$$

The degrees of freedom is $(r-1)(c-1)$. Here, there are $r = 3$ rows and $c = 2$ columns in the table, so the appropriate number of degrees of freedom is

$$(r-1)(c-1) = (3-1)(2-1) = 2$$

From Table 7 in the Appendix, we find

$$\chi^2_{2,0.005} = 10.60$$

Therefore, the null hypothesis of no association is very clearly rejected, even at the 0.5% level. The evidence against this hypothesis is overwhelming.

Table 16.10 Observed (and Expected) Numbers in Each Cross-Classification for Reservations

RESERVATION METHOD	FEMALE	MALE	TOTAL
Used a travel agent	256 (233.5)	74 (96.5)	330
Booked on the Internet	41 (58.7)	42 (24.3)	83
Called the airline's toll-free number	66 (70.8)	34 (29.2)	100
Total	**363**	**150**	**513**

It should be noted, as was the case for the goodness-of-fit tests in earlier sections, that the figures used in calculating the statistic must be the *actual numbers* observed and not, for example, percentages of the total.

Computer Applications

Various software packages are used by professional research organizations for the types of procedures discussed in this chapter. Example 16.5 illustrates Minitab. Example 16.5 illustrates Minitab for a university library study.

Library

Example 16.5   Library Study: Rank Versus Variety (Minitab)

As part of an exploratory study, a team of students conducted a survey on their college campus. Students were asked to complete a brief survey concerning their college library: Should the library hours be extended? Is it easy to locate books in the library? Are there sufficient databases available for research? Is the technology current? The results are contained in the data file **Library** (Reference 14). Is there any association between students' class rank (1: first year; 2: sophomore; 3: junior; 4: senior) and the responses to the question "Does the library have an adequate variety of books? (1: yes; 2: no)."

Solution   From the data file **Library** we see that a total of 355 students responded to both of these questions. Figure 16.1 shows the cross-classification of the responses and the Minitab output. Each of the expected values is greater than 5. If this assumption was not valid, a warning message would appear in the Minitab output, and adjacent classes could be combined. The small p-value indicates rejection of the null hypothesis of no association.

Figure 16.1   Class Rank Versus Adequate Variety (Minitab Output)

Tabulated Statistics: Class Rank, Adequate Variety

```
        Rows: Class      Columns: Adequate
              Rank                 Variety

                 No         Yes        All

         1       73          71        144
               54.76       89.24     144.00

         2       26          76        102
               38.79       63.21     102.00

         3       19          47         66
               25.10       40.90      66.00

         4       17          26         43
               16.35       26.65      43.00

       All      135         220        355
              135.00      220.00     355.00

       Chi-Square = 19.040, DF = 3, P-Value = 0.000
```

Although the use of the chi-square test for association may indicate that there is a relationship between two variables, this procedure does not indicate the direction or strength of the relationship.

EXERCISES

Application Exercises

16.17 Do commercial-free cable programs promote better citizenship among our school-aged children? (See Reference 7.) Many teachers and administrators believe that the use of commercial-free cable programs can enhance a student's interest in the democratic process in the years prior to the voting age. Other educators think that television is the enemy of education. Suppose that in a study in Texas a random sample of 150 high school history teachers was asked "Would you like to use commercial-free cable programs in your classroom?" The following contingency table gives the teachers' responses to this question as well as their opinions concerning whether or not such programming enhances citizenship. Is there evidence of a relationship between the responses to these two questions?

	Use Commercial-Free Cable Programs?	
Effect	Yes	No
Promotes better citizenship	78	25
Doesn't promote better citizenship	37	10

16.18 University administrators have collected the following information concerning student grade point average and the school of the student's major.

School	GPA < 3.0	GPA 3.0 or Higher
Arts & Sciences	50	35
Business	45	30
Music	15	25

Determine if there is any association between GPA and major.

16.19 Should all college students be required to own a laptop computer? Although this policy does exist at many universities, the added expense for students at small private schools should be considered. One business school recently surveyed its students to determine their reaction to this possible policy. The responses are given in the table below along with the students' major.

	Laptop Required?	
Major	Yes	No
Accounting	68	42
Finance	40	15
Management	60	50
Marketing	30	25

Do the data indicate that there is an association between one's major and the response to this question?

16.20 How do customers first hear about a new product? A random sample of 200 users of a new product was surveyed to determine the answer to this question. Other demographic data such as age were also collected. The respondents included 50 people under the age of 21 and 90 people between the ages of 21 and 35; the remainder were over 35 years of age. Of those under 21, 60% heard about the product from a friend, and the remainder saw an advertisement in the local paper. One-third of the people in the age category from 21 to 35 saw the advertisement in the local paper. The other two-thirds heard about it from a friend. Of those over 35, only 30% heard about it from a friend, while the remainder saw the local newspaper advertisement. Set up the contingency table for the variables age and method of learning about the product. Is there an association between the consumer's age and the method by which he or she heard about the new product?

16.21 Following a presidential debate, people were asked how they might vote in the forthcoming election. Is there any association between one's gender and choice of presidential candidate?

	Gender	
Candidate Preference	Male	Female
Candidate A	150	130
Candidate B	100	120

SUMMARY

In this chapter you studied some of the applications of the chi-square distribution. Goodness-of-fit tests were used to test the hypothesis that data are generated by a fully specified probability distribution. This technique is often used by market researchers to determine if products are equally preferred by potential customers or to check if the market shares for several brands of a product have changed over a given period of time.

In addition, the goodness-of-fit procedure was used to determine if data are generated by some distribution, such as the binominal, the Poisson, or the normal distribution, without assuming knowledge of the parameters of that distribution. The Bowman-Shelton test for normality was introduced. Other normality tests can be performed with various statistical software packages.

Finally, tests of association between two variables were considered. For larger contingency tables, it is convenient to use a software package to determine the test statistic and p-value.

KEY WORDS

- Bowman-Shelton test for normality, 620
- Chi-Square random variable, 614
- Chi-Square random variable: contingency tables, 623
- goodness-of-fit test, 614
- goodness-of-fit test: estimated parameters, 618
- goodness-of-fit test: specified probabilities, 615
- test of association, 624

CHAPTER EXERCISES AND APPLICATIONS

16.22 Suppose that a random sample of firms with impaired assets was classified according to whether discretionary write-downs of these assets were taken and also according to whether there was evidence of subsequent merger or acquisition activity. Using the data in the accompanying table, test the null hypothesis of no association between these attributes.

	Merger or Acquisition Activity?	
Write-Down	Yes	No
Yes	32	48
No	25	57

16.23 A manufacturer of a certain product has three factories located across the United States. There are three major causes of defects in this product, which we will identify as A, B, and C. During a recent week the reported occurrences of product defects in the three factories were as follows:

Factory 1	A, 15;	B, 25;	C, 23
Factory 2	A, 10;	B, 12;	C, 21
Factory 3	A, 32;	B, 28;	C, 44

Based on these frequencies, can we conclude that the defect patterns in the different factories are the same?

16.24 The human resources department is attempting to determine if an employee's undergraduate major influences the performance of this employee. The majors considered are business, economics, mathematics, and all others. Personnel ratings are grouped as excellent, strong, and average. The classifications are based on employees with two to four years of experience, as follows:

Business major	excellent, 21;	strong, 18;	average, 10
Economics major	excellent, 19;	strong, 15;	average, 5
Mathematics major	excellent, 10;	strong, 5;	average, 5
Other major	excellent, 5;	strong, 15;	average, 13

Do these data indicate that there is a difference in ratings based on undergraduate major?

16.25 A random sample of people from three different job classifications labeled A, B, and C was asked to indicate their preferences for three brands of camping lanterns: Big Star, Lone Star, and Bright Star. The preferences were as follows:

Group A	Big Star, 54;	Lone Star, 67;	Bright Star, 39
Group B	Big Star, 23;	Lone Star, 13;	Bright Star, 44
Group C	Big Star, 69;	Lone Star, 53;	Bright Star, 59

Do these data indicate that there is a difference in ratings for the three different groups?

16.26 A liberal arts college was interested in determining if there were different graduate school patterns for students with undergraduate majors in history and economics. They surveyed a random sample of recent graduates and found that a large number obtained graduate degrees in business, law, and theology. The frequency of persons in the various combinations is shown below. Based on these results, is there evidence that undergraduate economics and history majors pursue different graduate school programs?

	Graduate Studies		
Undergraduate	Business	Law	Theology
Economics	30	20	10
History	6	34	20

16.27 Suppose that you have collected market survey data for gender and product purchase. Perform a chi-square test to determine if there is a different probability of purchase among men and women. Include in your answer the expected cell values under the null hypothesis.

	Gender	
Decision	Male	Female
Purchase	150	150
No purchase	50	250

16.28 Sally Smith is a long-time political campaign manager from Chicago. In the primary election there are four candidates. She wishes to determine if voter preference is different over the four major districts. A random sample survey results in the candidate preference frequencies by district is shown in the contingency table. Perform an appropriate statistical test to determine if candidate preference is related to the district.

	Preference for Candidates in Primary Election				
District	A	B	C	D	Total
1	52	34	80	34	200
2	33	15	78	24	150
3	66	54	141	39	300

16.29 A manufacturer of household appliances wanted to determine if there was a relationship between family size and the size of washing machine purchased. The manufacturer was preparing guidelines for sales personnel and wanted to know if the sales staff should make specific recommendations to customers. A random sample of 300 families was asked about family size and size of washing machine. For the 40 families with one or two people, 25 had an 8-pound washer, 10 had a 10-pound washer, and 5 had a 12-pound washer. The 140 families with three or four people included 37 with the 8-pound, 62 with the 10-pound, and 41 with the 12-pound. For the remaining 120 families with five or more people, 8 had an 8-pound, 53 had a 10-pound, and 59 had a 12-pound. Based on these results, what can be concluded about family size and size of washer? Construct a two-way table, state the hypothesis, compute the statistics, and state your conclusion.

16.30 The gear-cutting department in a large manufacturing firm produces high-quality gears. The number produced per hour by a single machinist is 1, 2, or 3, as shown in the table. Company management is interested in determining the effect of worker experience on the number of units produced per hour. Worker experience is classified in three subgroups: 1 year or less, 2 to 5 years, and more than 5

years. Use the data in the table to determine if experience and number of parts produced per hour are independent.

	Units Produced/Hour			
Experience	1	2	3	Total
≤ 1 year	10	30	10	50
2–5 years	10	20	20	50
> 5 years	10	10	30	50
Total	30	60	60	150

16.31 Agnes Larson has been working on a plan for new store locations as part of her regional expansion. In one city proposed for expansion there are three possible locations: north, east, and west. From past experience she knows that the three major profit centers in her stores are tools, lumber, and paint. In selecting a location, the demand patterns in the different parts of the city were important. She commissioned a sampling study of the city, which resulted in a two-way table for the variables residential location and product purchased. This table was prepared by the market research department using data obtained from the random sample of households in the three major residential areas of the city. Each residential area had a separate phone number prefix, and the last four digits were chosen using a computer random number generator. Is there a difference in the demand patterns for the three major items among the different areas of the city?

	Product Demand		
Area	Tools	Lumber	Paint
East	100	50	50
North	50	95	45
West	65	70	75

16.32 The Speedi-Flex delivery service is conducting a study of its delivery operations. As part of this study it collected data on package type by originating source for one day's operation for one district office in the Southeast. These data are shown in the table. The major originating sources were identified as (1) small cities (towns), (2) central business districts (CBDs), (3) light manufacturing districts (factories), and (4) suburban residential communities (suburbs). Three major size and rate categories classify the items handled. Overnight envelopes must weigh 3 pounds or less and have a fixed charge of $12 anywhere in the United States. Small packages weigh from 4 to 10 pounds and have dimension restrictions. Large packages can weigh from 11 to 75 pounds and have the lowest rate per pound and the longest delivery time.

| Package Source | Package Size (LB) | | | |
	≤ 3	4–10	11–75	Total
Towns	40	40	20	100
CBDs	119	63	18	200
Factories	18	71	111	200
Suburbs	69	64	17	150

a. Are there any differences in the patterns of packages originated at the various locations?
b. Which two combinations have the largest percentage deviation from a uniform pattern?

16.33 A travel agent randomly sampled individuals in her target market and asked, "Did you use a travel agent to book your last airline flight?" By cross-referencing the answers to this question with the responses to the rest of the questionnaire, the agent obtained data such as that in the following contingency table:

| Age | Did You Use a Travel Agent to Book Your Last Flight? | |
	Yes	No
Under 30	15	30
30 to 39	20	42
40 to 49	47	42
50 to 59	36	50
60 or older	45	20

Determine if there is an association between the respondent's age and whether the respondent used a travel agent to make reservations for his or her last flight.

16.34 When the law was passed to give the same legal status to e-signatures as to handwritten signatures, nearly 60% of small business owners thought that digital signatures would not help them do business on-line (Reference 13). Suppose that the following data were obtained in a similar study of small business owners classified by the number of years that the company has existed and the CEO's opinion on the ability of e-signatures to increase business.

| Age of Company | Will Digital Signatures Have a Positive Effect on Your Business? | | |
	Yes	No	Uncertain
Less than 5 years	80	68	10
5 to 10 years	60	90	15
More than 10 years	72	63	12

Is there any relationship between the age of the company and the owner's opinion concerning the effectiveness of e-signatures?

16.35 The American Society for Quality (ASQ) offers its members exclusive recruiting tools available on-line. "Only members seeking to hire quality professionals can post jobs to these free bulletins and only members have access to these jobs online" (Reference 2). Suppose that a random sample of companies was surveyed and asked to indicate if they had used an Internet career service site to search for prospective employees. The companies were also asked questions concerning the posting fee for use of such a site. Is there a relationship between use of such a site and management's opinion on the posting fee?

| Posting Fee | Have You Used an Internet Career Service Site? | |
	Yes	No
Fee is too high	36	50
Fee is about right	82	28

16.36 *Business Florida* is the official guide to business growth and development in Florida. It is published annually by Enterprise Florida Inc.; the Florida Economic Development Council, Inc.; and *Florida Trend* magazine. In *Business Florida 2001* (Reference 12), 10 reasons are given to encourage a company to select Florida as "a site for business development and expansion." Suppose that in a follow-up study a random sample of businesses that located in Florida within the last three years is surveyed. Do the data in the following contingency table show any relationship between the primary reason for the company's move to Florida and the industry type?

| Primary Reason | Industry Type | | |
	Manufacturing	Retail	Tourism
Emerging technology	53	25	10
Tax credits	67	36	20
Labor force	30	40	33

16.37 Should large retailers offer banking services? Retail giants, such as Nordstrom and Federated Department Stores (corporate parent of Macy's and Bloomingdale's), began offering various banking services by the end of 2000 (Reference 3). Some incentives to attract customers included longer grace periods for late payments, reduced fees for such services as wire transfers, and auto or home improvement loans. Small community banks may be concerned about their future if more retailers enter the world of banking. Suppose that a market research company conducted a national survey for one retailer that is considering offering banking services to its customers. The respondents were asked to indicate the provider (bank, retail store, other) that they most likely would use for certain banking services (assuming that rate is not a factor). Is there a relationship between these two variables?

Service	Provider		
	Bank	Retail Store	Other
Checking account	100	45	10
Savings account	85	25	45
Home mortgage	30	10	80

16.38 Many easy-weight-loss products are just gimmicks that attract people with the hope of a fast way to a slimmer body. Diet industry groups, health professionals, and federal officials warn that deceptive advertising can lure consumers into danger (Reference 4). Suppose that a random sample of residents in one community was asked if they had ever tried a quick-weight-reduction product. Then they were asked if they thought that there should be stricter advertising controls to prohibit deceptive weight-loss advertising.

Advertising	Used a Quick-Weight-Loss Product?	
	Yes	No
Stricter controls needed	85	40
Stricter controls not needed	25	64

Are respondents' views on advertising controls dependent on whether or not they had ever used a quick-weight-loss product?

16.39 "Rattled by the trembling stock market, online enterprises began what will no doubt be a long run of layoffs" (Reference 5). Although the economy is new, apparently the same old downsizing is taking place among dot-com companies. These e-companies claim that firings are necessary to increase profits and save costs. Suppose that the following contingency table shows the number of layoffs in three dot-com companies and the months of service by those employees that were laid off. Is there any relationship between theses two variables?

Age	Dot-Com Company		
	A	B	C
Less than 6 months	23	40	12
6 months to 1 year	15	21	12
More than 1 year	12	9	6

16.40 Some marketing research studies indicate the "positive impact of store brand penetration on store profitability as measured by market share" (Reference 8). Two years ago the manager of a local supermarket that sells three national brands (brands A, B, and C) and one store brand (brand D) of orange juice found that brands A and C were equally preferred; 33% preferred brand B; and 27%

preferred the store brand, D. Now, the manager thinks that there has been a change in customer preferences and that the preference for store brand orange juice has increased and perhaps will positively contribute to increased profits. The results from a recent random sample of shoppers indicate the following preferences.

Favorite Brand	A	B	C	D (Store Brand)
Number	56	70	28	126

Has there been a change in customer preferences from the study 2 years ago?

16.41 By late fall 2000 customers who wanted wireless Internet service could choose from four basic categories of hardware: Palm handhelds and their offspring that use the Palm operating system; Pocket PCs; Web-enabled phones; and mobile e-mail devices (Reference 11). Analyzing the data below, taken from a survey of wireless Internet service users, does satisfaction depend on the hardware category selected?

Hardware Category	Are You Satisfied with Your Purchase?	
	Yes	No
Palm handhelds	128	40
Pocket PCs	45	15
Web-enabled phones	30	8
Mobile e-mail devices	30	6

16.42 ⬤ As part of an exploratory market study, students on one college campus were asked to answer a brief survey concerning their college library (Reference 14). One question asked if students thought that the library hours should be extended.

a. Test for a relationship between students' responses to this question and their class standing. The data are stored in the data file **Library**.
b. What recommendations would you suggest to the library staff?

16.43 ⬤ Can a student easily find books in the college library? This question was also included in the college library survey (Reference 14).

a. Test for any relationship between students' responses to this question and their class standing. The data are stored in the data file **Library**.
b. What recommendations would you suggest to the library staff?

16.44 ⬤ The Institutional Research Office (IRO) at a major university annually conducts surveys of freshmen, sophomores, and juniors to determine levels of satisfaction with student services, facilities, and policies of the university. Seniors are surveyed separately in the Senior Survey. Suppose that the director of the IRO at one university provides university administrators/faculty/staff with analyses of trends, comparisons, and other output useful for purpose of continuous improvement.

The 2002 Student Satisfaction Survey, conducted in the spring of 2002 from mid-March to early May, was mailed to a random sample of 600 students (200 freshmen, 200 sophomores, and 200 juniors). The response rate was 248, or 42.5% (after adjusting for undeliverable or unclaimed surveys). Demographic information included respondent's school or college of major, age, and gender. Suppose that selected data collected from the 2002 Student Satisfaction Survey are included in the data file **IRO**. Students were asked to indicate if they were satisfied with, neutral toward, or dissatisfied with on-line registration, the university bookstore, food service, the student accounts/billing office, student financial planning, the work-study program, and various other service providers on campus. From the data, numerous relationships can be investigated. Analyze the data, select and test several possible relationships, and write a summary of findings to be submitted to the university president. Include in your report discussion of any relationship between a student's satisfaction with library hours and the student's class standing, a student's satisfaction level with faculty advising, availability of internships, on-line registration, and overseas programs. Your report can be enhanced by descriptive measures, graphs, and estimations.

16.45 A recent study of computer usage (Reference 9) found that "children ages 2 to 5 averaged 27 minutes a day at the computer, while children 6 to 11 spent 49 minutes a day, and those 12 to 17 averaged 63 minutes a day." Most schools are now wired to the Internet, but how these computers are used in the classroom varies. According to Jay Becker, a professor at the University of California at Irvine, "schools serving poor children were more likely to emphasize word processing and other simple tasks while those serving more affluent students taught computer skills to promote problem-solving and a deeper understanding of an area of study." Suppose that a team of educational researchers under the direction of Dr. Joy Haugaard conducted a survey to test this hypothesis. The study involved 225 schools from both poorer communities and more affluent districts. The following table gives their responses to the question "Concerning computer usage, is your school more likely to emphasize basic tasks such as word processing or computer skills involving problem-solving?"

| | Economic Status | |
Content Emphasis	Poor Community	Affluent Community
Basic tasks (word processing)	75	40
Computer skills (problem solving)	30	80

Do the data from this study agree with Becker's conclusions?

16.46 There are several forms that people can use to file their federal income tax returns. One standard method is the 1040 form. Some people use other forms such as the telefile process. Others simply file for an extension (to extend the deadline beyond April 15). Suppose that in a particular locality a study of 200 randomly selected people filing returns was conducted. The filer's age was an important variable in this study. Proportional to the age demographics of the area, the study included 50 people under 25 and 90 people between the ages of 25 and 45; the remainder were over 45. Of those under the age of 25, 35 used a 1040 form, 8 used another form, and the remainder filed for an extension. Two-thirds of the people in the age category from 25 to 45 used the 1040 form, 20 used a different form, and the remainder filed for an extension. Seventy-five percent of the people over 45 used the 1040 form, 4 people filed for an extension, and the remainder used a different process. Determine if there is any association between a person's age and the method used to file income tax returns.

Appendix

We are able to solve Example 16.2 using Excel. To obtain the Poisson probabilities shown in Figure 16.2, we used the Function Arguments as illustrated in Figure 16.3 for $x = 0$, for each of the occurrences ($x = 0, 1, 2,$ and 3).

Figure 16.2   Excel Output to Test if Population Distribution Is Poisson

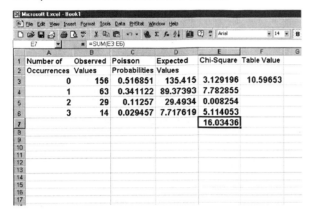

Figure 16.3   Poisson Probabilities Obtained with Excel Function Arguments

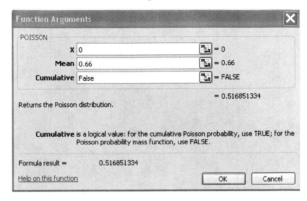

REFERENCES

1. Bera, A. K., and C. M. Jarque. "An Efficient Large-Sample Test for Normality of Observations and Regression Residuals." *Working Papers in Economics and Econometrics* 40, Australian National University (1981).

2. "Career Services Program Updated." *On Q* (American Society for Quality) 15, no. 4 (Fall 2000).

3. Coolidge, Carrie. "Socks and Bonds." *Forbes*, July 3, 2000, p. 62.

4. "Dieter Hunger for Gimmicks." *New York Times* article appearing in *Orlando Sentinel*, October 29, 2000, p. A11.

5. Godwin, Jennifer. "New Economy, Same Old Downsizing." *Forbes*, July 3, 2000, p. 60.

6. Jamison, Jane. "Survey Highlights Agents' Strength." *Travel Weekly*, October 25, 1999. pp. 10–47.

7. Keveney, Bill. "Classroom TV Brings Election to Students: Commercial-free Cable Programs Promote Citizenship." *USA Today*, October 30, 2000, p. 4D.

8. Lal, Rajiv, and Marcel CorstJensrajiv Lal. "Building Store Loyalty Through Store Brands." *Journal of Marketing Research* 37, no. 3 (August 2000): 281.

9. Lewin, Tamara. "Children's Computer Use Grows, but Gap Persist, Study Says." *New York Times*, January 22, 2001, p. A11.

10. Mosteller, F., and D. L. Wallace. *Interference and Disputed Authorship: The Federalist* © 1964, Addison-Wesley, Reading, Mass., Tables 2.3 and 2.4. Reprinted with permission.

11. Nadeau, Michael. "Cut the Cord." *Access: America's Guide to the Internet*. Special Magazine Supplement to *Orlando Sentinel*, October 29, 2000, pp. 12–14. *www.accessmagazine.com*.

12. Shepherd, Gary. "10 Reasons Why Your Business Belongs in Florida." *Business Trend's Business Florida 2001*, *www.businessflorida.com*.

13. "Sign Here Please," *USA Today*, October 30, 2000, p.1B. *www.office.com*.

14. Thorne, J. Renee, et al. "University Library Study," unpublished paper. Data available in data file **Library**.

Topic 12

Simple Regression

Chapter 12

Simple Regression

Introduction

The discussion to this point has focused on analysis and inference related to a single variable. In this chapter we extend our analysis to relationships between variables. We begin with a brief introduction to correlation analysis, followed by the development of simple regression analysis. Our discussion here follows Chapter 3, where we emphasized descriptive relationships including the use of scatter plots, correlation coefficients, and linear regression as tools to describe the relationships between variables. We assume that the reader is familiar with that material.

The analysis of business and economic processes makes extensive use of relationships between variables. These relationships are expressed mathematically as

$$Y = f(X)$$

where the function can follow many linear and nonlinear forms. In some of those cases the form of the relationship is not precisely known. Here, we will develop analyses that are based on linear relationships. In many cases linear relationships provide a good model of the process. In other cases we are interested in a limited portion of a nonlinear relationship that can be approximated by a linear relationship. In Section 13.7 we show how some important nonlinear relationships can also be analyzed using regression analysis. Thus, the correlation and regression procedures have wide application to a broad range of problems.

Linear relationships are very useful for many business and economic applications, as indicated in the following examples. The president of Amalgamated Materials, a manufacturer of sheetrock building material, believes that the mean annual quantity of sheetrock sold in her region is a linear function of the total value of building permits issued during the previous year. A grain dealer wants to know the effect of total output on price per ton. He is working on a prediction model that uses historical data. The marketing department needs to know how gasoline price affects total sales of gasoline. By using weekly price and sales data, the department plans to develop a linear model that will show how much sales change as the result of price changes.

With the advent of many high-quality statistical packages and spreadsheets such as Excel, it is now possible for almost anyone to compute correlation and regression statistics. Unfortunately, we also know that it is not possible for everyone to interpret and use these computer results correctly. Here, you will learn key insights that will guide your use of regression analysis. We will begin with a discussion of correlation analysis.

12.1 CORRELATION ANALYSIS

In this section we use correlation coefficients to study relationships between variables. In Chapter 3 the sample correlation coefficient was used to describe the relationship between variables indicated in the data. In Chapters 5 and 6 we learned about the population correlation. Here, we develop inference procedures that use the correlation coefficient for studying linear relationships between variables.

In principle, there are any number of ways in which a pair of random variables might be related to each other. As we begin our analysis, it is helpful to postulate some functional form for their relationship. It is often reasonable to conjecture, as a good approximation, that the association is linear. If the pair of linearly related random variables X and Y is being considered, a scatter plot of the joint observations on this pair will tend to be clustered around a straight line. Conversely, if a linear relationship does not exist, then the scatter plot will not follow a straight line. Not all of the relationships that we will study will be tightly clustered about a straight line. Many important relationships will have scatter plots that show a tendency toward a linear relationship, but with considerable deviation from a straight line. We saw a number of such examples in Chapter 2 scatter plots.

Correlations have wide applications in business and economics. In many applied economic problems we argue that there is an independent or exogenous variable X, whose values are determined by activities outside of the economic system being modeled, and that there is a dependent or endogenous variable Y, whose value depends on the value of X. If we ask if sales increase when prices are reduced, we are thinking about a situation in which a seller deliberately and independently adjusts prices up or down and observes changes in sales. Now suppose that prices and quantities sold result from equilibriums of supply and demand as proposed by the basic economic model. Then we could model prices and quantities both as random variables and ask if these two random variables are related to each other. The correlation coefficient can be used to determine if there is a relationship between variables in either of these situations.

Suppose that both X and Y are determined simultaneously by factors that are outside of the economic system being modeled. Therefore, a model in which both X and Y are random variables is often more realistic. In Chapter 5 the correlation coefficient ρ_{xy} was developed as a measure of the relationship between two random variables, X and Y. In those cases the population correlation coefficient, ρ_{xy}, was used to indicate a linear relationship without implying that one variable is independent and the other is dependent. In situations where one variable is logically dependent on a second variable, we can use regression analysis to develop a linear model as a logical next step after correlation analysis. This is the topic of the next section. Here, we develop statistical inference procedures that use sample correlations to determine characteristics of population correlations.

Hypothesis Test for Correlation

The sample correlation coefficient

$$r = \frac{s_{xy}}{s_x s_y}$$

$$s_{xy} = \frac{\sum (x_i - \bar{x})(y_i - \bar{y})}{n - 1}$$

is useful as a descriptive measure of the strength of linear association in a sample. We can also use the correlation to test the hypothesis that there is no linear association in the population between a pair of random variables; that is,

$$H_0 : \rho = 0$$

This particular null hypothesis of no linear relationship between a pair of random variables is of great interest in a number of applications. When we compute the sample correlation from data, the result is likely to be different from 0 even if the population correlation is 0. Thus, we would like to know how large a difference from 0 is required for a sample correlation to provide evidence that the population correlation is not 0.

We can show that, when the null hypothesis is true and the random variables have a joint normal distribution, then the random variable

$$t = \frac{r\sqrt{(n - 2)}}{\sqrt{(1 - r^2)}}$$

follows a Student's t distribution with $(n - 2)$ degrees of freedom. The appropriate hypothesis tests are shown in Equations 12.1 through 12.3.

Tests for Zero Population Correlation

Let r be the sample correlation coefficient, calculated from a random sample of n pairs of observations from a joint normal distribution. The following tests of the null hypothesis

$$H_0 : \rho = 0$$

have a significance value α:

1. To test H_0 against the alternative

$$H_1 : \rho > 0$$

the decision rule is

$$\text{Reject } H_0 \text{ if } \quad \frac{r\sqrt{(n-2)}}{\sqrt{(1-r^2)}} > t_{n-2,\alpha} \qquad (12.1)$$

2. To test H_0 against the alternative

$$H_1 : \rho < 0$$

the decision rule is

$$\text{Reject } H_0 \text{ if } \quad \frac{r\sqrt{(n-2)}}{\sqrt{(1-r^2)}} < -t_{n-2,\alpha} \qquad (12.2)$$

3. To test H_0 against the two-sided alternative

$$H_1 : \rho \neq 0$$

the decision rule is

$$\text{Reject } H_0 \text{ if } \quad \frac{r\sqrt{(n-2)}}{\sqrt{(1-r^2)}} < -t_{n-2,\alpha/2} \quad \text{or} \quad \frac{r\sqrt{(n-2)}}{\sqrt{(1-r^2)}} > t_{n-2,\alpha/2} \qquad (12.3)$$

Here, $t_{n-2,\alpha}$ is the number for which

$$P(t_{n-2} > t_{n-2,\alpha}) = \alpha$$

where the random variable t_{n-2} follows a Student's t distribution with $(n-2)$ degrees of freedom.

4. If we set $t_{n-2,\alpha/2} = 2.0$ in Equation 12.3, an approximate "rule of thumb" for testing the above hypothesis that the population correlation is 0 can be shown to be

$$|r| > \frac{2}{\sqrt{n}}$$

Example 12.1 Political Risk Score (Hypothesis Test for Correlation)

A research team was attempting to determine if political risk in countries is related to inflation for these countries. In this research a survey of political risk analysts produced a mean political risk score for each of 49 countries. (Data are from Reference 2.)

Solution   The political risk score is scaled such that the higher the score, the greater the political risk. The sample correlation between political risk score and inflation for these countries was 0.43.

We wish to determine if the population correlation, ρ, between these measures is different from 0. Specifically, we want to test

$$H_0 : \rho = 0$$

against

$$H_1 : \rho > 0$$

using the sample information

$$n = 49 \qquad r = 0.43$$

The test is based on the statistic

$$t = \frac{r\sqrt{(n-2)}}{\sqrt{(1-r^2)}} = \frac{0.43\sqrt{(49-2)}}{\sqrt{1-(0.43)^2}} = 3.265$$

Since there are $(n-2) = 47$ degrees of freedom, we have from the Student's t table 8 in the Appendix

$$t_{47,0.005} < 2.704$$

Therefore, we can reject the null hypothesis at the 0.5% significance level. As a result, we have strong evidence of a positive linear relationship between inflation and experts' judgments of political riskiness of countries. Note that from this result we cannot conclude that one variable caused the other, but only that they are related.

INTERPRETATION   We noted above that the null hypothesis $H_0 : \rho = 0$ can be rejected by using the approximate rule of thumb $|r| > 2/\sqrt{n}$. This result provides a quick test to determine if two variables are linearly related when one or more sample correlations are being examined. Thus, for a sample size $n = 25$ the absolute value of the sample correlation would have to exceed $2/\sqrt{25} = 0.40$. But for a sample of size $n = 64$ the absolute value of the sample correlation would have to exceed only $2/\sqrt{64} = 0.25$. This result has been found to be useful in many statistical applications.

EXERCISES

Basic Exercises

12.1   Given the following pairs of (x, y) observations, compute the sample correlation.

  a. (2, 5), (5, 8), (3, 7), (1, 2), (8, 15)
  b. (7, 5), (10, 8), (8, 7), (6, 2), (13, 15)
  c. (12, 4), (15, 6), (16, 5), (21, 8), (14, 6)
  d. (2, 8), (5, 12), (3, 14), (1, 9), (8, 22)

12.2   Test the null hypothesis

$$H_0 : \rho = 0$$

versus

$$H_1 : \rho \neq 0$$

given

a. A sample correlation of 0.35 for a random sample of size $n = 40$
b. A sample correlation of 0.50 for a random sample of size $n = 60$
c. A sample correlation of 0.62 for a random sample of size $n = 45$
d. A sample correlation of 0.60 for a random sample of size $n = 25$

12.3   An instructor in a statistics course set a final examination and also required the students to do a data analysis project. For a random sample of 10 students, the scores obtained are shown in the table. Find the sample correlation between the examination and project scores.

Examination	81	62	74	78	93	69	72	83	90	84
Project	76	71	69	76	87	62	80	75	92	79

Application Exercises

12.4   In the study of 49 countries discussed in Example 12.1, the sample correlation between the experts' political riskiness score and the infant mortality rate in these countries was 0.75. Test the null hypothesis of no correlation between these quantities against the alternative of positive correlation.

12.5   For a random sample of 353 high school teachers the correlation between annual raises and teaching evaluations was found to be 0.11. Test the null hypothesis that these quantities are uncorrelated in the population against the alternative that the population correlation is positive.

12.6   The sample correlation for 68 pairs of annual returns on common stocks in country A and country B was found to be 0.51. Test the null hypothesis that the population correlation is 0 against the alternative that it is positive.

It is recommended that the following exercises be solved by using the computer.

12.7   ● The accompanying table and the data file **Dow Jones** show percentage changes (x_i) in the Dow-Jones index over the first five trading days of each of 13 years and also the corresponding percentage changes (y_i) in the index over the whole year.

x	y	x	y
1.5	14.9	5.6	2.3
0.2	−9.2	−1.4	11.9
−0.1	19.6	1.4	27.0
2.8	20.3	1.5	−4.3
2.2	−3.7	4.7	20.3
−1.6	27.7	1.1	4.2
−1.3	22.6		

a. Calculate the sample correlation.
b. Test at the 10% significance level, against a two-sided alternative, the null hypothesis that the population correlation is 0.

12.8   ● A college administers for all its courses a student evaluation questionnaire. For a random sample of 12 courses the accompanying table and the data file **Student Evaluation** show both the average student ratings of the instructor (on a scale from 1 to 5), and the average expected grades of the students (on a scale from A = 4 to E = 0).

Instructor rating	2.8	3.7	4.4	3.6	4.7	3.5	4.1	3.2	4.9	4.2	3.8	3.3
Expected grade	2.6	2.9	3.3	3.2	3.1	2.8	2.7	2.4	3.5	3.0	3.4	2.5

a. Find the sample correlation between instructor ratings and expected grades.
b. Test at the 10% significance level the hypothesis that the population correlation coefficient is zero against the alternative that it is positive.

12.9   ● In an advertising study the researchers wanted to determine if there was a relationship between the per capita cost and the per capita revenue. The following variables were measured for a random sample of advertising programs:

x_i = Cost of Advertisement ÷ Number of Inquiries Received

y_i = Revenue from Inquiries ÷ Number of Inquiries Received

The sample data results are shown in the data file **Advertising Revenue**. Find the sample correlation, and test against a two-sided alternative the null hypothesis that the population correlation is 0.

12.2 LINEAR REGRESSION MODEL

Correlation coefficients are used to provide a measure of the strength of any linear association between a pair of random variables. The random variables are treated perfectly symmetrically, and it is a matter of indifference whether we speak of "the correlation between X and Y" or "the correlation between Y and X." In the remainder of this chapter we continue to discuss the linear relationship between a pair of variables, but in terms of dependency of one on the other. The symmetry of our previous discussion is now removed. Rather, the concept here is that, given that the random variable X takes a specific value, we expect a response in the random variable Y. That is, the value taken by X influences the value of Y. This can be thought of as a dependence of Y on X. Dependent or endogenous—Y—variables have values that depend on independent or exogenous—X—variables, whose values are, in turn, manipulated or influenced by factors external to a specific economic process.

INTERPRETATION

Linear models are not as restrictive as they might seem for applied business and economic analysis. First, linear models often provide a very good approximation of a relationship over the range being considered. Second, we will see in Chapters 13 and 14 that a number of nonlinear functions can be converted to implicit linear functions for regression analysis.

In this chapter we focus on a formal study of regression analysis and related statistical inference for simple linear models. In Chapters 2 and 3 we introduced scatter plots, correlation, and simple regression as tools for describing data. In Chapter 13 we will apply these ideas to multiple regression models that have more than one predictor variable. Then in Chapter 14 advanced procedures and applications will be developed that extend our capabilities for analyzing business and economic problems.

This discussion begins with an example that indicates a typical application of regression analysis and the kind of results that can be obtained.

Example 12.2 Sales Prediction for Northern Household Goods (Regression Model Estimation)

The president of Northern Household Goods has asked you to develop a model that will predict total sales for proposed new retail store locations. Northern is a rapidly expanding general retailer, and it needs a rational strategy for determining where new stores should be located. As part of the project you need to estimate a linear equation that predicts retail sales per household as a function of household disposable income. The company has obtained data from a national sampling survey of households, and the variables retail sales (Y) and income (X) per household will be used to develop the model.

Retail Sales

Solution Figure 12.1 is a scatter plot that shows the relationship between retail sales and disposable income for families. The actual data are shown in Table 12.1 and stored in a data file named **Retail Sales**. From economic theory we know that sales should increase with increases in disposable income, and the plot strongly supports that theory. Regression analysis provides us with a linear model that can be used to compute retail sales per household for various levels of disposable income. A line drawn on the graph represents the simple regression model

$$Y = 1{,}922.39 + 0.381517X$$

where Y is retail sales per household and X is disposable income per household. Thus, the regression equation provides us with the best linear model for predicting sales for a given disposable income based on the data. Notice that this model tells us that every \$1 increase in per capita disposable family income, X, is associated with an increase in the expected value of retail sales, Y, of \$0.38. Clearly, that

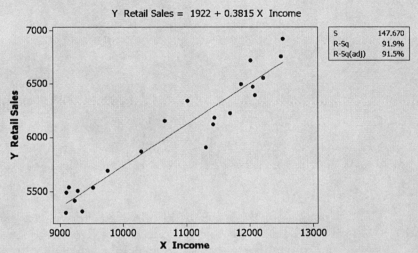

Figure 12.1 Retail Sales per Household Versus Per Capita Disposable Income

Y Retail Sales = 1922 + 0.3815 X Income

S	147.670
R-Sq	91.9%
R-Sq(adj)	91.5%

Table 12.1 Data on Disposable Income per Household (*X*) and Retail Sales per Household (*Y*)

YEAR	INCOME (X)	RETAIL SALES (Y)	YEAR	INCOME (X)	RETAIL SALES (Y)
1	9,098	5,492	12	11,307	5,907
2	9,138	5,540	13	11,432	6,124
3	9,094	5,305	14	11,449	6,186
4	9,282	5,507	15	11,697	6,224
5	9,229	5,418	16	11,871	6,496
6	9,347	5,320	17	12,018	6,718
7	9,525	5,538	18	12,523	6,921
8	9,756	5,692	19	12,053	6,471
9	10,282	5,871	20	12,088	6,394
10	10,662	6,157	21	12,215	6,555
11	11,019	6,342	22	12,494	6,755

result is important for forecasting retail sales. For example, we find that a family income of $50,000 would predict retail sales at $20,997 (1,922 + 50,000 × 0.3815).

INTERPRETATION

At this point we need to emphasize that the regression results summarize the information contained in the data and do not "prove" that increased income "causes" increased sales. Economic theory suggests that there is causation, and these results support that theory. Scatter plots, correlations, and regression equations cannot prove causation, but they can provide supporting evidence. Thus, in order to establish conclusions, we need a combination of theory—experience in business management and economics—and good statistical analysis.

From our study of economics we know that the quantity of goods purchased, *Y*, in a specific market can be modeled as a linear function of the disposable income, *X*. If income is a specific level, x_i, purchasers respond by purchasing a quantity, y_i. In the real world we know there are other factors that influence the actual quantity

Figure 12.2
Population Model
for Linear
Regression

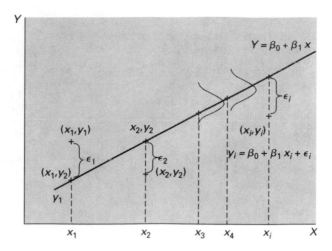

purchased. These include identifiable factors such as the price of the goods in question, advertising, and the prices of competing goods. In addition, there are other unknown factors that can influence the actual quantity purchased. In a simple linear equation we model the effect of these factors, other than income, by an error term labeled as ε.

Figure 12.2 presents an example of a set of observations that were generated by an underlying linear model of a process. The mean level of Y, for every X, is represented by the population equation

$$Y = \beta_0 + \beta_1 X$$

The linear regression model provides the expected value of the random variable Y when X takes on a specific value. The assumption of linearity implies that this expectation can be written

$$E(Y \mid X = x) = \beta_0 + \beta_1 X$$

where β_0 represents the Y intercept of the equation and β_1 is the slope. The actual observed value of Y for a given value of X is modeled as being equal to the expected value or population mean plus a random error, ε, that has mean 0 and variance σ^2:

$$y_i = \beta_0 + \beta_1 x_i + \varepsilon_i$$

The random error term ε represents the variation in Y that is not estimated by the linear relationship.

Least squares regression provides us with an estimated model of the linear relationship between an independent or exogenous variable and a dependent or endogenous variable. We begin the process of regression modeling by assuming a population model that has predetermined X values, and for every X there is a mean value of Y plus a random error term. We use the estimated regression equation—as shown in Figure 12.1—to estimate the mean value of Y for every value of X. Individual points vary about this line because of a random error term that has mean 0 and a common variance for all values of X. The random error represents all of the influences on Y that are not represented by the linear relationship between Y and X. Effects of these factors, which are assumed to be independent of X, behave like a random variable whose population mean is 0. The random deviations ε_i about the linear model are shown in Figure 12.2, and they are combined with the mean of Y_i for every X_i to obtain the observed value y_i.

Linear Regression Population Equation Model

In the application of regression analysis the process being studied is represented by a population model, and an estimated model, utilizing available data, is computed using least squares regression. The population model is specified as

$$y_i = \beta_0 + \beta_1 x_i + \varepsilon_i \qquad (12.4)$$

where β_0 and β_1 are the population model coefficients and ε is a random error term. For every observed value, x_i, an observed value, y_i, is generated by the population model. For purposes of statistical inference, as we develop in Section 12.4, ε is assumed to have a normal distribution with mean 0 and variance σ^2. Later we see that the central limit theorem can be used to relax the assumption of a normal distribution. The model of the linear relationship between Y and X is defined by the two coefficients, β_0 and β_1. Figure 12.2 represents the model schematically.

INTERPRETATION

In the least squares regression model we assume that values of the independent variable, x_i, are selected, and for each x_i there is a population mean of Y. The observed values of y_i contain the mean and the random deviation ε_i. A set of n (x_i, y_i) points is observed and used to obtain estimates of the model coefficients using the least squares procedure. We extend the concepts of classical inference developed in Chapters 8 through 11 to make inferences about the underlying population model by using the estimated regression model. In Chapter 13 we will see how several independent variables can be considered simultaneously using multiple regression.

The estimated regression model as shown schematically in Figure 12.3 is given by the equation

$$y_i = b_0 + b_1 x_i + e_i$$

where b_0 and b_1 are the estimated values of the coefficients and e is the difference between the predicted value of Y on the regression line, defined as

$$\hat{y}_i = b_0 + b_1 x_i$$

Figure 12.3
Estimated
Regression Model

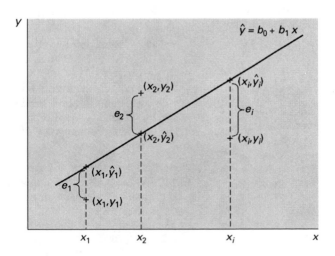

and the observed value y_i. The difference between y_i and $\hat{y}_i$ for each value of X is defined as the residual

$$e_i = y_i - \hat{y}_i$$
$$= y_i - (b_0 + b_1 x_i)$$

Thus, for each observed value of X there is a predicted value of Y from the estimated model and an observed value. The difference between the observed and predicted values of Y is defined as the residual, e_i. The residual, e_i, is not the model error, ε, but is the combined measure of the model error and errors in estimating b_0 and b_1 and, in turn, the errors in estimating the predicted value.

We determine the estimated regression model by obtaining estimates, b_0 and b_1, of the population coefficients using the process called least squares analysis, which we will develop in Section 12.3. These coefficients are, in turn, used to obtain predicted values of Y for every value of X.

Linear Regression Outcomes
Linear regression provides two important results:

1. Predicted values of the dependent or endogenous variable as a function of the independent or exogenous variable
2. Estimated marginal change in the endogenous variable that results from a one-unit change in the independent or exogenous variable

EXERCISES

Basic Exercises

12.10 Given the regression equation

$$Y = 100 + 10X$$

a. What is the change in Y when X changes by +3?
b. What is the change in Y when X changes by –4?
c. What is the predicted value of Y when $X = 12$?
d. What is the predicted value of Y when $X = 23$?
e. Does this equation prove that a change in X causes a change in Y?

12.11 Given the regression equation

$$Y = -50 + 12X$$

a. What is the change in Y when X changes by +3?
b. What is the change in Y when X changes by –4?
c. What is the predicted value of Y when $X = 12$?
d. What is the predicted value of Y when $X = 23$?
e. Does this equation prove that a change in X causes a change in Y?

12.12 Given the regression equation

$$Y = 43 + 10X$$

a. What is the change in Y when X changes by +8?
b. What is the change in Y when X changes by –6?
c. What is the predicted value of Y when $X = 11$?
d. What is the predicted value of Y when $X = 29$?
e. Does this equation prove that a change in X causes a change in Y?

12.13 Given the regression equation

$$Y = 100 + 21X$$

a. What is the change in Y when X changes by +5?
b. What is the change in Y when X changes by –7?
c. What is the predicted value of Y when $X = 14$?
d. What is the predicted value of Y when $X = 27$?
e. Does this equation prove that a change in X causes a change in Y?

Application Exercises

12.14 What is the difference between a population linear model and an estimated linear regression model?

12.15 Explain the difference between the residual e_i and the model error ε_i.

12.16 Suppose that we obtained an estimated equation for the regression of weekly sales of "palm pilots" and the price charged during the week. Interpret the constant b_0 for the product brand manager.

12.17 A regression model of total grocery sales on disposable income was estimated using data from small isolated towns in the western United States. Prepare a list of factors that might contribute to the random error term.

12.3 LEAST SQUARES COEFFICIENT ESTIMATORS

The population regression line is a useful theoretical construct, but for applications we need to determine an estimate of the model using available data. Suppose that we have n pairs of observations, $(x_1, y_1), (x_2, y_2), \ldots, (x_n, y_n)$. We would like to find the straight line that best fits these points. To do this, we need to find estimators of the unknown coefficients β_0 and β_1 of the population regression line.

We obtain the coefficient estimators b_0 and b_1 with equations derived by using the least squares procedure. As shown in Figure 12.3, there is a deviation, e_i, between the observed value, y_i, and the predicted value, $\hat{y}_i$, in the estimated regression equation for each value of X, where $e_i = y_i - \hat{y}_i$. We then compute a mathematical function that represents the effect of squaring all of the residuals and computing the sum of the squared residuals. This function—whose left side is labeled *SSE*—includes the coefficients b_0 and b_1. The quantity *SSE* is defined as the *error sum of squares*. The coefficient estimators b_0 and b_1 are selected as the estimators that minimize the error sum of squares.

Least Squares Procedure
The least squares procedure obtains estimates of the linear equation coefficients b_0 and b_1 in the model

$$\hat{y}_i = b_0 + b_1 x_i \tag{12.5}$$

by minimizing the sum of the squared residuals e_i:

$$SSE = \sum e_i^2 = \sum \left(y_i - \hat{y}_i\right)^2 \tag{12.6}$$

The coefficients b_0 and b_1 are chosen so that the quantity

$$SSE = \sum_{i=1}^{n} e_i^2 = \sum_{i=1}^{n} [y_i - (b_0 + b_1 x_i)]^2 \tag{12.7}$$

is minimized. We use differential calculus to obtain the coefficient estimators that minimize *SSE*. The derivation of the estimators using calculus is presented in the chapter Appendix.

The resulting coefficient estimator is

$$b_1 = \frac{\sum_{i=1}^{n} (x_i - \bar{x})(y_i - \bar{y})}{\sum_{i=1}^{n} (x_i - \bar{x})^2} = \frac{\text{Cov}(x, y)}{s_x^2}$$

$$= \frac{\displaystyle\sum_{i=1}^{n}(x_i - \bar{x})}{\displaystyle\sum_{i=1}^{n}(x_i - \bar{x})x_i}\, y_i$$

Note that the numerator of the estimator is the sample covariance of X and Y and the denominator is the sample variance of X. The third line shows that the coefficient b_1 is a linear function of the Y's. We spend considerable time with the slope coefficient because for many applications this is the key result. The slope coefficient b_1 is an estimate of the change in Y when X changes by one unit. For example, if Y is total output and X is number of workers, then b_1 is an estimate of the marginal increase in output for each new worker. Results such as this explain why regression has become such an important analysis tool.

With some algebraic manipulations we can show that the coefficient estimator is also equal to

$$b_1 = r\frac{s_y}{s_x}$$

where r_{xy} is the sample correlation and s_y and s_x are the sample standard deviations for X and Y. This is an important result because it indicates how the standardized relationship between X and Y, the correlation r_{xy}, is directly related to the slope coefficient.

In the chapter Appendix we also show that the constant estimator is

$$b_0 = \bar{y} - b_1\bar{x}$$

Substituting this value for b_0 into the linear equation, we have

$$y = \bar{y} - b_1\bar{x} + b_1 x$$
$$y - \bar{y} = b_1(x - \bar{x})$$

From this equation we see that, when $x = \bar{x}$, then $y = \bar{y}$ and that the regression equation always passes through the point $(\bar{x}, \bar{y})$. The estimated value of the dependent variable, $\hat{y}_i$ is then obtained by using

$$\hat{y}_i = b_0 + b_1 x_i$$

or by using

$$\hat{y}_i = \bar{y} + b_1(x_i - \bar{x})$$

This latter form emphasizes that the regression line goes through the means of X and Y.

Least Squares Derived Coefficient Estimators
The slope coefficient estimator is

$$b_1 = \frac{\displaystyle\sum_{i=1}^{n}(x_i - \bar{x})(y_i - \bar{y})}{\displaystyle\sum_{i=1}^{n}(x_i - \bar{x})^2} = r\frac{s_y}{s_x}$$

and the constant or intercept estimator is

$$b_0 = \bar{y} - b_1 \bar{x}$$

We also note that the regression line always goes through the mean $\bar{x}, \bar{y}$.

The least squares procedure could be used to compute coefficient estimates b_0 and b_1, using any set of paired data. However, in most applications we want to make inferences about the underlying population model that is part of our economic or business problem. In order to make inferences it is necessary that we agree on certain assumptions. Given these assumptions, it can be shown that the least squares coefficient estimators are unbiased and have minimum variance.

Standard Assumptions for the Linear Regression Model

The following assumptions are used to make inferences about the population linear model by using the estimated model coefficients.

1. The Y's are linear functions of X plus a random error term
$$y_i = \beta_0 + \beta_1 x_i + \varepsilon_i$$

2. The x's are fixed numbers, or they are realizations of random variable X that are independent of the error terms, ε_i's. In the latter case inference is carried out conditionally on the observed values of the x's.

3. The error terms are random variables with mean 0 and the same variance, σ^2. The latter is called homoscedasticity or uniform variance.
$$E[\varepsilon_i] = 0 \quad \text{and} \quad E[\varepsilon_i^2] = \sigma^2 \quad \text{for } (i = 1, \dots, n)$$

4. The random error terms, ε_i, are not correlated with one another, so that
$$E[\varepsilon_i \varepsilon_j] = 0 \quad \text{for all } i \neq j$$

The second of these assumptions is generally, with justification, taken to be true, although in some advanced econometric work, it is untenable. (The assumption fails to hold, for example, when the x_i cannot be measured precisely or when the regression is part of a system of interdependent equations.) Here, however, we will take this assumption as given.

Assumptions 3 and 4 concern the error terms, ε_i, in the regression equation. The expected error term is 0, and all error terms have the same variance. Thus, we do not expect the variances of the error terms to be higher for some observations than for others. Figure 12.2 shows this pattern with the errors for all X values being sampled from populations with the same variance. Finally, it is assumed that the discrepancies are not correlated with one another. Thus, for example, the occurrence of a large positive discrepancy at one observation point does not help us predict the values of any of the other error terms. Assumptions 3 and 4 will be satisfied if the error terms, ε_i, can be viewed as a random sample from a population with mean 0. In the remainder of this chapter, these assumptions will hold. The possibility for relaxing some of these assumptions will be considered in Chapter 14.

Computer Computation of Regression Coefficient

Extensive application of regression analysis has been made possible by statistical computer packages and Excel. As you might suspect, the computations to obtain the regression coefficient estimates are tedious. The estimator equations and other important statistical computations are included in computer packages and Excel and are used to compute the coefficient estimates for specific problems. Excel can be used to obtain the basic regression output without too much difficulty. But if you wish to use some of the advanced applied regression analysis procedures or insightful graphical analysis, then you should use a good statistical computer package. Since we are primarily interested in applications, our most important task is proper analysis of the regression computations for these applications. This analysis should be guided by knowing the estimator equations and the related discussion. We do not, however, use these equations to actually compute the estimates or other regression statistics. *We assign the computation to computers—our tasks are to think, to analyze, and to make recommendations.*

Figure 12.4 presents a portion of the Minitab and Excel outputs for the retail sales example. Note the location of the estimates for the constant, b_0, and the slope coefficient, b_1, in the computer output. The remaining items on each line help interpret the quality of the estimates and are developed in subsequent sections.

Figure 12.4 Regression Analysis for Retail Sales (a) Using Minitab and (b) Using Excel

Results for: retail sales.MTW

Regression Analysis: Y Retail Sales versus X Income

```
The regression equation is
Y Retail Sales = 1922 + 0.382 X Income              ⟵ Coefficients b₀, b₁

Predictor        Coef      SE Coef        T        P
Constant       1922.4       274.9      6.99    0.000
X Income      0.38152     0.02529     15.08    0.000

S = 147.670      R-Sq = 91.9%      R-Sq(adj) = 91.5%
```

(a)

	A	B	C	D	E	F	G	
1	SUMMARY OUTPUT							
2								
3	*Regression Statistics*							
4	Multiple R	0.958748803						
5	R Square	0.919199267						
6	Adjusted R Square	0.91515923						
7	Standard Error	147.6697181						
8	Observations	22						
9								
10	ANOVA							
11		*df*	*SS*	*MS*	*F*	*Significance F*		
12	Regression	1	4961434.406	4961434	227.5225	2.17134E-12		
13	Residual	20	436126.9127	21806.35				
14	Total	21	5397561.318					
15								
16		*Coefficients*	*Standard Error*	*t Stat*	*P-value*	*Lower 95%*	*Upper 95%*	
17	Intercept	1922.392694	274.9493737	6.991806	8.74E-07	1348.858617	2495.92677	
18	X Income	0.38151672	0.025293061	15.08385	2.17E-12	0.328756343	0.4342771	
19								

Coefficients b_0, b_1

(b)

In this regression the estimated constant, b_0, is 1,922 and the estimated slope coefficient, b_1, is 0.382. These values were computed using the coefficient estimator equations previously developed. The estimated equation can be written as

$$\hat{y} = 1,922 + 0.382x$$

or, using the means $\bar{x} = 10,799$ and $\bar{y} = 6,042$, as

$$\hat{y} = 6,042 + 0.382(x - 10,799)$$

INTERPRETATION

Typically, regression models should be used only over the range of the observed X values where we have information about the relationship because the relationship may not be linear outside this range. The second form of the regression model is centered on the data means with a rate of change equal to b_1. By using this form, we focus on the mean location of the regression model and not on the intercept with the Y axis. Naïve users of regression analysis will sometimes attempt interpretations of the constant b_0, claiming certain conclusions about the dependent variable when the independent variable has a value of 0. Consider the example regression of retail sales on disposable income. Would we really claim that retail sales are $1,922 when disposable income is 0? In fact, we simply do not have data to support any sales amount when disposable income is 0. This is another example of the importance of good analysis instead of silly interpretations. As professional analysts we must be careful not to claim results that simply do not exist.

EXERCISES

Basic Exercise

12.18 Compute the coefficients for a least squares regression equation and write the equation, given the following sample statistics:

a. $\bar{x} = 50$; $\bar{y} = 100$; $s_x = 25$; $s_y = 75$; $r_{xy} = 0.6$; $n = 60$
b. $\bar{x} = 60$; $\bar{y} = 210$; $s_x = 35$; $s_y = 65$; $r_{xy} = 0.7$; $n = 60$
c. $\bar{x} = 20$; $\bar{y} = 100$; $s_x = 60$; $s_y = 78$; $r_{xy} = 0.75$; $n = 60$
d. $\bar{x} = 10$; $\bar{y} = 50$; $s_x = 100$; $s_y = 75$; $r_{xy} = 0.4$; $n = 60$
e. $\bar{x} = 90$; $\bar{y} = 200$; $s_x = 80$; $s_y = 70$; $r_{xy} = 0.6$; $n = 60$

Application Exercises

12.19 A company sets different prices for a particular DVD system in eight different regions of the country. The accompanying table shows the numbers of units sold and the corresponding prices (in hundreds of dollars).

Sales	420	380	350	400	440	380	450	420
Price	5.5	6.0	6.5	6.0	5.0	6.5	4.5	5.0

a. Plot these data, and estimate the linear regression of sales on price.
b. What effect would you expect a $100 increase in price to have on sales?

12.20 For a sample of 20 monthly observations a financial analyst wants to regress the percentage rate of return (Y) of the common stock of a corporation on the percentage rate of return (X) of the Standard and Poor's 500 Index. The following information is available:

$$\sum_{i=1}^{20} y_i = 22.6 \qquad \sum_{i=1}^{20} x_i = 25.4$$
$$\sum_{i=1}^{20} x_i^2 = 145.7 \qquad \sum_{i=1}^{20} x_i y_i = 150.5$$

a. Estimate the linear regression of Y on X.
b. Interpret the slope of the sample regression line.
c. Interpret the intercept of the sample regression line.

12.21 A corporation administers an aptitude test to all new sales representatives. Management is interested in the extent to which this test is able to predict their eventual success. The accompanying table records average weekly sales (in thousands of dollars) and aptitude test scores for a random sample of eight representatives.

Weekly sales	10	12	28	24	18	16	15	12
Test score	55	60	85	75	80	85	65	60

a. Estimate the linear regression of weekly sales on aptitude test scores.
b. Interpret the estimated slope of the regression line.

12.22 It was hypothesized that the number of bottles of an imported premium beer sold per evening in the restaurants of a city depends linearly on the average costs of meals in the restaurants. The following results were obtained for a sample of $n = 17$ restaurants, of approximately equal size, where

y = Number of bottles sold per evening
x = Average cost, in dollars, of a meal

$$\bar{x} = 25.5 \quad \bar{y} = 16.0$$

$$\frac{\sum_{i=1}^{n}(x_i - \bar{x})^2}{n-1} = 350 \qquad \frac{\sum_{i=1}^{n}(x_i - \bar{x})(y_i - \bar{y})}{n-1} = 180$$

a. Find the sample regression line.
b. Interpret the slope of the sample regression line.
c. Is it possible to provide a meaningful interpretation of the intercept of the sample regression line? Explain.

It is recommended that the following exercises be solved by using a computer.

12.23 Refer to the data of Exercise 12.7 on percentage change (X) in the Dow-Jones index over the first five trading days of the year and percentage change (Y) in the index over the whole year.
a. Estimate the linear regression of Y on X.
b. Provide interpretations of the intercept and slope of the sample regression line.

12.24 On Friday, November 13, 1989, prices on the New York Stock Exchange fell steeply; the Standard and Poor's 500-share index was down 6.1% on that day. The data file **New York Stock Exchange Gains and Losses** shows the percentage losses (y) of the 25 largest mutual funds on November 13, 1989. Also shown are the percentage gains (x), assuming reinvested dividends and capital gains, for these same funds for 1989, through November 12.
a. Estimate the linear regression of November 13 losses on pre–November 13, 1989, gains.
b. Interpret the slope of the sample regression line.

12.25 Ace Manufacturing is studying worker absence. The data in the file **Employee Absence** were found for annual change in overall absentee rate and annual change in mean employee absence rate due to own illness.
a. Estimate the linear regression of change in mean employee absence rate due to own illness on change in absentee rate.
b. Interpret the estimated slope of the regression line.

12.4 THE EXPLANATORY POWER OF A LINEAR REGRESSION EQUATION

The estimated regression model that we have developed can be viewed as an attempt to explain the changes in a dependent variable Y that results from changes in an independent variable X. If we had observations only of the dependent variable, Y, then the central tendency of Y would be represented by the mean $\bar{y}$, and the total variability about Y would be represented by the numerator of the sample variance estimator, $\Sigma(y_i - \bar{y})^2$. When we also have measures of X, we have shown that the central tendency of Y can now be expressed as a function of X. We expect that the linear equation would be closer to the individual values of Y, and, thus, the variability about the linear equation would be smaller than the variability about the mean.

Now we are ready to develop measures that indicate how effectively the variable X explains the behavior of Y. In our retail sales example shown in Figure 12.1, retail sales, Y, tends to increase with disposable income, X, and, thus, disposable income explains some of the differences in retail sales. The points, however, are not all on the line, so the explanation is not perfect. Here, we will develop measures, based on the partitioning of variability, that measure the capability of X to explain Y in a specific regression application.

The analysis of variance, ANOVA, for least squares regression is developed by partitioning the total variability of Y into an explained component and an error

Figure 12.5
Partitioning of
Variability

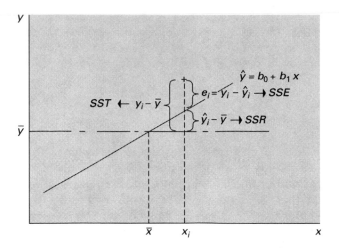

Figure 12.5
Partitioning of
Variability

component. In Figure 12.5 we show that the deviation of an individual Y value from its mean can be partitioned into the deviation of the predicted value from the mean and the deviation of the observed value from the predicted value

$$y_i - \bar{y} = (\hat{y}_i - \bar{y}) + (y_i - \hat{y}_i)$$

We square each side of the equation—because the sum of deviations about the mean is equal to 0—and sum the result over all n points

$$\sum_{i=1}^{n}(y_i - \bar{y})^2 = \sum_{i-1}^{n}(\hat{y}_i - \bar{y})^2 + \sum_{i=1}^{n}(y_i - \hat{y})^2$$

Some of you may note the squaring of the right-hand side should include the cross product of the two terms in addition to their squared quantities. It can be shown that the cross-product term goes to 0. This equation is expressed as

$$SST = SSR + SSE$$

Here, we see that the total variability—*SST*—can be partitioned into a component— *SSR*—that represents variability that is explained by the slope of the regression equation. (The mean of Y is different at different levels of X.) The second component— *SSE*—results from the random or unexplained deviation of points from the regression line. This variability provides an indication of the uncertainty that is associated with the regression model. We define the left side as the *total sum of squares.*

$$SST = \sum_{i=1}^{n}(y_i - \bar{y})^2$$

The amount of variability explained by the regression equation is defined as the *regression sum of squares* and computed as

$$SSR = \sum_{i=1}^{n}(\hat{y}_i - \bar{y})^2 = b_1^2 \sum_{i=1}^{n}(x_i - \bar{x})^2$$

We see that the variability explained by the regression depends directly on the size of the coefficient b_1 and on the spread of the independent, X, variable data. The deviations about the regression line, e_i, that are used to compute the unexplained or *error sum of squares* can be defined using the following algebraic forms

$$SSE = \sum_{i=1}^{n} (y_i - (b_0 + b_1 x_i))^2 = \sum_{i=1}^{n} (y_i - \hat{y}_i)^2 = \sum_{i=1}^{n} e_i^2$$

For a given set of observed values of the dependent variables, Y, the SST is fixed as the total variability of all observations from the mean. We see that in this partitioning larger values of SSR and hence smaller values of SSE indicate a regression equation that "fits" or comes closer to the observed data. This partitioning is shown graphically in Figure 12.5. From the equation for SSR we see that explained variability, SSR, is directly related to the spread of the independent or X variable. Thus, as we are thinking about regression applications, we know that we should try to obtain data that have a large range for the independent variable so that the resulting regression model will have a smaller unexplained variability.

Analysis of Variance

The total variability in a regression analysis, *SST*, can be partitioned into a component explained by the regression, *SSR*, and a component due to unexplained error, *SSE*:

$$SST = SSR + SSE \tag{12.8}$$

with the components defined as follows.
   Total sum of squares:

$$SST = \sum_{i=1}^{n} (y_i - \bar{y})^2 \tag{12.9}$$

Error sum of squares:

$$SSE = \sum_{i=1}^{n} (y_i - (b_0 + b_1 x_i))^2 = \sum_{i=1}^{n} (y_i - \hat{y}_i)^2 = \sum_{i=1}^{n} e_i^2 \tag{12.10}$$

Regression sum of squares:

$$SSR = \sum_{i=1}^{n} (\hat{y}_i - \bar{y})^2 = b_1^2 \sum_{i=1}^{n} (x_i - \bar{x})^2 \tag{12.11}$$

Retail Sales

With this background let us return to our retail sales example (Example 12.2) with data file **Retail Sales** and look at how we use the partitioned variability to determine how well our model explains the process being studied. Table 12.2 shows the detailed calculations of residuals, e_i; deviations of Y from the mean; and deviations of predicted values of Y from the mean. These provide us with the components to compute SSE, SST, and SSR. The sum of squared deviations for column 5 is $SSE = 436,127$. The

Table 12.2

Actual and Predicted Values for Retail Sales per Household and Residuals from Its Linear Regression on Income per Household

YEAR	INCOME (X)	RETAIL SALES (Y)	PREDICTED RETAIL SALES	RESIDUAL	OBSERVED DEVIATION FROM THE MEAN	PREDICTED DEVIATION FROM THE MEAN
1	9,098	5,492	5,394	98	−550	−649
2	9,138	5,540	5,409	131	−502	−633
3	9,094	5,305	5,392	−87	−737	−650
4	9,282	5,507	5,464	43	−535	−578
5	9,229	5,418	5,444	−26	−624	−599
6	9,347	5,320	5,489	−169	−722	−554
7	9,525	5,538	5,557	−19	−504	−486
8	9,756	5,692	5,645	47	−350	−397
9	10,282	5,871	5,846	25	−171	−197
10	10,662	6,157	5,991	166	115	−52
11	11,019	6,342	6,127	215	300	84
12	11,307	5,907	6,237	−330	−135	194
13	11,432	6,124	6,284	−160	82	242
14	11,449	6,186	6,291	−105	144	248
15	11,697	6,224	6,385	−161	182	343
16	11,871	6,496	6,452	44	454	409
17	12,018	6,718	6,508	210	676	465
18	12,523	6,921	6,701	220	879	658
19	12,053	6,471	6,521	−50	429	479
20	12,088	6,394	6,535	−141	352	492
21	12,215	6,555	6,583	−28	513	541
22	12,494	6,755	6,689	66	713	647
		Sum of squared values		436,127	5,397,561	4,961,434

sum of squared deviations for column 6 is $SST = 5,397,561$. Finally, the sum of squared deviations for column 7 is $SSR = 4,961,434$. Figure 12.6 presents the Minitab and Excel regression outputs with the analysis of variance section included.

Coefficient of Determination R^2

We have seen that the fit of the regression equation to the data is improved as SSR increases and SSE decreases. The ratio of the regression sum of squares, SSR, divided by the total sum of squares, SST, provides a descriptive measure of the proportion or percent of the total variability that is explained by the regression model. This measure is called the *coefficient of determination*— or, more generally, R^2.

$$R^2 = \frac{SSR}{SST} = 1 - \frac{SSE}{SST}$$

The coefficient of determination is often interpreted as the percent of variability in Y that is explained by the regression equation. Previously, we showed that SSR increases directly with the spread of the independent variable X:

$$SSR = \sum_{i=1}^{n} (\hat{y}_i - \bar{y})^2 = b_1^2 \sum_{i=1}^{n} (x_i - \bar{x})^2$$

Figure 12.6 Regression Analysis for Retail Sales on Disposable Income: (a) Minitab Output; (b) Excel Output

Results for: retail sales.MTW

Regression Analysis: Y Retail Sales versus X Income

```
The regression equation is
Y Retail Sales = 1922 + 0.382 X Income

Predictor        Coef    SE Coef        T        P
Constant       1922.4      274.9     6.99    0.000
X Income      0.38152    0.02529    15.08    0.000                    ─── s_e, Standard error of the estimate

S = 147.670   R-Sq = 91.9%    R-Sq(adj) = 91.5%
                                                                      ─── R², Coefficient of determination
Analysis of Variance

Source          DF        SS        MS        F        P
Regression       1   4961434   4961434   227.52    0.000
Residual Error  20    436127     21806                                ─── s²_e, Model error variance
Total           21   5397561

                                                                      ─── SSR = 4,961,434
Unusual Observations                                                      SSE = 436,127
                   Y                                                      SST = 5,397,561
                 Retail
Obs X   Income   Sales      Fit   SE Fit   Residual   St Resid
12       11307   5907.0   6236.2     34.0     -329.2     -2.29R

R denotes an observation with a large standardized residual.
```

(a)

	A	B	C	D	E	F	G
1	SUMMARY OUTPUT						
2				s_e, Standard error of the estimate			
3	*Regression Statistics*						
4	Multiple R	0.958748803					
5	R Square	0.919199267		R^2, Coefficient of determination			
6	Adjusted R Square	0.91515923					
7	Standard Error	147.6697181					
8	Observations	22					
9						s^2_e, Model error variance	
10	ANOVA						
11		*df*	*SS*	*MS*	*F*	*Significance F*	
12	Regression	1	4961434.406	4961434	227.5225	2.17134E-12	SSR = 4,961,434
13	Residual	20	436126.9127	21806.35			SSE = 436,127
14	Total	21	5397561.318				SST = 5,397,561
15							
16		*Coefficients*	*Standard Error*	*t Stat*	*P-value*	*Lower 95%*	*Upper 95%*
17	Intercept	1922.392694	274.9493737	6.991806	8.74E-07	1348.858617	2495.92677
18	X Income	0.38151672	0.025293061	15.08385	2.17E-12	0.328756343	0.4342771

(b)

Thus, we see that R^2 also increases directly with the spread of the independent variable. When you are seeking data to estimate a regression model, it is important to choose the observations of the independent variable that provide the largest possible spread in X so that we obtain a regression model with the highest R^2.

Coefficient of Determination R^2

The coefficient of determination for a regression equation is defined as

$$R^2 = \frac{SSR}{SST} = 1 - \frac{SSE}{SST}$$

(12.12)

This quantity varies from 0 to 1, and higher values indicate a better regression. Caution should be used in making general interpretations of R^2 because a high value can result from either a small SSE or a large SST or both.

R^2 can vary from 0 to 1, since SST is fixed and $0 < SSE < SST$. A larger R^2 implies a better regression, everything else being equal. In the regression output—Figure 12.6—we see that the R^2 for the retail sales regression is 0.919 or 91.9%. One popular interpretation is that R^2 is the *percent explained variability*.

INTERPRETATION

The second form of the equation emphasizes that R^2 depends on the ratio of SSE divided by SST. We can have a high R^2 because there is a small SSE—the desired goal—or because there is a large SST or both. General interpretations of R^2 that apply to all regression equations are dangerous. Two regression models with the same set of observed y_i's can always be compared using R^2, and the model with the larger R^2 provides a better explanation of Y. But global comparisons of R^2—stating that a model is good because its R^2 is above a particular value—are misleading. Generally, experienced analysts have found that R^2 is 0.80 and above for models based on time series data. Cross-section data models (e.g., cities, states, firms) have values in the 0.40 to 0.60 range, and models based on data from individual people often have R^2 in the 0.10 to 0.20 range.

To illustrate the problem of global interpretations of R^2, consider two regression models—whose plots are shown in Figure 12.7—each of which is based on a total of

Figure 12.7
Comparison of R^2 for Two Regression Models: (a) High R^2; (b) Low R^2

Regression Model with High R Squared

Y1 = 10.3558 + 1.99676 X

S = 0.881993   R-Sq = 99.7 %   R-Sq(adj) = 99.6 %

(a)

**Figure 12.7
Continued**

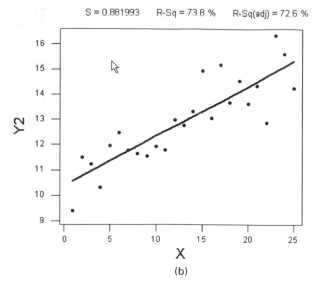

Regression Model with Low R Squared

Y2 = 10.3558 + 0.196759 X

S = 0.881993   R-Sq = 73.8 %   R-Sq(adj) = 72.6 %

(b)

25 observations. Both models have *SSE* equal to 17.89, so the fit of the regression equation to the data points is the same. But the first model has a total sum of squares equal to 5,201.05, while the second has *SST* equal to 68.22. The R^2 values for the two models are as follows.

Model 1:

$$R^2 = 1 - \frac{SSE}{SST} = 1 - \frac{17.89}{5,201.05} = 0.997$$

Model 2:

$$R^2 = 1 - \frac{SSE}{SST} = 1 - \frac{17.89}{68.22} = 0.738$$

Since both models have the same *SSE*, and thus the same goodness of fit, one cannot claim that model 1 fits the data better. Yet model 1 has a substantially higher R^2 compared to model 2. As we see here, one should be very careful about global interpretations of R^2. Note that the two different vertical axis intervals in Figure 12.7 result from different values for *SST*.

The correlation coefficient can also be linked with R^2, as shown, by noting that the correlation squared is equal to the coefficient of determination. Another interpretation of the correlation is that it is the square root of the percent explained variability.

Correlation and R^2

The coefficient of determination, R^2, for simple regression is equal to the simple correlation squared:

$$R^2 = r^2 \tag{12.13}$$

This provides an important link between correlation and the regression model.

The error sum of squares can be used to obtain an estimate of the variance of the model error ε_i. As we will see, the estimator for the variance of the model error will be used for regression model statistical inference. Recall that we have assumed that the population error, ε_i, is a random error with mean 0 and variance σ^2. The estimator for σ^2 is computed as follows.

Estimation of Model Error Variance

The quantity *SSE* is a measure of the total squared deviation about the estimated regression line and e_i is the residual. An estimator for the variance of the population model error is

$$\hat{\sigma}^2 = s_e^2 = \frac{\sum_{i=1}^{n} e_i^2}{n-2} = \frac{SSE}{n-2} \tag{12.14}$$

Division by $n-2$ instead of $n-1$ results because the simple regression model uses two estimated parameters, b_0 and b_1, instead of one. In the next section we see that this variance estimator is the basis for statistical inference in the regression model.

EXERCISES

Basic Exercise

12.26 Compute *SSR*, *SSE*, s_e^2, and the coefficient of determination, given the following statistics computed from a random sample of pairs of X and Y observations:

a. $\sum_{i=1}^{n} (y_i - \bar{y})^2 = 100{,}000; \quad r^2 = 0.50; \quad n = 52$

b. $\sum_{i=1}^{n} (y_i - \bar{y})^2 = 90{,}000; \quad r^2 = 0.70; \quad n = 52$

c. $\sum_{i=1}^{n} (y_i - \bar{y})^2 = 240; \quad\quad r^2 = 0.80; \quad n = 52$

d. $\sum_{i=1}^{n} (y_i - \bar{y})^2 = 200{,}000; \quad r^2 = 0.30; \quad n = 74$

e. $\sum_{i=1}^{n} (y_i - \bar{y})^2 = 60{,}000; \quad r^2 = 0.90; \quad n = 40$

Application Exercises

12.27 Let the sample regression line be

$$y_i = b_0 + b_1 x_i + e_i = \hat{y}_i + e_i \quad (i = 1, 2, \dots, n)$$

and let $\bar{x}$ and $\bar{y}$ denote the sample means for the independent and dependent variables, respectively.

a. Show that

$$e_i = y_i - \bar{y} - b(x_i - \bar{x})$$

b. Using the result in part (a), show that

$$\sum_{i=1}^{n} e_i = 0$$

c. Using the result in part (a), show that

$$\sum_{i=1}^{n} e_i^2 = \sum_{i=1}^{n} (y_i - \bar{y})^2 - b^2 \sum_{i=1}^{n} (x_i - \bar{x})^2$$

d. Show that

$$\hat{y}_i - \bar{y} = b_i(x_i - \bar{x})$$

e. Using the results in parts (c) and (d), show that

$$SST = SSR + SSE$$

f. Using the result in part (a), show that

$$\sum_{i=1}^{n} e_i(x_i - \bar{x}) = 0$$

12.28 Let

$$R^2 = \frac{SSR}{SST}$$

denote the coefficient of determination for the sample regression line.

a. Using part (d) of Exercise 12.27, show that

$$R^2 = b_1^2 \frac{\sum\limits_{i=1}^{n} (x_i - \bar{x})^2}{\sum\limits_{i=1}^{n} (y_i - \bar{y})^2}$$

b. Using the result in part (a), show that the coefficient of determination is equal to the square of the sample correlation between X and Y.

c. Let b_1 be the slope of the least squares regression of Y on X, b_1^* the slope of the least squares regression of X on Y, and r the sample correlation between X and Y. Show that

$$b_1 \cdot b_1^* = r^2$$

12.29   Find and interpret the coefficient of determination for the regression of DVD system sales on price, using the following data.

Sales	420	380	350	400	440	380	450	420
Price	5.5	6.0	6.5	6.0	5.0	6.5	4.5	5.0

12.30   ◐ Find and interpret the coefficient of determination for the regression of the percentage change in the Dow-Jones index in a year on the percentage change in the index over the first five trading days of the year, continuing the analysis of Exercise 12.7. Compare your answer with the sample correlation found for these data in Exercise 12.7. Use the data file **Dow Jones**.

12.31   ◐ Find the proportion of the sample variability in mutual fund percentage losses on November 13, 1989, explained by their linear dependence on 1989 percentage gains through November 12, based on the data of Exercise 12.24. Use the data file **New York Stock Exchange Gains and Losses**.

12.32   ◐ Refer to the data on employee absence rate in Exercise 12.25. Use data file **Employee Absence**.

a. Find the predicted values, $\hat{y}_i$, and the residuals, e_i, for the least squares regression of change in mean employee absence rate due to own illness on change in unemployment rate.

b. Find the sums of squares SST, SSR, and SSE, and verify that

$$SST = SSR + SSE$$

c. Using the results in part (b), find and interpret the coefficient of determination.

12.33   Refer to the data on weekly sales and aptitude test scores achieved by sales representatives given in Exercise 12.21.

a. Find the predicted values, $\hat{y}_i$, and residuals, e_i, for the least squares regression of weekly sales on aptitude test scores.

b. Find the sums of squares SST, SSR, and SSE, and verify that

$$SST = SSR + SSE$$

c. Using the results in part (b), find and interpret the coefficient of determination.

d. Find directly the sample correlation coefficient between sales and aptitude test scores, and verify that its square is equal to the coefficient of determination.

12.34   In a study it was shown that for a sample of 353 college faculty the correlation was 0.11 between annual raises and teaching evaluations. What would be the coefficient of determination of a regression of annual raises on teaching evaluations for this sample? Interpret your result.

12.5 STATISTICAL INFERENCE: HYPOTHESIS TESTS AND CONFIDENCE INTERVALS

Now that we have developed the coefficient estimators and an estimator for σ^2, we are ready to make population model inferences. The basic approach follows that developed in Chapters 8 through 11. We develop variance estimators for the coefficient estimators, b_0 and b_1, and then use the estimated parameters and variances to test hypotheses and compute confidence intervals using the Student's t distribution. Inferences from regression analysis will help us understand the process being modeled and make decisions about the process. Initially, we assume that random model errors, ε, are normally distributed. Later this assumption will be replaced by the central limit theorem assumption. We begin by developing variance estimators and useful test forms. Then we apply these using our retail sales data.

In Section 12.2 we defined the population model for simple regression as

$$y_i = \beta_0 + \beta_1 x_i + \varepsilon_i$$

with the x_i's being predetermined values and not random variables. From our work in Chapters 5 and 6 on linear functions of random variables, we know that, if ε_i is a normally distributed random variable with variance σ^2, then y_i is also normally distributed with the same variance. The right-hand side is a linear function of X except for the random variable ε_i. If we add a function of X to a random variable, we do not change the variance. In Section 12.3 we found that the estimator for the slope coefficient, b_1, is

$$
\begin{aligned}
b_1 &= \frac{\displaystyle\sum_{i=1}^{n}(x_i - \bar{x})(y_i - \bar{y})}{\displaystyle\sum_{i=1}^{n}(x_i - \bar{x})^2} \\
&= \sum \left(\frac{(x_i - \bar{x})}{\sum(x_i - \bar{x})^2} \right) y_i \\
&= \sum a_i y_i
\end{aligned}
$$

where

$$a_i = \frac{(x_i - \bar{x})}{\displaystyle\sum_{i=1}^{n}(x_i - \bar{x})^2}$$

In this estimator we see that b_1 is a linear function of the random variable y_i whose variance is σ^2. The y_i's are independent random variables. Thus, the variance of b_1 is a simple transformation of the variance of Y. Using the results from Chapter 6, the linear function can be written as

$$
\begin{aligned}
b_1 &= \sum_{l=1}^{n} a_i y_i \\
a_i &= \frac{(x_i - \bar{x})}{\displaystyle\sum_{i=1}^{n}(x_i - \bar{x})^2} \\
\sigma_{b_1}^2 &= \sum_{i=1}^{n} a_i^2 \sigma^2
\end{aligned}
$$

$$
\begin{aligned}
\sigma_{b_1}^2 &= \sum_{i=1}^{n}\left(\frac{(x_i - \bar{x})}{\displaystyle\sum_{i=1}^{n}(x_i - \bar{x})^2} \right)^2 \sigma^2 = \frac{\displaystyle\sum_{i=1}^{n}(x_i - \bar{x})^2}{\left(\displaystyle\sum_{i=1}^{n}(x_i - \bar{x})^2 \right)^2} \sigma^2 \\
&= \frac{\sigma^2}{\displaystyle\sum_{i=1}^{n}(x_i - \bar{x})^2}
\end{aligned}
$$

Since y_i is normally distributed and b_1 is a linear function of independent normal variables, this linear function implies that b_1 is also normally distributed. From this analysis we can derive the population and sample variances.

Sampling Distribution of the Least Squares Coefficient Estimator

If the standard least squares assumptions hold, then b_1 is an unbiased estimator for β_1 and has a population variance

$$\sigma_{b_1}^2 = \frac{\sigma^2}{\displaystyle\sum_{i=1}^{n}(x_i - \overline{x})^2} = \frac{\sigma^2}{(n-1)s_x^2} \qquad (12.15)$$

and an unbiased sample variance estimator

$$s_{b_1}^2 = \frac{s_e^2}{\displaystyle\sum_{i=1}^{n}(x_i - \overline{x})^2} = \frac{s_e^2}{(n-1)s_x^2} \qquad (12.16)$$

The regression constant estimator, b_0, is also a linear function of the random variable y_i, and, thus, it can be shown to be normally distributed, and its variance estimator can be derived as

$$s_{b_0}^2 = \left(\frac{1}{n} + \frac{\overline{x}^2}{(n-1)s_x^2}\right)s_e^2$$

It is important to observe that the variance of the slope coefficient, b_1, depends on two important quantities:

1. The distance of the points from the regression line measured by s_e^2. Higher values imply greater variance for b_1.
2. The total deviation of the X values from the mean measured by $(n-1)s_x^2$. Greater spread in the X values implies smaller variance for the slope coefficient.

INTERPRETATION

These two results are very important as one is thinking about choices of data for a regression model. Previously, we noted that a wider spread in the independent, X, variable resulted in a higher R^2, indicating a stronger relationship. Now, we see that a wider spread in the independent variable—measured by s_x^2—results in a smaller variance for the estimated slope coefficient, b_1. It follows that smaller variance slope coefficient estimators imply a better regression model. We need to also add that many research conclusions and policy decisions are based on the change in Y that results from a change in X, as estimated by b_1. Thus, we would like to have the variance of this important decision variable, b_1, be as small as possible.

In applied regression analysis we first would like to know if there is a relationship. In the regression model we see that if β_1 is 0, then there is no linear relationship—Y would not continuously increase or decrease with increases in X. To determine if there is a linear relationship, we can test the hypothesis

$$H_0 : \beta_1 = 0$$

versus

$$H_1 : \beta_1 \neq 0$$

Given that b_1 is normally distributed, we can test this hypothesis using the Student's t statistic

$$t = \frac{b_1 - \beta_1}{s_{b_1}} = \frac{b_1 - 0}{s_{b_1}} = \frac{b_1}{s_{b_1}}$$

that is distributed as Student's t with $n - 2$ degrees of freedom. The hypothesis test can also be performed for values of β_1 other than 0. One rule of thumb is to conclude that a relationship exists if the absolute value of the t statistic is greater than 2. This result holds exactly for a two-tailed test with $\alpha = 0.05$ and 60 degrees of freedom and provides a close approximation for $n > 30$.

> ## Basis for Inference About the Population Regression Slope
> Let β_1 be a population regression slope and b_1 its least squares estimate based on n pairs of sample observations. Then, if the standard regression assumptions hold and it can also be assumed that the errors, ε_i, are normally distributed, the random variable
>
> $$t = \frac{b_1 - \beta_1}{s_{b_1}} \qquad (12.17)$$
>
> is distributed as Student's t with $(n - 2)$ degrees of freedom. In addition, the central limit theorem enables us to conclude that this result is approximately valid for a wide range of non-normal distributions and large enough sample sizes, n.

The coefficient standard deviation and Student's t statistic—for $\beta_1 = 0$—are routinely computed in most regression programs. Example outputs from Minitab and Excel are shown in Figure 12.8.

For the retail sales model the slope coefficient is $b_1 = 0.382$ with a standard deviation $s_{b_1} = 0.02529$. To decide if there is a relationship between retail sales, Y, and disposable income, X, we can test the hypothesis

$$H_0 : \beta_1 = 0$$

versus

$$H_1 : \beta_1 \neq 0$$

Under the null hypothesis the ratio of the coefficient estimator, b_1, to its standard deviation has a Student's t distribution. For the retail sales example we find that the computed Student's t statistic is

$$t = \frac{b_1 - \beta_1}{s_{b_1}} = \frac{b_1 - 0}{s_{b_1}} = \frac{0.38152 - 0}{0.02529} = 15.08$$

The resulting Student's t statistic, $t = 15.08$, as shown in the regression output, provides strong evidence to reject the null hypothesis and conclude that there is a strong

Figure 12.8   Retail Sales Model: Coefficient Variance Estimators: (a) Minitab Output; (b) Excel Output

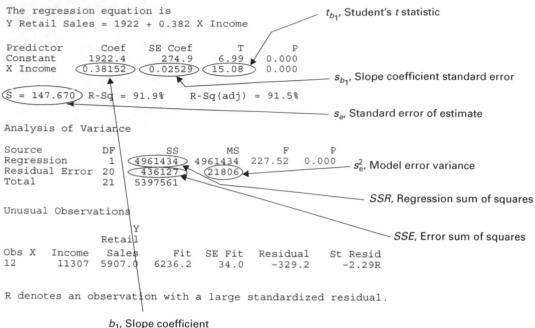

Results for: retail sales.MTW

Regression Analysis: Y Retail Sales versus X Income

```
The regression equation is                         t_{b_1}, Student's t statistic
Y Retail Sales = 1922 + 0.382 X Income

Predictor       Coef    SE Coef        T       P
Constant      1922.4      274.9     6.99   0.000
X Income     0.38152    0.02529    15.08   0.000       s_{b_1}, Slope coefficient standard error

S = 147.670    R-Sq = 91.9%    R-Sq(adj) = 91.5%
                                                        s_e, Standard error of estimate
Analysis of Variance

Source           DF        SS       MS       F       P
Regression        1    4961434  4961434  227.52   0.000    s_e^2, Model error variance
Residual Error   20     436127    21806
Total            21    5397561
                                                        SSR, Regression sum of squares

Unusual Observations
                                                        SSE, Error sum of squares
                      Y
                  Retail
Obs  X  Income   Sales      Fit   SE Fit  Residual   St Resid
12       11307  5907.0   6236.2     34.0    -329.2     -2.29R

R denotes an observation with a large standardized residual.
```

b_1, Slope coefficient

(a)

	A	B	C	D	E	F	G
1	SUMMARY OUTPUT						
2							
3	*Regression Statistics*						
4	Multiple R	0.958748803					
5	R Square	0.919199267					
6	Adjusted R Square	0.91515923					
7	Standard Error	147.6697181					
8	Observations	22					
9							
10	ANOVA						
11		*df*	*SS*	*MS*	*F*	*Significance F*	
12	Regression	1	4961434.406	4961434	227.5225	2.17134E-12	
13	Residual	20	436126.9127	21806.35			
14	Total	21	5397561.318				
15							
16		*Coefficients*	*Standard Error*	*t Stat*	*P-value*	*Lower 95%*	*Upper 95%*
17	Intercept	1922.392694	274.9493737	6.991806	8.74E-07	1348.858617	2495.92677
18	X Income	0.38151672	0.025293061	15.08385	2.17E-12	0.328756343	0.4342771
19							

s_e, Standard error of estimate

SSR Regression sum of squares

SSE Error sum of squares

s_e^2, Model error variance

t_{b_1}, Student's t statistic

s_{b_1}, Slope coefficient standard error

b_1, Slope coefficient

(b)

relationship between retail sales and disposable income. We also note that the *p*-value for b_1 is 0.000, providing alternative evidence that β_1 is not equal to 0. Recall from Chapter 10 that the *p*-value is the smallest significance level at which the null hypothesis can be rejected.

Hypothesis tests could also be performed on the equation constant, b_0, using the standard deviation previously developed and shown in the Minitab output. However, because we are usually interested in rates of change—measured by b_1—tests involving the constant are generally less important.

If the sample size is large enough for the central limit theorem to apply, then we can perform such hypothesis tests even if the errors, ε_i, are not normally distributed. The key question concerns the distribution of b_1. If b_1 has an approximate normal distribution, then the hypothesis test can be performed.

Tests of the Population Regression Slope

If the regression errors, ε_i, are normally distributed and the standard least squares assumptions hold (or if the distribution of b_1 is approximately normal), the following tests have significance level α.

1. To test either null hypothesis

$$H_0: \beta_1 = \beta_1^* \quad \text{or} \quad H_0: \beta_1 \leq \beta_1^*$$

against the alternative

$$H_1: \beta_1 > \beta_1^*$$

the decision rule is

$$\text{Reject } H_0 \text{ if} \quad \frac{b_1 - \beta_1^*}{s_{b_1}} \geq t_{n-2,\alpha} \tag{12.18}$$

2. To test either null hypothesis

$$H_0: \beta_1 = \beta_1^* \quad \text{or} \quad H_0: \beta_1 \geq \beta_1^*$$

against the alternative

$$H_1: \beta_1 < \beta_1^*$$

the decision rule is

$$\text{Reject } H_0 \text{ if} \quad \frac{b_1 - \beta_1^*}{s_b} \leq -t_{n-2,\alpha} \tag{12.19}$$

3. To test the null hypothesis

$$H_0: \beta_1 = \beta_1^*$$

against the two-sided alternative

$$H_1: \beta_1 \neq \beta_1^*$$

the decision rule is

$$\text{Reject } H_0 \text{ if} \quad \frac{b_1 - \beta_1^*}{s_{b_1}} \geq t_{n-2,\alpha/2} \quad \text{or} \quad \frac{b_1 - \beta_1^*}{s_{b_1}} \leq -t_{n-2,\alpha/2} \tag{12.20}$$

We can derive confidence intervals for the slope β_1 of the population regression line by using the coefficient and variance estimators we have developed and the rationale presented in Chapter 8.

Confidence Intervals for the Population Regression Slope β_1

If the regression errors, ε_i, are normally distributed and the standard regression assumptions hold, a $100(1 - \alpha)\%$ confidence interval for the population regression slope β_1 is given by

$$b_1 - t_{n-2,\alpha/2}s_{b_1} < \beta_1 < b_1 + t_{n-2,\alpha/2}s_{b_1} \tag{12.21}$$

where $t_{n-2,\alpha/2}$ is the number for which

$$P(t_{n-2} > t_{n-2,\alpha/2}) = \alpha/2$$

and the random variable t_{n-2} follows a Student's t distribution with $(n-2)$ degrees of freedom.

From the regression output for the retail sales on disposable income regression in Figure 12.8, we know that

$$n = 22 \qquad b_1 = 0.3815 \qquad s_{b.} = 0.0253$$

For a 99% confidence interval for β_1 we have $1 - \alpha = 0.99$, and $n - 2 = 20$ degrees of freedom, and, thus, from Table 8 of the Appendix

$$t_{n-2,\alpha/2} = t_{20,0.005} = 2.845$$

Therefore, we have the 99% confidence interval

$$0.3815 - (2.845)(0.0253) < \beta_1 < 0.3815 + (2.845)(0.0253)$$

or

$$0.3095 < \beta_1 < 0.4535$$

We see that the 99% confidence interval for the expected increase in retail sales per household associated with a $1 increase in disposable income per household covers the range from $0.3095 to $0.4353. Figure 12.9 shows the 90%, 95% and 99% confidence intervals for the population regression slope.

Figure 12.9
Confidence Intervals for the Retail Sales Population Regression Slope at Confidence Levels 90%, 95%, and 99%

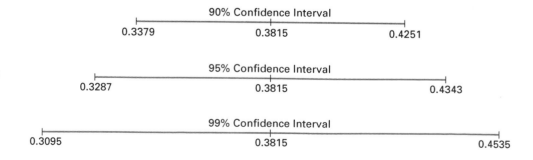

Hypothesis Test for Population Slope Coefficient Using the *F* Distribution

There is an alternative test for the hypothesis that the slope coefficient, β_1, is equal to 0:

$$H_0 : \beta_1 = 0$$

$$H_1 : \beta_1 \neq 0$$

This test is based on the partitioning of variability that we developed in Section 12.4. The assumption for this test is that, if the null hypothesis is true, then both *SSE* and *SSR* can be used to obtain independent estimators of the model error variance σ^2. To perform this test, we obtain two sample estimates of the population standard deviation σ. These are defined as mean square terms. The regression sum of squares, *SSR*, has one degree of freedom, since it refers to the single slope coefficient, and the mean square for regression, *MSR*, is

$$MSR = \frac{SSR}{1} = SSR$$

If the null hypothesis—no relationship—is true, then *MSR* is an estimate of the overall model variance, σ^2. We also use the error sum of squares as before to obtain the mean square for error, *MSE*:

$$MSE = \frac{SSE}{n-2} = s_e^2$$

In Section 11.4 we introduced the *F* distribution as the ratio of independent sample estimates of variance, given equal population variances. It can be shown that *MSR* and *MSE* are independent and that under H_0 both are estimates of the population variance, σ^2. Thus, if H_0 is true, then we can show that the ratio

$$F = \frac{MSR}{MSE} = \frac{SSR}{s_e^2}$$

has an *F* distribution with 1 degree of freedom for the numerator and $n-2$ degrees of freedom for the denominator. It should also be noted that the *F* statistic is equal to the squared *t* statistic for the slope coefficient. This can be shown algebraically. From distribution theory we can show that a squared Student's *t* with $n-2$ degrees of freedom and the *F* with 1 degree of freedom for the numerator and $n-2$ degrees of freedom for the denominator are equal:

$$F_{\alpha,1,n-2} = t_{\alpha/2,n-2}^2$$

The analysis of variance for the retail sales regression from the Minitab output is shown in Figure 12.8(a). In our retail sales example the error sum of squares is divided by the 20 degrees for freedom to compute the *MSE*:

$$MSE = \frac{436{,}127}{20} = 21{,}806$$

Then the *F* ratio is computed as the ratio of the two mean squares:

$$F = \frac{MSR}{MSE} = \frac{4{,}961{,}434}{21{,}806} = 227.52$$

This F ratio is substantially larger than the critical value for $\alpha = 0.01$ with 1 degree of freedom for the numerator and 20 degrees of freedom for the denominator $(F_{1,20,0.01} = 8.10)$ from the Appendix Table 9. The Minitab output—Figure 12.8(a)—for the retail sales regression shows the p-value for this computed F as 0.000, providing alternative evidence to reject H_0. Also note that the F statistic is equal to t^2 where the Student's t statistic is computed for the slope coefficient, b_1:

$$F = t^2$$
$$227.52 = 15.08^2$$

F Test for Simple Regression Coefficient

We can test the hypothesis

$$H_0 : \beta_1 = 0$$

against the alternative

$$H_1 : \beta_1 \neq 0$$

using the F statistic

$$F = \frac{MSR}{MSE} = \frac{SSR}{s_e^2} \qquad (12.22)$$

The decision rule is

$$\text{Reject } H_0 \text{ if } F \geq F_{1,n-2,\alpha} \qquad (12.23)$$

We can also show that the F statistic is

$$F = t_{b_1}^2 \qquad (12.24)$$

for any simple regression analysis.

From this result we see that hypothesis tests relating to the population slope coefficient will provide exactly the same result when using either the Student's t or the F distribution. We will learn in Chapter 13 that the F distribution—when used in a multiple regression analysis—also provides the opportunity for testing the hypothesis that several population slope coefficients are simultaneously equal to 0.

EXERCISES

Basic Exercises

12.35   Given the simple regression model

$$Y = \beta_0 + \beta_1 X$$

and the regression results that follow, test the null hypothesis that the slope coefficient is 0 versus the alternative hypothesis of greater than zero using probability of Type I error equal to 0.05, and determine the two-sided 95% and 99% confidence intervals.

a. A random sample of size $n = 38$ with $b_1 = 5$ and $s_{b_1} = 2.1$

b. A random sample of size $n = 46$ with $b_1 = 5.2$ and $s_{b_1} = 2.1$

c. A random sample of size $n = 38$ with $b_1 = 2.7$ and $s_{b_1} = 1.87$

d. A random sample of size $n = 29$ with $b_1 = 6.7$ and $s_b = 1.8$

12.36   Use a simple regression model to test the hypothesis

$$H_0 : \beta_1 = 0$$

versus

$$H_1 : \beta_1 \neq 0$$

with $\alpha = 0.05$, given the following regression statistics:

a. The sample size is 35, $SST = 100,000$, and the correlation between X and Y is 0.46.
b. The sample size is 61, $SST = 123,000$, and the correlation between X and Y is 0.65.
c. The sample size is 25, $SST = 128,000$, and the correlation between X and Y is 0.69.

Application Exercises

12.37 Consider the linear regression of DVD system sales on price, based on the data of Exercise 12.29.

a. Use an unbiased estimation procedure to find an estimate of the variance of the error terms in the population regression.
b. Use an unbiased estimation procedure to find an estimate of the variance of the least squares estimator of the slope of the population regression line.
c. Find a 90% confidence interval for the slope of the population regression line.

12.38 A fast-food chain decided to carry out an experiment to assess the influence of advertising expenditure on sales. Different relative changes in advertising expenditure, compared to the previous year, were made in eight regions of the country, and resulting changes in sales levels were observed. The accompanying table shows the results.

Increase in advertising expenditure (%)	0	4	14	10	9	8	6	1
Increase in sales (%)		2.4	7.2	10.3	9.1	10.2	4.1	7.6	3.5

a. Estimate by least squares the linear regression of increase in sales on increase in advertising expenditure.
b. Find a 90% confidence interval for the slope of the population regression line.

12.39 A liquor wholesaler is interested in assessing the effect of the price of a premium scotch whiskey on the quantity sold. The results in the accompanying table on price, in dollars, and sales, in cases, were obtained from a sample of eight weeks of sales records.

Price	19.2	20.5	19.7	21.3	20.8	19.9	17.8	17.2
Sales	25.4	14.7	18.6	12.4	11.1	15.7	29.2	35.2

Find a 95% confidence interval for the expected change in sales resulting from a $1 increase in price.

It is recommended that a computer be used for the following exercises.

12.40 Continue the analysis of Exercise 12.30 of the regression of the percentage change in the Dow-Jones index in a year on the percentage change in the index over the first five trading days of the year. Use the data file **Dow Jones**.

a. Use an unbiased estimation procedure to find a point estimate of the variance of the error terms in the population regression.
b. Use an unbiased estimation procedure to find a point estimate of the variance of the least squares estimator of the slope of the population regression line.
c. Find and interpret a 95% confidence interval for the slope of the population regression line.
d. Test at the 10% significance level, against a two-sided alternative, the null hypothesis that the slope of the population regression line is 0.

12.41 Consider the model for mutual fund losses on November 13, 1989, based on the data of Exercise 12.24. Use the data file **New York Stock Exchange Gains and Losses**.

a. Use an unbiased estimation procedure to obtain a point estimate of the variance of the error terms in the population regression.
b. Use an unbiased estimation procedure to obtain a point estimate of the variance of the least squares estimator of the slope of the population regression line.
c. Find 90%, 95%, and 99% confidence intervals for the slope of the population regression line.

12.6 PREDICTION

Regression models can be used to compute predictions or forecasts for the dependent variable, given an assumed future value for the independent variable. Suppose that we are interested in forecasting the value of the dependent variable, given that the independent variable is equal to a specified value, x_{n+1}, and that the linear relationship between dependent and independent variables continues to hold. The corresponding value of the dependent variable will then be

$$y_{n+1} = \beta_0 + \beta_1 x_{n+1} + \varepsilon_{n+1}$$

which, given x_{n+1}, has expectation

$$E[y_{n+1} \mid x_{n+1}] = \beta_0 + \beta_1 x_{n+1}$$

Two distinct options are of interest:

1. We might want to estimate the actual value that will result for a single observation, y_{n+1}. This option is shown in Figure 12.10.
2. We might want to estimate the conditional expected value, $E[y_{n+1} \mid x_{n+1}]$—that is, the average value of the dependent variable when the independent variable is fixed at x_{n+1}. This option is shown in Figure 12.11.

Given that the standard regression assumptions continue to hold, the same point estimate results for either option. We simply replace the unknown β_0 and β_1 by their least squares estimates, b_0 and b_1. That is, $(\beta_0 + \beta_1 x_{n+1})$ is estimated by $(b_0 + b_1 x_{n+1})$. We know that the corresponding estimator is the best linear unbiased estimator for Y, given X. With the first option we are interested in the best forecast for a single occurrence of the process. But for the second option we are interested in the expected value or long-term average for the process. For both options, an appropriate point estimate under our assumptions is

$$\hat{y}_{n+1} = b_0 + b_1 x_{n+1}$$

This follows because we do not know anything useful about the random variable, ε_{n+1}, except that its mean is 0. Thus, without other information we will use 0 as its point estimate.

However, we usually want intervals in addition to point estimates, and for that purpose the two options are different. This is because the variance estimators are different for the two different quantities being estimated. The results for these different variance estimators lead to the two different intervals. The interval for the first option is generally defined as a prediction interval because we are predicting the

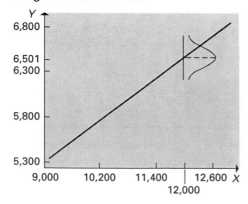

Figure 12.10 Least Squares Estimated Regression Line of Retail Sales on Disposable Income for a Single Observed Value

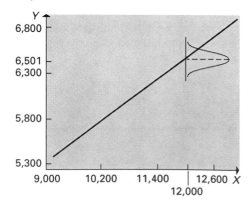

Figure 12.11 Least Squares Estimated Regression Line of Retail Sales on Disposable Income for the Expected Value

value for a single point. The interval for the second option is referred to as a confidence interval because it is the interval for the expected value.

Forecast Confidence Intervals and Prediction Intervals

Suppose that the population regression model is

$$y_i = \beta_0 + \beta_1 x_i + \varepsilon_i \quad (i = 1, \ldots, n+1)$$

that the standard regression assumptions hold, and that the ε_i are normally distributed. Let b_0 and b_1 be the least squares estimates of β_0 and β_1, based on $(x_1, y_1), (x_2, y_2), \ldots, (x_n, y_n)$. Then it can be shown that the following are $100(1 - \alpha)\%$ intervals.

1. For the forecast of the actual value resulting for Y_{n+1}, the prediction interval is

$$\hat{y}_{n+1} \pm t_{n-2,\alpha/2} \sqrt{\left[1 + \frac{1}{n} + \frac{(x_{n+1} - \bar{x})^2}{\sum_{i=1}^{n}(x_i - \bar{x})^2} \right]} s_e \qquad (12.25)$$

2. For the forecast of the conditional expectation $E(Y_{n+1} \mid x_{n+1})$, the confidence interval is

$$\hat{y}_{n+1} \pm t_{n-2,\alpha/2} \sqrt{\left[\frac{1}{n} + \frac{(x_{n+1} - \bar{x})^2}{\sum_{i=1}^{n}(x_i - \bar{x})^2} \right]} s_e \qquad (12.26)$$

where

$$\bar{x} = \frac{\sum_{i=1}^{n} x_i}{n} \quad \text{and} \quad \hat{y}_{n+1} = b_0 + b_1 x_{n+1}$$

Example 12.3 Forecasting Retail Sales (Regression Model Forecasting)

Retail Sales

We illustrate the interval computation using the retail sales and disposable income from Example 12.2. We have been asked to determine the following forecast values for retail sales per household when disposable income per household is $12,000: the actual value for next year and the expected value for the long run. In addition, we have been asked to compute prediction intervals and confidence intervals for these forecasts. Use the data file **Retail Sales**.

Solution   The forecast values for next year and for the long run are both

$$\hat{y}_{n+1} = b_0 + b_1 x_{n+1}$$
$$= 1,922 + (0.3815)(12,000) = 6,501$$

Thus, we find that the estimated sales are $6,501 when disposable income is $12,000. We have also found that

$$n = 22 \qquad \bar{x} = 10{,}799 \qquad \sum (x_i - \bar{x})^2 = 34{,}110{,}178 \qquad s_e^2 = 21{,}806$$

Hence, the standard error for a predicted single observation of Y is

$$\sqrt{\left[1 + \frac{1}{n} + \frac{(x_{n+1} - \bar{x})^2}{\displaystyle\sum_{i=1}^{n}(x_i - \bar{x})^2}\right]} s_e = \sqrt{\left[1 + \frac{1}{22} + \frac{(12{,}000 - 10{,}799)^2}{34{,}110{,}178}\right]} \sqrt{21{,}806} = 154.01$$

Similarly, we find that the standard error for the expected value of Y is

$$\sqrt{\left[\frac{1}{n} + \frac{(x_{n+1} - \bar{x})^2}{\displaystyle\sum_{i=1}^{n}(x_i - \bar{x})^2}\right]} s_e = \sqrt{\left[\frac{1}{22} + \frac{(12{,}000 - 10{,}799)^2}{34{,}110{,}178}\right]} \sqrt{21{,}806} = 43.76$$

Suppose that 95% intervals are required for the forecasts with $\alpha = 0.05$ and

$$t_{n-2, \alpha/2} = t_{20, 0.025} = 2.086$$

Using these results, we find that the 95% prediction interval for next year's retail sales when disposable income is $12,000 is computed as

$$6{,}501 \pm (2.086)(154.01)$$
$$6{,}501 \pm 321$$

Thus, the 95% prediction interval for sales in a single year in which income is $12,000 runs from $6,180 to $6,822.

For the confidence interval for the expected value of retail sales when disposable income is $12,000, we have

$$6{,}501 \pm (2.086)(43.76)$$
$$6{,}501 \pm 91$$

Hence, the 95% confidence interval for the expected value runs from $6,410 to $6,592.

INTERPRETATION

The distinction between these two interval estimation problems is illustrated in Figures 12.10 and 12.11. We see in each figure the estimated regression line for our retail sales–disposable income data. Also, in Figure 12.10 we see a probability density function representing our uncertainty about the value that retail sales will take in any specific year in which disposable income is $12,000. The probability density function in Figure 12.11 represents our uncertainty about expected, or average, retail sales in years when disposable income is $12,000. Of course, we would be less certain about sales in a single specific year than about average sales, and this is reflected in the shapes of the two density functions. We see that both are centered on retail sales of $6,501, but that the density function in Figure 12.10 has greater dispersion. As a result, the prediction interval for a specific value is wider than the confidence interval for expected retail sales.

We can obtain some further insights by studying the general forms of the prediction and confidence intervals. As we have seen, the wider the interval, the greater the uncertainty surrounding the point forecast. From these formulas we make four observations:

1. All other things being equal, the larger the sample size n, the narrower the confidence interval. Thus, we see that the more sample information we have available, the more sure we will be of our inference.

2. All other things being equal, the larger s_e^2 is, the wider is the confidence interval. Again, this is to be expected, since s_e^2 is an estimate of σ^2, the variance of the regression errors, ε_i. Since these errors

$$\varepsilon_i = y_i - \beta_0 - \beta_1 x_i$$

represent the discrepancy between the observed values of the dependent variables and their expectations, given the independent variables, the bigger the magnitude of this discrepancy is, the more imprecise will be our inference.

3. Consider now the quantity $\left(\sum_{i=1}^{n} (x_i - \bar{x})^2 \right)$. This is simply a multiple of the sample variance of the observations of the independent variable. A large variance implies that we have information for a wide range of values of this variable, which allows more precise estimates of the population regression line and correspondingly narrower confidence intervals.

4. We also see that larger values of the quantity $(x_{n+1} - \bar{x})^2$ result in wider confidence intervals for the predictions. Thus, confidence intervals become wider as we move from the mean of the independent variable, X. Since our sample data are centered at the mean $\bar{x}$, we would expect to be more definitive about our inference when the independent variable is relatively close to this central value than when it is some distance away.

INTERPRETATION

Extrapolation of the regression equation outside the range of the data used for estimation is not recommended. Suppose that you are asked to predict retail sales per household in a year when disposable income is $30,000. Referring to the data in Table 12.1 and the regression line in Figure 12.11, we see that $30,000 is well outside the range of the data used to develop the regression model. An inexperienced analyst might use the procedures previously developed to estimate a prediction or a confidence interval. From the equations we can see that the resulting intervals would be very wide, and, thus, the forecast would be of limited value. However, there is a more fundamental problem with forecasts made outside the range of the original data: We simply have no evidence to indicate the nature of the relationship outside of the range of the data. There is no reason in economic theory that requires absolutely that the relationship will remain linear with the same rate of change when we move outside of the range of the data used to estimate the regression model coefficients. Any extrapolation of the model outside of the range of the data to obtain predicted values must be based on knowledge or evidence beyond that contained in the regression analysis on the available data. Major errors can result when analysts have attempted this kind of extrapolation.

EXERCISES

Basic Exercises

12.42 Given a simple regression analysis, suppose that we have obtained a fitted regression model

$$\hat{y}_i = 12 + 5x_i$$

and also

$$s_e = 9.67 \qquad \bar{x} = 8 \qquad n = 32 \qquad \sum_{i=1}^{n}(x_i - \bar{x})^2 = 500$$

Find the 95% confidence interval and 95% prediction interval for the point where $x = 13$.

12.43 Given a simple regression analysis, suppose that we have obtained a fitted regression model

$$\hat{y}_i = 14 + 7x_i$$

and also

$$s_e = 7.45 \qquad \bar{x} = 8 \qquad n = 25 \qquad \sum_{i=1}^{n}(x_i - \bar{x})^2 = 300$$

Find the 95% confidence interval and 95% prediction interval for the point where $x = 12$.

12.44 Given a simple regression analysis, suppose that we have obtained a fitted regression model

$$\hat{y}_i = 22 + 8x_i$$

and also

$$s_e = 3.45 \qquad \bar{x} = 11 \qquad n = 22 \qquad \sum_{i=1}^{n}(x_i - \bar{x})^2 = 400$$

Find the 95% confidence interval and 95% prediction interval for the point where $x = 17$.

12.45 Given a simple regression analysis, suppose that we have obtained a fitted regression model

$$\hat{y}_i = 8 + 10\,x_i$$

and also

$$s_e = 11.23 \qquad \bar{x} = 8 \qquad n = 44 \qquad \sum_{i=1}^{n}(x_i - \bar{x})^2 = 800$$

Find the 95% confidence interval and 95% prediction interval for the point where $x = 17$.

Application Exercises

12.46 A sample of 25 blue-collar employees at a production plant was taken. Each employee was asked to assess his or her own job satisfaction (x) on a scale from 1 to 10. In addition, the numbers of days absent (y) from work during the last year were found for these employees. The sample regression line

$$\hat{y} = 12.6 - 1.2x$$

was estimated by least squares for these data. Also found were

$$\bar{x} = 6.0 \qquad \sum_{i=1}^{25}(x_i - \bar{x})^2 = 130.0 \qquad SSE = 80.6$$

a. Test at the 1% significance level against the appropriate one-sided alternative the null hypothesis that job satisfaction has no linear effect on absenteeism.
b. A particular employee has job satisfaction level 4. Find a 90% interval for the number of days this employee would be absent from work in a year.

12.47 Doctors are interested in the relationship between the dosage of a medicine and the time required for a patient's recovery. The following table shows, for a sample of five patients, dosage levels (in grams) and recovery times (in hours). These patients have similar characteristics except for medicine dosages.

Dosage level	1.2	1.0	1.5	1.2	1.4
Recovery time	25	40	10	27	16

a. Estimate the linear regression of recovery time on dosage level.
b. Find and interpret a 90% confidence interval for the slope of the population regression line.
c. Would the sample regression derived in part (a) be useful in predicting recovery time for a patient given 2.5 grams of this drug? Explain your answer.

12.48 For the stock rate-of-return problem of Exercise 12.20 it was found that

$$\sum_{i=1}^{20} y_i^2 = 196.2$$

a. Test the null hypothesis that the slope of the population regression line is 0 against the alternative that it is positive.
b. Test against the two-sided alternative the null hypothesis that the slope of the population regression line is 1.

12.49 Using the data of Exercise 12.21, test the null hypothesis that representatives' weekly sales are not linearly related to their aptitude test scores against the alternative that there is positive association.

12.50   Refer to the data of Exercise 12.41. Test against a two-sided alternative the null hypothesis that mutual fund losses on Friday, November 13, 1989, did not depend linearly on previous gains in 1989.

12.51   Denote by r the sample correlation between a pair of random variables.

a. Show that

$$\frac{1-r^2}{n-2} = \frac{s_e^2}{SST}$$

b. Using the result in part (a), show that

$$\frac{r}{\sqrt{(1-r^2)/(n-2)}} = \frac{b}{s_e/\sqrt{\sum (x_i - \bar{x})^2}}$$

c. Using the result in part (b), deduce that the test of the null hypothesis of 0 population correlation, given in Section 12.1, is the same as the test of the 0 population regression slope, given in Section 12.5.

12.52   For the problem of Exercise 12.22, on sales of premium beer in restaurants, it was found that

$$\frac{\sum (y_i - \bar{y})^2}{n-1} = 250$$

Test against a two-sided alternative the null hypothesis that the slope of the population regression line is 0.

12.53   For a sample of 74 monthly observations the regression of the percentage return on gold (y) against the percentage change in the consumer price index (x) was estimated. The sample regression line, obtained through least squares, was

$$y = -0.003 + 1.11x$$

The estimated standard deviation of the slope of the population regression line was 2.31. Test the null hypothesis that the slope of the population regression line is 0 against the alternative that the slope is positive.

12.54   Refer to the data of Exercise 12.39. Test at the 5% level against the appropriate one-sided alternative the null hypothesis that sales do not depend linearly on price for this premium scotch whiskey.

12.55   Refer to the data of Exercise 12.29.

a. Find a point estimate for the volume of sales when the price of the DVD system is $480 in a given region.

b. If the price of the system is set at $480, find 95% confidence intervals for the actual volume of sales in a particular region and the expected number of sales in that region.

12.56   Continue the analysis of Exercise 12.7. If the Dow-Jones index increases by 1.0% in the first five trading days of a year, find 90% confidence intervals for the *actual* and also the *expected* percentage changes in the index over the whole year. Discuss the distinction between these intervals.

12.57   ◗ Refer to the data in Exercise 12.25 (data file **Employee Absence**). For a year in which there is no change in the unemployment rate, find 90% confidence intervals for the *actual* and also the *expected* changes in mean employee absence rate due to own illness.

12.58   Use the data of Exercise 12.20 to find 90% and 95% confidence intervals for the expected return on the corporation's stock when the rate of return on the Standard and Poor's 500 Index is 1%.

12.59   A new sales representative for the corporation of Exercise 12.21 scores 70 on the aptitude test. Find 80% and 90% confidence intervals for the value of weekly sales he will achieve.

12.7 GRAPHICAL ANALYSIS

We have developed the theory and analysis procedures that provide the capability to perform regression analysis and build linear models. Using hypothesis tests and confidence intervals, we can determine the quality of our model and identify certain important relationships. These inferential procedures initially assume that the model errors are normally distributed. But we also know that the central limit theorem will help us perform hypothesis tests and construct confidence intervals as long as the sampling distributions of the coefficient estimators and predicted values are approximately normal. The regression model is also based on a set of assumptions.

However, there are many ways that regression analysis applications can go wrong, including assumptions that are not satisfied if the data do not follow the assumed patterns.

The example of retail sales regressed on disposable income—Figure 12.1—has a scatter plot that follows the pattern assumed in regression analysis. That pattern, however, does not always occur when new data are studied. One of the best ways to detect potential problems for simple regression analysis is to prepare scatter plots and observe the pattern. Here, we will consider some analysis tools and regression examples that can help us prepare better regression analysis applications.

In this section graphical analysis will be used to show the effect on regression analysis of points that have extreme X values and points that have Y values that deviate considerably from the least squares regression equation. In later chapters we show how residuals analysis can be used to examine other deviations from standard data patterns.

Extreme points are defined as points that have X values that deviate substantially from the X values for the other points. Refer to Equation 12.26, which presents the confidence interval for the expected value of Y at a specific value of X. Central to this confidence interval is a term typically called the *leverage*, h_i, for a point, which is defined as

$$h_i = \frac{1}{n} + \frac{(x_i - \bar{x})^2}{\sum_{i=1}^{n} (x_i - \bar{x})^2}$$

This leverage term will increase the standard deviation of the expected value as data points are farther from the mean of X and thus lead to a wider confidence interval. A point i is defined as an extreme point if its value of h is substantially different from the h values for all other data points. We see in the example below that Minitab will identify points that have a high leverage with an X if $h_i > 3\,p/n$, where p is the number of predictors including the constant. The same feature is available in most good statistical packages, but not in Excel. Using this capability, extreme points can be identified, as shown in Example 12.4.

Outlier points are defined as those that deviate substantially in the Y direction from the predicted value. Typically, these points are identified by computing the standardized residual as

$$e_{is} = \frac{e_i}{s_e \sqrt{1 - h_i}}$$

That is, the standardized residual is the residual divided by the standard error of the residual. Note that in the above equation points with high leverage—large h_i—will have a smaller standard error of the residual. This occurs because points with high leverage are likely to influence the location of the estimated regression line, and, hence, the observed and expected values of Y will be closer. Minitab will mark observations that have an absolute value of the standardized residual greater than 2.0 with an R to indicate them as outliers. This capability is also available in most good statistical packages, but not in Excel. Using this capability, outlier points can be identified, as shown in Example 12.5.

INTERPRETATION

In the next two examples we will see that extreme points and outliers have a great influence on the estimated regression equation compared to other observations. In any applied analysis either these unusual points are part of the data that represent the process being studied, or they are not. In the former case they should be included in the data set, and in the latter case they should not. The analyst must decide! Typically, these decisions require a good understanding of the process and good judgment. First, the individual points should be examined carefully and their source checked. These unusual points could have resulted from measurement or recording errors and thus would be eliminated or corrected. Further investigation may reveal unusual circumstances that are not expected to be part of the standard process, and this would indicate exclusion of the data points. Decisions concerning what a standard process is and other related decisions require careful judgment and examination of other information about the process being studied. A good analyst uses the above statistical computations to identify observations that should be examined more carefully, but does not rely exclusively on these measures for unusual observations to make the final decision.

Example 12.4   The Effect of Extreme *X* Values (Scatter Plot Analysis)

We are interested in determining the effect of extreme *X* values on the regression. In this example the effect of points with *X* values that are substantially different from the other points will be investigated using two samples that differ in only two points. These comparative examples, while somewhat unusual, are used to emphasize the effect of extreme points on a regression analysis.

Figure 12.12   Scatter Plot with Two Extreme *X* Points: Positive Slope

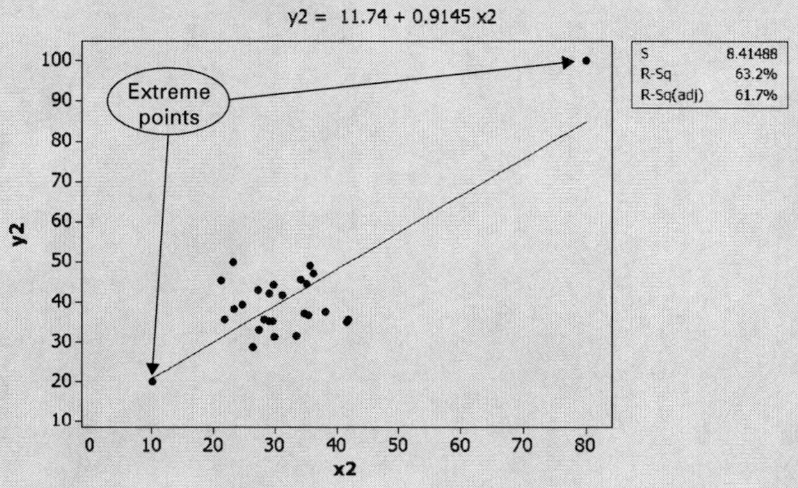

$$y2 = 11.74 + 0.9145\ x2$$

S	8.41488
R-Sq	63.2%
R-Sq(adj)	61.7%

Extreme points

y2 vs x2

Solution Figure 12.12 is a scatter plot with a regression line drawn on the points, and Figure 12.13 is the output from the regression analysis computed with the data. The regression slope is positive and $R^2 = 0.632$. But note that two extreme points seem to determine the regression relationship. Now let us consider the effect of changing the two extreme data points, as shown in Figures 12.14 and 12.15.

Figure 12.13 Regression Analysis with Two Extreme X Points: Positive Slope (Minitab Output)

Regression Analysis: Y2 versus x2

```
The regression equation is
Y2 = 11.74 + 0.9145 x2


S = 8.41488   R-Sq = 63.2%   R-Sq(adj) = 61.7%

Analysis of Variance

Source       DF        SS        MS       F      P
Regression    1   3034.80   3034.80   42.86  0.000
Error        25   1770.26     70.81
Total        26   4805.05
```

Fitted Line: y2 versus x2

Figure 12.14 Scatter Plot with Two Extreme X Points: Negative Slope

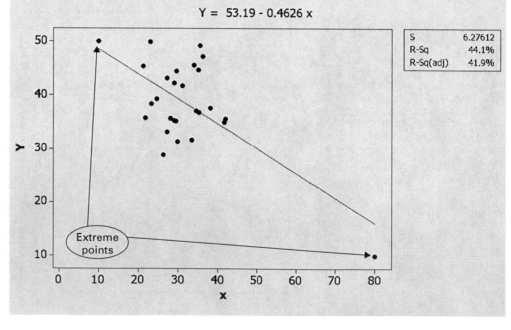

$$Y = 53.19 - 0.4626 \ x$$

Figure 12.15 Regression Analysis with Two Extreme *X* Points: Negative Slope (Minitab Output)

Regression Analysis: Y versus X

```
The regression equation is
Y1 = 53.2 - 0.463 X


Predictor        Coef     SE Coef        T        P
Constant       53.195       3.518    15.12    0.000
X1            -0.4626      0.1042    -4.44    0.000


s = 6.27612   R-Sq = 44.1%   R-Sq(adj) = 41.9%


Analysis of Variance

Source           DF        SS        MS        F        P
Regression        1    776.56    776.56    19.71    0.000
Residual Error   25    984.74     39.39
Total            26   1761.30
```

Observation 26 is an extreme point with large influence.

```
Unusual Observations

Obs     X       Y     Fit   Se Fit   Residual   St Resid
 7   35.5   49.14   36.78     1.27      12.37      2.01R
26   80.0   10.00   16.19     5.17      -6.19     -1.74 X


R denotes an observation with a large standardized residual.
X denotes an observation whose X value gives it large influence.
```

As a result of changing only two data points, the relationship now has a statistically significant negative slope, and the predictions would be substantially different. Without examining the scatter plots we would not know why we had either a positive or a negative slope. We might have thought that our results represented a standard regression situation such as we saw in the retail sales scatter plot. Note that in Figure 12.15 that observation 26 has been labeled as an extreme observation by the symbol *X*.

INTERPRETATION

This example demonstrates a common problem when historical data are used. Suppose that *X* is the number of workers employed on a production shift and *Y* is the number of units produced on that shift. Most of the time the factory operates with a relatively stable workforce, and output depends in large part on the amount of raw materials available and the sales requirements. The operation adjusts up or down over a narrow range in response to demands and to the available workforce, *X*. Thus, we see that in most cases the scatter plot covers a narrow range for the *X* variable. But occasionally there is a very large or small workforce—or the number of workers has been recorded incorrectly. On those days the production might be unusually high or low—or might be recorded incorrectly. As a result, we have extreme points that can have a major influence on the regression model. These few days determine the regression results. Without the extreme points the regression would indicate little or no relationship. If these extreme points represent extensions of the relationship, then the estimated model is useful. But if these points result from unusual conditions or recording errors, the estimated model is misleading.

In a particular application we may find that these outlier points are correct and should be used to determine the regression line. But the analyst needs to make that decision knowing that all of the other data points do not support a significant relationship. In fact, you do need to think carefully in order to understand the system and process that generated the data and to evaluate the available data.

Example 12.5 The Effect of Outliers in the *Y* Variable (Scatter Plot Analysis)

In this example we consider the effect of outliers in the *y* or vertical direction. recall that the regression analysis model assumes that all of the variation is in the *Y* direction. Thus, we know that outliers in the *Y* direction will have large residuals, and these will result in a higher estimate of the model error. In this example we will see that the effects can be even more extreme.

Solution To begin, observe the scatter plot and regression analysis in Figures 12.16 and 12.17. In this example we have a strong relationship between the *X* and *Y* variables. The scatter plot clearly supports a linear relationship with $b_1 = 11.88$. In addition, the regression model R^2 is close to 1, and the Student's *t* statistic is very large. Clearly, we have strong evidence to support a linear model.

Now let us consider the effect of changing two observations to outlier data points, as shown in Figure 12.18. This could occur because of a data recording error or because of a very unusual condition in the process being studied.

The regression slope is still positive, but now $b_1 = 6.40$, and the slope estimate has a larger standard error, as shown in Figure 12.19. The confidence interval is much wider, and the predicted value from the regression line is not as accurate.

Figure 12.16 Scatter Plot with Anticipated Pattern

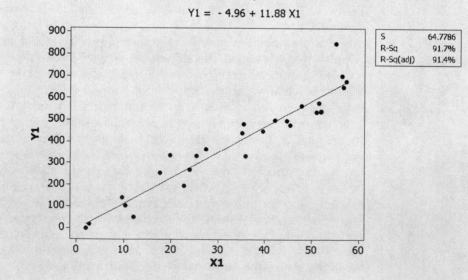

$$Y1 = -4.96 + 11.88\ X1$$

S	64.7786
R-Sq	91.7%
R-Sq(adj)	91.4%

Figure 12.17   Regression with Anticipated Pattern (Minitab Output)

Regression Analysis: Y1 versus X1

```
The regression equation is
Y1 = -4.96 + 11.88 X1


s = 64.7786  R-Sq = 91.7%  R-Sq(adj) = 91.4%


Analysis of Variance

Source       DF        SS        MS       F      P
Regression    1   1160171   1160171  276.48  0.000
Error        25    104907      4196
Total        26   1265077
```

Fitted Line: Y1 versus X1

Figure 12.18   Scatter Plot with *Y* Outlier Points

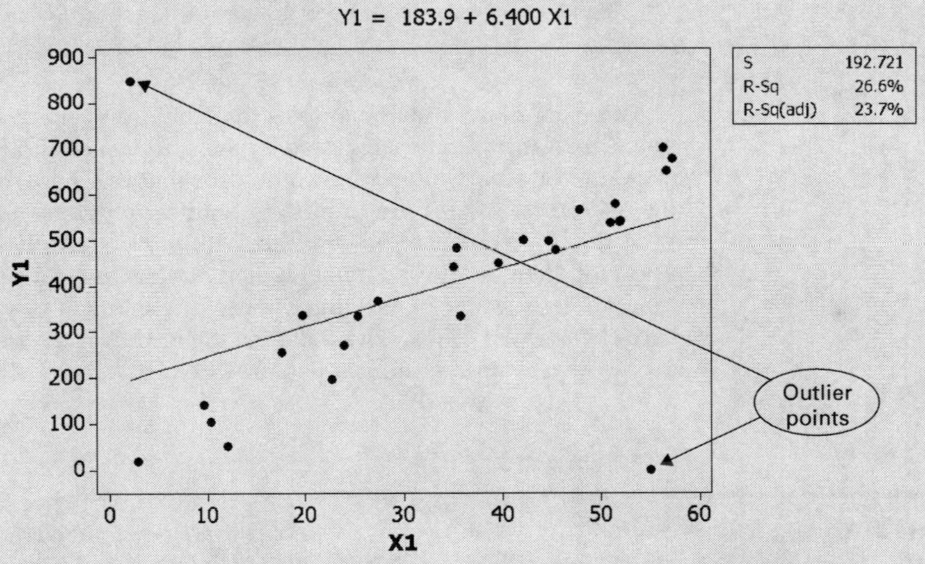

Y1 = 183.9 + 6.400 X1

S	192.721
R-Sq	26.6%
R-Sq(adj)	23.7%

The correct regression model is now not as clear. Minitab identifies observations 26 and 27 as outliers by printing an R next to the standardized residual. Standardized residuals whose absolute value is greater than 2 are indicated in the output. If the two outlier points actually occurred in the normal operation of the process, then you must include them in your analysis. But the fact that they deviate so strongly from the pattern indicates that you should carefully investigate the data situations that generated those points and study the process that you are modeling.

Figure 12.19   Regression with Y Outlier Points (Minitab Output)

```
Regression Analysis: Y1 versus X1

The regression equation is
Y1 = 184 + 6.40 X1

Predictor      Coef    SE Coef       T       P
Constant     183.92      82.10    2.24   0.034
X1            6.400      2.126    3.01   0.006

S = 192.721   R-Sq = 26.6%   R-Sq(adj) = 23.7%

Analysis of Variance

Source          DF        SS       MS      F      P
Regression       1    336540   336540   9.06  0.006
Residual Error  25    928537    37141
Total           26   1265077

Unusual Observations

Obs   X1     Y1     Fit   Se Fit   Residual   St Resid          Outliers marked
26   2.0  850.0   196.7    78.3      653.3      3.71R      ←    with R
27  55.0    0.0   535.9    57.3     -535.9     -2.91R

R denotes an observation with a large standardized residual.
```

There are many other examples that could be generated. You might find that a nonlinear relationship is suggested by the scatter plot and thus would provide a better model for a particular application problem. In Chapters 13 and 14 we will learn how we can use regression to model nonlinear relationships. You will see many different data patterns as you proceed with various applications of regression. The important point is that you must regularly follow analysis procedures—including the preparation of scatter plots—that can provide as much insight as possible. As a good analyst, you must **"Know thy data!"** In the next chapter we will consider how residuals can also be used graphically to provide further tests of regression models.

EXERCISES

Basic Exercise

12.60   Frank Anscombe, senior research executive, has asked you to analyze the following four linear models using data contained in the data file **Anscombe**.

$$Y_1 = \beta_0 + \beta_1 X_1$$
$$Y_2 = \beta_0 + \beta_1 X_1$$
$$Y_3 = \beta_0 + \beta_1 X_1$$
$$Y_4 = \beta_0 + \beta_1 X_1$$

Use your computer package to obtain a linear regression estimate for each model. Prepare a scatter plot for the data used in each model. Write a report, including regression and graphical outputs, that compares and contrasts the four models.

Application Exercise

12.61   John Foster, president of Public Research Inc., has asked for your assistance in a study of the occurrence of crimes in different states before and after a large federal government expenditure to reduce crime. As part of this study he wants to know if the crime rate for selected crimes after the expenditure can be predicted using the crime rate before the expenditure. He has asked you to test the hypothesis that crime before predicts crime after for Total Crime rate and for the Murder, Rape, and Robbery rates. The data for your analysis are contained in the data file **Crime Study**. Perform appropriate analysis and write a report that summarizes your results.

SUMMARY

In this chapter we developed the two variable or simple least squares models. We built on some of the initial descriptive concepts developed in Chapter 3. The simple regression model assumes that a set of exogenous or independent variables has a linear relationship to the expected value of an endogenous or dependent random variable. By developing estimates of the coefficients of this model, we can better understand business and economic processes and can predict values of the endogenous variable as a function of the exogenous variable. Our study included the development of estimators for coefficients and for dependent variables. We also developed measures of regression goodness of fit—analysis of variance and R^2.

Following that study, we developed statistical inference procedures—hypothesis testing and confidence intervals for the key regression estimators. We also considered correlation analysis—simply examining the relationship between two variables. Finally, we discussed the importance of scatter plots and graphical analysis in the development and testing of regression models.

KEY WORDS

- analysis of variance
- assumptions for the least squares coefficient estimators
- basis for inference about the population regression slope
- coefficient estimators
- coefficient of determination, R^2
- confidence intervals for predictions
- confidence intervals for the population regression slope b_1
- correlation and R^2
- estimation of model error variance
- F test for simple regression coefficient
- least squares procedure
- linear regression outcomes
- linear regression population equation model
- sampling distribution of the least squares coefficient estimator
- tests for zero population correlation
- tests of the population regression slope

CHAPTER EXERCISES AND APPLICATIONS

12.62 What is meant by the statement that a pair of random variables are positively correlated? Give examples of pairs of random variables for which you would expect:

  a. Positive correlation
  b. Negative correlation
  c. Zero correlation

12.63 A random sample of five sets of observations for a pair of random variables yielded the results given in the table.

X	4	1	0	1	4
Y	−2	−1	0	1	2

  a. Find the sample correlation coefficient.
  b. In light of the fact that each y_i value is the square of the corresponding x_i value, comment on your answer in part (a).

12.64 For a random sample of 53 building supply stores in a chain the correlation between annual euro sales per square meter of floor space and annual euro rent per square meter of floor space was found to be 0.37. Test the null hypothesis that these two quantities are uncorrelated in the population against the alternative that the population correlation is positive.

12.65 For a random sample of 526 firms the sample correlation between the proportion of a firm's officers who are directors and a risk-adjusted measure of return on the firm's stock was found to be 0.1398. Test against a two-sided alternative the null hypothesis that the population correlation is 0.

12.66 For a sample of 66 months the correlation between the returns on Canadian and Hong Kong 10-year bonds was found to be 0.293. Test the null hypothesis that the population correlation is 0 against the alternative that it is positive.

12.67 For a random sample of 192 female employees, a sample correlation of −0.18 was found between age and a measure of willingness to relocate. Given only this information, derive all the conclusions you can about the regression of willingness to relocate on age.

12.68 Based on a sample on n observations, (x_1, y_1), $(x_2, y_2), \ldots, (x_n, y_n)$, the sample regression of y on x is calculated. Show that the sample regression line passes through the point $(x = \bar{x}, y = \bar{y})$, where $\bar{x}$ and $\bar{y}$ are the sample means.

12.69 ● A company routinely administers an aptitude test to all new management trainees. At the end of the first year with the company, these trainees are graded by their immediate supervisors. For a random sample of 12 trainees, the results shown in the data file **Employee Test** were obtained.

a. Estimate the regression of supervisor's grade on aptitude score.
b. Interpret the slope of the sample regression line.
c. Is it possible to give a useful interpretation of the intercept of the sample regression line? Explain.
d. Find and interpret the coefficient of determination for this regression.
e. Test against the obvious one-sided alternative the null hypothesis that the slope of the population regression line is 0.
f. Find a 95% confidence interval for the supervisor's grade that would be obtained by a particular trainee who had an aptitude score of 70.

12.70 An attempt was made to evaluate the inflation rate as a predictor of the spot rate in the German treasury bill market. For a sample of 79 quarterly observations the estimated linear regression

$$\hat{y} = 0.0027 + 0.7916x$$

was obtained, where

y = Actual change in the spot rate
x = Change in the spot rate predicted by the inflation rate

The coefficient of determination was 0.097, and the estimated standard deviation of the estimator of the slope of the population regression line was 0.2759.

a. Interpret the slope of the estimated regression line.
b. Interpret the coefficent of determination.
c. Test the null hypothesis that the slope of the population regression line is 0 against the alternative that the true slope is positive, and interpret your result.
d. Test against a two-sided alternative the null hypothesis that the slope of the population regression line is 1, and interpret your result.

12.71 The table shows, for eight vintages of select wine, purchases per buyer (y) and the wine buyer's rating in a year (x).

x	3.6	3.3	2.8	2.6	2.7	2.9	2.0	2.6
y	24	21	22	22	18	13	9	6

a. Estimate the regression of purchases per buyer on the buyer's rating.
b. Interpret the slope of the estimated regression line.
c. Find and interpret the coeffient of determination.
d. Find and interpret a 90% confidence interval for the slope of the population regression line.
e. Find a 90% confidence interval for expected purchases per buyer for a vintage for which the buyer's rating is 2.0.

12.72 For a sample of 306 students in a basic business statistics course the sample regression line

$$y = 58.813 + 0.2875x$$

was obtained. Here,

y = Final student score at the end of the course
x = Score on a diagnostic statistics test given at the beginning of the course

The coefficient of determination was 0.1158, and the estimated standard deviation of the estimator of the slope of the population regression line was 0.04566.

a. Interpret the slope of the sample regression line.
b. Interpret the coefficient of determination.
c. The information given allows the null hypothesis that the slope of the population regression line is 0 to be tested in two different ways against the alternative that it is positive. Carry out these tests and show that they reach the same conclusion.

12.73 Based on a sample of 30 observations, the population regression model

$$y_i = \beta_0 + \beta_1 x_i + \varepsilon_i$$

was estimated. The least squares estimates obtained were

$$b_0 = 10.1 \quad \text{and} \quad b_1 = 8.4$$

The regression and error sums of squares were

$$SSR = 128 \quad \text{and} \quad SSE = 286$$

a. Find and interpret the coefficient of determination.
b. Test at the 10% significance level against a two-sided alternative the null hypothesis that β_1 is 0.
c. Find

$$\sum_{i=1}^{30} (x_i - \bar{x})^2$$

12.74 Based on a sample of 25 observations, the population regression model

$$y_i = \beta_0 + \beta_1 x_i + \varepsilon_i$$

was estimated. The least squares estimates obtained were

$$b_0 = 15.6 \quad \text{and} \quad b_1 = 1.3$$

The total and error sums of squares were

$$SST = 268 \quad \text{and} \quad SSE = 204$$

a. Find and interpret the coefficient of determination.
b. Test against a two-sided alternative at the 5% significance level the null hypothesis that the slope of the population regression line is 0.
c. Find a 95% confidence interval for β_1.

12.75 An analyst believes that the only important determinant of banks' returns on assets (Y) is the ratio of loans to deposits (x). For a random sample of 20 banks the sample regression line

$$Y = 0.97 + 0.47x$$

was obtained with coefficient of determination 0.720.

a. Find the sample correlation between returns on assets and the ratio of loans to deposits.
b. Test against a two-sided alternative at the 5% significance level the null hypothesis of no linear association between the returns and the ratio.
c. Find

$$\frac{s_e}{\sqrt{\sum (x_i - \bar{x})^2}}$$

12.76 Comment on the following statement:

> If a regression of the yield per acre of corn on the quantity of fertilizer used is estimated using fertilizer quantities in the range typically used by farmers, the slope of the estimated regression line will certainly be positive. However, it is well known that, if an enormously high amount of fertilizer is used, corn yield will be very low. Therefore, regression equations are not of much use in forecasting.

The following exercises require the use of a computer.

12.77 🔵 A college's Economics Department is attempting to determine if verbal or mathematical proficiency is more important for predicting academic success in the study of economics. The department faculty have decided to use the grade point average (GPA) in economics courses for graduates as a measure of success. Verbal proficiency is measured by the SAT verbal and the ACT English entrance examination test scores. Mathematical proficiency is measured by the SAT mathematics and the ACT mathematics entrance examination scores. The data for 112 students are available in a data file named **Student GPA**, which is available on your data disk. The designation of the variable columns is presented at the beginning of the data file. You should use your local statistical computer program to perform the analysis for this problem.

a. Prepare a graphical plot of economics GPA versus each of the two verbal proficiency scores and each of the two mathematical proficiency scores. Which variable is a better predictor? Note any unusual patterns in the data.
b. Compute the linear model coefficients and the regression analysis statistics for the models that predict economics GPA as a function of each verbal and each mathematics score. Using both the SAT mathematics and verbal measures and the ACT mathematics and English measures, determine whether mathematical or verbal proficiency is the best predictor of economics GPA.
c. Compare the descriptive statistics—mean, standard deviation, upper and lower quartiles, range—for the predictor variables. Note the differences and indicate how these differences affect the capability of the linear model to predict.

12.78 🔵 The administrator of the National Highway Traffic Safety Administration (NHTSA) wants to know if the different types of vehicles in a state have a relationship to the highway death rate in the state. She has asked you to perform several regression analyses to determine if average vehicle weight, percentage imported cars, percentage light trucks, or average car age is related to crash deaths in automobiles and pickups. The data for the analysis are located in the data file named **Crash**, which is located on your data disk. The variable descriptions and locations are contained in the data file catalog in the Appendix.

a. Prepare graphical plots of crash deaths versus each of the potential predictor variables. Note the relationship and any unusual patterns in the data points.

b. Prepare a simple regression analysis of crash deaths on the potential predictor variables. Determine which, if any, of the regressions indicate a significant relationship.

c. State the results of your analysis and rank the predictor variables in terms of their relationship to crash deaths.

12.79 The Department of Transportation wishes to know if states with a larger percentage of urban population have higher automobile and pickup crash death rates. In addition, it wants to know if the average speed on rural roads or the percentage of rural roads that are surfaced is related to crash death rates. Data for this study are included in the data file **Crash**, stored on your data disk.

a. Prepare graphical plots of crash deaths versus each of the potential predictor variables. Note the relationship and any unusual patterns in the data points.

b. Prepare a simple regression analysis of crash deaths on the potential predictor variables. Determine which, if any, of the regressions indicate a significant relationship.

c. State the results of your analysis and rank the predictor variables in terms of their relationship to crash deaths.

12.80 An economist wishes to predict the market value of owner-occupied homes in small midwestern cities. He has collected a set of data from 45 small cities for a two-year period and wants you to use this as the data source for the analysis. The data are stored in the file **Citydat**, which is stored on your data disk. He wants you to develop two prediction equations: one that uses the size of the house as a predictor and a second that uses the tax rate as a predictor.

a. Plot the market value of houses (hseval) versus size of house (sizense) and then versus tax rate (taxrate). Note any unusual patterns in the data.

b. Prepare regression analyses for the two predictor variables. Which variable is the stronger predictor of the value of houses?

c. A business developer in a midwestern state has stated that local property tax rates in small towns need to be lowered because if they are not, no one will purchase a house in these towns. Based on your analysis in this problem, evaluate the business developer's claim.

12.81 Stuart Wainwright, the vice president of purchasing for a large national retailer, has asked you to prepare an analysis of retail sales by state. He wants to know if either the percent unemployment or the per capita personal income is related to per capita retail sales. Data for this study are stored in the data file named **Retail**, which is stored on your data disk and described in the data file catalog in the Appendix.

a. Prepare graphical plots and regression analyses to determine the relationships between per capita retail sales and unemployment and personal income. Compute 95% confidence intervals for the slope coefficients in each regression equation.

b. What is the effect of a $1,000 decrease in per capita income on per capita sales?

c. For the per capita income regression equation what is the 95% confidence interval for retail sales at the mean per capita income and at $1,000 above the mean per capita income?

12.82 A major national supplier of building materials for residential construction is concerned about total sales for next year. It is well known that the company's sales are directly related to the total national residential investment. Several New York bankers are predicting that interest rates will rise about 2 percentage points next year. You have been asked to develop a regression analysis that can be used to predict the effect of interest rate changes on residential investment. The time series data for this study are contained in the data file named **Macro2003**, which is stored on your data disk and described in the Chapter 14 Appendix.

a. Develop two regression models to predict residential investment, using the prime interest rate for one and the federal funds interest rate for the other. Analyze the regression statistics and indicate which equation provides the best predictions.

b. Determine the 95% confidence interval for the slope coefficient in both regression equations.

c. Based on each model, predict the effect of a 2-percentage-point increase in interest rates on residential investment.

d. Using both models, compute 95% confidence intervals for the change in residential investment that results from a 2-percentage-point increase in interest rates.

Appendix

In this appendix we derive the least squares estimates of the population regression parameters. We want to find the values b_0 and b_1 for which the sum of squared discrepancies

$$SSE = \sum_{i=1}^{n} e_i^2 = \sum_{i=1}^{n} (y_i - b_0 - b_1 x_i)^2$$

is as small as possible.

As a first step, we keep b_1 constant and differentiate with respect to b_0, giving

$$\frac{\partial SSE}{\partial b_0} = 2\sum_{i=1}^{n} (y_i - b_0 - b_1 x_i)$$

$$= -2\left(\sum y_i - nb_0 - b_1 \sum x_i\right)$$

Since this derivative must be 0 for a minimum, we have

$$\sum y_i - nb_0 - b_1 \sum x_i = 0$$

Hence, dividing through by n yields

$$b_0 = \bar{y} - b_1 \bar{x}$$

Substituting this expression for b_0 gives

$$SSE = \sum_{i=1}^{n} [(y_i - \bar{y}) - b_1(x_i - \bar{x})]^2$$

Differentiating this expression with respect to b_1 then gives

$$\frac{\partial SSE}{\partial b_1} = 2\sum_{i=1}^{n} (x_i - \bar{x})[(y_i - \bar{y}) - b_1(x_i - \bar{x})]$$

$$= -2\left(\sum (x_i - \bar{x})(y_i - \bar{y}) - b_1 \sum (x_i - \bar{x})^2\right)$$

This derivative must be 0 for a minimum, so we have

$$\sum (x_i - \bar{x})(y_i - \bar{y}) = b_1 \sum (x_i - \bar{x})^2$$

Hence,

$$b_1 = \frac{\sum (x_i - \bar{x})(y_i - \bar{y})}{\sum (x_i - \bar{x})^2}$$

References

1. Dhalla, N. K. "Short-Term Forecasts of Advertising Expenditures." *Journal of Advertising Research* 19, no. 1 (1979): 7–14.

2. Mampower, J. L., S. Livingston, and T. J. Lee. "Expert Judgments of Political Risk." *Journal of Forecasting* 6 (1987): 51–65.

Appendices

Appendix 1

Basic Mathematics

CHAPTER **12**
....

Basic mathematics

Objectives
....

By the end of this chapter you should be able to:
- ▶ deal with arithmetic problems involving whole numbers, fractions and decimals;
- ▶ 'round off' to a given number of decimal places or significant figures;
- ▶ perform calculations involving percentages and ratios;
- ▶ handle expressions involving powers or roots of a variable;
- ▶ be familiar with the simple rules of algebra;
- ▶ draw graphs and solve problems involving linear and non-linear equations;
- ▶ solve pairs of simultaneous equations.

Introduction
....

In this chapter we briefly review some of the key ideas in mathematics which are the building blocks for any course in quantitative methods. Many of these you will already have met in previous courses at school or college, though some may be new. The intention is to be *selective* rather than exhaustive and to give you the opportunity to revise and practice some important numerical skills. By following through the various Worked examples and trying the Self-check and Review questions (with answers) it is hoped that you will gain confidence in handling numbers and data, which is so important for your success in Quantitative methods.

Where you feel further help is required on any particular technique the 'Further reading' section (p. 313) will direct you to alternative sources.

Answers to the 'Self-check questions', responses to each 'Pause for thought' and answers to the 'Review questions' can be found at the end of the book.

12.1 Whole numbers, fractions and decimals
....

Whole numbers

Numbers such as 3, 5, 9 are referred to as whole numbers or *integers*.

Such numbers can be positive (+3) or negative (–3).

Some simple rules apply to situations involving negative numbers.

Negative number arithmetic

* To *add two negative numbers*, add the 'numbers' and make the answer negative.

Example:

$-4 + -3$ or $-4 - 3 = -7$

▶ To *add a negative and a positive number,* take the smaller number away from the bigger number and give your result the sign of the 'bigger number'.

Examples:

$-11 + 4 = -(11 - 4) = -7$

$5 + -7$ or $5 - 7 = -(7 - 5) = -2$

▶ To *subtract a negative number,* you read the two minuses $(- -)$ as a $+$

Example

$5 - -3 = 5 + 3 = 8$

These various rules involving negative numbers can usefully be illustrated by the *Number Line.* Look at the number line in Figure 12.1. The 0 is in the middle. All numbers to the right of 0 are the *positive* numbers, and all those to the left of 0 are the *negative* numbers.

▶ When we *add a negative number,* it is the same as *subtracting a positive number:* we always move towards the left on the number line. Check the following examples in Figure 12.1.

(a) $3 + -2 = 1$ or $3 - 2 = 1$
(b) $-1 + -3 = -4$ or $-1 - 3 = -4$
(c) $-2 + -3 = -5$ or $-2 - 3 = -5$

figure 12.1
Adding a negative number (same as subtracting a positive number)

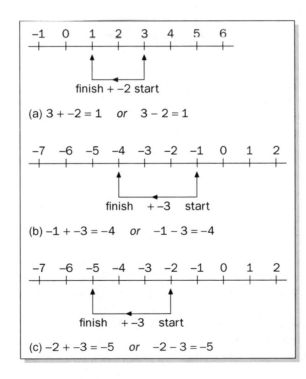

(a) $3 + -2 = 1$ *or* $3 - 2 = 1$

(b) $-1 + -3 = -4$ *or* $-1 - 3 = -4$

(c) $-2 + -3 = -5$ *or* $-2 - 3 = -5$

▶ When we *subtract a negative number*, it is the same as *adding a positive number*: we always move towards the right on the number line. Check the following example in Figure 12.2.

(a) $3 - -2 = 5$ or $3 + 2 = 5$
(b) $-6 - -4 = -2$ or $-6 + 4 = -2$
(c) $-1 - -3 = 2$ or $-1 + 3 = 2$

figure 12.2
Subtracting a negative number (same as adding a positive number)

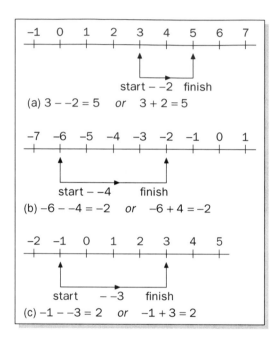

(a) $3 - -2 = 5$ *or* $3 + 2 = 5$

(b) $-6 - -4 = -2$ *or* $-6 + 4 = -2$

(c) $-1 - -3 = 2$ *or* $-1 + 3 = 2$

▶ The rules for *multiplying and dividing with negative numbers* are very easy after you have learnt the rules for addition and subtraction:
If the signs are the same, the answer is a positive
If the signs are different, the answer is a negative

Examples:

$2 \times 5 = 10$ $-3 \times -4 = 12$ $-18 \div -3 = 6$
$-2 \times 5 = -10$ $3 \times -4 = -12$ $18 \div -3 = -6$

Fractions

A **fraction** is usually part of something. It can be defined as the ratio of two numbers, one (the *numerator*) placed on top of another (the *denominator*).
    Work through the following rules involving fractions.

Addition and subtraction of fractions
To add or subtract two fractions, change them to *equivalent fractions* (see below) with the same bottom number. Then we can add or subtract.

WORKED EXAMPLE 12.1

$$\frac{1}{3} + \frac{2}{5} = \frac{5}{15} + \frac{6}{15} = \frac{11}{15}$$

We use 15 since it is the smallest multiple of both 3 and 5.

WORKED EXAMPLE 12.2

$$\frac{7}{8} - \frac{5}{6} = \frac{21}{24} - \frac{20}{24} = \frac{1}{24}$$

We use 24 since it is the smallest multiple of both 8 and 6.

Multiplication of fractions

To multiply two fractions you simply need to multiply the top numbers and the bottom numbers of the fractions.

WORKED EXAMPLE 12.3

$$\frac{3}{5} \times \frac{3}{4} = \frac{9}{20}$$

Division of fractions

To divide two fractions, you turn the second fraction upside-down and then multiply the two fractions together.

WORKED EXAMPLE 12.4

$$\frac{2}{3} \div \frac{4}{5} = \frac{2}{3} \times \frac{5}{4} = \frac{10}{12} = \frac{5}{6}$$

Cancelling fractions

Worked example A4 illustrates the fraction 10/12 being cancelled down to 5/6 by dividing both top and bottom by the same number, in this case a 2.

Equivalent fractions

These are fractions that have the same value. For example, 1/4, 3/12, 6/24 are all equivalent to each other, and so are called equivalent fractions.

Decimals

Decimals are simply found by dividing the top (numerator) of the fraction by the bottom (denominator) of the fraction.

WORKED EXAMPLE 12.5

Change $\frac{5}{8}$ to a decimal number. Divide 5 by 8 to give 0.625.

When a number is written in decimal form, the digits on the right-hand side of the decimal point are called the *decimal places*.

WORKED
EXAMPLE **12.6**
• • • • • • • • • • • • • •

83.7 is written to one decimal place (1 d.p.).
0.439 is written to three decimal places (3 d.p.).

12.2 Rounding-off
• •

In many tasks you will need to 'round-off' your answer to a suitable number of *decimal places* (d.p.) or *significant figures* (s.f.)

Decimal places

▶ Decide on the number of decimal places you wish to round-off to, say to two decimal places.
▶ Look at the number in the next (here third) decimal place.
▶ If it is less than 5, then the two decimal places remain the same.
▶ If it is 5 or more than 5, then think of the first two decimal place numbers as together forming a number between 1 and 99, and then add 1 to this. This new number now represents your two decimal places.

WORKED
EXAMPLE **12.7**
• • • • • • • • • • • • • •

9.5427 will round-off to 9.54 (the 2 of the third decimal place is less than 5, so we keep 54).

11.1873 will round-off to 11.19 (the 7 of the third decimal place is more than 5, so we need to add 1 to 18, making 19).

23.6154 will round-off to 23.62 (the 5 of the third decimal place causes us to add 1 to 61, making 62).

Significant figures

Counting the number of actual *digits* (numbers) will often tell us the number of significant figures involved.

WORKED
EXAMPLE **12.8**
• • • • • • • • • • • • • •

8	has 1 significant figure
9.3	has 2 significant figures
47.7	has 3 significant figures
0.1845	has 4 significant figures

However, when 0s are in the number, we must know when to count them as a significant figure and when not to.

▶ When the 0s come at the end of the number or at the beginning of the number, then we do *not* count them as significant figures.

WORKED EXAMPLE 12.9

60	has 1 significant figure
500	has 1 significant figure
57,000	has 2 significant figures
0.68	has 2 significant figures
0.009	has 1 significant figure
0.00013	has 2 significant figures

▶ When the 0s come between digits, we *do* count them as significant figures.

WORKED EXAMPLE 12.10

105 has 3 significant figures
2070 has 3 significant figures
5002 has four significant figures

The rules for rounding off for significant figures are similar to those for decimal places.

▶ Decide on the number of significant figures you wish to round-off to. Look at the next digit which then 'has to go'.
▶ If this is less than 5, then leave the digits on the left (if there are any) alone.
▶ If the digit is 5 or more than 5, then add 1 to the digit on the left.
▶ Then put 0s in to keep the place value of the original number.

WORKED EXAMPLE 12.11

832 to 1 s.f. is 800 since the 3 is less than 5
8.7621 to 2 s.f. is 8.8 since the 6 is more than 5

Look at the following table to see how these rules work for the numbers chosen:

Number	Correct to 1 s.f.	Correct to 2 s.f.	Correct to 3 s.f.
34.87	30	35	34.9
159.2	200	160	159
10.942	10.000	11.000	10.900
0.07158	0.07	0.072	0.0716

12.3 Percentages and ratios

Percentages

A percentage means 'out of a hundred'. So:

▶ 1% means 1 out of a 100 or 1/100 or 0.01.
▶ 3% means 3 out of a 100 or 3/100 or 0.03.

Changes of form

Fractions to percentages
To change any *fraction* into a percentage, all you need to do is to multiply the fraction by 100. What this is doing is finding the fraction of 100.

For example:

$\frac{5}{8}$ would become $\frac{5}{8} \times 100 = 62.5\%$

You should know the common fractions expressed as a percentage.

$\frac{1}{2} = 50\%$ $\frac{1}{4} = 25\%$ $\frac{3}{4} = 75\%$ $\frac{1}{10} = 10\%$ $\frac{1}{5} = 20\%$ $\frac{1}{3} = 33\frac{1}{3}\%$

Percentages to fractions
To change a *percentage* into a fraction, simply express the percentage as a fraction over 100 and then cancel down. For example:

$45\% = \frac{45}{100} = \frac{9}{20}$ (cancelled by 5s)

$31\% = \frac{31}{100}$ (will not cancel)

Decimals to percentages
To change any *decimal* into a percentage, simply multiply by 100. For example:

0.35 becomes $0.35 \times 100 = 35\%$ as a percentage.
1.26 becomes $1.26 \times 100 = 126\%$ as a percentage.

Percentages to decimals
To change a *percentage* to a decimal, simply divide the percentage by 100. This is done by moving the decimal point two places to the left. For example:

35% becomes 0.35 as a decimal
6% becomes 0.06 as a decimal.

Percentage of
To calculate the *percentage of* something you first change the percentage to a decimal and then multiply.

WORKED EXAMPLE 12.12

Find 8% of £135.
Calculate $0.08 \times 135 = £10.80$. So 8% of £135 is £10.80.

Percentage increase
Change the percentage to a decimal, add 1, then multiply by the figure that needs increasing.

WORKED EXAMPLE 12.13

Increase £6 by 5%.
Change 5% to a decimal, add 1, then multiply by £6.
1.05 × £6 = £6.30

Percentage decrease
Change the percentage to a decimal and take it away from 1, then multiply it by the original figure.

WORKED EXAMPLE 12.14

Decrease £8 by 4%. Change 4% to a decimal and take it away from 1.
1 − 0.04 = 0.96
Multiply this by the original
0.96 × £8 = £7.68

'As a percentage'
We express one quantity *as a percentage* of another by setting up the two numbers as a fraction of each other and converting that fraction to a percentage by simply multiplying by 100.

WORKED EXAMPLE 12.15

Express £7 as a percentage of £25
Set up the fraction $\frac{7}{25}$ and multiply by 100. This becomes (7 ÷ 25) × 100 = 28%

Reverse percentage
There are times when we know a certain percentage and we wish to get back to the original amount.

WORKED EXAMPLE 12.16

The 31 pupils who were absent represented only 4 per cent of the pupils in the school. How many pupils should have been at school?
Since 4 per cent represents 31 pupils, then 1 per cent will represent 31 ÷ 4 pupils = 7.75, so 100 per cent will be represented by
(7.75 × 100) = 775 pupils

Ratios

To divide any amount in a given ratio, you simply multiply the amount by the fraction of the ratio.

Divide £60 between John and Kevin in the ratio of 2:3.

From the ratio we see that John receives $\frac{2}{5}$ and Kevin receives $\frac{3}{5}$. Hence

John receives £60 $\times \frac{2}{5}$ = £24 and

Kevin receives £60 $\times \frac{3}{5}$ = £36

Sometimes you may know only part of the information.

Two business partners Sue and Trish divide their profits in the ratio 3:5. If Sue receives £1,800, how much does Trish receive?

Sue receives £1,800 which is $\frac{3}{8}$ of the whole profit. So $\frac{1}{8}$ = £1,800 ÷ 3 = £600.

So Trish's share which is $\frac{5}{8}$ will be £600 × 5 = £3,000.

**SELF-CHECK
QUESTIONS**

12.1 Solve

    (a) −4 + −2   (b) −4 − −2   (c) −4 × −2
    (d) −4 ÷ −2   (e) −16 × −6   (f) −81 ÷ −9

12.2 Correct each of the following to the number of decimal places or significant figures indicated.

    (a) 2.643 (2 d.p.)   (b) 1.338 (2 d.p.)   (c) 17.64 (1 d.p.)
    (d) 7.5474 (2 s.f.)   (e) 17.6 (1 s.f.)   (f) 0.00587 (1 s.f.)

12.3 Express each of the following as a percentage (to no more than 1 d.p.).

    (a) £5 out of £24   (b) 4 kg out of 32 kg.
    (c) 2.5 m out of 10 m.   (d) 40 cm out of 3 m.

12.4 (a) Divide £3.25 in the ratio of 2:3
    (b) Three footballers score 21, 15 and 9 goals respectively. Their club pays out £9,000 in bonus money to these players. They share the bonus in the same ratio as the goals they score. Calculate the share of the bonus for each player.

Note: **Answers can be found on p. 367.**

12.4 Powers and roots
· ·

In the expressions x^4 and x^2, the letter x is called the *base* and the numbers 4 and 2 are called the *powers* (or *indices* or *exponents*).

$x^4 = x \times x \times x \times x$

$x^2 = x \times x$

Rules for powers

Whenever powers have the *same base*, then a number of rules can be applied. You should make sure that you are familiar with these simple rules.

Multiplying powers (indices)

$4^3 \times 4^2 = (4 \times 4 \times 4) \times (4 \times 4) = 4 \times 4 \times 4 \times 4 \times 4 = 4^5$

To multiply, just add the powers

i.e. $x^a \times x^b = x^{a+b}$

Dividing powers (indices)

$3^5 \div 3^2 = \dfrac{3 \times 3 \times 3 \times 3 \times 3}{3 \times 3} = 3 \times 3 \times 3 = 3^3$

To divide, just subtract the powers

i.e. $x^a \div x^b = x^{a-b}$

The power zero

e.g. $2^3 \div 2^3 = 2^{3-3} = 2^0$

but $2^3 \div 2^3 = \dfrac{8}{8} = 1$

so $2^0 = 1$

$x^0 = 1$

Negative powers

e.g. $3^1 \div 3^3 = 3^{1-3} = 3^{-2}$

but $3^1 \div 3^3 = \dfrac{3}{27} = \dfrac{1}{9} = \dfrac{1}{3^2}$

so $3^{-2} = \dfrac{1}{3^2}$

$x^{-a} = \dfrac{1}{x^a}$

Fractional powers

Fractional powers will be used to indicate *roots* (see below)

$x^{\frac{1}{2}} = \sqrt{x}$

$x^{\frac{1}{3}} = \sqrt[3]{x}$

$x^{\frac{1}{n}} = \sqrt[n]{x}$

and $x^{\frac{2}{3}} = \sqrt[3]{x^2} = \left(\sqrt[3]{x}\right)^2$

$x^{\frac{m}{n}} = \sqrt[n]{x^m} = \left(\sqrt[n]{x}\right)^m$

Roots

A root is the mathematical word for a solution of a *quadratic* equation.

Root of a number

The root of a number is generally taken to be the *square root*. So, root 9 will be 3 or –3.

The Nth root

The Nth root of a number A is that number which, when multiplied by itself N times, gives A.

Examples:

▶ The square root of 25: $\sqrt{25}$ = 5 or –5, because $5 \times 5 = 25$ and $-5 \times -5 = 25$.
▶ The cube (3rd) root of 64 : $\sqrt[3]{64}$ = 4, because $4 \times 4 \times 4 = 64$.
▶ The 4th root of 81, $\sqrt[4]{81}$ = 3 or –3, because $3 \times 3 \times 3 \times 3 = 81$ and $-3 \times -3 \times -3 \times -3 = 81$.

You can use your calculator to find any root of any number by using the $x^{1/y}$ key, where y is the Nth root you want. You will most likely need to use the shift or inv or 2ndf key also. For example, if you want to find the 5th root of 7776, key in 7776 $x^{1/y}$ 5: this will give the result 6.

SELF-CHECK QUESTIONS

Solve the following using your knowledge of the rules for dealing with powers.

12.5 (a) $t^3 \times t^4$ (b) $m^2 \times m$ (c) $3x^2 \times 2x^5$
      (d) $5p \times 3p^4$ (e) $7m^3 \times 4m$ (f) $3w \times 4w^2$

12.6 (a) $x^7 \div x^3$ (b) $p^6 \div p^4$ (c) $8d^3 \div 2d$
      (d) $6m^4 \div 3m^3$ (e) $12c^3 \div 6c^3$ (f) $9m^4 \div 6m^3$

12.7 (a) $3^8 \div 3^5$ (b) $2^9 \div 2^7$ (c) $10^3 \div 10^2$
      (d) $10^9 \div 10^3$ (e) $7^7 \div 7^6$ (f) $19^8 \div 19^7$

12.8 Write the following in fraction form:

      (a) 7^{-2} (b) 8^{-3} (c) x^{-4} (d) m^{-1}

      (e) $4g^{-2}$ (f) $5m^{-2}$ (g) $(2t)^{-3}$ (h) $\frac{1}{2}t^{-4}$

12.9 (a) $6m + 3m^2$ (b) $8t^2 + 6t^5$ (c) $9x^3 + 6x^4$ (d) $cd^3 + d^5$
      (e) $a^2b + ab$ (f) $3ab + b^2$ (g) $9q^2 + 5q^3$ (h) $12m^2 + 6mp$
      (i) $3x + 4x$ (j) $15x^2 + 3x^2$ (k) $4t^2 + 3t^{-1}$ (l) $5t^{-1} + 2t^{-1}$

12.10 Write each of the following as a power

      (a) $\sqrt{3}$ (b) $\sqrt{4^2}$ (c) $\frac{1}{\sqrt{7}}$

      (d) $\frac{1}{\sqrt{5^2}}$ (e) $\sqrt[3]{3^2}$ (f) $\sqrt[4]{5^3}$

Note: Answers can be found on pp. 367–368.

12.5 Simple algebra
· ·

Algebra is the use of letters for numbers and is often known as the language of mathematics. A number of processes are often involved.

Substitution

One of the most important features of algebra is the use of expressions and formulae and the substitution of real numbers into them.

The value of an expression such as $3x + 2$ will change with the different values of x *substituted* into it.

WORKED
EXAMPLE **12.19**
· · · · · · · · · · · · · · · ·

Suppose the formula is given by $A = \dfrac{h(a + b)}{2}$

Then if $a = 4$, $b = 7$ and $h = 8$

$A = \dfrac{8(4 + 7)}{2} = 44$

Transposition

It is often necessary to be able to change a formulae round to help you find a particular piece of information.

This changing round of formulae is called *transposition* of formulae and what we are doing is changing the subject of a formulae. The *subject* of a formula is the single letter, or word, usually on the left-hand side all by itself.

For example:

t is the subject of the formula $t = \dfrac{d}{v}$

Here are some rules for changing the subjects of formulae:

Rule 1
You can move any letter, or word, from one side of the equation to the other as long as it is operating on *all* the rest of that side.

For example, in the formula $v = u + 6t$, the u can be moved since it is adding to the rest of that side, but the t cannot be moved yet as it is only multiplying the 6.

This simple list of formulae should help you see when we can move terms:

▶ $v = u + 6t$ we could move either the u or the $6t$
▶ $A = lb$ we could move either the l or the b
▶   wage = hours × hourly rate   we could move either hours or hourly rate
▶ $t = \dfrac{d}{v}$ we could move either the d or the v
▶ $x = \dfrac{y + 1}{7}$ we could move either the 7 or the $(y + 1)$
▶ $w = n(y - 10)$ we could move either the n or the $(y - 10)$

Rule 2
When a letter, or word, has been moved from one side to the other, it does the *opposite thing* to the other side.

For example, if something was added, then when it moved it would be subtracted, or if something was multiplied then when it moved it would divide.

WORKED EXAMPLE 12.20

The following examples will help to illustrate these points:

▶ $v = u + 6t$ can be changed to $v - u = 6t$
or $v - 6t = u$

▶ $A = lb$ can be changed to $\dfrac{A}{l} = b$
or $\dfrac{A}{b} = l$

▶ $t = \dfrac{d}{v}$ can be changed to $tv = d$
or $\dfrac{t}{d} = \dfrac{1}{v}$

▶ $y = 6x - 10$ can be changed to $y + 10 = 6x$
or $y - 6x = -10$

All your transposition or manipulation involving algebra can be summarised in the following principle.

If it is doing what it is doing to everything else on that side of the equation, then it can be moved to the other side and perform the opposite job.

Simplification

This is what we do in algebra to make expressions look as simple as possible. Only *like* terms can be added or subtracted, as follows:

$$3x + 4x = 7x \qquad 6x - 2x = 4x \qquad 3x^2 + 4x^2 = 7x^2$$
$$5y + y = 6y \qquad 4t - t = 3t \qquad 3y^3 + 2y^3 = 5y^3$$

Simplification can also involve either the *expansion* of brackets or the opposite process, namely *factorisation*, whereby a more complex expression is reduced to a simpler one involving brackets.

Expansion

'Expand' in mathematics means to multiply out the brackets.

For example,

Expand $3(2x - 5)$

means multiply the 3 by everything inside the bracket to give $6x - 15$.

If you are asked to expand $(x + 6)(x + 4)$ you need to multiply everything inside the first bracket by everything inside the second bracket, i.e.

$$(x + 6)(x + 4) = x(x + 4) + 6(x + 4)$$
$$= x^2 + 4x + 6x + 24$$
$$= x^2 + 10x + 24$$

This can be illustrated with a diagram.

figure 12.3

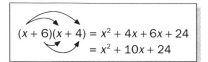

$$(x + 6)(x + 4) = x^2 + 4x + 6x + 24$$
$$= x^2 + 10x + 24$$

Factorisation

This means to separate an expression into the parts that will multiply together to give that expression. The two (or more) parts are usually connected by brackets.

For example

$4x + 8y$ would factorise and simplify to $4(x + 2y)$
$3y - 3x$ would factorise and simplify to $3(y - x)$

As we note below, these examples of factorisation involve *linear* expressions. However we are often faced with examples involving *quadratic* (highest power is a square) expressions.

Quadratic factorisation

For example:

Factorise and simplify the quadratic expression

$6x^2 + 5x - 6$

This process is the opposite to that shown in Figure 12.3 above for a quadratic expansion. We know that quadratic factorisation will involve *two* brackets. The quadratic expression can be thought to be of the general type:

$ax^2 + bx + c$

1   When the last sign in the quadratic $ax^2 + bx + c$ is *positive*, then both signs in the brackets are the *same as the first sign* in the quadratic. For example:

$$x^2 + 5x + 4 = (\ \ + \ \ )(\ \ + \ \ )$$

and $x^2 - 5x + 4 = (\ \ - \ \ )(\ \ - \ \ )$

2   When the last sign in the quadratic $ax^2 + bx - c$ is *negative*, then the signs in the brackets are *different*. For example:

$$x^2 + 5x - 5 = (\ \ + \ \ )(\ \ - \ \ )$$
$$\text{or} = (\ \ - \ \ )(\ \ + \ \ )$$

Once you've sorted out the *signs*, then you need to look at the *numbers*. Follow through these two examples to see how to do this.

Factorise $6x^2 + 7x + 2$

Solution

By looking at the signs we see that the brackets both contain a '+', so:

$6x^2 + 7x + 2 = (\quad + \quad)(\quad + \quad)$.

We see that the end numbers in each bracket must multiply to give 2, and the only way to do this is to have 2×1.

Hence $6x^2 + 7x + 2 = (\quad + 2)(\quad + 1)$.

Now we see that the first numbers in each bracket must multiply to give 6, and we could have 3×2 or 2×3 or 6×1 or 1×6, but the combination we need must multiply with the 2 and the 1, so that their sum is 7. We ask ourselves which of the vertical pairs

$\{3 \times 1\} \{2 \times 1\} \{6 \times 1\}$ or $\{1 \times 1\}$

$\{2 \times 2\} \{3 \times 2\} \{1 \times 2\}$ $\{6 \times 2\}$

give a combined total of 7, and we see that the only one which does is

$\{3 \times 1\}$

$\{2 \times 2\}$

so the factorisation is $(3x + 2)(2x + 1)$

Factorise $2x^2 + 5x - 3$

Solution

We factorise by looking at the signs and noticing that both signs will be different, hence
$(\quad + \quad)(\quad - \quad)$. The -3 indicates we need a 3 and a 1 at the end of each bracket to give
$(\quad + 3)(\quad - 1)$ or $(\quad + 1)(\quad - 3)$. Now, a product of 2 for the first numbers in each bracket, i.e. 2 and 1, must combine with the 3 and 1 in such a way as to give a difference of $+5$. This will give us $(x + 3)(2x - 1)$.

12.6 Solving equations

To *solve* an equation is to find the value or values which satisfy that equation.

For example,

Solve $4x + 3 = 23$

This is a *linear* equation (highest power is 1) and has a unique solution, namely $4x = 23 - 3$, giving $x = 5$. Only when $x = 5$ is this equation satisfied. Linear equations have only one solution.

When we are solving *quadratic* equations, we may find up to two solutions, i.e. two values of the variable which satisfy that equation. In solving quadratic equations it is usual to use either *factorisation* or the *formula method*.

Factorising quadratic equations

Take the general form of the quadratic equation:

$ax^2 + bx + c = 0$

If we can *factorise* this equation, i.e. reduce it to two brackets multiplied together, then we can set *either* bracket = 0 and find a solution.

WORKED EXAMPLE 12.23

Solve $x^2 + 2x - 15 = 0$

Solution

This factorises into $(x - 3)(x + 5) = 0$

The only way that this expression can ever equal 0 is if one of the brackets is worth 0. Hence either

$(x - 3) = 0$ or $(x + 5) = 0$

hence $x - 3 = 0$ or $x + 5 = 0$

hence $x = 3$ or $x = -5$

The solutions then are $x = 3$ and -5

Whether or not an equation will factorise, the next method will always give you the solution to a quadratic equation (where a solution exists!).

Formula for solving quadratic equations

A formula has been derived that can be used to solve any quadratic equation (or used to tell you that there is no solution). For a quadratic equation of the general form $ax^2 + bx + c = 0$:

$$x = \frac{-b \pm \sqrt{(b^2 - 4ac)}}{2a}$$

The use of the $\pm$ reflects the fact that a square root has a positive and a negative solution.

WORKED
EXAMPLE **12.24**

Solve the equation $3x^2 - 8x + 2 - 0$, correct to 2 d.p.

Solution

Use $x = \dfrac{-b \pm \sqrt{(b^2 - 4ac)}}{2a}$ where $a = 3$, $b = -8$ and $c = 2$

$= \dfrac{8 \pm \sqrt{\{64 - 4(3)(2)\}}}{6}$

$= \dfrac{8 \pm \sqrt{40}}{6} = \dfrac{8 + \sqrt{40}}{6}$ and $\dfrac{8 - \sqrt{40}}{6}$

$= 2.39$ or 0.28

12.7 Simultaneous equations

In business and economic situations we may, for example, need to find the price at which supply equals demand. We call this the *equilibrium price* as it balances both supply and demand. Put another way, it is the price which solves both the demand and supply equations *at the same time* (i.e. simultaneously).

It is therefore important that you know how to go about solving simultaneous equations. The idea in the example below is to *eliminate* either the x or the y variable, whether by addition or subtraction, so that we are left with one equation with one unknown variable. Having solved this equation we can then use the result to solve for the other unknown variable. Work through these examples yourself.

WORKED
EXAMPLE **12.25**

Solve the simultaneous equations $6x + y = 15$

$4x + y = 11$

Solution

Since both equations have a y term the same we can *subtract* one equation from the other to give

$$2x = 4$$

which solves to give $\qquad x = 2$

We now substitute $x = 2$ into one of the first equations (usually the one with the smallest numbers involved). So substitute $x = 2$ into $4x + y = 11$ to give $8 + y = 11$ which gives

$$y = 11 - 8$$

$$y = 3$$

We test our solution in the other initial equation.

Substitute $x = 2$ and $y = 3$ into $6x + y$ to give $12 + 3 = 15$, which is correct. So we can confidently say that our solution is $x = 2$ and $y = 3$.

WORKED EXAMPLE 12.26

Solve the simultaneous equations $4x - 2y = 12$

$$2x + 2y = 18$$

Solution

Since both equations have a $2y$ term but one with a + and one with a − then we can *add* one equation to the other to give

$$6x = 30$$

$$x = 5$$

Substitute $x = 5$ into, say, the lower equation to get

$$2 \times 5 + 2y = 18$$

$$10 + 2y = 18$$

$$2y = 18 - 10 = 8$$

$$y = 4$$

The solution of $x = 5$ and $y = 4$ can be checked in the top equation to give

$$(4 \times 5) - (2 \times 4) = 20 - 8 = 12$$

which is correct. So our solution is $x = 5$ and $y = 4$.

WORKED EXAMPLE 12.27

Solve the simultaneous equations $4x + 2y = 32$

$$3x - y = 19$$

Here we do not have any equal terms so we have to start creating them because that is the only way we can solve simultaneous equations. We can see that by multiplying *all* of the second equation by 2 we get

$$(3x - y = 19) \times 2 \Rightarrow 6x - 2y = 38$$

Our pair of equations is now $4x + 2y = 32$

$$6x - 2y = 38$$

and we can solve these as we did in Worked Example 12.26 by *adding* them together.

WORKED EXAMPLE 12.28

Solve the simultaneous equations $5x + 4y = 22$

$$2x + 3y = 16$$

Solution

Notice that we cannot simply multiply one equation by anything to give us equal terms. So we have to multiply *both* equations.

The choice is now up to us: we can either make the x's the same or the y's the same. Sometimes there is an obvious choice; sometimes it does not matter. In this example it does not matter which you do since there is no great advantage in choosing either.

Let us choose the x's to be made equal. We will have to multiply the first equation through by 2 and the second equation through by 5. This gives

$$(5x + 4y = 22) \times 2 \Rightarrow 10x + 8y = 44$$

and $(2x + 3y = 16) \times 5 \Rightarrow 10x + 15y = 80$

We now solve these in the same way as we did in Worked Example 12.25 by *subtracting* them from each other.

12.8 Inequalities

Inequalities behave similarly to normal equations. The difference is that they have an inequality sign instead of an equals sign.

Linear inequalities

For linear inequalities we use the same rules to solve inequalities as we do linear equations.

WORKED EXAMPLE 12.29

Solve $\dfrac{5x + 7}{3} < 14$

Solution

$5x + 7 < 14 \times 3$

$5x + 7 < 42$

$5x < 42 - 7$

$5x < 35$

$x < 35 \div 5$

$x < 7$

WORKED EXAMPLE 12.30

Solve the inequality $1 < 5x + 3 \leq 17$.

Solution

We need to treat each side separately as

$$1 < 5x + 3 \qquad 5x + 3 \leq 17$$
$$1 - 3 < 5x \qquad 5x \leq 17 - 3$$
$$-2 < 5x \qquad 5x \leq 14$$
$$\frac{-2}{5} < x \qquad x \leq \frac{14}{5}$$
$$-0.4 < x \qquad x \leq 2.8$$

Hence $-0.4 < x \leq 2.8$

Inequalities involving x^2

Consider $x^2 < 16$. Now, the solution to $x^2 = 16$ is $x = +4$ and $x = -4$. When we look at the $x = 4$ part we can see that, yes, $x < -4$ just does not work. In fact the solution to do with $x = -4$ needs the inequality sign changing round to give us the solution $x > -4$ which can be turned to give $-4 < x$.

Put all this on to a number line and you see the solution (Figure 12.4).

figure 12.4

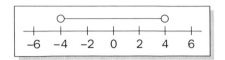

The solution is $-4 < x < 4$.

WORKED EXAMPLE **12.31**

Solve the inequality $x^2 > 25$

Solution

The solution to $x^2 > 25$ will be $x > 5$ and $x < -5$.
Notice the difference between the types $x^2 < a^2$ and the types $x^2 > a^2$.

12.9 Graphs and functions

A *function* is a rule describing the relationship between variables. Using the notation $y = f(x)$, we are indicating, in a type of shorthand, that the variable y *depends upon* (is a function of) some other variable x. We could then say that y is the *dependent variable* and x the *independent variable*, though our study of economics will alert us to the fact that relationships between variables are rarely in a single direction only.

The function or rule describing the relationship between variables may be specified more precisely. Thus $y = f(x) = 3x + 2$, will tell us that y takes the value 2 when $x = 0$ and rises by 3 units for every unit rise in x. This is an example of a *linear function*, of the general form $y = mx + c$, where c is the vertical intercept and m is the slope or gradient.

Linear Function

Where the highest power of the independent variable is 1, as in $y = 3x^1 + 2$, then we have a linear function or relationship. A *graph* or picture of this linear relationship between the variables is shown in Figure 12.5.

Quadratic Function

Where the highest power of the independent variable is 2, as in the case of $y = ax^2 + bx + c$, then we have a quadratic function or relationship. A graph of such a quadratic relationship between the variables is shown in Figure 12.6. The shape of this graph is called a *parabola*, and will be $\cup$-shaped where a is positive and $\cap$-shaped where a is negative. The vertical intercept will again be determined by the value of c.

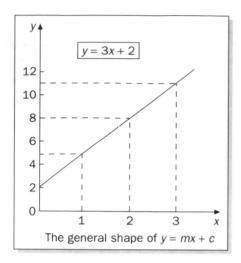

figure 12.5
Linear function

The general shape of $y = mx + c$

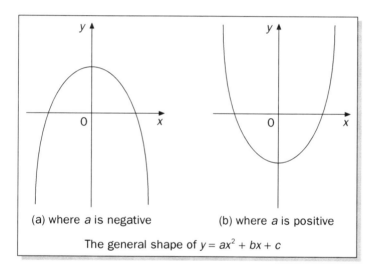

figure 12.6
Quadratic function

(a) where *a* is negative   (b) where *a* is positive

The general shape of $y = ax^2 + bx + c$

Cubic Function

Where the highest power of the independent variable is 3, as in the case of $y = ax^3 + bx^2 + cx + d$, then we have a cubic function or relationship. A graph of such a cubic relationship between the variables is shown in Figure 12.7.

You should, of course, be familiar with other functional relationships.

▶ **Exponential:** of the form $y = a^x$, where *a* is any constant > 1 and *x* is any variable. Figure 12.8 graphs the exponential relationship $y = 2^x$ over the values $x = 1$ to 5.

▶ **Reciprocal (Hyperbolic):** of the form $y = \dfrac{a}{x}$, where *a* is any constant and *x* any variable. Figure 12.9 graphs the reciprocal (hyperbolic) relationship of $y = \dfrac{6}{x}$ over the values $x = 1$ to 6.

figure 12.7
Cubic function

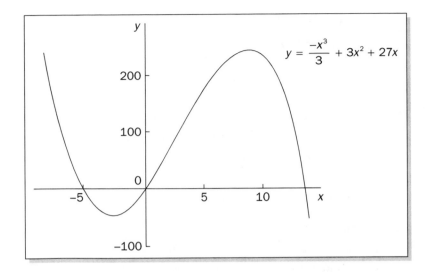

$$y = \frac{-x^3}{3} + 3x^2 + 27x$$

figure 12.8
Exponential function

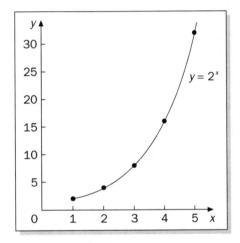

$y = 2^x$

figure 12.9
**Reciprocal
(hyperbolic function)**

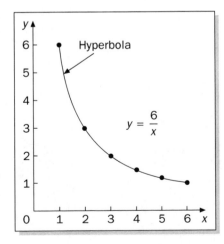

Hyperbola

$$y = \frac{6}{x}$$

Gradients to graphs

Linear Functions

The general form of the linear function is:

$y = mx + c$

where m is the gradient and c the vertical intercept.

The slope or gradient of the line joining two points measures how 'steep' the line is and is defined as the fraction:

$$\frac{\text{difference between the } y \text{ co-ordinates of the points}}{\text{difference between the } x \text{ co-ordinates of the points}}$$

Gradient between $(x_1 \; y_1)$, $(x_2 \; y_2)$

$$\text{Gradient} = \frac{(y_2 - y_1)}{(x_2 - x_1)}$$

$$\text{Gradient} = \frac{\text{vertical distance}}{\text{horizontal distance}}$$

In Figure 12.10

$$\text{Gradient} = \frac{7 - 3}{3 - 1} = \frac{4}{2} = +2$$

figure 12.10

Gradient of straight line

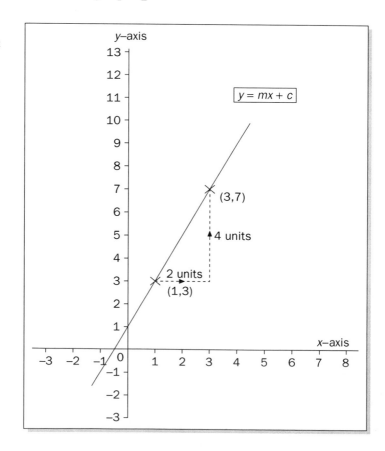

Non-linear Functions

Here we use *calculus* (see Chapter 11) to find the gradient to a point on a curve. The process by which we *differentiate* the function will give us the required gradient.

ACTIVITY **8**

A restaurant is considering a new vegetarian meal and has test marketed the product. The tests showed that if 280 pence is charged for the meal it will sell 1,600 units per restaurant per week, whilst at a price of 320 pence it sells 1,400 units.

Assuming that the demand curve for the product is linear, find its equation (i.e. find *m* and *c*).

$$P = c + mQ$$

1 Construct the demand schedule.
   (i)   Label column **A: Quantity** and column **B: Price (in pence)**.
   (ii) Enter the price data from 600 to 0 in increments of –25.
   (iii) Use the demand equation formula to calculate how many units can be sold at each of these prices.
         This will be easier to accomplish if the demand equation is rewritten to make Q the subject of the equation.
2 Plot the demand curve.
3 In column **C** calculate the firm's total revenue at each price.
   What price will maximise the firm's total revenue?
4 In column **D** calculate the price elasticity of demand (P.E.D.) at each price where:

$$P.E.D. = \left(\frac{\Delta Q}{\Delta P}\right) \times \left(\frac{P}{Q}\right)$$

   What is the price elasticity of demand when revenue is maximised?
5 Plot the graph showing the total revenue curve.
6 Using columns **E** and **F** construct data for total cost and profits at each potential level of output.
   The restaurant have estimated the total cost equation for the product (in pence) as:

$$TC = 100,000 + 2Q + 0.1Q^2$$

   Note that this is a quadratic equation where the 100,000 represents the fixed costs assigned to the product.

   Which output and price maximises profits?
   Is this the same output/price combination that maximises total revenue?

7 Plot a graph showing TR, TC and profits.
8 Use the spreadsheet to investigate changes in fixed costs on the profit maximising output/price combination – try increasing fixed costs by 20,000.
9 Return fixed costs to their original level.

10 From the previous graph find the levels of output where the firm breaks even (this will be approximate).

Try to get a more accurate answer from the spreadsheet by altering *P*.

11 Use the formula:

Profit = TR − TC

to solve the quadratic profit equation which will disclose the break-even output.

Responses and solutions to this activity can be found on pp. 471–472.

12.10 Progressions

Two types of progression are frequently used in quantitative solutions, namely arithmetic and geometric progressions.

Arithmetic progressions (AP)

This is a sequence of terms in which an initial term, *a*, changes by a constant absolute amount, called the 'common difference' (*d*).

An **arithmetic progression** involving *n* terms takes the following form:

$a, a + d, a + 2d, a + 3d, a + 4d \ldots a + (n - 1)d$

Examples: $5, 7, 9, 11, 13 \ldots (a = 5, \quad d = +2)$

$\qquad 43, 39, 35, 31, 27 \ldots (a = 43, d = -4)$

Note that the third term is $a + 2d$, the fourth terms is $a + 3d$, and so on, so that the *n*th term is $a + (n - 1)d$, where *n* can be any number.

If we sum the *n* terms of an arithmetic progression (AP), then we can use the formula:

Sum of Arithmetic Progression

$$S_n = \frac{n}{2}[2a + (n - 1)d]$$

where S_n = sum of AP over *n* terms
$\qquad n$ = number of terms
$\qquad a$ = initial term
$\qquad d$ = common difference

WORKED EXAMPLE 12.32

A businessman pays his employee a salary of £10,000 per annum; at the end of each year he receives an annual increment of £400.

Calculate (a) the employee's salary during the 6th year
$\qquad\qquad$ (b) the total salary received by the employee during the six years.

Solution

This is an arithmetic progression (AP) with an initial amount (*a*) of £10,000 which rises by a common difference (*d*) of £400 per annum.

(a) When *n* = 6, the sixth term of an AP will be $a + (n - 1)d$

$$= £10,000 + (6 - 1)£400$$

$$= £12,000$$

The employee receives £12,000 in the sixth year

(b) $S_n = \dfrac{n}{2}[2a + (n - 1)d]$

$S_6 = \dfrac{6}{2}[2(£10,000) + (6 - 1)£400]$

$S_6 = 3[£20,000 + £2,000]$

$S_6 = £66,000$

The employee receives £66,000 salary during the first six years of employment.

The box below gives a proof of the formula for summing an arithmetic progression

---

Proof of AP formula

$$S_n = a + [a + d] + [a + 2d] + \ldots [a + (n - 2)d] + [a + (n - 1)d]$$

S_n (backward) $= [a + (n - 1)d] + [a + (n - 2d)] + \ldots [a + d] + a$

∴ adding term by term

$$2S_n = [2a + (n - 1)d] + [2a + (n - 1)d] + [2a + (n - 1)d] + [2a + (n - 1)d] + [2a + (n - 1)d]$$

$2S_n = n[2a + (n - 1)d]$

$$S_n = \dfrac{n}{2}[2a + (n - 1)d]$$

Geometric progressions (GP)

A **geometric progression** occurs where an initial amount (*a*) changes by a 'common ratio' (*r*) in successive terms.

A geometric progression involving *n* terms takes the following form:

$a,\ ar,\ ar^2,\ ar^3 \ldots ar^{n-1}$

Examples

$3,\ 6,\ 12,\ 24,\ 48 \ldots (a = 3,\ r = 2)$

$200,\ 100,\ 50,\ 25,\ 12.5 \ldots (a = 200,\ r = \dfrac{1}{2})$

Note that the third term is ar^2, the fourth term is ar^3, and so on, so that the nth term is ar^{n-1}, where n can be any number.

If we sum the n terms of a geometric progression (GP), then we can use the formula

---

Sum of geometric progression

$$S_n = \frac{a\,(1 - r^n)}{(1 - r)}$$

where S_n = Sum of GP over n terms
n = number of terms
a = initial term
r = common ratio (as a fraction or a decimal)

WORKED
EXAMPLE **12.33**
....

An employee makes an annual investment of £1,000 in shares this year. He instructs his broker to increase this annual investment by 5 per cent each year.

(a) How much does he invest in the sixth year?
(b) How much does he invest altogether over the first six years?

Solution

This is a GP, with a = £1,000 and r = 1.05

(a) When $n = 6$, the sixth term of a GP will be:

$$ar^{n-1} = ar^{6-1} = ar^5$$

$$£1,000(1.05)^5 = £1,276.28$$

He invests £1,276.28 in the sixth year

(b) $S_n = \dfrac{a(1 - r^n)}{(1 - r)}$

$$S_6 = \frac{1,000[1 - (1.05)^6]}{(1 - 1.05)} = \frac{1,000[1 - 1.3401]}{-0.05}$$

$$S_6 = \frac{1,000[-0.3401]}{-0.05} = \frac{-340.1}{-0.05}$$

$$S_6 = £6,802$$

He invests £6,802 over the six years.

The box below gives a proof of the formula for summing a geometric progression.

Proof of GP formula

$$S_n = a + ar + ar^2 + \ldots + ar^{n-2} + ar^{n-1}$$

$$\therefore rS_n = \quad ar + ar^2 + \ldots + ar^{n-2} + ar^{n-1} + ar^n$$

$$S_n - rS_n = a \qquad\qquad\qquad\qquad\qquad\qquad - ar^n$$

$$\text{i.e.} \quad S_n(1 - r) = a - ar^n$$

$$S_n = \frac{a(1 - r^n)}{(1 - r)}$$

12.11 Make y the subject of the following formulae:

(a) $x = 2(y - 1)$ (b) $x = y(b + 7)$ (c) $t = 5y + \dfrac{p}{7}$

12.12 Expand the following and simplify:

(a) $(2x - 3)(4x + 1)$ (b) $(3x + 5)(x - 3)$ (c) $p(2m + t) - t(3m - p)$

12.13 Factorise the following:

(a) $3t + 7t^2$ (b) $2m^3 - 6m^2$ (c) $6mp^2 + 9m^2pt$

(d) $x^2 - 7x + 12$ (e) $x^2 - 25$ (f) $2x^2 - x - 15$

12.14 Solve the following equations:

(a) $2x - 3 = 11$ (b) $3 - 5x = 8$ (c) $4(2x - 3) = 7$

12.15 Solve the following quadratic equations, to 2 d.p. where necessary:

(a) $x^2 + 7x + 12 = 0$ (b) $5x^2 + 6x - 2 = 0$ (c) $x^2 + 4x - 117 = 0$

12.16 Solve the following pairs of simultaneous equations:

(a) $5x + y = 0$ (b) $7x + 3y = 18$

     $3x - 2y = 13$ $x + y = 4$

12.17 Solve the following inequalities:

(a) $5x > 32$ (b) $4t < 5t - 8$ (c) $x^2 < 36$ (d) $-2 \leq 5x + 3 < 4$

12.18 Complete this table of values for $y = x^2 + x - 6$:

x	−4	−3	−2	−1	0	1	2	3
x^2		9			0		4	
$+x$	−4	−3				1	2	3
−6	−6	−6			−6		−6	
y	6		−4	−6				

(a) Use the table to draw the graph of $y = x^2 + x - 6$ as x takes values from −4 to 3.

(b) Use your graph to solve $y = x^2 + x - 6 = 0$

12.19 Find the gradient of the straight line which connects the points (−2, −3) and (4, 9)

12.20 Use an appropriate *formula* to sum the following progressions to eight terms

(a) 42, 46, 50, 54 . . .
(b) 200, 195, 190, 185 . . .
(c) 4, 6, 9, 13.5 . . .
(d) 1,000, 500, 250, 125 . . .

Note: **Answers can be found on pp. 368–369.**

**REVIEW
QUESTIONS**

12.1 Nearly a third of large and medium sized companies said they regarded overqualified (graduate) applicants for low level unskilled jobs as a problem. In reply it was argued that in 1980 one in eight school leavers went on to take a degree. Today (2001) the proportion is one in three, meaning that as a group they cannot be regarded as high fliers. Find

(a) how many of the 474 companies interviewed were concerned about this problem?
(b) if the number of school leavers was constant over the period at 900,000 how many went to university in 1980 and 2001?

12.2 In a 2000 survey of British pop wealth in *Business Age* magazine, David Bowie came top with £550m, Paul McCartney came second with £520m and Gary Barlow 50th with £9.5m. The youngest person in the top 50 was Baby Spice with £14.5m.

(a) What percentage is Gary Barlow's wealth of Baby Spice's wealth?
(b) By what percentage would Paul McCartney's wealth have to increase by before it equalled that of David Bowie's?

12.3 On Monday 27 October 1997 the Dow Jones share index in New York fell by 7 per cent to 7,161.15 (the biggest one day fall since Black Monday in 1987). What was the index at the start of the day?

12.4 A company produces a product for which the variable cost per unit is £5 and the fixed costs are £20,000. If the selling price is £15 per unit

(a) how many units (Q) does the company need to sell in order to make £8,000 profit?
(b) At what level of output would the firm break even (i.e. total revenue = total costs)
(c) New environmental legislation increases the company's fixed costs by 20 per cent, by what percentage does this increase the break-even output?
(d) Plot the firms Fixed Costs, Total Costs (before and after the increase) and Total Revenue on a graph. Mark the break-even outputs of b) and c) on the graph.
Make use of the following relationships:

Total cost   = fixed costs + variable costs
Total revenue = price per unit × number of units sold
Profit   = total revenue – total cost

12.5 It is estimated that if a price of £15 per unit is charged for a product five units per period will be sold. If the price is lowered to £13, sales will be six units per period.

The supply curve for the product is given by $P = 3Q + 5$.

    (a) Assuming that the demand relationship is linear, find the demand equation.

    (b) Find the equilibrium price and quantity (i.e. the price where quantity demanded = quantity supplied).

12.6 *Note:* the intention of Question A6 is to practice your mathematics and graph drawing and not break-even analysis (see Chapter 10).

A firm's total revenue and total cost equations are given by:

Total costs $= Q^2 + 23$
Total revenue $= -2Q^2 + 26Q$

    (a) Find the output levels at which the firm just breaks even.

    (b) Plot the graph of total costs, total revenue and profits and show that the profit maximising output is mid-way between the break-even outputs.

Note: Answers to review questions can be found on pp. 456–458.

Further study and data
••••••••••••••••••••••••

Texts

Bancroft, G. and O'Sullivan, G. (1993), *Quantitative methods for accounting and business studies*, 3rd edn, McGraw Hill, chapters 1 and 2.

Curwin, J. and Slater, R. (1996), *Quantitative methods for business decisions*, 4th edn, International Thompson Business Press, chapter 6.

Morris, C. (1999), *Quantitative approaches in business studies*, 5th edn, Pitman, chapter 1.

Swift, L. (2001), *Quantitative methods for business, management and finance*, Palgrave Publishers, parts EM and MM.

Thomas, R. (1997), *Quantitative methods for business studies*, Prentice Hall, appendix.

Waters, D. (1997), *Quantitative methods for business*, 2nd edn, Addison Wesley Longman, chapters 1 and 2.

Wisniewski, M. with Stead, R. (1996), *Foundation quantitative methods for business*, Pitman, chapter 2.

On-line exercises
•••••••••••••••••••••

Check the web site *www.booksites.net/burton* to find extra questions, Spreadsheet and on-line exercises for this chapter.

Appendix 2

Σ Notation; E and V Operators; Using Logarithms

Appendix 1A Σ notation

The Greek symbol Σ (capital sigma) means 'add up' and is a shorthand way of writing what would otherwise be long algebraic expressions. For example, given the following observations on x:

x_1	x_2	x_3	x_4	x_5
3	5	6	4	8

then

$$\sum_{i=1}^{5} x_i = x_1 + x_2 + x_3 + x_4 + x_5 = 3 + 5 + 6 + 4 + 8 = 26$$

To expand the sigma expression, the subscript i is replaced by successive integers, beginning with the one below the Σ sign and ending with the one above it. Similarly

$$\sum_{i=2}^{4} x_i = x_2 + x_3 + x_4 = 5 + 6 + 4 = 15$$

When it is clear what range of values i takes, the formula can be simplified to $\Sigma_i x_i$ or Σx_i or even Σx.

When frequencies are associated with each of the observations, as in the data below:

i	1	2	3	4	5
x_i	3	5	6	4	8
f_i	2	2	4	3	1

then

$$\sum_{i=1}^{i=5} f_i x_i = f_1 x_1 + \ldots + f_5 x_5 = 2 \times 3 + \ldots + 1 \times 8 = 60$$

and

$$\Sigma f_i = 2 + 2 + 4 + 3 + 1 = 12$$

Thus the sum of the 12 observations is 60 and the mean is

$$\frac{\Sigma fx}{\Sigma f} = \frac{60}{12} = 5$$

Further examples are:

$$\Sigma x^2 = x_1^2 + x_2^2 + \ldots + x_5^2 = 150$$

$$(\Sigma x)^2 = (x_1 + x_2 + \ldots + x_5)^2 = 676$$

$$\Sigma fx^2 = f_1 x_1^2 + f_2 x_2^2 + \ldots + f_5 x_5^2 = 2 \times 3^2 + 2 \times 5^2 + \ldots + 1 \times 8^2 = 324$$

Using Σ notation we can see the effect of transforming x by dividing by 1000, as was done in calculating the average level of wealth. Instead of working with x we used kx, where $k = 1/1000$. In finding the mean we calculated

$$(1.34) \qquad \frac{\Sigma kx}{N} = \frac{kx_1 + kx_2 + \dots}{N} = \frac{k(x_1 + x_2 + \dots)}{N} = k\frac{\Sigma x}{N}$$

so to find the mean of the original variable x we had to divide by k again, i.e. multiply by 1000. In general, whenever each observation in a sum is multiplied by a constant, the constant can be taken outside the summation operator, as in (1.34) above.

Problems on Σ notation

Problem 1A.1   Given the following data on x_i: {4, 6, 3, 2, 5}, evaluate:

$$\Sigma x_i, \; \Sigma x_i^2, \; (\Sigma x_i)^2, \; \Sigma(x_i - 3), \; \Sigma x_i - 3, \; \sum_{i=2}^{4} x_i$$

Problem 1A.2   Given the following data on x_i: {8, 12, 6, 4, 10}, evaluate:

$$\Sigma x_i, \; \Sigma x_i^2, \; (\Sigma x_i)^2, \; \Sigma(x_i - 3), \; \Sigma x_i - 3, \; \sum_{i=2}^{4} x_i$$

Problem 1A.3   Given the following frequencies, f_i, associated with the x values in Problem A1: {5, 3, 3, 8, 5}, evaluate:

$$\Sigma fx, \; \Sigma fx^2, \; \Sigma f(x - 3), \; \Sigma fx - 3$$

Problem 1A.4   Given the following frequencies, f_i, associated with the x values in Problem 1.A2: {10, 6, 6, 16, 10}, evaluate:

$$\Sigma fx, \; \Sigma fx^2, \; \Sigma f(x - 3), \; \Sigma fx - 3$$

Problem 1A.5   Given the pairs of observations on x and y,

x	4	3	6	8	12
y	3	9	1	4	3

evaluate:

$$\Sigma xy, \; \Sigma x(y - 3), \; \Sigma(x + 2)(y - 1)$$

Problem 1A.6   Given the pairs of observations on x and y,

x	3	7	4	1	9
y	1	2	5	1	2

evaluate:

$$\Sigma xy, \; \Sigma x(y - 2), \; \Sigma(x - 2)(y + 1).$$

Problem 1A.7 Demonstrate that

$$\frac{\Sigma f(x - k)}{\Sigma f} = \frac{\Sigma fx}{\Sigma f} - k$$

where k is a constant.

Problem 1A.8 Demonstrate that

$$\frac{\Sigma f(x - \mu)^2}{\Sigma f} = \frac{\Sigma fx^2}{\Sigma f} - \mu^2$$

Appendix 1B   E and V operators

These operators are an extremely useful form of notation that we shall make use of later in the book. It is quite easy to keep track of the effects of data transformations using them. There are a few simple rules for manipulating them that allow some problems to be solved quickly and elegantly.

$E(x)$ is the mean of a distribution and $V(x)$ is its variance. We showed above in (1.34) that multiplying each observation by a constant k multiplies the mean by k. We can express this as:

(1.35) $E(kx) = kE(x)$

If a constant is added to every observation the effect is to add that constant to the mean (see Problem 1.23):

(1.36) $E(x + a) = E(x) + a$

(Graphically, the whole distribution is shifted a units to the right and hence so is the mean.) Combining (1.35) and (1.36):

(1.37) $E(kx + a) = kE(x) + a$

Similarly for the variance operator it can be shown that:

(1.38) $V(x + k) = V(x)$

Proof:

$$V(x + k) = \frac{\Sigma((x + k) - (\mu + k))^2}{N} = \frac{\Sigma((x - \mu) + (k - k))^2}{N} = \frac{\Sigma(x - \mu)^2}{N} = V(x)$$

(A shift of the whole distribution leaves the variance unchanged.) Also:

(1.39) $V(kx) = k^2V(x)$

(See Problem 1.24 above.) This is why, when the wealth figures were divided by 1000, the variance became divided by 1000^2. Applying (1.38) and (1.39):

(1.40) $V(kx + a) = k^2V(x)$

Finally, we should note that V itself can be expressed in terms of E:

(1.41) $V(x) = E(x - E(x))^2$

Appendix 1C — Using logarithms

Logarithms are less often used now that cheap electronic calculators are available. Formerly logarithms were an indispensable aid to calculation. However, the logarithmic transformation is useful in other contexts in statistics and economics so its use is briefly set out here.

The logarithm (to the base 10) of a number x is defined as the power to which 10 must be raised to give x. For example, $10^2 = 100$, so the log of 100 is 2 and we write $\log_{10} 100 = 2$ or simply $\log 100 = 2$.

Similarly, the log of 1000 is 3 ($1000 = 10^3$), of 10 000 it is 4, etc. We are not restricted to integer (whole number) powers of 10, so for example $10^{2.5} = 316.227766$ (try this if you have a scientific calculator), so the log of 316.227766 is 2.5. Every number x can therefore be represented by its logarithm.

Multiplication of two numbers

We can use logarithms to multiply two numbers x and y, based on the property

$$\log xy = \log x + \log y$$

For example, to multiply 316.227766 by 10:

$$\log(316.227766 \times 10) = \log 316.227766 + \log 10$$
$$= 2.5 + 1$$
$$= 3.5$$

The *anti-log* of 3.5 is given by $10^{3.5} = 3162.27766$ which is the answer.

Taking the anti-log (i.e. 10 raised to a power) is the inverse of the log transformation. Schematically we have:

$x \rightarrow$ take logarithms $\rightarrow a\ (= \log x) \rightarrow$ raise 10 to the power $a \rightarrow x$

Division

To divide one number by another we subtract the logs. For example, to divide 316.227766 by 100:

$$\log(316.227766/100) = \log 316.227766 - \log 100$$
$$= 2.5 - 2$$
$$= 0.5$$

and

$$10^{0.5} = 3.16227766$$

Powers and roots

Logarithms simplify the process of raising a number to a power. To find the square of a number, multiply the logarithm by 2, e.g. to find 316.227766^2:

$$\log(316.227766^2) = 2 \log(316.227766) = 5$$

and

$$10^5 = 100\ 000$$

To find the square root of a number (equivalent to raising it to the power $\frac{1}{2}$) divide the log by 2. To find the nth root, divide the log by n. For example, in the text we have to find the 32nd root of 16.936:

$$\frac{\log(16.936)}{32} = 0.0384$$

and

$$10^{0.0384} = 1.092$$

Common and natural logarithms

Logarithms to the base 10 are known as common logarithms but one can use any number as the base. *Natural* logarithms are based on the number e (= 2.71828 . . .) and we write ln x instead of log x to distinguish them from common logarithms. So, for example,

ln 316.227766 = 5.756462732

since

$$e^{5.756462732} = 316.227766$$

Natural logarithms can be used in the same way as common logarithms and have similar properties. Use the 'ln' key on your calculator just as you would the 'log' key, but remember that the inverse transformation is e^x rather than 10^x.

Problems on logarithms

Problem 1C.1 Find the common logarithms of: 0.15, 1.5, 15, 150, 1500, 83.7225, 9.15, –12.

Problem 1C.2 Find the log of the following values: 0.8, 8, 80, 4, 16, –37.

Problem 1C.3 Find the natural logarithms of: 0.15, 1.5, 15, 225, –4.

Problem 1C.4 Find the ln of the following values: 0.3, e, 3, 33, –1.

Problem 1C.5 Find the anti-log of the following values: –0.823909, 1.1, 2.1, 3.1, 12.

Problem 1C.6 Find the anti-log of the following values: –0.09691, 2.3, 3.3, 6.3.

Problem 1C.7 Find the anti-ln of the following values: 2.70805, 3.70805, 1, 10.

Problem 1C.8 Find the anti-ln of the following values: 3.496508, 14, 15, –1.

Problem 1C.9 Evaluate: $\sqrt[2]{10}$, $\sqrt[4]{3.7}$, $4^{1/4}$, 12^{-3}, $25^{-3/2}$.

Problem 1C.10 Evaluate: $\sqrt[3]{30}$, $\sqrt[6]{17}$, $8^{1/4}$, 15^0, 12^0, $3^{-1/3}$.

Appendix 3

Calculus and Business Applications

## CHAPTER 11

Calculus and business applications

Objectives
....

When you have read this chapter you should be able to:

▶ use the process of *differentiation* to calculate turning points, both maximum and minimum;

▶ apply differentiation to situations involving two variables *and* to situations involving more than two variables (*partial differentiation*);

▶ solve a variety of business related problems using the process of differentiation, such as the output/ price the business must set if it seeks the maximisation of revenue or profit, or the minimisation of cost, etc.;

▶ use the process of *integration* to calculate areas under a curve;

▶ solve a variety of business related problems using the process of integration, such as the total revenue, profit or cost of producing various levels of output, etc.

Introduction
....

In this chapter we look at the idea of **calculus** and its application to the solution of a number of business related problems. We have already seen (Chapter 10) how we can find maximum or minimum solutions involving *linear* relationships between variables. Here we see how calculus helps us find maximum or minimum solutions involving *non-linear* relationships between variables.

Calculus can, for our purposes, be regarded as involving two key processes, namely **differentiation** and **integration**. We consider each of these processes separately, beginning with differentiation.

Some basic mathematical techniques are reviewed in Chapter 12 (p. 284) and may help you with this chapter.

Answers to the 'Self-check questions', responses to each 'Pause for thought' and answers to the 'Review questions' can be found at the end of the book.

11.1 Differentiation
....

Differentiation refers to the process whereby we calculate the gradient to a curve at any point. Clearly for a *linear function* or equation $y = mx + c$, the gradient, m, is a constant at every point. In Figure 12.5 (p. 304) the gradient of the curve $y = 3x + 2$ is clearly + 3 at all points along that curve.

However to find the gradient to a *non-linear function*. We would need to draw a straight line touching the curve at each particular point (the *tangent* to that point) and then find the slope (*gradient*) of that tangent. Clearly in Figure 12.6 ((a) and (b), p. 304) gradients to these non-linear (quadratic) functions will be changing at each and every point (i.e. for different values of *x*). It would be extremely tedious to draw and measure the gradients to a large number of points along non-linear functions.

We can short-circuit this whole process by using the technique of *differentiation*. We can then establish a formula which will give the value of the

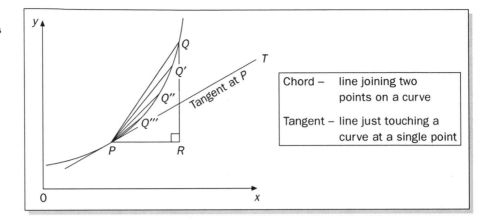

figure 11.1
Gradients and limits

Chord – line joining two points on a curve

Tangent – line just touching a curve at a single point

tangent drawn at any point on the curve. This formula is often referred to as the *first derivative* of the curve. So important is this technique to understanding much of the analysis underpinning the solution of business related problems that we shall consider it in some detail.

Gradients and limits

The idea of **limits** is central to understanding the process of differentiation. In fact we shall see that the slope of a *tangent* just touching a curve is in fact the limit of the slope of a *chord* joining two points along that curve. In Figure 11.1 we can connect two separate points on the curve, namely P and Q, by drawing the straight line PQ. This chord can easily be depicted as the hypotenuse of the right-angled triangle PQR, and from trigonometry we know that the tan. of angle QPR will give us the slope of the chord.

Slope of chord PQ = tan. QPR

$$= \frac{\text{side opposite}}{\text{side adjacent}}$$

$$= \frac{QR}{PR}$$

PAUSE FOR THOUGHT 11.1 *Can you suggest three other examples illustrating the idea of a limit?*

We can always calculate the slope of a chord since we can find the actual values for QR and PR. However we cannot actually calculate the slope of a tangent. But what we can do is take the *limit* of the slope of a chord as a close approximation to the slope of a tangent to that point on the curve. It will be useful to use Figure 11.1 to explain this.

As Q approaches (gets nearer to) P along the curve, the slope of the chord PQ gets closer and closer to the slope of the *tangent* at P, namely PT. Of course another way of expressing the idea of Q approaching P is to say that PR (the base of the triangle) tends to zero, i.e. $PR \rightarrow 0$. As long as P and Q are separate

figure 11.2
**Process of
differentiation**

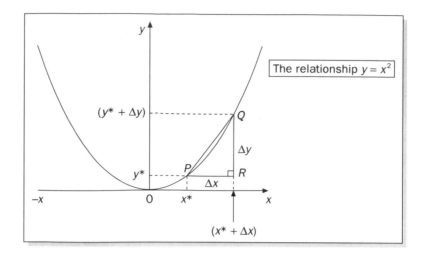

points along the curve, the slope of PQ will never actually equal the slope of PT, but it will become so close to the value of PT that for all intents and purposes it can be regarded as identical. We can use the following shorthand to express this idea (using Figure 11.1 on page 251).

Slope of tangent PT = limit to the slope of the chord PQ, as Q approaches P

i.e. Slope of tangent $PT = \underset{PR \to 0}{\text{limit}} \left(\dfrac{QR}{PR} \right)$

We now apply these ideas to curves involving the dependent variable y and the independent variable x. For purposes of illustration we shall use the simple *quadratic* relationship $y = x^2$ as in Figure 11.2. The symbol Δ refers to a *change* in any variable.

We construct a chord PQ connecting point P (with co-ordinates x^*, y^*) and point Q (with co-ordinates $x^* + \Delta x$, $y^* + \Delta y$).

Following our earlier reasoning we can state the following:

Slope of tangent to curve at $P = \underset{PR \to 0}{\text{limit}} \left(\dfrac{QR}{PR} \right)$

Slope of tangent to curve at $P = \underset{\Delta x \to 0}{\text{limit}} \left(\dfrac{\Delta y}{\Delta x} \right)$

Slope of tangent to curve at $P = \dfrac{dy}{dx}$

The expression $\dfrac{dy}{dx}$ is merely shorthand for the expression directly above it, and is termed the *first derivative*. Put another way we have *differentiated* the variable y with respect to x. Of course what we have done is to find an expression for the slope of the *tangent* to any point on the curve as being the limit of a known expression for the slope of the *chord* to that curve.

From Figure 11.2 we can show that for the curve $y = x^2$, the first derivative will always be $\dfrac{dy}{dx} = 2x$ at each and every point on that curve. The workings behind this solution are indicated in Box 1 at the end of this chapter (p. 279).

This extremely powerful result tells us that for any given value of x we can find the slope of the tangent to the curve at that point.

Thus for $x = 1$, the slope of the tangent to the curve at $x = 1$ is

$$\frac{dy}{dx} = 2x = 2(1) = 2;$$

for $x = 2$, the slope of the tangent to the curve at $x = 2$ is

$$\frac{dy}{dx} = 2x = 2(2) = 4; \text{ and so on.}$$

If we repeat this process for other curves then we shall see that a *pattern* emerges which forms the basis for an important formula used in differentiation.

Suppose we differentiate (find $\dfrac{dy}{dx}$ for) the curve $y = 3x^2$ using our earlier approach. As we can see from Box 2 at the end of this chapter (p. 279), the solution will be that $\dfrac{dy}{dx} = 6x$.

Thus for $x = 1$, the slope of the tangent to the curve $y = 3x^2$ at $x = 1$ is

$$\frac{dy}{dx} = 6x = 6(1) = 6;$$

for $x = 2$, the slope of the tangent to the curve at $x = 2$ is

$$\frac{dy}{dx} = 6x = 6(2) = 12;$$

and so on.

General Formula for Differentiation

In fact the pattern which will always result from such differentiation will give us the following general formula.

> If $y = ax^n$
>
> when a = any constant
>
> x = any variable
>
> n = any power
>
> then $\dfrac{dy}{dx} = nax^{n-1}$

Thus if $y = 1x^2$

$$\frac{dy}{dx} = 2 \cdot 1x^{2-1} = 2x$$

and if $y = 3x^2$

$$\frac{dy}{dx} = 2 \cdot 3x^{2-1} = 6x$$

and so on.

This extremely powerful result will allow us to find (in the limit) the slope of the tangent drawn to any point on a particular curve.

PAUSE FOR THOUGHT 11.2 *Can you suggest what we get if we differentiate, respectively, the equations for the following curves:*

(a) Total cost
(b) Total revenue
(c) Total profit?

SELF-CHECK QUESTIONS

11.1 Use the 'rule' for differentiation to find the gradient ($\frac{dy}{dx}$) to each of the following expressions

(a) $y = 9x$ (b) $y = 4x^2$ (c) $y = 3x^3$ (d) $y = 5x^4$

(e) $y = \frac{x^3}{3}$ (i.e. $y = \frac{1}{3}x^3$)   (f) $y = \frac{x^4}{4}$ (i.e. $y = \frac{1}{4}x^4$)

(g) $y = \sqrt{x}$ (i.e. $y = x^{\frac{1}{2}}$)   (h) $y = \sqrt[3]{x}$ (i.e. $y = x^{\frac{1}{3}}$)

(i) $y = \sqrt[3]{x^2}$ (i.e. $y = x^{\frac{2}{3}}$)   (j) $y = 10$ (i.e. $y = 10x^0$)

Note: question (g) to (h) make use of your knowledge of powers/ indices – see Chapter 12, p. 293).

11.2 For each of the curves or lines given by the expressions in Question 11.1 above, find the value of the gradient at:

(i) $x = 1$
(ii) $x = 2$

Note: Answers can be found on p. 360.

11.2 Turning points
....

Clearly the ideas of *maxima* and *minima* (i.e. **turning points**) are vital to many business related problems. As we can see from Figure 11.3(a) the value of the first derivative (the gradient) $\frac{dy}{dx}$ will be zero for any turning point, whether maximum or minimum. In other words we can differentiate the equation of the curve $y = x^3$ by finding $\frac{dy}{dx}$. If we plot $\frac{dy}{dx} (= 3x^2)$ against x, as in Figure 11.3(b), set $\frac{dy}{dx} = 0$ and solve for x, then for a quadratic equation we can expect two solutions for the turning points x_1 and x_2.

Unfortunately we will not, at this stage, be able to distinguish between the maximum and minimum solutions. However by taking second derivatives (i.e. finding the gradient of the gradient), we can distinguish between the different turning points.

figure 11.3

Using differentiation to identify turning points

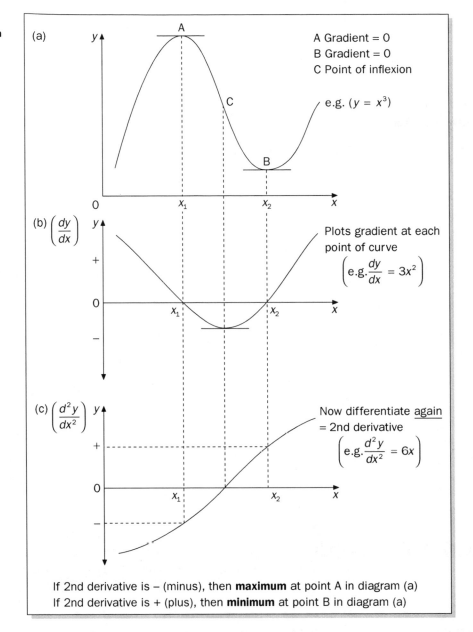

(a) A Gradient = 0
B Gradient = 0
C Point of inflexion

e.g. $(y = x^3)$

(b) $\left(\dfrac{dy}{dx}\right)$ Plots gradient at each point of curve

$\left(\text{e.g.}\dfrac{dy}{dx} = 3x^2\right)$

(c) $\left(\dfrac{d^2y}{dx^2}\right)$ Now differentiate <u>again</u> = 2nd derivative

$\left(\text{e.g.}\dfrac{d^2y}{dx^2} = 6x\right)$

If 2nd derivative is – (minus), then **maximum** at point A in diagram (a)
If 2nd derivative is + (plus), then **minimum** at point B in diagram (a)

Figure 11.3(c) shows the gradient $\left(\dfrac{dy}{dx}\right)$ of the gradient $\left(\dfrac{dy}{dx}\right)$ already displayed in Figure 11.3(b). This is known as finding the *second derivative* and is expressed as $\dfrac{d^2y}{dx^2}\left(\dfrac{dy}{dx} \text{ of } \dfrac{dy}{dx}\right)$.

▶ Where we have the **maximum** at x_1, the value of the first derivative is zero, and the value of the second derivative (at x_1) is *negative*.

► Where we have the **minimum** at x_2, the value of the first derivative is zero, and the value of the second derivative (at x_2) is *positive*.

The following worked example illustrates this approach.

WORKED EXAMPLE 11.1

$y = x^3 - 27x + 3$

Find the turning points for this equation.
Distinguish between maximum and minimum turning points.

Solution

$\dfrac{dy}{dx} = 0$ at a turning point

i.e. $\dfrac{dy}{dx} = 3x^2 - 27 = 0$ (applying our general formula for differentiation to each term separately)

$$3x^2 = 27$$

$$x^2 = 9$$

$\underline{x = +3 \text{ or } -3 \text{ are the turning points}}$

$\dfrac{d^2y}{dx^2} = 6x$ (second derivative, applying $\dfrac{dy}{dx}$ to the previous $\dfrac{dy}{dx}$)

At $x = +3$, second derivative $= +18$

$\underline{x = +3 \text{ is a minimum}}$

At $x = -3$, second derivative $= -18$

$\underline{x = -3 \text{ is a maximum}}$

PAUSE FOR THOUGHT 11.3 *Can you suggest how this idea of finding turning points might be helpful to managers in achieving their objectives, given that statisticians have worked out equations showing how revenue and cost vary with output?*

SELF-CHECK QUESTIONS

11.3 Find the maximum and/or minimum turning points for the following curves.

(a) $y = x^2 - 10x + 16$ (b) $y = 9 - 6x + x^2$

(c) $y = 12 + 4x - x^2$ (d) $y = x^3 - 27x + 6$

(e) $y = x^3 - 3x^2$ (f) $y = \dfrac{x^3}{3} - \dfrac{7}{2}x^2 + 12x$

(*Note:* use your 'rule' to differentiate each term separately, not forgetting the sign in front of each term).

Note: Answers can be found on p. 360.

11.3 Rules for differentiation

We can set out our earlier 'rule' for differentiating an expression more formally. In all the examples above we were differentiating an expression involving sums (plus signs) or differences (minus signs). However there are other types of expression to which our rule could apply, such as those involving multiplication (product) or division (quotient).

In all the following 'rules' we use the letters u and v to stand for parts of the expression we are differentiating, with each of these parts involving the variable x in some way (i.e. u and v are functions of x).

The derivative of a sum or difference

If $y = u + v$ or $y = u - v$ (where u and v are functions of x)

$$\frac{dy}{dx} = \frac{du}{dx} + \frac{dv}{dx} \text{ or } \frac{dy}{dx} = \frac{du}{dx} - \frac{dv}{dx}$$

WORKED EXAMPLE 11.2

$y = 2x^4 - 4x^2$

Solution

$$\frac{dy}{dx} = 8x^3 - 8x$$

The derivative of a product

If $y = uv$ (where u and v are functions of x)

$$\frac{dy}{dx} = u\frac{dv}{dx} + v\frac{du}{dx}$$

WORKED EXAMPLE 11.3

$y = (3x + 1)(3x^2)$ $(u = 3x + 1, \frac{du}{dx} = 3$

$v = 3x^2, \frac{dv}{dx} = 6x)$

Solution

$$\frac{dy}{dx} = (3x + 1) \cdot (6x) + (3x^2) \cdot (3)$$

$$\frac{dy}{dx} = 18x^2 + 6x + 9x^2$$

$$\frac{dy}{dx} = 27x^2 + 6x$$

The derivative of a quotient

$y = \dfrac{u}{v}$ (where u and v are functions of x)

$$\frac{dy}{dx} = \frac{u\dfrac{dv}{dx} - v\dfrac{du}{dx}}{v^2}$$

WORKED EXAMPLE 11.4

$y = \dfrac{3x - 2}{5x + 3}$ $[u = 3x - 2, \dfrac{du}{dx} = 3$

$v = 5x + 3, \dfrac{dv}{dx} = 5]$

Solution

$$\frac{dy}{dx} = \frac{(3x - 2) \cdot (5) - (5x + 3) \cdot (3)}{(5x + 3)^2}$$

$$\frac{dy}{dx} = \frac{15x - 10 - 15x - 9}{25x^2 + 30x + 9}$$

$$\frac{dy}{dx} = \frac{-19}{25x^2 + 30x + 9}$$

The derivative of a function of a function

If $y = f(u)$ where $u = f(x)$

$$\frac{dy}{dx} = \frac{dy}{du} \cdot \frac{du}{dx}$$

WORKED EXAMPLE 11.5

$y = (3x^2 + 2)^4$ $[y = u^4, \dfrac{dy}{du} = 4u^3$

$u = 3x^2 + 2, \dfrac{du}{dx} = 6x]$

Solution

$$\frac{dy}{dx} = 4u^3 \cdot 6x$$

$$= 24x \cdot u^3$$

$$= 24x \cdot (3x^2 + 2)^3$$

SELF-CHECK QUESTIONS

11.4 Differentiate each of the following expressions using an appropriate rule

(a) $y = 7x^5 + 3x^2$ (b) $y = 4x^5 - 4x^3$

(c) $y = (2x + 3)(2x^3)$ (d) $y = (3x + 4)(3x^4)$

(e) $y = \dfrac{(2x + 3)}{2x^2}$ (f) $y = \dfrac{4x^2 - 2}{2x^2 + 4}$

(g) $y = (2x^2 + 3)^2$ (h) $y = (3x^3 + 4)^3$

Note: Answers can be found on p. 362.

11.4 Applications of differentiation

Revenue, cost and profit

Obviously turning points, involving maximum or minimum outcomes, are likely to have widespread applications in economics or business. These applications make use of some introductory ideas involving revenue, cost or profit.

▶ Total revenue (TR)   = price (average revenue) × quantity

   Average revenue (AR)   = price = $\dfrac{TR}{\text{quantity}}$

▶ Total cost (TC)   = total fixed cost (TFC) + total variable cost (TVC)

   Average total cost (ATC) = $\dfrac{TC}{\text{quantity}}$

▶ Total profit (TP)   = total revenue − total cost

Suppose that statisticians employed by a large firm have estimated the demand (average revenue) curve and average total cost curve for the firm as follows

$$D = AR = 21 - x$$

$$ATC = \frac{x^2}{3} - 3x + 9$$

where x = output in units

       AR − average revenue (£)

    ATC = average total cost (£)

The firm can use *differentiation* to find, for example, the output which maximises either total revenue or total profit.

Maximum total revenue

Total Revenue = average revenue (price) × quantity (output)

$$TR = AR \times x$$

$$TR = (21 - x) \times x$$

$$TR = 21x - x^2$$

If we let $y = TR$

then $\dfrac{dy}{dx} = 0$ for a turning point

i.e. $21 - 2x = 0$

$$21 = 2x$$

$$\underline{10.5 = x}$$

2nd derivative $= \dfrac{d^2 y}{dx^2} = -2$

So the turning point is a maximum since the 2nd derivative is negative.

<u>An output of 10.5 units will maximise total revenue</u>

Maximum total profit

Remember total profit (TP) = total revenue − total cost

Total revenue (TR) = average revenue × quantity (output)

Total cost (TC) = average total cost × quantity (output)

So TR $= (21 - x) \cdot x = 21x - x^2$

$$TC = \left(\dfrac{x^2}{3} - 3x + 9 \right) \cdot x = \dfrac{x^3}{3} - 3x^2 + 9x$$

TP = TR − TC

$$TP = [21x - x^2] - \left[\dfrac{x^3}{3} - 3x^2 + 9x \right]$$

$$TP = -\dfrac{x^3}{3} + 2x^2 + 12x$$

If we let $y = $ TP

then $\dfrac{dy}{dx} = 0$ for a turning point

i.e. $-x^2 + 4x + 12 = 0$

$(-x + 6)(x + 2) = 0$ (factorising)

<u>i.e. $x = 6$ and $x = -2$ are the solutions.</u>

Taking the 2nd derivative

$$\dfrac{d^2 y}{dx^2} = -2x + 4$$

▶ when $x = +6$, 2nd derivative is negative (-8)
   so $x = +6$ is a maximum
▶ when $x = -2$, 2nd derivative is positive $(+8)$
   so $x = -2$ is a minimum.

<u>An output of six units will maximise total profit</u>

The (maximum) Total Profit earned at an output of 6 units is:

$$TP = -\frac{6^3}{3} + 2(6)^2 + 12(6)$$

i.e. $TP = -72 + 72 + 72$

$\underline{TP = £72}$

Price

We can, of course, easily find the *price* at which the above outputs must be sold. Remember price = average revenue.

Price = AR = $21 - x$

▶   when $x = 10.5$ (maximum total revenue), price = $21 - 10.5 = £10.5$
▶   when $x = 6$ (maximum total profit), price = $21 - 6 = £15$

Minimum cost

The firm in our previous example has estimated that its average total cost (ATC) is given by the expression

$$ATC = \frac{x^2}{3} - 3x + 9$$

where ATC = average total cost (£)
           x = output in units

We may now wish to find the 'technical optimum' output, i.e. that level of output for which ATC is a minimum. Again we can use our rules of differentiation to solve such a problem.

Let y = ATC

$\frac{dy}{dx} = 0$ for a turning point

$\frac{2}{3}x - 3 = 0$

$\frac{2}{3}x = 3$

$\underline{x = 4.5}$

To check that this turning point is a minimum, we find the 2nd derivative.

$\frac{d^2y}{dx^2} = +\frac{2}{3}$

The sign of the 2nd derivative is positive, so the turning point is a minimum.

<u>An output of 4.5 units will minimise average total cost, i.e. be a technically efficient output.</u>

Figure 11.4 presents a visual overview of these solutions involving revenue, profit, price and cost.

figure 11.4
Finding turning points: revenue, cost and profit

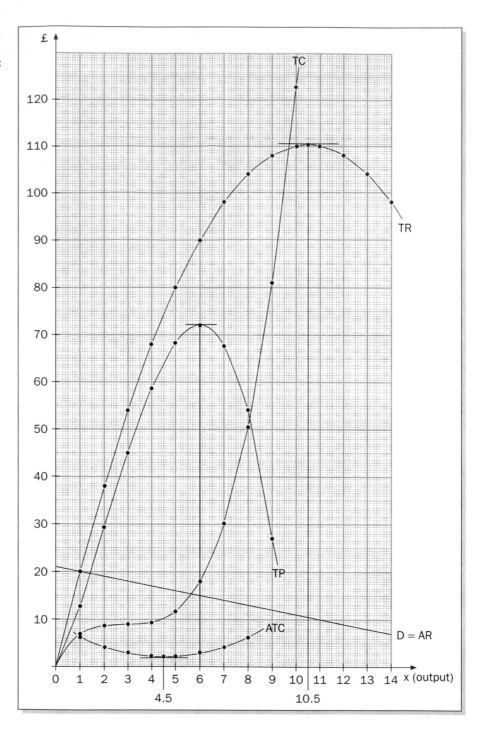

figure 11.4
Finding turning points: revenue, cost and profit

11.5 Average revenue (£) $= 32 - \dfrac{2}{3}x^2$

Average cost (£) $= \dfrac{1}{3}x^2 - x + 11$

where x = output in units

(a) Find an expression for (i) total revenue
    (ii) total cost
    (iii) total profit

(b) At what output is total profit a maximum?
How much profit is earned at this output?
What price is charged for this output?

11.6 For a firm, total revenue and total cost are indicated below:

$TR = 40x - 8x^2$

$TC = 8 + 16x - x^2$

where TR = Total Revenue (£)
    TC = Total Cost (£)
    x = output (in 1,000 units)

(a) Find the level of output at which total profit (y) is a maximum. What price will be charged for this output? How much profit will be earned?

(b) If the firm were to seek to maximise Total Revenue rather than profit, how would your output target differ from (a) above? What profit would be earned at this new output level?

11.7 Suppose the total cost function is as follows:

$$TC = \frac{x^3}{3} - x^2 + 11x$$

where TC = total cost (£)
    x = output (in 1,000 units)

What output would make average total cost a minimum?

Note: Answers can be found on pp. 363–365.

Marginal analysis

In some of the solutions to problems involving revenue, cost and profit we needed to differentiate (find the gradient to) the total revenue, total cost and total profit curves respectively. When we did this we were in fact finding the expressions for *marginal* revenue, *marginal* cost and *marginal* profit respectively.

We can usefully illustrate this idea in terms of marginal revenue (MR). Remember that marginal revenue is the addition to total revenue (TR) from selling the last unit of output. We can therefore say that MR is, in the *limit*, the rate of change of total revenue with regard to output. In other words MR is the slope of the tangent to any particular point on the total revenue curve. We have already noted that the slope of that tangent is *zero* (i.e. MR = 0) when total revenue is a maximum.

If we differentiate (find the gradient to) the total revenue, total cost and total profit curves respectively, then we will find marginal revenue, marginal cost and marginal profit curves.

▶ If total revenue (TR) $= y$

then marginal revenue (MR) $= \dfrac{dy}{dx}$

▶ If total cost (TC) $= y$

then marginal cost (MC) $= \dfrac{dy}{dx}$

▶ If total profit (TP) $= y$

then marginal profit (MP) $= \dfrac{dy}{dx}$

**SELF-CHECK
QUESTIONS**

11.8 Total Revenue = $y = 20x - 2x^2$

   (a) Find an expression for marginal revenue.
   (b) Plot the total revenue and marginal revenue curves on a graph ($x = 0$ to $x = 8$)

11.9 Total Cost $= y = \dfrac{1}{3}x^3 - 3x^2 + 9x$

   (a) Find an expression for marginal cost.
   (b) Plot the total cost and marginal cost curves on a graph ($x = 0$ to $x = 6$)

Note: Answers can be found on p. 365.

Price elasticity of demand

Price elasticity of demand (PED) is a measure of the responsiveness of demand for a product to a change in its own price. It is an extremely important concept for business since its value will impact directly on the pricing strategy of the firm.

$$PED = \frac{\% \text{ change in quantity demanded of } x}{\% \text{ change in price of } x}$$

Here we use P for the original price and Q for the original quantity, and Δ for any change in that price or quantity. We can now say that:

$$PED = \frac{\dfrac{\Delta Q}{Q} \cdot 100}{\dfrac{\Delta P}{P} \cdot 100}$$

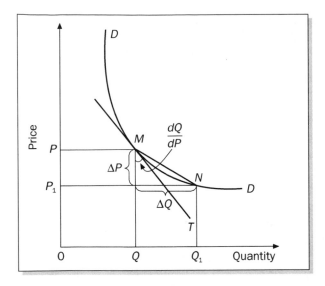

figure 11.5

Using differentiation to calculate price elasticity of demand at a point on the demand curve

$$PED = \frac{\Delta Q}{Q} \div \frac{\Delta P}{P} \text{ (100s cancel out)}$$

$$PED = \frac{\Delta Q}{Q} \cdot \frac{P}{\Delta P} \text{ (to change divide to multiply, turn one fraction on its head)}$$

$$PED = \frac{P}{Q} \cdot \frac{\Delta Q}{\Delta P} \text{ (collect } \Delta\text{s on one side)}$$

Clearly the ratio $\Delta Q/\Delta P$ in Figure 11.5 will now vary depending on the *direction* of price change from P and on the *magnitude* of the price change from P.

However, at the point M there is a *unique* value for price elasticity of demand. In other words when demand is non-linear, only for infinitely small changes in price around the original price do we have a unique value of PED. We call this **point elasticity of demand** and it can be expressed as:

$$\text{Point price elasticity of demand} = \frac{P}{Q} \cdot \frac{dQ}{dP}$$

$$\left[\text{where } \frac{dQ}{dP} = \lim_{\Delta P \to 0} \left(\frac{\Delta Q}{\Delta P} \right) \right]$$

In terms of Figure 11.5, as N approaches M (ΔP tends to zero), the slope of the chord MN (measured as angle QMN), namely $\Delta Q/\Delta P$, becomes closer and closer to the slope of the tangent MT (measured as angle QMT) at point M. In the *limit*, as N gets extremely close to M, we can regard the two slopes as identical, even though they will never quite be identical so long as N is a separate point from M on the demand curve.

In other words, at the *point M*, price elasticity of demand can be found by multiplying the ratio of initial price to initial quantity by the slope of the tangent (MT) to M. The slope of MT is expressed using derivatives (dQ/dP).

For anything other than an infinitely small change in price around the initial price, we must admit however that price elasticity of demand will vary with both the direction and magnitude of the price change.

WORKED EXAMPLE 11.6

The quantity demanded (Q) of a product and its own price (P) are related in the following way

$$Q = 400 - P^2$$

where Q = quantity of x in units

P = price of x in £s

What is the (point) price elasticity of demand? Calculate this price elasticity at a price of £5.

Solution

$$PED = \frac{P}{Q} \cdot \frac{dQ}{dP}$$

where $\frac{dQ}{dP} = -2P$ (use our earlier 'rule' (p. 253) but Q replacing y and P replacing x)

So $PED = \frac{P}{Q} \cdot (-2P)$

At $P = £5$

$$Q = 400 - 5^2$$

i.e. $Q = 400 - 25 = 375$

So $PED = \frac{5}{375} \cdot (-10)$

So $PED = \frac{1}{75} \cdot (-10) = \frac{-10}{75}$

$PED = -0.13$

Strictly speaking price E of D is negative (−0.13 here) since the demand curve slopes downwards from left to right. However the negative sign is often ignored in practice. Any value for PED less than 1 implies a *relatively price inelastic* demand, and suggests that a price cut will reduce total revenue, whereas a price rise will increase total revenue.

Of course demand for a product depends on many variables other than its own price, such as the price of any substitutes or complements in consumption, the income of the household, etc. Often we want to find the rate of change between two variables (say quantity demanded of x and its own price) while assuming that the value of each of these other variables remains constant at some particular level. We are then involved in the process of **partial differentiation**, to which we now turn.

Inventory (stock) control

As we shall see (Box 3, p. 280) the use of differentiation can play an important part in deriving a formula for minimising the cost of holding **inventory** (stock).

A firm will need to hold inventories of its products for a variety of reasons.

▶ A stock of raw materials and work-in-progress is often needed so that the production sequence is not interrupted by shortages.
▶ A stock of finished goods can help by acting as a buffer between customer demand and the often erratic supply from the production process.
▶ A stock of tools and spare parts may be required for the maintenance of essential plant and machinery.

However stock represents cash tied up in either the production process or in goods on the shelves. There may therefore be a conflict between the financial department, which would like to keep stocks to a minimum in order to release as much capital for other uses, and the production and marketing departments which would like to see adequate levels of stocks to ensure against breakdown, down-time or late delivery. The purpose of inventory (stock) control is to find the *optimum* level of stocks which reconciles these two views.

Useful terminology

When considering inventory control, some important terms are frequently encountered.

▶ *Lead or procurement time* The period of time, often expressed in days, weeks, months, etc. between ordering and replenishment, i.e. when the goods become available for use.
▶ *Demand* The amount required by sales, production, etc. Usually expressed as a rate of demand per week, month, year, etc.
▶ *Usage rate* The number of stock items used per unit of time.
▶ *Economic order quantity (EOQ)* This is the ordering quantity which minimises the sum of inventory carrying costs and ordering costs.
▶ *Buffer stock or safety stock* A stock allowance to cover errors in forecasting the lead time or the demand during the lead time.

Figure 11.6 shows a simple stock-level diagram applying some of these ideas. Here the lead time and usage rates are constant and the goods arrive just as the minimum stock level is reached (i.e. replenishment is instantaneous at the end of the lead time).

We can calculate the *re-order level* in Figure 11.6 if we have information on usage rate and lead time.

figure 11.6
Stock model

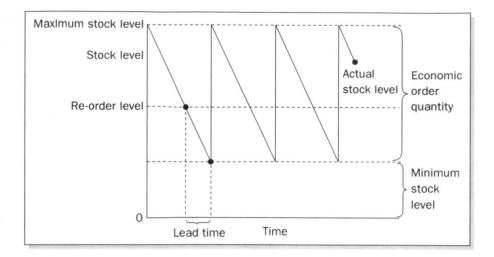

WORKED EXAMPLE 11.7

Calculate the re-order level in a situation where there is a constant usage rate of 30 items per week and a lead time of three weeks.

Solution

Re-order level = usage rate × lead time

Re-order level = 30 × 3

Re-order level = 90 units

When stocks reach 90 units a new order should be placed which will take three weeks to arrive, in which time the existing stock will be just enough to cover the usage rate of 30 per week. This assumes that the delivery will be exactly on time and that usage will be constant at 30 units per week. Any increase in the usage rate or delay in delivery will produce a stock-out; therefore most firms also carry a safety or buffer-stock. This is the minimum stock level held to cover any possible deviation in the average demand and supply.

There are three broad categories of costs involving inventories. The cost of holding stock (**carrying costs**), costs of obtaining stock (**ordering costs**) and the costs of failing to have adequate stock (**stock-out costs**).

Inventory costs include the following:

▶ **Holding or carrying costs.** These might include insurance, storage costs (staff, equipment, handling, deterioration, obsolescence, security). These might also include opportunity costs, i.e. the financial cost in terms of alternatives foregone (e.g. interest) through having capital tied up.

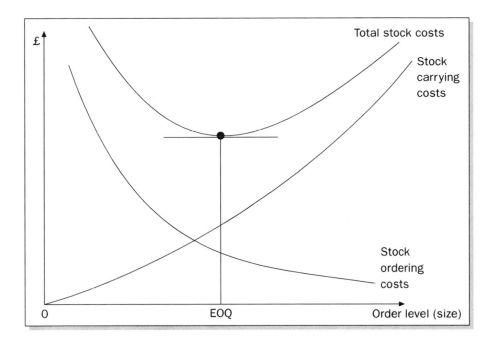

figure 11.7
Finding the economic order quantity (EOQ)

▶ **Order costs.** These occur when obtaining stock and might include the cost of clerical and administrative work in raising an order, any associated transport costs and inspection of stock on arrival, etc.

▶ **Stock – out costs.** These are difficult to quantify but might include the following:

stock-out of raw materials and work-in-progress, which may result in machine and operator idle time and possibly the need for overtime payments to catch up on missed production.
stock-out of finished goods, which may result in:

(i)   missed orders from occasional customers
(ii)   missed delivery dates resulting in a deterioration in customer/ supplier relations
(iii) penalty clauses incurred for late delivery

stock-out of tools and spares, which may result in an increase in downtime of machinery and loss of production.

Stock carrying costs can be expected to *rise* as the order size increases, for reasons already discussed. However stock ordering costs can be expected to *fall* as the order size increases. (See Figure 11.7.)

If we ignore stock-out costs which are notoriously difficult to quantify, then total (inventory) costs can be regarded as the sum of the carrying and ordering costs. These will be at a minimum for the following value of Q (output).

Economic Order Quantity (EOQ)

$$Q = \sqrt{\frac{2 \cdot CoD}{Cc}}$$

where Q = economic order quantity
Co = ordering cost for one order
D = annual demand for stock
Cc = carrying cost for one item p.a.

Note: A proof of this formula can be found in Box 3 (p. 280).

WORKED EXAMPLE 11.8

A firm uses 100,000 components per annum in its manufacturing process each of which cost the firm £10 to purchase from its supplier. The carrying costs of stocking these components is estimated as 15 per cent per annum of the purchase price. The ordering costs are estimated at £200 per order. Find the economic order quantity.

Solution

$$EOQ = \sqrt{\frac{2 \cdot CoD}{Cc}}$$

where Co = £10 per order

$\qquad D$ = 100,000 units p.a.

$\qquad Cc$ = £10 × 0.15 = £1.50 per item per annum.

i.e. $EOQ = \sqrt{\dfrac{2 \cdot (10) \cdot (100{,}000)}{1.50}}$

i.e. EOQ = 1,155 units

Of course more complex inventory control situations with variable usage rates, variable lead times and gradual (rather than instantaneous) replenishment may be encountered by firms (See Further Study).

SELF-CHECK QUESTIONS

11.10 Mondeo Ltd. produce transmission systems, assembling these using four main components, of which EL3 is one component. Since June, Mondeo has been using a new supplier who can supply EL3 at a much cheaper cost. The graph in Figure 11.8 shows stocks of EL3 for Mondeo Ltd., and indicates the usage of EL3 since January.

    (a) Using the graph, find the:
       (i) lead time for EL3
       (ii) minimum stock level
       (iii) re-order quantity; and
       (iv) stock-out point
    (b) (i) Explain the possible reasons for the change in the stock level after July.

figure 11.8

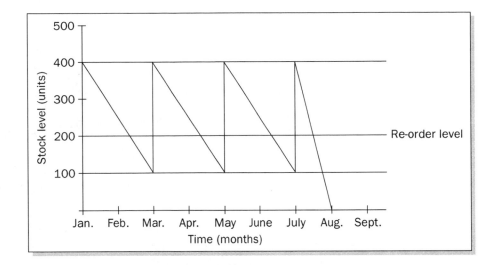

(ii) What are the consequences for production from July of the change in stock levels?

(c) Calculate the economic order quantity if each order of EL3 components costs the firm £200, there is a carrying cost of £2 per EL3 component per annum and an annual demand for 5,000 EL3 components.

PAUSE FOR THOUGHT 11.4 *What is meant by just-in-time manufacturing and how might Mondeo Ltd. benefit from its introduction?*

11.5 Partial differentiation

Many functions have *more than one* independent variable. A function with two independent variables could be expressed:

$y = f(x,z)$.

Similarly, a function with three independent variables could be expressed:

$y = f(w,x,z)$.

If we differentiate the function with respect to *one* of these variables, keeping *all other variables constant*, we are using the process of **partial differentiations** and are finding the partial derivatives.

We can illustrate the idea of partial differentiation using Figure 11.9 which shows a situation where the variable y depends upon two variables, x and z. Clearly we now have a three dimensional diagram.

▶ When we partially differentiate y with respect to x, we use the terminology $\dfrac{\partial y}{\partial x}$, replacing the letter d with ∂ to indicate partial differentiation. Essentially we are seeking to find the rate of change of y with respect to x, everything else (in this case z) assumed constant.

figure 11.9
Using partial differentiation to find the gradient to a segment of a surface at a particular value of some other variable

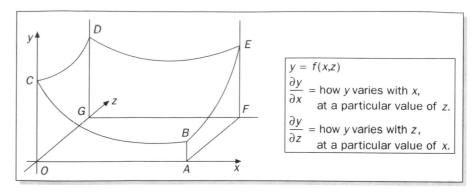

Suppose z is assumed to be constant at the specific value OG, then we are finding the gradient (rate of change) to segment DE of the surface at each value of x.

▶ Alternatively we may be seeking to partially differentiate y with respect to z, using the terminology $\dfrac{\partial y}{\partial z}$. In this case we are seeking to find the rate of change of y with respect to z, everything else (in this case x) assumed constant. Suppose x is assumed to be constant at the specific value OA, then we are finding the gradient (rate of change) to segment BE of the surface at each value of z. On the other hand, if x is assumed to be constant at the specific value 0 (zero), then we are finding the gradient (rate of change) to segment CD of the surface at each value of z.

Strictly speaking, finding *own-price elasticities of demand* often involves the 'other things equal' assumption for variables other than the price of the product in question, and is therefore a partial elasticity. The same is true of calculations involving *cross-elasticities of demand*, where only the price of the other product is allowed to change. The *particular values* of these other variables might then affect the own-price or cross-elasticity of demand calculations, as is illustrated in the following examples.

Calculating partial derivatives

To differentiate a function with respect to *one* of its variables, treat the remaining variables as constants and proceed in the usual way already considered for differentiation. Here the dependent variable (y) depends on two independent variables, x and z.

WORKED EXAMPLE 11.9

Give the partial derivatives of

$$y = x^2 + 3xz - 4z^2$$

$$\frac{\partial y}{\partial x} = 2x + 3z \text{ (treat } z \text{ as a constant when differentiating)}$$

This measures the rate of change of y with respect to x, all other variables (here z) held constant.

$\dfrac{\partial y}{\partial z} = 3x - 8z$ (treat x as a constant when differentiating)

This measures the rate of change of y with respect to z, all other variables (here x) held constant.

Note that the value of each partial derivative is influenced by the particular value of the 'other variable', whether z or x.

WORKED
EXAMPLE 11.10

Give the partial derivatives of

$$y = w^3 - w^2x + x^2z - z^2$$

$\dfrac{\partial y}{\partial w} = 3w^2 - 2wx$ (treat x and z as constants when differentiating)

$\dfrac{\partial y}{\partial x} = -w^2 + 2xz$ (treat w and z as constants when differentiating)

$\dfrac{\partial y}{\partial z} = x^2 - 2z$ (treat w and x as constants when differentiating)

11.6 Integration

This is the *opposite* process to differentiation. As Figure 11.10 illustrates, if we have gone from a particular expression or function (e.g. $y = x^2$) to the first derivative (e.g. $\dfrac{dy}{dx} = 2x$) using *differentiation*, then we go backwards from $2x$ to x^2 using *integration*.

The function $y = x^2$ in Figure 11.10 is differentiated using our earlier 'rule' (p. 253) to give the gradient $\dfrac{dy}{dx} = 2x$. But suppose we are told that the result of differentiating some function is $2x$ and are asked to find the original function! In this case we must *reverse* the differentiation process in Figure 11.10 and instead use the integration process.

figure 11.10
Integration as the opposite of differentiation

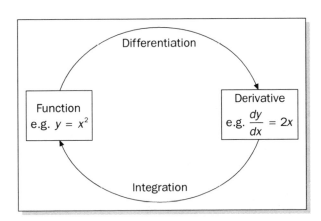

Unfortunately we will encounter an immediate problem in finding an *exact* original function whose derivative is $2x$. For example we could work back from $\frac{dy}{dx} = 2x$ to get *all* of the following original functions (y).

$\frac{dy}{dx}$	y
$2x$	$x^2 + 1$
$2x$	$x^2 + 2$
$2x$	$x^2 + 3$
.	.
.	.
.	.
$2x$	$x^2 + C$

So if we know the derivative $\left(\frac{dy}{dx}\right)$ of a function is $2x$, we must write that the original function (y) is $x^2 + C$ where C is any constant.

The standard symbol for the integration process is $\int$, which looks rather like an extended letter 's'. Whenever we are integrating we must also remember that we are integrating with respect to some variable; here the variable is x, so we must write dx at the end of the function to be integrated.

We can now write our integration as:

$$\int 2x\,dx = x^2 + C$$

Examples

$$\int 2x\,dx = x^2 + C$$

$$\int 4x\,dx = 2x^2 + C$$

$$\int 6x\,dx = 3x^2 + C$$

$$\int 8x\,dx = 4x^2 + C$$

Can you see a pattern emerging from these examples?

$\frac{dy}{dx}$	y
$2x^1$	$\frac{2x^2}{2} + C$
$4x^1$	$\frac{4x^2}{2} + C$
$6x^1$	$\frac{6x^2}{2} + C$
$8x^1$	$\frac{8x^2}{2} + C$

We can express this pattern as a general formula.

> General Formula for integration
>
> If $y = ax^n$
>
> $$\int y\,dx = \frac{ax^{n+1}}{n+1} + C$$
>
> for all values of n except $n = -1$

Of course you could *check* this general formula by reversing the process, i.e. differentiating

If $y = \dfrac{ax^{n+1}}{n+1} + C$

Then using our general formula for differentiating (p. 253)

$$\frac{dy}{dx} = \frac{(n+1)ax^n}{n+1} = ax^n$$

In other words, our process works both ways, except for the uncertainty as to C. We call C the **constant of integration**.

WORKED EXAMPLE 11.11

$$\int 3x^7 dx = \frac{3x^{7+1}}{7+1} + C = \frac{3x^8}{8} + C$$

WORKED EXAMPLE 11.12

$$\int 4x^8 dx = \frac{4x^{8+1}}{8+1} + C = \frac{4x^9}{9} + C$$

Integrating functions with more than one term

When the function has several terms, we apply our general formula to each term separately. However we only apply the constant of integration, C, at the end of the process.

WORKED EXAMPLE 11.13

$$y = \underset{\left(\substack{a=8 \\ n=3}\right)}{8x^3} + \underset{\left(\substack{a=6 \\ n=2}\right)}{6x^2} - \underset{\left(\substack{a=5 \\ n=1}\right)}{5x} + \underset{\left(\substack{a=8 \\ n=0}\right)}{8}$$

Note: 8 is the same as $8x^0$ (see Chapter 12, p. 293)

Solution

We can write this integration of each term separately, as:

$$\int 8x^3 dx + \int 6x^2 dx - \int 5x\,dx + \int 8\,dx + C$$

$$\int y\,dx = \frac{8x^{3+1}}{3+1} + \frac{6x^{2+1}}{2+1} - \frac{5x^{1+1}}{1+1} + \frac{8x^{0+1}}{0+1} + C$$

$$\int y\,dx = \frac{8x^4}{4} + \frac{6x^3}{3} - \frac{5x^2}{2} + 8x + C$$

$$\int y\,dx = 2x^4 + 2x^3 - 2.5x^2 + 8x + C$$

Finding the value of C

To find the value of C, the **constant of integration**, we need more specific information. In the example below we are given the co-ordinates to the curve at which the derivative $\left(\dfrac{dy}{dx}\right)$ has been calculated. We can then integrate the derivative and find C in the original function.

WORKED EXAMPLE 11.14

Find the equation of the curve whose gradient at the point (1,1) is given by $1 - 3x^2$

Solution

Since $\dfrac{dy}{dx} = 1 - 3x^2$ then $y = \displaystyle\int (1 - 3x^2)\,dx$

$$\int 1\,dx - \int 3x^2\,dx + C$$

$$= \frac{x^{0+1}}{0+1} - \frac{3x^{2+1}}{2+1} + C$$

$$= x - \frac{3x^3}{3} + C$$

$$y = x - x^3 + C$$

When $x = 1$, $y = 1$ so $\qquad 1 = 1 - 1 + C$

giving $\qquad\qquad\qquad C = 1$

The equation of the curve then is $\underline{y = x - x^3 + 1}$

Definite integrals

So far we have only considered *indefinite integrals*, whereby the process of integration has resulted in a general function, with or without a specific value for C, the constant of integration.

However we are often interested in a *specific range* of a function. In this case we use the **definite integral** which evaluates the function at two specific points and allows us to find the difference between the value of the function at these points.

▶ $\displaystyle\int 4x\,dx = 2x^2 + C$ **Indefinite integral**

▶ $\displaystyle\int_{1}^{3} 4x\,dx = \left|2x^2\right|_{1}^{3}$ **Definite integral**

$$= 2(3)^2 - 2(1)^2$$

$$= 18 - 2$$

$$= 16$$

Notice that for the definite integral we place the specific values of the function around the integration sign. These specific values are often called the **limits of integration**. Here we are interested in finding the *difference* between the value of $\int 4x\,dx$ at $x = 3$ and at $x = 1$.

Because we are subtracting, the constant of integration, C, cancels out and can be ignored.

The indefinite integral, without the C, is then found and enclosed by vertical lines, with the limits of integration (the 3 and the 1) placed after the second vertical line. By convention we subtract the value of the integral at the bottom limit from the value of the integral at the top limit.

Using the definite integral helps us to eliminate C, and therefore avoid having to find it. A further benefit is that using the definite integral focuses on *summing* the function over particular values of the variable. This is required when we wish to calculate the *area beneath a curve* over a particular range of that curve. This is important in a variety of business applications, such as summing marginal revenue, marginal cost or marginal profit (all first derivatives) to find total revenue, total cost or total profit respectively.

Area under a curve

The area between a curve $y = f(x)$, the x axis and the lines $x = a$, $x = b$ is defined by $\int_{a}^{b} f(x)\,dx$.

The worked example which follows illustrates the use of integration in such situations.

figure 11.11
The definite integral and the area beneath a curve

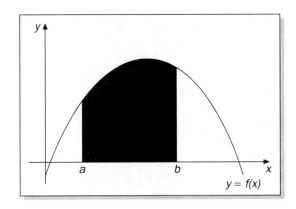

Find the area included between the curve $y = 2x + x^2 + x^3$, the x-axis and the lines $x = 1$ and $x = 2$.

Solution

$$\text{Area} = \int_1^2 (2x + x^2 + x^3)dx$$

$$\text{Area} = \left[\frac{2x^2}{2} + \frac{x^3}{3} + \frac{x^4}{4}\right]_1^2 = \left[x^2 + \frac{x^3}{3} + \frac{x^4}{4}\right]_1^2$$

$$\text{Area} = \left(4 + \frac{8}{3} + \frac{16}{4}\right) - \left(1 + \frac{1}{3} + \frac{1}{4}\right)$$

$$\text{Area} = 9\frac{1}{12} \text{ units}^2$$

11.11 Solve the following indefinite integrations

(a) $\int 6x\,dx$ (b) $\int 3x^5\,dx$ (c) $\int 4x^6\,dx$

(d) $\int (4x^3 + 5x^2 - 3x + 4)dx$ (e) $\int (2x^4 - 4x^3 + 7x)dx$

11.12 Find the equation of the curve whose gradient at the point (1,1) is given by $2 - 4x^2$.

11.13 Find the area included between the curve $y = 3x + 2x^2 + x^3$, the x axis and the lines $x = 1$ and $x = 2$.

Note: **Answers can be found on pp. 366–367.**

11.1 A firm has estimated that L workers on a production line will produce Q units per day where $Q = 80L^2 - 0.1L^4$. Find the number of workers that maximise output per day

11.2 The manager of a manufacturing company has estimated that the relationship between a firm's sales (X) and it's profits (Y) can be approximated by:

$Y = 0.6X - 0.002X^2$

where Y = profits (£000)
       X = sales (000 units)

Find the level of sales that would maximise the firm's profits.

11.3 For the straight line demand equation $P = 8 - 0.05Q$, verify that the demand is price elastic when $P = 6$ and price inelastic when $P = 2$. At what price does the demand curve have unitary elasticity?

Box 1

The relationship $y = x^2$ (See Figure 11.2, p. 252)

$$y^* + \Delta y = (x^* + \Delta x)^2$$

or

$$y^* + \Delta y = x^{*2} + 2x^*\Delta x + (\Delta x)^2 \text{ (see note below)}$$

but $\qquad y^* = x^{*2}$

Subtracting $\quad \Delta y = 2x^*\Delta x + (\Delta x)^2$

and dividing throughout by Δx

gives $\qquad \dfrac{\Delta y}{\Delta x} = 2x^* + \Delta x$

and $\qquad \underset{\Delta x \to 0}{\text{limit}} \dfrac{\Delta y}{\Delta x} = 2x^*$

i.e. $\qquad \dfrac{dy}{dx} = 2x^*$

Note

$(x^* + \Delta x)(x^* + \Delta x)$

$x^{*2} + x^*\Delta x + x^*\Delta x + \Delta x\Delta x$

$x^{*2} + 2x^*\Delta x + (\Delta x)^2$

Box 2

The relationship $y = 3x^2$

$$y^* + \Delta y = 3(x^* + \Delta x)^2$$

or

$$y^* + \Delta y = 3x^{*2} + 6x^*\Delta x + 3(\Delta x)^2$$

but $\qquad y^* = 3x^{*2}$

Subtracting $\quad \Delta y = 6x^*\Delta x + 3(\Delta x)^2$

and dividing throughout by Δx

gives $\qquad \dfrac{\Delta y}{\Delta x} = 6x^* + 3\Delta x$

and $\qquad \underset{\Delta x \to 0}{\text{limit}} \dfrac{\Delta y}{\Delta x} = 6x^*$

i.e. $\qquad \dfrac{dy}{dx} = 6x^*$

Box 3   Derivation of basic EOQ formula

Let D = annual demand
  Q = order quantity
  Co = cost of ordering for one order
  Cc = carrying cost for one item p.a.

$$\text{Average Stock} = \frac{Q}{2}$$

$$\text{Total annual stock holding cost} = \frac{QCc}{2}$$

$$\text{Number of orders per annum} = \frac{D}{Q}$$

$$\text{Annual ordering costs} = \frac{DCo}{Q}$$

$$\text{Total (inventory) Cost} = \frac{QCc}{2} + \frac{D}{Q}Co$$

The order quantity which makes the total (inventory) cost (TC) a minimum is obtained by differentiating with respect to Q and equating the derivative to zero.

$$\frac{dTC}{dQ} = \frac{Cc}{2} - \frac{DCo}{Q^2}$$

and when $\frac{dTC}{dQ} = 0$ costs are at a minimum

$$\text{i.e. } 0 = \frac{Cc}{2} - \frac{DCo}{Q^2}$$

and to find Q

$$\frac{DCo}{Q^2} = \frac{Cc}{2}$$

$$2DCo = Q^2Cc$$

$$\frac{2DCo}{Cc} = Q^2$$

$$\text{Q (i.e. the EOQ)} = \sqrt{\frac{2 \cdot CoD}{Cc}}$$

11.4　Suppose a total cost function is given by $TC = 0.01Q^2 + 5Q + 100$, where TC is total cost (£'s) and Q is output (units). Find the output level that minimises average total cost (ATC).

11.5　Investment in new machines increases output and hence revenue whilst at the same time increasing costs. Suppose each machine costs £1,800 and revenue (£) from sales occurs as follows, $R = 5,000X - 20X^2$ where X is the number of machines.

(a) Find the number of machines that maximise revenue.
(b) Find the number of machines that maximise profits (revenue – cost of machines)
(c) What is the break even number of machines?

11.6　A supply of 10 cm by 16 cm tin plates is available to a manufacturer. Rectangular boxes are to be made by cutting out squares from each corner and then folding up the sides. How long should the sides of the square be if the manufacturer wishes to maximise the volume of the boxes?

11.7　The demand equation for a firm's product is given by $P = -5Q + 3,000$. The firm's total cost equation is given by $TC = 50Q + 10,000$. All values are in £'s and quantities in units. Determine

(a) The quantity that maximises revenue.
(b) The quantity and price that maximise profits.
(c) The maximum profit.

11.8　Suppose the government wishes to discourage the consumption of the good produced by the firm in the previous example. It imposes a tax of £60 per unit produced, so that the new total cost relationship is $TC = 50Q + 10,000 + 60Q = 110Q + 10,000$.

(a) How does this affect profit maximising output and price?
(b) What is the new maximum profit?
(c) What proportion of the tax is passed on to the consumer?

11.9　The total revenue a textile firm obtains from selling x football shirts and y cricket jumpers is given by the function

$$TR = -2x^2 + 6x - 3y^2 + 6y + 10xy + 50$$

Find

(a) the marginal revenue from selling 1 additional football shirt, when $x = 4$ and $y = 3$
(b) the marginal revenue from selling one extra cricket jumper when $x = 4$ and $y = 3$

11.10　The demand for a good depends on its own price (P), the income of consumers (Y) and the price of another good (P_B). The demand equation is given by

$$Q = -2P^2 + 4P_BY$$

if $P = 5$, $P_B = 4$ and $Y = 50$

Find

(a) the own price elasticity of demand
(b) the income elasticity of demand
(c) the cross elasticity of demand (CED). Are the goods substitutes or complements?

11.11 A firms production function is given $Q = 160K^{0.25}L^{0.75}$ where K and L are the number of machines and workers used. Find the marginal productivities of both factors when 400 units of capital and 81 units of labour are used.

11.12 The marginal revenue function for a firm is as follows:

$$MR = \frac{dTR}{dQ} = 100 - 40Q - 6Q^2$$

Find the firm's demand equation.

11.13 In the manufacture of a product, fixed costs are £500 per week. Suppose the marginal cost function of the manufacturer is given by $MC = 2.4Q^2 - 0.8Q + 10$, where Q is weekly output. Find the total cost of producing 100 units per week.

11.14 An economy's marginal propensity to save (MPS), depends on its national income(Y) in the following way:

$$MPS = 0.4 - 0.3Y^{-0.5}$$

If savings $(S) = 0$ when $Y = 100$, find

(a) the equation of total savings and
(b) savings when national income is 400

11.15 The management of an investment fund is considering investing in one of two possible firms in two years time when resources become available. Analysts have estimated that the equations for net profits over the next 8 years for the respective firms are as follows:

Y = net profits (£000,000) and X = the year in question from 1 to 8

Company A: $Y = 30 + 10X - X^2$

Company B: $Y = \dfrac{80}{X^2} + 8X - 10$

Calculate the total net profits that each firm is expected to make from the end of the second year to the end of the eighth year (i.e. evaluate from years 2 to 8).

11.16 A firm invests continuously over time. The rate of net investment (I) at time t (in years) is given by:

$$I = -t^2 + 6t + 10$$

Find out how much capital the firm will have accumulated

(a) in the first two years
(b) from years $t = 2$ to $t = 5$

11.17 A manufacturers marginal cost function is:

$$MC = \frac{dTC}{dQ} = 0.8Q + 9$$

Production is currently set at Q = 50 units per day. How much more would it cost to increase output to 80 units per day?

Note: Answers to Review questions can be found on pp. 451–456.

Further study and data
. . . .

Texts

Bancroft, G. and O'Sullivan, G. (1993), *Quantitative methods for accounting and business studies*, 3rd edn, McGraw Hill, chapter 5.

Curwin, J. and Slater, R. (1996), *Quantitative methods for business decisions*, 4th edn, International Thompson Business Press, chapter 8.

Swift, L. (2001), *Quantitative methods for business, management and finance*, Palgrave Publishers, parts EM and MM.

Waters, D. (1997), *Quantitative methods for business*, 2nd edn, Addison Wesley Longman, chapter 12.

Wisniewski, M. with Stead, R. (1996), *Foundation quantitative methods for business*, Pitman, chapter 11.

On-line exercises
. . . .

Check the web site *www.booksites.net/burton* to find extra questions, Spreadsheet and on-line exercises for this chapter.

Appendix 4

Answers to Selected Even-Numbered Exercises from Newbold

ANSWERS TO SELECTED EVEN-NUMBERED EXERCISES

Chapter 1

1.2 Various answers. Marketing decisions under uncertainty could include pricing decisions, promotion decisions, advertising decisions, packaging decisions, etc.

1.4 a. Various answers. A population parameter could be the true overall population mean income of all families living in West Palm Beach, Florida.
b. Various answers. A population parameter could be the true overall population standard deviation of all stocks traded on the New York Stock Exchange.
c. Various answers. A population parameter could be the true population mean costs of all medical insurance claims received by a company in a given year.
d. Various answers. A population parameter could be the true population mean values of all accounts receivable for a corporation.

1.6 a. The population consists of all of the airline's scheduled flights at Orlando International Airport.
b. The sample consists of the randomly selected 200 flights.
c. The statistic is the 1.5% that were found to depart later than the scheduled time for the 200 randomly selected flights.
d. 1.5% is a sample statistic.

1.8 a. Descriptive—to describe information about a one-week sample.
b. Inferential statistics—to estimate the true percentage of all employees who arrive to work late.
c. Inferential statistics—to predict the relationship between years of experience and pay scale.

Chapter 2

2.2 a. Categorical data. The measurements levels are qualitative—nominal. yes/no response.
b. Categorical data. The measurement levels are are qualitative—nominal.
c. Numerical data. Dollar amounts are generally considered continuous, even though we may truncate dollar amounts and treat dollar amounts as if they were the same as discrete.

2.4 a. Categorical—Qualitative—ordinal
b. Numerical—Quantitative—discrete
c. Categorical—Qualitative—nominal
d. Categorical—Qualitative—nominal

2.6 a. Categorical—Qualitative—nominal
b. Numerical—Quantitative—discrete
c. Categorical—Qualitative—nominal; yes/no response
d. Categorical—Qualitative—ordinal

2.8 a. Various answers—Categorical variable with ordinal responses: Health consciousness
b. Various answers—Categorical variable with nominal responses: Gender

2.10

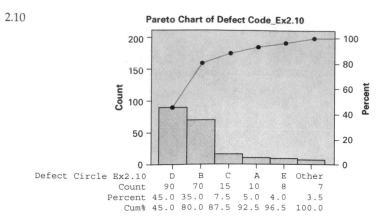

Defect Circle Ex2.10	D	B	C	A	E	Other
Count	90	70	15	10	8	7
Percent	45.0	35.0	7.5	5.0	4.0	3.5
Cum%	45.0	80.0	87.5	92.5	96.5	100.0

2.12

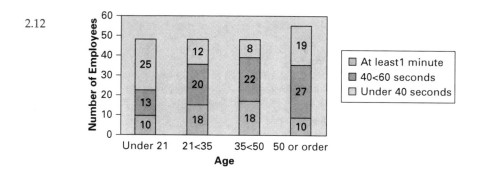

2.14   a.

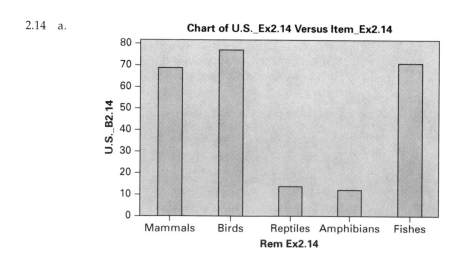

Chart of U.S._Ex2.14 Versus Item_Ex2.14

b.

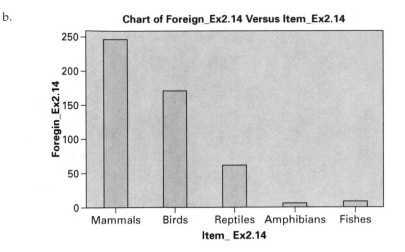

c.

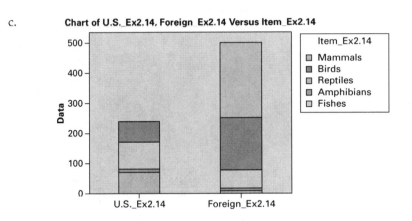

2.16   Describe the data graphically.

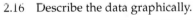

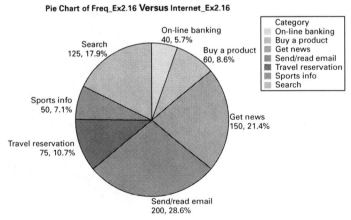

2.18 a.

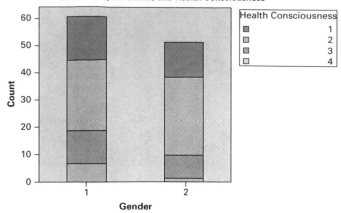

b.

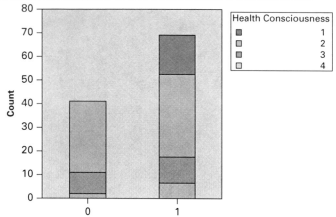

2.20

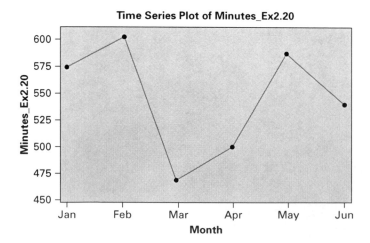

2.22 a.

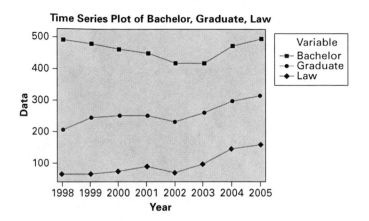

b. The number of law and graduate degrees awarded is increasing. The number of bachelor degrees awarded declined from 1998 to 2002, leveled off in 2003, then began an upward trend in 2004. Enrollment restrictions may be in order if class sizes are becoming too large or if crowding conditions occur.

2.24

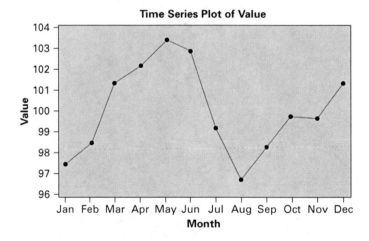

2.26

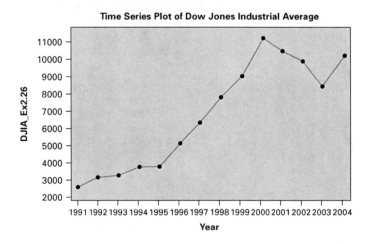

2.28

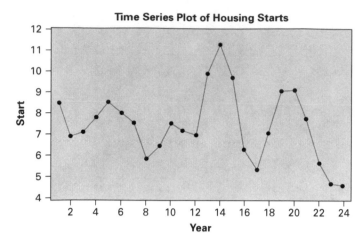

2.30 a. 5 – 7 classes
      b. 7 – 8 classes
      c. 8 – 10 classes
      d. 8 – 10 classes
      e. 10 – 11 classes

2.32 a.

Classes	Frequency
10 < 20	5
20 < 30	3
30 < 40	7
40 < 50	4
50 < 60	5
60 < 70	4

b. histogram and c. ogive

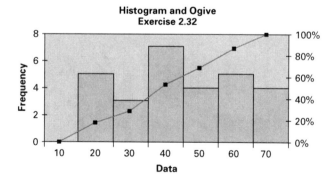

d.

Stem-and-Leaf Display: Data_Ex2.32

Stem-and-leaf of Data N = 28
Leaf Unit = 1.0

```
  5    1   23557
  8    2   148
 (7)   3   2567799
 13    4   0144
  9    5   14699
  4    6   2455
```

2.34

Classes	Frequency	a. Relative Frequency	b. Cumulative Frequency	c. Relative Cumulative Frequency
0<10	8	16.33%	8	16.33%
10<20	10	20.41%	18	36.74%
20<30	13	26.53%	31	63.27%
30<40	12	24.49%	43	87.76%
40<50	6	12.24%	49	100.00%
Total	49	100.00%		

2.36   Various answers – one possibility is to use 7 classes with a width of 0.1

Classes	Frequency	Cumulative %
3.5 < 3.6	1	1.33%
3.6 < 3.7	8	12.00%
3.7 < 3.8	29	50.67%
3.8 < 3.9	22	80.00%
3.9 < 4.0	13	97.33%
4.0 < 4.10	1	98.67%
4.10 < 4.20	1	100.00%

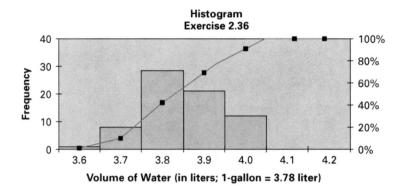

**Histogram
Exercise 2.36**

Volume of Water (in liters; 1-gallon = 3.78 liter)

Stem-and-Leaf Display: Weights
```
Stem-and-leaf of Weights  N = 28
Leaf Unit = 0.010

    1    35  7
    3    36  34
    9    36  577799
   21    37  111122344444
  (17)   37  55566777777889999
   37    38  0111112222244
   24    38  556677899
   15    39  01334444
    7    39  56689
    2    40
    2    40  6
    1    41  1
```

2.38   a. Histogram and c. Ogive of the **Returns** data

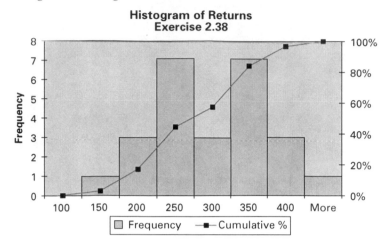

b.

Stem-and-Leaf Display: Returns
```
Stem-and-leaf of Weights  N = 25
Leaf Unit = 10

   1    1   3
   4    1   899
  11    2   0014444
  (3)   2   589
  11    3   0000122
   4    3   689
   1    4
   1    4
   1    5   0
```

2.40

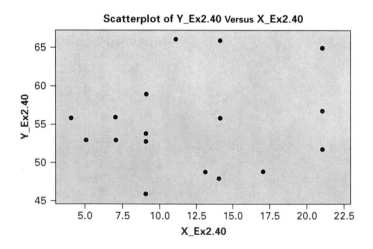

2.42 a.

Subcontractor	Defective Parts	Non-Defective Parts	Parts Supplied
A	4	54	58
B	10	60	70
C	6	66	72
Total	20	180	200

b.

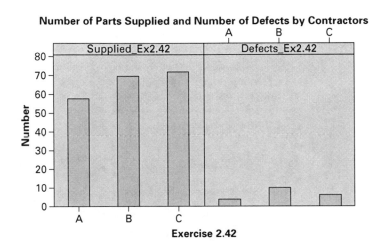

2.44

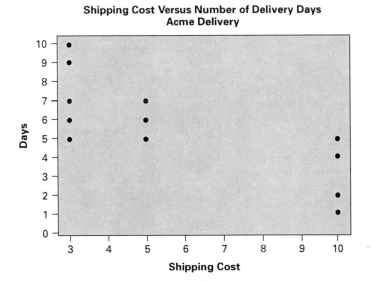

The relationship appears to be negative; however there is significant variability in delivery time at each of the three shipping costs—regular, $3; fast, $5; and lightning, $10.

2.46

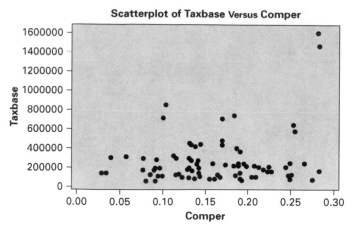

No relationship between the two variables and hence no evidence that emphasis on attracting a larger percentage of commercial property increases the tax base. The two outlier points on the right side of the plot might be used to argue that a very high amount of commercial property will provide a larger tax base. That argument, however, is contrary to the overall pattern of the data.

2.48   a.

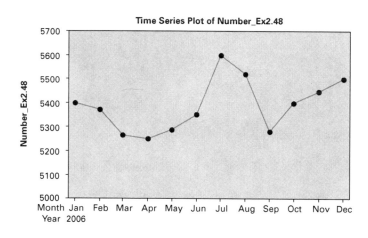

b.

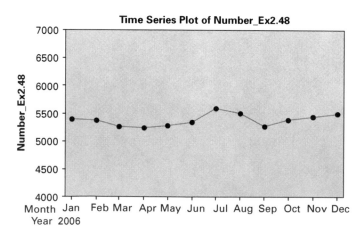

c. Differences between the two graphs include the variability of the data series. One graph suggests greater variability in the data series while the other one suggests a relatively flat line with less variability. Keep in mind the scale on which the measurements are made.

2.50

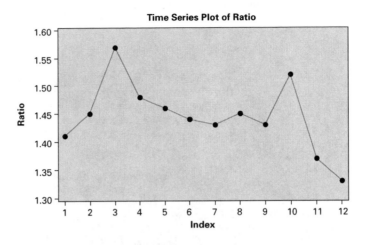

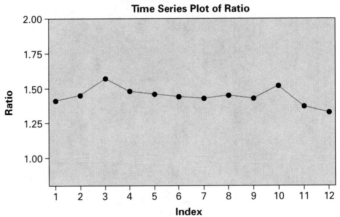

Differences between the two graphs include the variability of the data series. One graph suggests greater variability in the data series while the other one suggests a relatively flat line with less variability. Keep in mind the scale on which the measurements are made.

2.52 a.

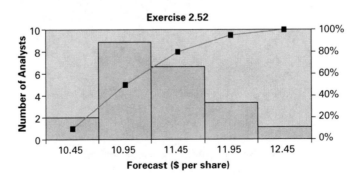

Answer to b., c. and d. are:

	(b)	(c)	(d)	
Forecast of Earnings per Share	Frequency	Relative Freq.	Cumulative Freq.	Cumulative %
9.95	2	0.1	2	10.00%
10.45	8	0.4	10	50.00%
10.95	6	0.3	16	80.00%
11.45	3	0.15	19	95.00%
11.95	1	0.05	20	100.00%

d. Cumulative relative frequencies are in the last column of the table above. These numbers indicate the percent of analysts who forecast that level of earnings per share and all previous classes, up to and including the current class.

2.54

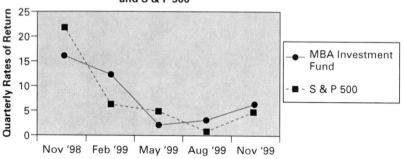

2.56   a.

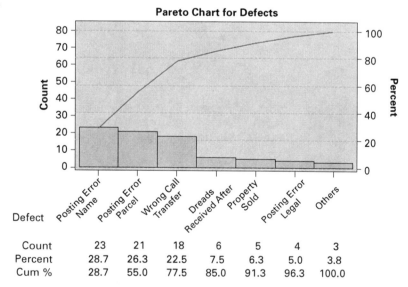

Defect	Posting Error Name	Posting Error Parcel	Wrong Call Transfer	Dreads Received After	Property Sold	Posting Error Legal	Others
Count	23	21	18	6	5	4	3
Percent	28.7	26.3	22.5	7.5	6.3	5.0	3.8
Cum %	28.7	55.0	77.5	85.0	91.3	96.3	100.0

b. Recommendations should include a discussion of the data entry process. The data entry was being made by individuals with no knowledge of the data. Training of the data entry personnel should be a major recommendation. Increasing the size of the monitors used by the data entry staff would also reduce the number of errors.

2.58

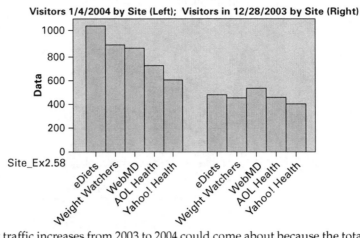

Weekly traffic increases from 2003 to 2004 could come about because the total number of users of the Internet has increased, an increasing awareness of health Internet sites, or an aging baby boom population that is more concerned about health issues.

2.60

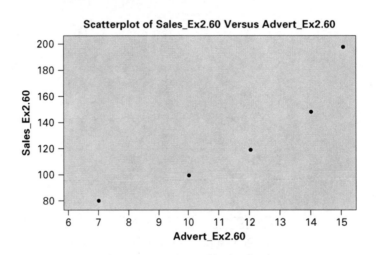

2.62

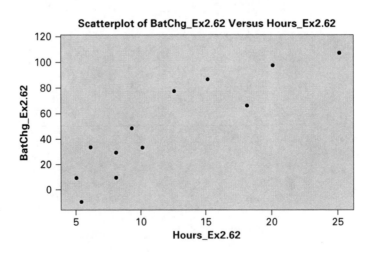

It appears that the number of hours spent per week in a special weight-training program is positively related to the change in their batting averages from the previous season.

2.64 a.

Age	Friend	Newspaper	Subtotal
<21 years	30	20	50
21–35	60	30	90
>35	18	42	60
Subtotal	108	92	200

b.

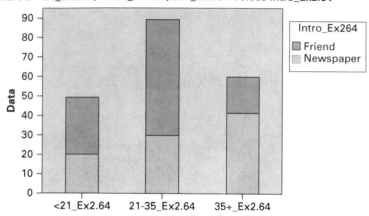

Chart of <21_Ex2.64, 21-35_Ex2.64, 35+_Ex2.64 Versus Intro_Ex2.64

2.66 a.

Health Consciousness	Male	Female	Subtotal
Very	16	13	29
Moderately	26	29	55
Slightly	12	8	20
Not very	7	2	9
Subtotal	61	52	113

b. Do you like a protein supplement in your smoothie?

Health Consciousness	No	Yes	Subtotal
Very	12	17	29
Moderately	19	36	55
Slightly	9	11	20
Not very	2	7	9
Subtotal	42	71	113

2.68 a.

Payment	M	T	W	Th	F	S	Total
Am Ex	7	0	3	4	3	6	23
MC	1	4	4	2	4	9	24
Visa	6	6	4	5	8	10	39
Cash	3	1	0	0	3	9	16
Other	2	0	4	4	7	6	23
Subtotal	19	11	15	15	25	40	125

b.

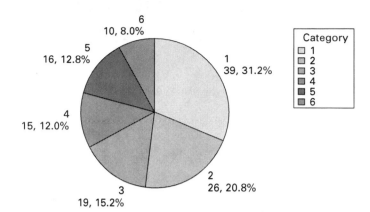

Pie Chart of Preference for Color of Roses

Chapter 3

3.2   a. 12   b. 13   c. 8

3.4   a. 5.94   b. 6.35
      c. The distribution is relatively symmetric since the mean of 5.94 is relatively close to
         the median of 6.35. Since the mean is slightly less than the median, the distribution
         is slightly skewed to the left.

3.6   a. 53.57. The mean demand for one-gallon bottles is 53.57 which is the balancing
         point of the distribution. The median of 55 indicates that half of the distribution
         had larger sales than 55 bottles and half had smaller sales. No unique mode exists
         in the distribution.
      b. Comment on symmetry or skewness. Since the mean is slightly less than the
         median, the distribution is slightly skewed to the left.

3.8   a. 25.58   b. 22.50   c. 22

3.10 a. 8.545   b. 9.0
      c. The distribution is slightly skewed to the left since the mean is less than the median.

3.12 $s^2 = 5.143$ and $s = 2.268$

3.14 $\bar{x} = 9$; $s^2 = 2.5$; $s = 1.581$; $CV = 17.57$

3.16 a. IQR = 24.25; $Q_1 = 49.5$; $Q_3 = 73.75$
      b. 77.2
      c. 83.64

3.18 a. 190 and 310. At least 88.9% of the observations are within 3 standard deviations
         from the mean.
      b. 210 and 290. At least 75% of the observations are within 2 standard deviations from
         the mean.
      c. 230 and 270. At least 0% of the observations are within 1 standard deviation from
         the mean.

3.20 a. $\mu_{stocks} = 8.16$, $\mu_{Tbills} = 5.786$
         The mean annual % return on stocks is higher than the return for U.S. Treasury bills.
      b. $\sigma_{stocks} = 20.648$, $\sigma_{Tbills} = 1.362$
         The variability of the U.S. Treasury bills is much smaller than the return on stocks.

3.22 a. range = 0.54, standard deviation = 0.1024, variance = 0.010486
      b. Five number summary:

Min	Q1	Median	Q3	Max
3.57	3.74	3.79	3.87	4.11

      c. IQR = 0.13. This tells that the range of the middle 50% of the distribution is 0.13
      d. 0.02689 or 2.689%

3.24 a. s = 3.8696
      b. The distribution is mounded. Therefore, the empirical rule applies. Approximately
         95% of the distribution is expected to be within +/− 2 standard deviations of the
         mean.

3.26 a. 4.2   b. 4.583

3.28 32,299.519

3.30 a. 1.40   b. $s^2 = 3.0612$, s = 1.7496

3.32 a. 11.025   b. 0.520

3.34 a. 261.54545 b. 17.370

3.36 a. 1392.5   b. 0.9930

3.38 a. 4.268
      b. 0.128
      c. Weak positive association between the number of drug units and the number of
         days to complete recovery. Recommend low or no dosage units.

3.40 a. 0.65   b. 4.40   c. $\hat{y} = b_0 + b_1 x = 4.40 + 0.65x$

3.42 a. Covariance = −99.762, Correlation = −0.927136
      b. $b_1 = -18.217$. For a one dollar increase in the price per gallon of paint, we estimate
         that the quantity sold per seven days of operation would decrease by 18.217 gallons
         of paint.
      c. $b_0 = 268.70$. If the price of the paint were $0 per gallon, we would expect to sell 268.7
         gallons per seven days of operation. Interpret with caution—note that we are
         extrapolating the results beyond the observed data.
      d. 141.181

3.44 a. $Cov(x,y) = 9.96429$ r = 0.985
      b. $b_1 = 3.695$ and $b_0 = -3.69536$
      c. The regression equation provides an estimation of the impact that additional
         retail experience has on weekly sales (in hundreds of dollars). It appears that as
         retail experience increases, the weekly sales also increases. This estimate is based
         on retail experience between 2 and 6 years with weekly sales of $400 to $2,000.

3.46 a. 18.1325   b. Sample variance = 204.7017,   s = 14.307

3.48 a.

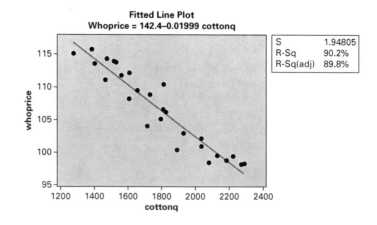

b. $\hat{y} = 142.398 - 0.0199937x$; marginal effect is -0.0199937

c.

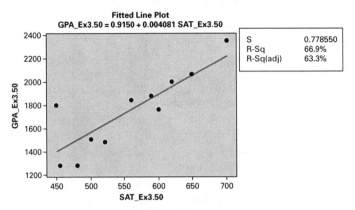

3.50 a.

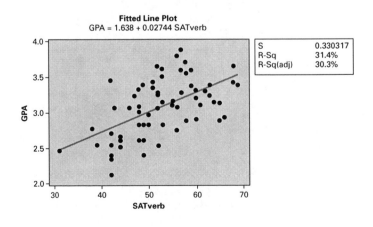

Direction is positive with a relatively strong ($r = 0.818$) correlation between the two variables. There is a positive relationship between the Math SAT score and the GPA at the time of graduation.

b. $b_1 = 0.004081$. For a one point increase in the Math SAT score, we estimate that GPA at the time of graduation will increase by 0.004081

c. $b_0 = 0.9150$

d. 3.078

e. Based on this data, can you predict GPA for a 375 Math SAT?
The value of 375 for the Math SAT score is outside of the observed data. We would have to extrapolate beyond the observed data in order to make a statement about the graduating GPA. The results outside of the observed data are much less meaningful.

3.52 a.

Fitted Line Plot
GPA = 1.638 + 0.02744 SATverb

S	0.330317
R-Sq	31.4%
R-Sq(adj)	30.3%

b. Describe the data numerically

Covariances: GPA, SATverb

```
                    GPA   SATverb
GPA        0.169284
SATverb    1.791637  65.293985
```

Correlations: GPA, SATverb

```
Pearson correlation of GPA and SATverb=0.560
P-Value=0.000
```

Regression Analysis: GPA versus SATverb

```
The regression equation is
GPA=1.64 + 0.0274 SATverb
```

    c. 3.06

3.54   a. 195.46 up to 394.54

       b. 137.50 up to 452.50

3.56   a. 23,000 to 35,000

       b. 15,583.59 to 42,416.41

Chapter 4

4.2   a. (E_3, E_9)

       b. $(E_1, E_2, E_3, E_7, E_8, E_9)$

       c. A union B is not collectively exhaustive—it does not contain all of the possible sample points.

4.4   a. (E_3, E_6)

       b. $(E_3, E_4, E_5, E_6, E_9, E_{10})$

       c. A union B is not collectively exhaustive—it does not contain all of the possible sample points.

4.6   a. $(\underline{A} \cap B)$ is the event that the Dow-Jones average rises on both days which is O_1. $(\overline{A} \cap B)$ is the event the Dow-Jones average does not rise on the first day but it rises on the second day which is O_3. The union between these two will be O_1 or O_3 either of which by definition is event B: the Dow-Jones average rises on the second day.

       b. Since $(\overline{A} \cap B)$ is the event the Dow-Jones average does not rise on the first day but rises on the second day which is O_3 and because A is the event that the Dow-Jones average rises on the first day, then the union will be O_2, either the Dow-Jones average does not rise on the first day but rises on the second day or the Dow-Jones average rises on the first day or both. This is the definition of A∪B.

4.8   .53

4.10   .3709

4.12   .0123

4.14 a. .54   b. .18

       c. A complement is the event that the rate of return is not more than 10%.

       d. .46

       e. The intersection between more than 10% and return will be negative is the null or empty set.

       f. 0

       g. The union of A and B is the event that are the rates of return of; less than −10%, −10% to 0%, 10% to 20%, and more than 20%.

       h. .72

       i. A and B are mutually exclusive because their intersection is the null set.

       j. A and B are not collectively exhaustive because their union does not equal 1

4.16 A and $\overline{A}$ of exercise 4-1 are not mutually exclusive. Since $P(A) = .68$ and $P(\overline{A}) = .75$, check if $P(A \cup \overline{A}) = P(A) + P(\overline{A}) = .68 + .75 = 1.43 > 1$. Therefore, if two events are not mutually exclusive, the probability of their union cannot equal the sum of their individual probabilities.

4.18   a. .87
      b. .35
      c. By the third probability postulate, the sum of the probabilities of all outcomes in the sample space must sum to 1

4.20   0

4.22   .75

4.24   .80, A and B are independent since the P(A | B) of .80 equals the P(A) of .80

4.26   .625, A and B are not independent since the P(A | B) of .625 does not equal the P(A) of .70

4.28   a. 5,040
      b. 0.0001984

4.30   .00833

4.32   .0167

4.34   28

4.36   a. 150   b. .2667   c. .20

4.38   .35

4.40   a. No, the two events are not mutually exclusive because $P(A \cap B) \neq 0$
      b. No, the two events are not collectively exhaustive because $P(A \cup B) \neq 1$
      c. No, the two events are not statistically independent because $P(A \cap B) = .15 \neq .06 = P(A)P(B)$.

4.42   a. .069

4.44   a. .5556   b. .8333

4.46   .1292

4.48   a. .9   b. .88   c. .925

4.50   a. 0.867
      b. Check if $P(A \cap B) = P(A)P(B)$. Since $.04 \neq .06$, the two events are not independent events.

4.52   .2

4.54   .05

4.56   .05

4.58   .1667

4.60   .40

4.62   Odds $= \dfrac{.5}{1 - .5} = 1$ to 1 odds

4.64   2.00

4.66   a. .12
      b. .7037
      c. Check if $P(F \cap N) = P(F)P(N)$. Since $.19 \neq .2133$, the two events are not independent.
      d. .3333
      e. Check if $P(I \cap O) = P(I)P(O)$. Since $.07 \neq .0399$, the two events are not independent.
      f. .79
      g. .27
      h. .87

4.68   a. .25   b. .32   c. .16   d. .125   e. .2121

4.70 a. .32   b. .25   c. .375   d. .48   e. .4375
      f. No, since $P(A \cap Y)$ which is .12 $\neq$ $P(A)P(Y)$ which is .08

4.72 a. .76   b. .77   c. .4348

4.74 a. .025   b. .445   c. .2697

4.76 a. .475   b. .3684   c. .8571

4.78 .375

4.80 .3636

4.82 .6667

4.84 .6923

4.86 .444

4.88 a. True   b. False   c. True   d. True   e. True
      f. True   g. False

4.90 Bayes' theorem is a summary of the relationship between a specific event that has occurred and the effect on a subsequent event. The occurrence of the specific event is the prior information or 'prior probability' that is known. This prior knowledge can be analyzed to understand the effect on the probability of a subsequent event. The subsequent event is the 'posterior probability.'

4.92 Various answers. By definition, *Joint Probability* is the probability that two events will occur together e.g. P(female and Liberal Arts major).
      Marginal probability is defined as the probability of an individual event e.g. P(female).
      Conditional probability is the probability of occurrence of one event given that another event has occurred. e.g. P(female given Liberal Arts Major).

4.94 $P(A \cup B) = P(A) + P(B) - P(A \cap B) = P(A) + P(B) - [P(A \mid B)P(B)]$
      $= P(A) + P(B)[1 - P(A \mid B)]$

4.96 a. .4211   b. .6316   c. .2526

4.98 a. .125   b. .3571   c. .875
      d. No, since $P(HM \cap S)$ which is .125 $\neq$ .175 which is $P(HM)P(S)$.
      e. No, their intersection is not zero, hence the two events cannot be mutually exclusive. $P(HM \cap S) = .125 \neq 0$
      f. No, the probability of their union does not equal 1. $P(HM \cup S) = P(HM) + P(S) - P(HM \cap S) = .35 + .5 - .125 = .725$ which is less than 1

4.100 a. .48   b. .11   c. .7273
      d. No, check if $P(M \cap G)$ which is .8 $\neq$ .088 which is $P(M)P(G)$.
      e. .191

4.102 a. 1,820   b. .089

4.104 a. .075   b. .1429   c. 10!90!/100!

4.106 .2581

4.108 .6364

4.110 a. .4526   b. .6632   c. .9406
      d. No, since $P(G \cap JC)$ which is (.78)(.27) = .2106 $\neq$ .1791 which is $P(G)P(JC)$ = (.6632)(.27)

4.112 a. .58   b. .6034   c. .3966

4.114 .0128

4.116 .5085

Chapter 5

5.2   Discrete random variable

5.4   Discrete random variable

5.6   Total sales, advertising expenditures, competitor's sales

5.8   Discrete

5.10   Probability distribution of number of heads in one toss

X-number of heads	P(x)
0	.5
1	.5

5.12   Various answers OK

X – # of Times Missing Class	P(x)	F(x)
0	.65	.65
1	.15	.80
2	.10	.90
3	.09	.99
4	.01	1.00

5.14   a. Cumulative probability function: OK

X	0	1	2	3	4	5	6	7	8	9
P(x)	.10	.08	.07	.15	.12	.08	.10	.12	.08	.10
F(x)	.10	.18	.25	.40	.52	.60	.70	.82	.90	1.00

   b. .48
   c. .57

5.16   a. Probability distribution function

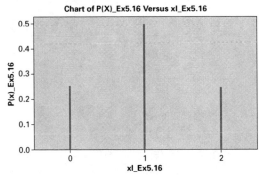

   b. Cumulative probability function

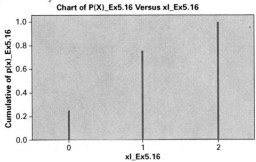

c. $\mu_x = 1.00$ d. $\sigma^2_x = 0.50$

5.18   a. Probability function:

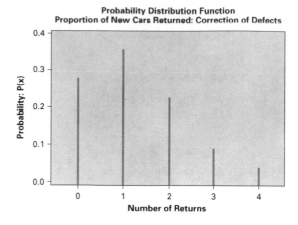

b. Cumulative probability function:

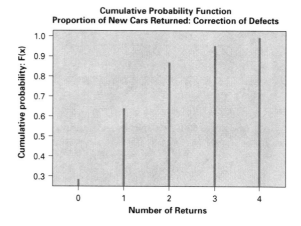

c. 1.25 defects
d. 1.1675 defects

5.20   a. Probability function

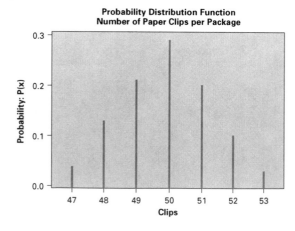

b. Cumulative probability function

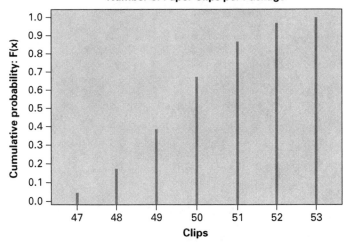

Cumulative Probability Function
Number of Paper Clips per Package

c. .70
d. .8556
e. $\mu = 49.9$ $\sigma_x = 1.3964$

	M	N	O	P	Q
1	Clips	P(x)	F(x)	Mean	Variance
2	47	0.04	0.04	1.88	0.3364
3	48	0.13	0.17	6.24	0.4693
4	49	0.21	0.38	10.29	0.1701
5	50	0.29	0.67	14.5	0.0029
6	51	0.20	0.87	10.2	0.242
7	52	0.10	0.97	5.2	0.441
8	53	0.03	1.00	1.59	0.2883
9		1.00		49.9	1.95
10					

Microsoft Excel - Book1

File Edit View Insert Format Tools QIC Data Window Help

Arial

W12   =

f. $\mu = \$.342$, $\sigma_\pi = \$.0279$

5.22 a. Probability function

X	0	1	2
P(x)	0.81	0.18	.01

b. $P(Y = 0) = 153/190$
$P(Y = 1) = 36/190$
$P(Y = 2) = 1/190$
The answer in part b. is different from part a. because in part b. the probability of picking a defective part on the second draw depends upon the result of the first draw.
c. $\mu = 0.2$ defects, $\sigma_x^2 = .18$
d. $\mu = 0.2$ defects, $\sigma_y^2 = .1705$

5.24 "One and one" $E(X) = 1.3125$
"Two-shot foul" $E(X) = 1.50$
The "two-shot foul" has a higher expected value.

5.26 $\mu = 3.29$ $\sigma = 1.1515$

5.28 a. $\mu = 1.82$, $\sigma = 1.0137$
b. Cost: $\mu = \$2,730$, $\sigma = \$1,520.559$

5.30 $\mu_x = .5$
$\sigma_x^2 = .25$

5.32 $P(x = 7) = .06181$, $P(x < 6) = .7805$

5.34 $P(x = 12) = .1873$, $P(x < 6) = .000269$

5.36 a. $P(x \geq 1) = .7627$
b. $P(x \geq 3) = .1035$

5.38 $P(x \geq 4) = .5$

5.40 a. $P(x = 5) = .0102$
b. $P(x \geq 3) = .3174$
c. $P(x \geq 2) = .5248$
d. $E(X) = 2$ games. Unless of course you are a Cubs fan and then you would *hope* the Cubs would win all of the games but you would *expect* them to win none of the games.
e. $E(X) = 2.6$ games

5.42 a. .5248   b. $E(X) = 1.6$, $\sigma_x = .9798$

5.44 a. $E(X) = 64$, $\sigma_x = 7.871$
b. $E(Z) = \$640$, $\sigma_z = \$78.71$

5.46 a. $E(X) = 483.6$, $\sigma_x = 10.3146$
b. $E(Z) = \$967.20$, $\sigma_z = \$20.6292$

5.48 The acceptance rules have the following probabilities:
(i) Rule 1: $P(X = 0) = (.8)^{10} = .1074$
(ii) Rule 2: $P(X \leq 1) = (.8)^{20} + 20(.2)(.8)^{19} = .0692$

The second acceptance rule will have the smaller probability of accepting a shipment containing 20% defectives.

5.50 .210376

5.52 .151769

5.54 .1999

5.56 .3808

5.58 .2619

5.60 .1336

5.62 .857614

5.64 .4232

5.66 .7898

5.68 .0884

5.70 .9380

5.72 Two models are possible—the poisson distribution is appropriate when the warehouse is serviced by many thousands of independent truckers where the mean number of 'successes' is relatively small. However, under the assumption of a small fleet of 10 trucks with a probability of any truck arriving during a given hour is .1, then the binomial distribution is the more appropriate model. Both models yield similar, although not identical, probabilities.

Cumulative Distribution Function
Poisson with mean = 1

x	P(X <= x)
0	0.36788
1	0.73576
2	0.91970
3	0.98101
4	0.99634
5	0.99941
6	0.99992
7	0.99999
8	1.00000
9	1.00000
10	1.00000

Cumulative Distribution Function
Binomial with n = 10 and p = 0.1

x	P(X <= x)
0	0.34868
1	0.73610
2	0.92981
3	0.98720
4	0.99837
5	0.99985
6	0.99999
7	1.00000
8	1.00000
9	1.00000
10	1.00000

5.74 a.

		X		
Y		1	2	P(y)
	0	0.2	0.25	0.45
	1	0.3	0.25	0.55
P(x)		0.5	0.5	1

b. $Cov(X, Y) = -.025$, $\rho = -.1005$

5.76 a. Compute marginal probability distributions for X and Y.

		X		
Y		1	2	P(y)
	0	0.3	0.2	0.5
	1	0.25	0.25	0.5
P(x)		0.55	0.45	1

b. $Cov(X, Y) = .025$, $\rho = .0326$
c. $\mu_W = 3.4$, $\sigma^2_W = 9.75$

5.78 a.

		X		
Y		1	2	P(y)
	0	0.25	0.25	0.5
	1	0.25	0.25	0.5
P(x)		0.5	0.5	1

b. $Cov(X, Y) = 0.0$, $\rho = 0.0$
c. $\mu_W = 2.0$, $\sigma^2_W = .50$

5.80 a.

	X		
Y	1	2	P(y)
0	0	0.6	0.6
1	0.4	0	0.4
P(x)	0.4	0.6	1

b. $Cov(X, Y) = -0.24$, $\rho = -1.00$
c. $\mu_W = 1.6$, $\sigma^2_W = .48$

5.82 a. $Px(0) = .22$ $Px(1) = .26$ $Px(2) = .43$ $Px(3) = .09$ $\mu_x = 1.39$
      b. $Py(0) = .23$ $Py(1) = .21$ $Py(2) = .30$ $Py(3) = .26$ $\mu_y = 1.59$
      c. $P_{Y|X}(0|3) = .1111$ $P_{Y|X}(1|3) = .1111$
        $P_{Y|X}(2|3) = .3333$ $P_{Y|X}(3|3) = .4444$
      d. $Cov(X, Y) = .3399$
      e. No, because $Cov(X,Y) \neq 0$

5.84 a. $Py(0) = .12$ $Py(1) = .24$ $Py(2) = .23$ $Py(3) = .23$ $Py(4) = .18$
      b. $P_{Y|X}(y|3) = 1/26; 3/26; 6/26; 8/26; 8/26$
      c. No, because $Px,y(3,4) = .08 \neq .0468 = Px(3)Py(4)$

5.86 a.

Y/X	0	1	Total
0	.704	.168	.872
1	.096	.032	.128
Total	.80	.20	1.00

b. $P_{Y|X}(y|0) = .88; .12$
c. $Px(0) = .80$ $Px(1) = .20$ $Py(0) = .872$ $Py(1) = .128$
d. $Cov(X, Y) = .0064$
      The covariance indicates that there is a positive association between X and Y, professors are more likely to be away from the office on Friday than during the other days.

5.88 Number of total complaints (food complaints + service complaints) has a mean of $(1.36 + 1.64) = 3.00$. If the two types of complaints are independent, then the variance of total complaints is equal to the sum of the variance of the two types of complaints because the covariance would be zero. $(.8104 + .7904) = 1.6008$. The standard deviation will be the square root of the variance $= 1.26523$

If the number of food and service complaints are not independent of each other, then the covariance would no longer be zero. The mean would remain the same; however, the standard deviation would change. The variance of the sum of the two types of complaints becomes the variance of one plus the variance of the other plus two times the covariance.

5.90 a. No, not necessarily. There is a probability distribution associated with the rates of return in the mutual fund and not all rates of return will equal the expected value.
      b. Which fund to invest in will depend not only on the expected value of the return but also on the riskiness of each fund and how risk averse the client is.

5.92 a. 2.21
      b. 1.3513
      c. Mean Salary = \$913. Standard deviation of salary = \$405.39
      d. To earn a salary of \$1,000 or more, the salesperson must sell at least 3 cars. $P(X \geq 3) = .16 + .12 + .07 = .35$

5.94 a. Positive covariance: Consumption expenditures and Disposable income
      b. Negative covariance: Price of cars and the number of cars sold
      c. Zero covariance: Dow Jones stock market average and rainfall in Brazil

5.96 a. .17
      b. $\mu_x = 2.59$, $\mu_y = 1.1$
      c. Cov(X,Y) = .191. This implies that there is a positive relationship between the number of years in school and the number of visits to a museum in the last year.

5.98 a. .3369   b. .5931
      c. $\mu = 44$. The proportion is .55. $\sigma = 4.4497$. The proportion is .05562

5.100 To evaluate the effectiveness of the analyst's ability, find the probability that x is greater than or equal to 3 at random. $P(x \geq 3) = .16683$

5.102 a. $P(0) = .09072$ b. $P(x > 3) = .2213$

5.104 $P(x = 0) = .0907$. Let Y be the number of stalls for both lines. Find the $P(Y \geq 1) = .99177$

5.106 $\mu_W = 10$, $\sigma^2_W = 22.5$

Chapter 6

6.2   0.45

6.4   0.35

6.6   a.

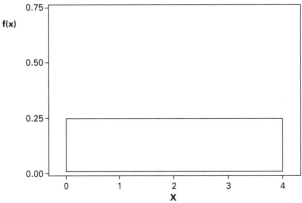

b.

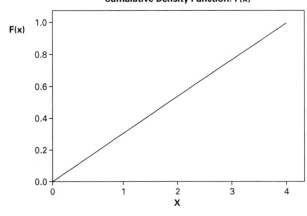

c. .25
d. .25

6.8 a. .2 b. .4 < P(X < 400) < .6

6.10 $\mu_W = 900$, $\sigma^2_W = 360$

6.12 $\mu_W = 4,000$, $\sigma^2_W = 8,100$

6.14 $\mu_Y = \$26.4$ million, $\sigma_Y = \$1$ million

6.16 $\mu_Y = \$54,000$, $\sigma_Y = \$14,400$

6.18 a. .52 b. −.67 c. .84 d. −.25

6.20 a. .9772 b. .3674 c. = .0062 d. 92.8 e. X = 70 and 90

6.22 a. .6554 b. .6554
c. The graph should show the property of symmetry—the area in the tails equidistant from the mean will be equal.
d. .6006
e. The area under the normal curve is equal to .8 for an infinite number of ranges—merely start at a point that is marginally higher. The shortest range will be the one that is centered on the z of zero. The z that corresponds to an area of .8 centered on the mean is a Z of ±1.28. This yields an interval of the mean plus and minus $64: [$316, $444]

6.24 a. .2266 b. .2266 c. .5468
d. (i) The graph should show the property of symmetry—the area in the tails equidistant from the mean will be equal.
e. (ii) The answers to a, b, c sum to one because the events cover the entire area under the normal curve which by definition, must sum to 1

6.26 a. .2148 b. .1587 c. .3692
d. The answer to a. will be larger because 10 grams is closer to the mean than is 15 grams. Thus, there would be a greater area remaining less than 10 grams than will be the area above 15 grams.

6.28 .0668

6.30 $\mu = 15.265$, $\sigma^2 = 14.317$

6.32 For Investment A, the probability of a return higher than 10%

$$P(Z > \frac{10 - 10.4}{1.2}) = P(Z > -.33) = F_Z(.33) = .6293$$

For Investment B, the probability of a return higher than 10%

$$P(Z > \frac{10 - 11.0}{4}) = P(Z > -.25) = F_Z(.28) = .5987$$

Therefore, Investment A is a better choice.

6.34 a. 98.8 b. 183.6 c. .9487

6.36 a. .3721 b. 522.4 c. 400 – 439 d. 520 – 559 e. .2922

6.38 .4990

6.40 a. .0054 b. .0002 c. .9892
d. X = 1573.741 ≈ 1,574 successes
e. X = 1616.46 ≈ 1616 successes

6.42 a. .0000 b. .0005 c. .9990
d. P = 38.971% e. P = 41.642%

6.44   a. .0475   b. .3372

6.46   .0207

6.48   .2877

6.50   .864665

6.52   .2019

6.54   .4866

6.56   .3012

6.58   a. $P(X > 3) = 1 - [1 - e^{-(3/\mu)}] = e^{-3\lambda}$ since $\lambda = 1/\mu$
        b. $P(X > 6) = 1 - [1 - e^{-(6/\mu)}] = e^{-(6/\mu)} = e^{-6\lambda}$
        c. $P(X > 6 \mid X > 3) = P(X > 6)/P(X > 3) = e^{-6\lambda}/e^{-3\lambda}] = e^{-3\lambda}$
            The probability of an occurrence within a specified time in the future is not related to how much time has passed since the most recent occurrence.

6.60 $\mu_W = 1{,}300$, $\sigma^2_W = 4{,}900$

6.62 $\mu_W = 1{,}700$, $\sigma^2_W = 4{,}900$

6.64 $\mu_X = 28{,}000$, $\sigma_X = 12{,}000$

6.66 $\mu_Y = 162{,}000$

        $\sigma_Y = 18{,}027.76$

6.68   The calculation of the mean is correct, but the standard deviations of two random variables cannot be summed. To get the correct standard deviation, add the variances together and then take the square root. The standard deviation: $\sigma = \sqrt{5(16)^2} = 35.7771$

6.70   a. $\mu_W = 2{,}850$, $\sigma^2_W = 992{,}500$
        b. $\mu_W = 2{,}850$, $\sigma^2_W = 332{,}500$

6.72   a. $\mu_W = 100$, $\sigma^2_W = 256.90465$
        b. .3483

6.74   a. $\mu_W = -5$, $\sigma^2_W = 21.79449$
        b. .4090

6.76   a.

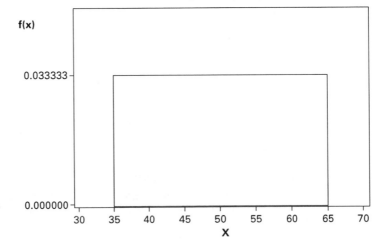

Probability Density Function: f(x)

b. Cumulative density function

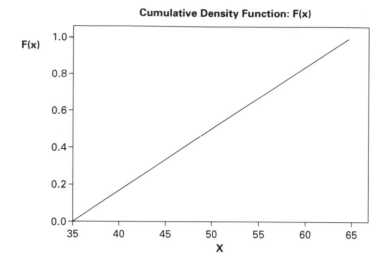

Cumulative Density Function: F(x)

    c. 10/30
    d. 50

6.78 a. $\mu_Y = 3{,}360$ b. $\sigma_Y = 80$

6.80 Given that the variance of both predicted earnings and forecast error are both positive and given that the variance of actual earnings is equal to the sum of the variances of predicted earnings and forecast error, then the Variance of predicted earnings must be less than the variance of actual earnings.

6.82 a. .2119   b. .3759   c. 3.24   d. .7190   e. .3789

6.84 a. .3085
      b. .6826
      c. $Xi = 149.35$
      d. .9916
      e. 0.0417
      f. 90 – 109
      g. 130 – 149

6.86 .0436

6.88 $P(Z < 6.45) \approx 1.0000$

6.90 .0084

6.92 a. .0475
      b. 236.95 (237 listeners)

6.94 .975

6.96 a. $\mu_W = 200$, $\sigma^2_W = 3{,}204.919$
      b. Option 1: $\sigma^2_1 = 3{,}813.744$, Option 2: $\sigma^2_2 = 2{,}665.66$
      To reduce the variance of the porfolio, select Option 2.

6.98 a. .1020   b. .2764

Chapter 7

7.2 a.

Probability Density Function

Binomial with n = 2 and p = 0.5

x	p(X = x)
0	0.25
1	0.50
2	0.25

b.

Probability Density Function

Binomial with n = 4 and p = 0.5

x	p(X = x)
0	0.0625
1	0.2500
2	0.3750
3	0.2500
4	0.0625

c.

Probability Density Function

Binomial with n = 10 and p = 0.5

x	P(X = x)
0	0.000977
1	0.009766
2	0.043945
3	0.117188
4	0.205078
5	0.246094
6	0.205078
7	0.117188
8	0.043945
9	0.009766
10	0.000977

7.4 The response should note that there will be errors in taking a census of the entire population as well as errors in taking a sample. Improved accuracy can be achieved via sampling methods versus taking a complete census (see reference to Hogan, 90). By using sample information, we can make valid inferences about the entire population without the time and expense involved in taking a census.

7.6 a. $\mu_{\bar{x}} = \mu = 100$, $\sigma_{\bar{x}}^2 = 30$
b. .0505
c. .7337
d. .8997

7.8 a. $\mu_{\bar{x}} = \mu = 400$, $\sigma_{\bar{x}}^2 = 45.7143$
b. .0384
c. .7016
d. .0516

7.10 a. $E(\bar{X}) = \mu_{\bar{x}} = 1{,}200$
b. $\sigma_{\bar{x}}^2 = 17{,}778$
c. $\sigma_{\bar{x}} = 33.33$
d. .1292

7.12 a. .9772   b. .5762   c. .3108   d. \$114,000 − \$116,000
e. Even with non-normal populations, the sampling distribution of the sample means will be normal for sufficient sample n. Since n is ≥ 30, the sampling distribution of the sample means can be assumed to be a normal distribution.

7.14 a. $\sigma_{\bar{x}} = 5.5$ b. .9909   c. .8980   d. .4329
e. Higher, higher, lower. The graph will show that the standard error of the sample means will decrease with an increased sample size.

7.16 a. $\sigma_{\bar{x}} = 4$ b. .1056   c. .1587   d. .4532

7.18 a. Difference = .2632
b. Difference = −.2048
c. Difference = ±.2304

7.20 a. $n = 68$ b. smaller   c. larger

7.22 a. $N = 20$, correction factor $= \dfrac{0}{19}$

        $N = 40$, correction factor $= \dfrac{20}{39}$

        $N = 100$, correction factor $= \dfrac{80}{99}$

        $N = 1{,}000$, correction factor $= \dfrac{980}{999}$

        $N = 10{,}000$, correction factor $= \dfrac{9{,}980}{9{,}999}$

   b. When the population size (N) equals the sample size (n), then there is no variation away from the population mean and the standard error will be zero. As the sample size becomes relatively small compared to the population size, the correction factor tends towards 1 and the correction factor becomes less significant in the calculation of the standard error.

   c. The correction factor tends toward a value of 1 and becomes progressively less important as a modifying factor when the sample size decreases relative to the population size.

7.24 a. .2546   b. .0951   c. $= .0086$

7.26 a. .1539   b. .0122   c. .8339

7.28 a. .1112   b. .0071   c. .8372

7.30 a. .424   b. .00244   c. .0494   d. .0618

7.32 a. .20   b. .000889   c. .0298   d. .0465

7.34 .7372

7.36 a. .0351   b. .9222   c. .4314   d. Higher, higher

7.38 The largest value for σ_p is when $p = .5$. In this case, $\sigma_p = \sqrt{\dfrac{(.5)(.5)}{100}} = .05$

7.40 a. .0395
   b. Difference $= .0506$
   c. Difference $= .065$
   d. Difference $= .0409$

7.42 .0057

7.44 a. .03934   b. .0384   c. .0054

7.46 $P(Z > 4.61) \approx .0000$

7.48 a. .1587
   b. $s^2 < 57.702$
   c. $s^2 > 151.879$

7.50 Between .01 and .025 (.0201 exactly)

7.52 a. Just greater than .1 (.1187 exactly)
   b. Between .01 and .025 (.0118 exactly)

7.54 a. Between .025 and .05 (.0428 exactly)
   b. Less than .005 (.0004 exactly)

7.56

Descriptive Statistics: C1, C2, C3, C4, C5, C6, C7, C8, ...

Variable	Mean	Variance
C1	4.500	3.667
C2	4.75	4.92
C3	5.00	6.67
C4	4.75	4.92
C5	5.00	6.67
C6	5.25	7.58
C7	5.25	4.92
C8	5.50	6.33
C9	5.75	6.92
C10	5.75	6.92
C11	5.750	1.583
C12	6.000	2.667
C13	6.250	2.917
C14	6.250	2.917
C15	6.750	0.917

$$\bar{x} = \frac{70.518}{15} = 4.7012 \quad E(s^2) = \frac{15(3.91667)}{(14)} = 4.1964$$

which is not equal to $\sigma^2 = \frac{47}{12} = 3.91667$

7.58 a. 163.11%
b. The probability is .95 that the sample variance is between 30% and 211.33% of the population variance.
c. The interval in part b. will be smaller.

7.60 a. 41.55%
b. 50.73%
c. The probability is .95 that the sample variance is between 34.727% and 199.27% of the population variance.

7.62 Less than .90 (.5438 exactly)

7.64 a. 15 possible samples
b. (41, 39), (41, 35), (41, 35), (41, 33), (41, 38), (39, 35), (39, 35), (39, 33), (39, 38), (35, 35), (35, 33), (35, 38), (35, 33), (35, 38), (33, 38)

c. $\frac{2}{15}$ for 34 and 36.5

$\frac{1}{15}$ for all others

d. $34P_{\bar{X}}(34) = 34\frac{2}{15} = 4.5333$ $37P_{\bar{X}}(37) = 37\frac{3}{15} = 7.4$

$35P_{\bar{X}}(35) = \frac{35}{15} = 2.3333$ $38P_{\bar{X}}(38) = 38\frac{2}{15} = 5.0667$

$35.5P_{\bar{X}}(35.5) = \frac{35.5}{15} = 2.3667$ $38.5P_{\bar{X}}(38.5) = \frac{38.5}{15} = 2.5667$

$36P_{\bar{X}}(36) = \frac{36}{15} = 2.4$ $39.5P_{\bar{X}}(39.5) = \frac{39.5}{15} = 2.6333$

$36.5P_{\bar{X}}(36.5) = 36.5\frac{2}{15} = 4.8667$ $40P_{\bar{X}}(40) = \frac{40}{15} = 2.6667$

The mean of the sampling distribution of the sample mean is $\sum \bar{x}P_{\bar{x}}(\bar{x}) = 36.8333$ which is exactly equal to the population mean: $\dfrac{1}{N}\sum x_i = 36.8333$. This is the result expected from the Central Limit Theorem.

7.66 a. .0668 b. .7745 c. 445.6 d. 394.4
     e. $s_{\bar{x}} = 123.1868$ f. $s_{\bar{x}} = 75.966$ g. Smaller

7.68 a. .0228 b. .9544 c. $X_i = 13.3825$
     d. $s_{\bar{x}} = 8.1414$ e. Smaller

7.70 Let $n = N$, then $\bar{X} = \mu_x$:

$$E[\sum_{i-1}^{N}(X_i - \bar{X})^2] = n\sigma_x^2 - n\frac{\sigma_x^2}{n}\frac{N-n}{N-1} = n\sigma_x^2 - \frac{N-n}{N-1}\sigma_x^2 =$$

$$\frac{\sigma_x^2}{N-1}(nN - n - N + n) = \frac{N\sigma_x^2}{N-1}(n-1)$$

Therefore, $E[\dfrac{1}{n-1}\sum (X_i - \bar{X})^2] = \dfrac{1}{n-1}E[\sum (X_i - \bar{X})^2] = \dfrac{N\sigma_x^2}{N-1}$

7.72 a. .0262 b. .3446 c. .2709 d. .3210

7.74 .005

7.76 .6826

7.78 a. .3739 b. .4397 c. Difference = ±.0322

7.80 a. More than .99 (.9979 exactly)
     b. Between .9 and .95 (.9354 exactly)

Chapter 8

8.2 a.

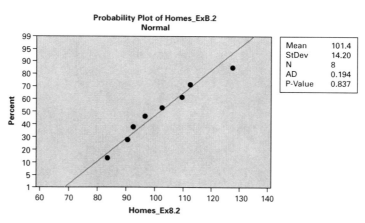

No evidence of non-normality.
  b. The minimum variance unbiased point estimator of the population mean is the sample mean: $\bar{x} = 101.375$
  c. The unbiased point estimator of the variance of the sample mean:
    $s^2 = 201.6964$
    $Var(\bar{X}) = 25.2121$
  d. $\hat{p} = .375$

8.4 a. Unbiased point estimator of the population mean is the sample mean: $\bar{x} = 24.42$
  b. The unbiased point estimator of the population variance: $s^2 = 85.72$
  c. Unbiased point estimator of the variance of the sample mean $Var(\bar{X}) = 7.1433$

d. Unbiased estimator of the population proportion: $\hat{p} = .25$

e. Unbiased estimator of the variance of the sample proportion: $Var(\hat{p}) = .015625$

8.6   a. $E(\overline{X}) = \dfrac{1}{2}E(X_1) + \dfrac{1}{2}E(X_2) = \dfrac{\mu}{2} + \dfrac{\mu}{2} = \mu$

$E(Y) = \dfrac{1}{4}E(X_1) + \dfrac{3}{4}E(X_2) = \dfrac{\mu}{4} + \dfrac{3\mu}{4} = \mu$

$E(Z) = \dfrac{1}{3}E(X_1) + \dfrac{2}{3}E(X_2) = \dfrac{\mu}{3} + \dfrac{2\mu}{3} = \mu$

b. $Var(\overline{X}) = \dfrac{\sigma^2}{n} = \dfrac{1}{4}Var(X_1) + \dfrac{1}{4}Var(X_2) = \dfrac{\sigma^2}{4}$

$Var(Y) = \dfrac{1}{16}Var(X_1) + \dfrac{9}{16}Var(X_2) = \dfrac{5\sigma^2}{8}$

$Var(Z) = \dfrac{1}{9}Var(X_1) + \dfrac{4}{9}Var(X_2) = \dfrac{5\sigma^2}{9}$

$\overline{X}$ is most efficient since $Var(\overline{X}) < Var(Y)$ and $Var(\overline{X}) < Var(Z)$

c.   Relative efficiency between Y and $\overline{X}$: $\dfrac{Var(Y)}{Var(\overline{X})} = 2.5$

Relative efficiency between Z and $\overline{X}$: $\dfrac{Var(Z)}{Var(\overline{X})} = 2.222$

8.8   a.   No evidence of the data distribution coming from a non-normal population.

b.   The minimum variance unbiased point estimator of the population mean is the sample mean: $\bar{x} = 3.8079$

c.   Minimum variance unbiased point estimator of the population variance is the sample variance $s^2 = 0.0105$

8.10   a.   3.495   b.   23.552

8.12   a.   40.2 to 59.8   b.   81.56 to 88.44   c.   506.2652 to 513.73478

8.14   a.   1.75   b.   .63246   c.   2.2136

8.16   a.   3.9926 up to 4.1474   b.   narrower
       c.   narrower   d.   wider

8.18   a.   13.9182   b.   19.007   c.   3.493   d.   7.5407

8.20   a.   541.424 to 578.576   b.   156.28 to 163.72   c.   49.9474 to 66.0526

8.22   a.   83.9685   b.   24.1428   c.   34.22

8.24   a.   519.379 to 522.517   b.   narrower

8.26   5.9152

8.28 $41,104.28 up to $44,375.72

8.30   a.   .02898   b.   .03761   c.   .010897

8.32   a.   .079055 to .120945   b.   0.0 to .031696   c.   0.4555 to 0.5445

8.34   .5846 up to .8260

8.36   95% confidence interval: .2026 up to .2974

8.38   84.14%

8.40   .1079 up to .2173

8.42   a.   235.4318 up to 278.5628
       assume that the population is normally distributed
       b.   [95%]: 230.39 up to 283.61
       [98%]: 223.815 up to 290.185

8.44   29.0229 up to 30.9771

8.46 a. 0.0613 up to 0.2721   b. 0.0782 up to 0.2552

8.48 95.96%

8.50 a. The sample mean $\bar{x} = 8.545$ b. 1.3568

8.52 a. .03098
      b. Margin of Error for a 95% confidence interval = 0.0607
      c. 0.3457 up to 0.4542

8.54 a. 0.5392 up to 0.71742   b. 0.1609 up to 0.3523
      c. 0.6093 up to 0.7535

8.56 a. $\bar{x} = 50.48$
         assume a 95% confidence level: 48.19 up to 52.77 years
      b. 0.0267 up to 0.1173
      c. Estimate the population mean by the sample mean = $52.65.

8.58 99.38%

8.60 a. .0623   b. smaller

Chapter 12

12.2 a. $t = 2.303$, $t_{38,.05} \approx 2.021$, $t_{38,.01} \approx 2.704$, therefore, reject H_0 at the 5% level. Insufficient evidence to reject H_0 at the 1% level.

  b. $t = 4.397$, $t_{58,.05} \approx 2.000$, $t_{58,.01} \approx 2.660$, therefore, reject H_0 at the 1% level.

    c. $t = 5.18$, $t_{43,.05} \approx 2.021$, $t_{43,.01} \approx 2.704$, therefore, reject H_0 at the 1% level.

    d. $t = 3.597$, $t_{23,.05} \approx 2.069$, $t_{23,.01} \approx 2.807$, therefore, reject H_0 at the 1% level.

12.4 $t = 7.7736$, $t_{47,.05} \approx 1.684$, $t_{47,.01} \approx 2.423$, therefore, reject H_0 at all common levels of alpha.

12.6 $t = 4.8168$, therefore, reject H_0 at the 5% level since $4.8168 > 1.671 \approx t_{66,.05}$

12.8   a.

```
Pearson correlation of Instructor Rating and Expected Grade = 0.722, p-value = 0.008
```

    b. $t = 3.2971$, therefore, reject H_0 at the 10% level since $3.2971 > 1.372 = t_{10,.10}$

12.10 a. Y changes by +30

     b. Y changes by -40

     c. $\hat{y} = 220$

     d. $\hat{y} = 330$

     e. Regression results do not "prove" that increased values of X "cause" increased values of Y. Theory will help establish conclusions of causation.

12.12 a. Y changes by +80

     b. Y changes by -60

     c. $\hat{y} = 153$

     d. $\hat{y} = 333$

     e. Regression results do not "prove" that increased values of X "cause" increased values of Y. Theory will help establish conclusions of causation.

12.14 A population regression equation consists of the true regression coefficients β_i's and the true model error ε_i. By contrast, the estimated regression model consists of the estimated regression coefficients b_i's and the residual term e_i. The population regression equation is a model that purports to measure the actual value of Y as a function of X while the sample regression equation is an estimate of the predicted value of the dependent variable Y as a function of X.

12.16 The constant represents an adjustment for the estimated model and not the number sold when the price is zero.

12.18 a. $b_1 = 1.80$ $b_0 = 10$ $\hat{y}_i = 10 + 1.80x_i$

     b. $b_1 = 1.30$ $b_0 = 132$ $\hat{y}_i = 132 + 1.30x_i$

     c. $b_1 = .975$ $b_0 = 80.5$ $\hat{y}_i = 80.5 + .975x_i$

     d. $b_1 = .30$ $b_0 = 47$ $\hat{y}_i = 47 + .30x_i$

     e. $b_1 = .525$ $b_0 = 152.75$ $\hat{y}_i = 152.75 + .525x_i$

12.20 a. $b_1 = 1.0737$, $b_0 = -.2336$, $\hat{y}_i = -.2336 + 1.0737x_i$

     b. For a one unit increase in the rate of return of the S&P 500 index, we estimate that the rate of return of the corporation's stock will increase by 1.07%.

     c. When the percentage rate of return of the S&P 500 index is zero, we estimate that the corporation's rate of return will be $-.2336\%$.

12.22 a. $b_1 = .5143$, $b_0 = 2.8854$, $\hat{y} = 2.8854 + .5143x$

     b. For a one unit increase in the average cost of a meal, we would estimte that the number of bottles sold would increase by .5148%.

     c. Yes. 2.8854 bottles are estimated to be sold, regardless of the price paid for a meal.

12.24 a. $\hat{y} = 1.89 + 0.0896x$

     b. 0.0896%. For a one percent pre-November 13 gain, we would estimate that there would be a loss of .0896% on November 13.

12.26 a. SSR = 50,000. SSE = 50,000. $s_e^2 = 1,000$, $R^2 = 0.50$

     b. SSR = 63,000. SSE = 27,000. $s_e^2 = 540$, $R^2 = 0.70$

     c. SSR = 192. SSE = 48. $s_e^2 = .96$, $R^2 = 0.80$

     d. SSR = 60,000. SSE = 140,000. $s_e^2 = 1,944.444$, $R^2 = 0.30$

     e. SSR = 54,000. SSE = 6,000. $s_e^2 = 157.8947$, $R^2 = 0.90$

12.28 a. $R^2 = \dfrac{\Sigma(\hat{y}_i - \bar{y})^2}{\Sigma(y_i - \bar{y})^2} = \dfrac{\Sigma[(b_1(x_i - \bar{x})]^2}{\Sigma(y_i - \bar{y})^2} = b_1^2 \dfrac{\Sigma(x_i - \bar{x})^2}{\Sigma(y_i - \bar{y})^2}$

b. $R^2 = b_1^2 \dfrac{\Sigma(x_i - \bar{x})^2}{\Sigma(y_i - \bar{y})^2} = b_1 \dfrac{\Sigma(x_i - \bar{x})(y_i - \bar{y})}{\Sigma(y_i - \bar{y})^2} = \dfrac{[\Sigma(x_i - \bar{x})(y_i - \bar{y})]^2}{\Sigma(x_i - x)^2 \Sigma(y_i - y)^2} = r^2$

c. $b_1 b_1^* = \dfrac{\Sigma(x_i - \bar{x})(y_i - \bar{y})}{\Sigma(x_i - \bar{x})^2}\dfrac{\Sigma(x_i - \bar{x})(y_i - \bar{y})}{\Sigma(y_i - \bar{y})^2} = r^2$

12.30 a. $R^2 = .1653$, from Exercise 12.7: $r = -.4066$, $r^2 = .1653 = R^2$

12.32 a.

Regression Analysis: Change in Mean a Versus Change in Absent
```
The regression equation is
Change in Mean absence illness = 0.0449 - 0.224 Change in Absentee Rate
Predictor                      Coef    SE Coef    T     P
Constant                    0.04485  0.06347   0.71  0.498
Change in Absentee Rate -0.22426  0.05506  -4.07  0.003
S = 0.207325   R-Sq = 64.8%   R-Sq(adj) = 60.9%
```

b. $SST = \Sigma y^2 - n\bar{y}^2 = 1.1 - 25(0.0)^2 = 1.1$
   $SSR = \Sigma(\hat{y}_i - \bar{y})^2 = .713$
   $SSE = \Sigma e_i^2 = .387$
   $SST = 1.1 = .713 + .387 = SSR + SSE$

c. $R^2 = SSR/SST = .713/1.1 = .648$, 64.8% of the variation in the dependent variable mean employee absence rate due to own illness can be explained by the variation in the change in absentee rate.

12.34 $R^2 = r^2 = .0121$. 1.21% of the variation in the dependent variable annual raises can be explained by the variation in teaching evaluations.

12.36 a. $F = 8.857$. $F_{\alpha,1,n-2} = 4.170$, therefore, at the .05 level, reject H_0
   b. $F = 43.165$. $F_{\alpha,1,n-2} = 4.00$, therefore, at the .05 level, reject H_0
   c. $F = 20.902$. $F_{\alpha,1,n-2} = 4.281$, therefore, at the .05 level, reject H_0

12.38 a. $b_1 = .5391$, $b_0 = 3.2958$, $\hat{y}_i = 3.2958 + .5391x_i$
   b. 2406 up to .8376

12.40 a. $s_e^2 = 144.4686$
   b. $s_b^2 = 1.8991$
   c. -5.0673 up to .9991
   d. $t = -1.476$, therefore, do not reject H_0 at the 10% level since $t = -1.476 > -1.796 = -t_{11,.05}$

12.42 95% Prediction Interval: (56.467, 97.533)
   95% Confidence Interval: (71.371, 82.629)

12.44 95% Prediction Interval: (150.331, 165.669)
   95% Confidence Interval: (155.351, 160.649)

12.46 a. $t = -7.303$, therefore, reject H_0 at the 1% level since $t = -7.303 > -2.807 = -t_{23,.005}$
   b. $y_{n+1} = 12.6 - 1.2(4) = 7.8$, 90% interval: (4.4798, 11.1203)

12.48 a. $t = 7.689$, therefore, reject H_0 at the 1% level since $t = 7.689 > 2.878 = t_{18,.005}$
   b. $t = .5278$, therefore, do not reject H_0 at the 20% level since $t = .5278 < 1.33 = t_{18,.10}$

12.50 $t = 5.1817$, therefore, reject H_0 at the 1% level since $t = 5.1817 > 2.807 = t_{23,.005}$

12.52 $t = 2.969$, therefore, reject H_0 at the 1% level since $t = 2.969 > 2.947 = t_{15,.005}$

12.54 $t = -10.251$, therefore, reject H_0 at the .5% level since $t = -10.251 < -3.707 = t_{6,.005}$

12.56 The 90% confidence interval for prediction of the actual value: $(-11.5212$ up to $33.337)$
   The 90% confidence interval for prediction of the expected value: (4.8197 up to 16.9961)

The distinction between the two lies in the uncertainty about the expected or mean value as compared to the uncertainty about a single specific value. Both are centered on the same value; however, the uncertainty surrounding a single specific value will be larger as compared to the expected or mean value, because the variation of both the expected value and the individual value about the expected value is included.

12.58 The 90% confidence interval for prediction of the expected value: (.2591 up to .14211) 95% confidence interval for the prediction of the expected value: (.1362 up to 1.544)

12.60 Note that the computed values for the Minitab regression output are exactly the same for all four data sets, but the scatter plots indicate very different patterns of the data and hence different models:
The model of $Y_1 = f(X_1)$ is a good fit for a linear model.
The model of $Y_2 = f(X_2)$ is a non-linear model.
The model of $Y_3 = f(X_3)$ has a significant outlier at the largest value of X1
The model of $Y_4 = f(X_4)$ has only two values of the independent variable.

12.62 Two random variables are positively correlated if low values of one are associated with low values of the other and high values of one are associated with high values of the other:
a. Total consumption expenditures are positively correlated with disposable income.
b. Price of a good or service are negatively related with the quantity sold.
c. The price of peanut butter and the sales of wrist watches are uncorrelated.

12.64 $t = 2.844$, therefore, reject H_0 at the .5% level since t = 2.844 > 2.660 ≈ $t_{51,.005}$

12.66 $t = 2.452$, therefore, reject H_0 at the 1% level since t = 2.452 > 2.39 ≈ $t_{60,.01}$

12.68 To show this, let $x = \bar{x}$ for the regression of y on x, $y = b_0 + b_1 x$
$\hat{y} = b_0 + b_1 \bar{x} = \bar{y} - b_1 \bar{x} + b_1 \bar{x} = \bar{y}$

12.70 a. For a one unit change in the inflation rate, we estimate that the actual spot rate will change by .7916 units.
b. $R^2 = 9.7\%$. 9.7% of the variation in the actual spot rate can be explained by the variations in the spot rate predicted by the inflation rate.
c. $t = 2.8692$, therefore, reject H_0 at the .5% level since $t = 2.8692 > 2.66 = t_{77,.005}$
d. $t = -.7553$, therefore, do not reject H_0 at any common level of alpha.

12.72 a. For each unit increase in the diagnostic statistics test, we estimate that the final student score at the end of the course will increase by .2875 points.
b. 11.58% of the variation in the final student score can be explained by the variation in the diagnostic statistics test.
c. The two methods are (1) the test of the significance of the population regression slope coefficient (β) and (2) the test of the significance of the population correlation coefficient (ρ).
(1) $H_0 : \beta = 0, H_1 : \beta > 0$
$t = 6.2965$. Therefore, reject H_0 at any common level of alpha.
(2) $H_0 : \rho = 0, H_1 : \rho > 0, r = .3403, t = 6.3098$. Therefore, reject H_0 at any common level of alpha.

12.74 a. $R^2 = 23.88\%$ of the variation of the dependent variable can be explained by the variability of the independent variable x.
b. $t = 2.6863$, therefore, reject H_0 at the 5% level since t = 2.6863 > 2.069 = $t_{23,.025}$
c. (.2987 up to 2.3013)

12.76 The linear regression model could still be appropriate if the quantity of fertilizer used were within the range of values that were utilized in estimating the regression equation. To extrapolate out beyond the range of values is where the regression equations may not be as useful in forecasting.

12.78 a. The graph with vehicle weight as the independent variable shows a slight positive relationship to crash deaths. The simple regression $R^2 = 5.9\%$. Percent imported cars has a slight negative relationship with a simple regression $R^2 = 8.1\%$. Deaths versus light trucks is a much stronger positive association with a simple regression $R^2 = 52.7\%$. And car age has a weak negative association with a simple regression $R^2 = 17.8\%$. All graphs show an unusual data point of an outlier of .55 crash deaths at the 49th observation of the data set. This data point is much higher than expected given the levels of the independent variables.

b.

Regression Analysis: Deaths Versus vehwt
```
The regression equation is
deaths = -0.346+0.000147 vehwt
Predictor      Coef     SE Coef      T       P
Constant    -0.3458      0.3022  -1.14   0.258
vehwt      0.00014697 0.00008528  1.72   0.091

S = 0.0786123 R-Sq = 5.9% R-Sq(adj) = 3.9%
```

Regression Analysis: Deaths Versus impcars
```
The regression equation is
deaths = 0.224-0.00478 impcars
Predictor     Coef    SE Coef     T      P
Constant    0.22371   0.02662  8.40  0.000
impcars   -0.004776  0.002351 -2.03  0.048

S = 0.0777183 R-Sq = 8.1% R-Sq(adj) = 6.1%
```

Regression Analysis: Deaths Versus lghttrks
```
The regression equation is
deaths = 0.0137 + 0.00974 lghttrks
Predictor     Coef   SE Coef     T      P
Constant    0.01375  0.02359  0.58  0.563
lghttrks   0.009742 0.001346  7.24  0.000

S = 0.0557321 R-Sq = 52.7% R-Sq(adj) = 51.7%
```

Regression Analysis: Deaths Versus carage
```
The regression equation is
deaths = 5.26 - 0.0723 carage
Predictor    Coef  SE Coef     T      P
Constant    5.263    1.594  3.30  0.002
carage   -0.07234  0.02266 -3.19  0.003

S = 0.0734818 R-Sq = 17.8% R-Sq(adj) = 16.1%
```

c. Independent variables are ranked based on the R^2 of the simple regression.

Variable	R-Sq	Rank
Light trucks	52.7%	1
Car age	17.8%	2
Imported cars	8.1%	3
Vehicle weight	5.9%	4

Crash deaths are positively related to both weight and percent of light trucks. Deaths are negatively related to percent import cars and the age of the vehicle. Light trucks has the strongest linear association followed by age and then vehicle weight.

12.80 a. The scatter plots show market value is positively related to the size of house. Outliers include several houses with a much higher than expected valuation based on their size. Market value is negatively related to tax rate where unusual patterns include homes with the highest market valuation but among the lowest tax rates.

b.

Regression Analysis: hseval Versus sizehse

```
The regression equation is
hseval = -40.1 + 11.2 sizehse
```

Predictor	Coef	SE Coef	T	P
Constant	-40.15	10.11	-3.97	0.000
sizehse	11.169	1.844	6.06	0.000

```
S = 4.188    R-Sq = 29.4%    R-Sq(adj) = 28.6%
```

Regression Analysis: hseval Versus taxrate

```
The regression equation is
hseval = 26.6 -208 taxrate
```

Predictor	Coef	SE Coef	T	P
Constant	26.650	1.521	17.52	0.000
taxrate	-207.60	53.27	-3.90	0.000

```
S = 4.603    R-Sq = 14.7%    R-Sq(adj) = 13.7%
```

Size of house is a stronger predictor than is the taxrate.

c. Whether tax rates are lowered or not does not have as large an impact as does the size of the house on the evaluation.

12.82 a. Fixed Residential Investment vs. Bank Prime Rate:

Regression Analysis: FRH Versus FBPR

```
The regression equation is
FRH = 132 + 10.5 FBPR
210 cases used 8 cases contain missing values
```

Predictor	Coef	SE Coef	T	P
Constant	132.004	9.828	13.43	0.000
FBPR	10.529	1.233	8.54	0.000

```
S = 64.19    R-Sq = 26.0%    R-Sq(adj) = 25.6%
```

Fixed Private Residential Investment vs. Federal funds rate:

Regression Analysis: FRH Versus FFED

```
The regression equation is
FRH = 191 + 5.01 FFED
184 cases used 34 cases contain missing values
```

Predictor	Coef	SE Coef	T	P
Constant	190.67	10.25	18.60	0.000
FFED	5.013	1.480	3.39	0.001

```
S = 66.41    R-Sq = 5.9%    R-Sq(adj) = 5.4%
```

Better predictions are provided by the first regression model with a coefficient of determination of 26.0% versus only 5.9% for the second model.

b. 95% confidence intervals for the slope coefficient:
Bank prime rate: 8.112 up to 12.946
Federal funds rate: 2.112 up to 7.914

c. Two point increase in interest rates:
Bank prime rate: $\hat{Y} = 153.062$
Federal funds rate: $\hat{Y} = 200.696$

d. 95% confidence intervals given a 2 percentage point increase in interest rates:
Given a 2% increase in each interest rate:
For bank prime rate: 152.8559 up to 153.2681
For federal funds rate: 200.5225 up to 200.8695

Chapter 16

16.2 H_0: Mutual fund performance is equally likely to be in the 5 performance quintiles.
H_1: otherwise

Mutual Funds	Top 20%	2nd 20%	3rd 20%	4th 20%	5th 20%	Total
Observed number	13	20	18	11	13	75
Probability (Ho)	0.2	0.2	0.2	0.2	0.2	1
Expected number	15	15	15	15	15	75
Chi-square calculation	0.266667	1.666667	0.6	1.066667	0.266667	3.8667

$\chi^2 = 3.8667$, $\chi^2_{(4,.1)} = 7.78$. Therefore, do not reject H_0 at the 10% level.

16.4 H_0: Quality of the output conforms to the usual pattern.
H_1: otherwise

Electronic Component	No Faults	1 Fault	>1 Fault	Total
Observed number	458	30	12	500
Probability (Ho)	0.93	0.05	0.02	1
Expected number	465	25	10	500
Chi-square calculation	0.105376344	1	0.4	1.505376

$\chi^2 = 1.505$, $\chi^2_{(2,.05)} = 5.99$ $\chi^2_{(2,.10)} = 4.61$. Therefore, do not reject H_0 at the 5% or the 10% level.

16.6 H_0: Student opinion of business courses is the same as that for all courses.
H_1: Otherwise

Opinion16-6	Very Useful	Somewhat	Worthless	Total
Observed number	68	18	14	100
Probability (Ho)	0.6	0.2	0.2	1
Expected number	60	20	20	100
Chi-square calculation	1.066666667	0.2	1.8	3.066667

$\chi^2 = 3.067$, $\chi^2_{(2,.10)} = 4.61$. Therefore, do not reject H_0 at the 10% level.

16.8 H_0: Consumer preferences for soft drinks are equally spread across 5 soft drinks.
H_1: Otherwise

Drink16-8	A	B	C	D	E	Total
Observed number	20	25	28	15	27	115
Probability (Ho)	0.2	0.2	0.2	0.2	0.2	1
Expected number	23	23	23	23	23	115
Chi-square calculation	0.391304	0.173913	1.086957	2.782609	0.695652	5.130435

$\chi^2 = 5.130$, $\chi^2_{(4,.10)} = 7.78$. Therefore, do not reject H_0 at the 10% level.

16.10 H_0: Statistics professors preferences for software packages are equally divided across 4 packages.
H_1: Otherwise

Software16-10	M	E	S	P	Total
Observed number	100	80	35	35	250
Probability (Ho)	0.25	0.25	0.25	0.25	1
Expected number	62.5	62.5	62.5	62.5	250
Chi-square calculation	22.5	4.9	12.1	12.1	51.6

$\chi^2 = 51.6$, $\chi^2_{(3,.005)} = 12.84$. Therefore, reject H_0 at the .5% level.

16.12 H_0: Population distribution of arrivals per minute is Poisson.
H_1: Otherwise

Arrivals	0	1	2	3	4+	Total
Observed number	10	26	35	24	5	100
Probability (Ho)	0.1496	0.2842	0.27	0.171	0.1252	1
Expected number	14.96	28.42	27	17.1	12.52	100
Chi-square calculation	1.6445	.2061	2.3704	2.7842	4.5168	11.522

$\chi^2 = 11.52$, $\chi^2_{(3,.01)} = 11.34$ $\chi^2_{(3,.005)} = 12.84$. Therefore, reject H_0 at the 1% level but not at the .5% level.

16.14 H_0: Resistance of electronic components is normally distributed.
H_1: Otherwise
$B = 9.625$. From Table 16.7—Significance points of the Bowman–Shelton statistic; 5% point ($n = 100$) is 4.29. Therefore, reject H_0 at the 5% level.

16.16 H_0: Monthly balances for credit card holders of a particular card are normally distributed.
H_1: Otherwise
$B = 6.578$. From Table 16.7—Significance points of the Bowman–Shelton statistic; 5% point ($n = 125$) is 4.34. Therefore, reject H_0 at the 5% level.

16.18 a. H_0: No association exists between gpa and major.
H_1: Otherwise
Chi-Sq $= 0.226 + 0.276 + 0.341 + 0.417 + 2.227 + 2.722 = 6.209$
DF $= 2$, p-value $= 0.045$, $\chi^2_{(2,.05)} = 5.99$. Therefore, reject H_0 of no association at the 5% level.

16.20 a.

	Method of Learning About Product		
Age	Friend	Ad	Collective Total
<21	30	20	50
21–35	60	30	90
35+	18	42	60
Row total	108	92	200

b. H_0: No association exists between the method of learning about the product and the age of the respondent.
H_1: Otherwise
Chi-Sq $= 0.333 + 0.391 + 2.674 + 3.139 + 6.400 + 7.513 = 20.451$
DF $= 2$, p-value $= 0.000$, $\chi^2_{(2,.005)} = 10.6$. Therefore, reject H_0 of no association at the .5% level.

16.22 H_0: No association exists between write-downs of assets and merger activity.
H_1: Otherwise
Chi-Sq $= 0.527 + 0.286 + 0.514 + 0.279 = 1.607$
DF $= 1$, p-value $= 0.205$, $\chi^2_{(1,.10)} = 2.71$. Therefore, do not reject H_0 at the 10% level.

16.24 H_0: No association exists between personnel rating and college major.
H_1: Otherwise
Chi-Sq $= 0.186 + 0.010 + 0.188 + 0.943 + 0.008 + 1.867 + 0.620 + 0.843 + 0.022 + 4.814$
$+ 0.543 + 3.605 = 13.648$

DF $= 6$, p-value $= 0.034$, 1 cells with expected counts less than 5.0
$\chi^2_{(6,.05)} = 12.59$. Therefore, reject H_0 at the 5% level.

16.26 H_0: No association exists between graduate studies and college major
H_1: Otherwise
Chi-Sq $= 8.000 + 1.815 + 1.667 + 8.000 + 1.815 + 1.667 = 22.963$
DF $= 2$, p-value $= 0.000$, $\chi^2_{(2,.005)} = 10.60$. Therefore, reject H_0 at the .5% level.

16.28 H_0: No association exists between primary election candidate preferences and voting district.
H_1: Otherwise
Chi-Sq $= 0.660 + 0.168 + 1.565 + 0.578 + 0.098 + 3.235 + 1.174 + 0.117 + 0.196 + 0.878$
$+ 0.065 + 0.743 = 9.478$
DF $= 6$, p-value $= 0.148$, $\chi^2_{(6,.10)} = 10.64$. Therefore, do not reject H_0 at the 10% level.

16.30 H_0: No association exists between years of experience and parts produced per hour.
H_1: Otherwise
Chi-Sq $= 0.000 + 5.000 + 5.000 + 0.000 + 0.000 + 0.000 + 0.000 + 5.000 + 5.000 = 20.000$
DF $= 4$, p-value $= 0.000$, $\chi^2_{(4,.005)} = 14.86$. Therefore, reject H_0 at the .5% level.

16.32 a. H_0: No association exists between package weight and package source.
H_1: Otherwise

Chi-Sq $= 0.123 + 0.313 + 1.201 + 24.779 + 1.429 + 21.420 + 43.973 + 0.068 + 70.301$
$+ 2.635 + 1.500 + 11.852 = 179.594$
DF $= 6$, p-value $= 0.000$, $\chi^2_{(6,.005)} = 18.55$. Therefore, reject H_0 at the .5% level.
b. The combinations with the largest percentage gap between observed and expected frequencies are 1) between factories and 11-75 pound packages, and 2) between factories and under 3 pound packages.

16.34 H_0: No association exists between the age of the company and the owner's opinion regarding the effectiveness of digital signatures.
H_1: Otherwise
Chi-Sq $= 1.070 + 0.533 + 0.478 + 2.796 + 1.987 + 0.311 + 0.489 + 0.542 + 0.016 = 8.222$
DF $= 4$, p-value $= 0.084$, $\chi^2_{(4,.05)} = 9.49$ $\chi^2_{(4,.10)} = 7.78$. Therefore, do not reject H_0 at the 5% level; but do reject at 10%.

16.36 H_0: No association exists between reason for moving to Florida and industry type.
H_1: Otherwise
Chi-Sq $= 2.858 + 0.386 + 3.320 + 1.156 + 0.321 + 0.887 + 7.495 + 1.424 + 7.362 = 25.210$
DF $= 4$, p-value $= 0.000$, $\chi^2_{(4,.005)} = 14.86$. Therefore, reject H_0 at the .5% level.

16.38 H_0: No association exists between opinions on stricter advertising controls of weight loss products and useage of quick weight reduction product.
H_1: Otherwise
Chi-Sq $= 6.700 + 7.086 + 9.410 + 9.952 = 33.148$
DF $= 1$, p-value $= 0.000$, $\chi^2_{(1,.005)} = 7.88$. Therefore, reject H_0 at the .5% level.

16.40 H_0: No difference in current and past customer preferences.
H_1: Otherwise

	A	B	C	D
Observed frequency	56	70	28	126
Expected frequency	56	92.4	56	75.6
$(O_i - E_i)^2/E_i$	0	5.43	14	33.6

Chi-square Test Statistic $= 53.03$, $\chi^2_{(3,.005)} = 12.84$. Therefore, reject H_0 at the .5% level.

16.42 a. H_0: No association exists between class standing and opinions on whether library hours should be extended.
H_1: Otherwise
Here we used Mintab and included only the responses from 340 students who had an opinion about the extension of the library hours.

```
Tabulated statistics: Class, Hours Extension
Rows: Class    Columns: Hours Extension
            Yes      No      All
1            86      53      139
            98.12   40.88   139.00

2            79      21      100
            70.59   29.41   100.00

3            46      15       61
            43.06   17.94    61.00

4            29      11       40
            28.24   11.76    40.00
Missing       0       1        *
              *       *        *
All         240      100     340
            240.00  100.00  340.00
Cell Contents:      Count
                    Expected count
Pearson Chi-Square = 9.250, DF = 3, p-value = 0.026
Likelihood Ratio Chi-Square = 9.262, DF = 3, P-Value = 0.026
```
$\chi^2_{(3,0.025)} = 9.35$

Do not Reject H_0 at the 2.5% level.

b. Recommendations should include better orientation with the freshmen class in order to better acquaint the students with the library and the hours that the library is open. Also, extending library hours, particularly during heavy usage, would be appropriate.

16.44 Answers will vary.

16.46 H_0: No association exists between method of filing tax returns and the person's age.
H_1: Otherwise

```
Chi-Sq = 7.143, DF = 4, p-value = 0.129
```

$\chi^2_{(4,.10)} = 7.78$. Therefore, do not reject H_0 at the 10% level.
There is not a statistically significant relationship between the method of filing income tax returns and the person's age.

Chapter 21

21.2   D is dominated by C. Therefore, D is inadmissible.

21.4   a. D is dominated by C. Hence D is inadmissible and removed from further consideration.

Maximin criterion would select production process C:

Actions	States of Nature			
Prod. Process	Low Demand	Moderate Demand	High Demand	Min Payoff
A	100,000	350,000	900,000	100,000
B	150,000	400,000	700,000	150,000
C	250,000	400,000	600,000	250,000

b. Minimax regret criterion would select production process A:

Actions	Regrets or Opportunity Loss Table			
Prod. Process	Low Demand	Moderate Demand	High Demand	Max Regret
A	150,000	50,000	0	150,000
B	100,000	0	200,000	200,000
C	0	0	300,000	300,000

21.6

Actions	States of Nature			
Prod. Process	Low Demand	Moderate Demand	High Demand	Min Payoff
A	70,000	120,000	200,000	70,000
B	80,000	120,000	180,000	80,000
C	100,000	125,000	160,000	100,000
D*	100,000	120,000	150,000	Inadmissible
E	60,000	115,000	220,000	60,000

*inadmissible

Therefore, production process C would be chosen using the Maximin Criterion.

Actions	Regrets or Opportunity Loss Table			
Prod. Process	Low Demand	Moderate Demand	High Demand	Max Regret
A	30,000	5,000	20,000	30,000
B	20,000	5,000	40,000	40,000
C	0	0	60,000	60,000
D*				Inadmissible
E	40,000	10,000	0	40,000

*inadmissible

Therefore, production process A would be chosen using the Minimax Regret Criterion.

21.8

Action	S1	S2
A1	M_{11}	M_{12}
A2	M_{21}	M_{22}

Then action A1 will be chosen by both the Maximin and the Minimax Regret Criteria if for: $M_{11} > M_{21}$ and $M_{12} < M_{22}$ and $(M_{11} - M_{21}) > (M_{22} - M_{12})$

21.10 a.

Actions	Offered Better Position	Not Offered Better Position
Interview	4500	−500
Don't interview	0	0

b. EMV(Interview) = −250
EMV(Don't Interview) = 0
Therefore, the optimal action: Don't Interview.

21.12 a. EMV(Certificate of Deposit) = 1200
EMV(Low risk stock fund) = 1280
EMV(High risk stock fund) = 1270
Therefore, the optimal action: Low risk stock fund

b. Decision tree:

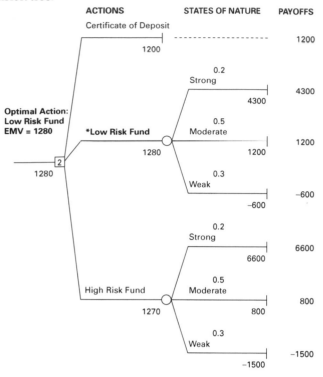

21.14 a. i) false ii) true iii) true
b. No

21.16 a. EMV(New) = 74,000
EMV(Old) = 58,000
Therefore, the optimal action: New center
b. Decision tree:

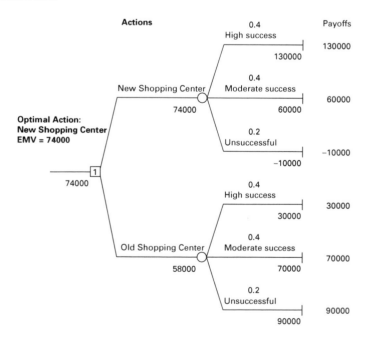

21.18 a. EMV(A) = 660,000 − 550,000p
           EMV(B) = 535,000 − 300,000p
           EMV(C) = 495,000 − 200,000p
           EMV(D) = 460,000 − 150,000p
           EMV(A) > EMV(B) when p < .5
           EMV(A) > EMV(C) when p < .471
           EMV(A) > EMV (D) when p < .5
           For p < .471, the EMV criterion chooses action A, same decision as in 21.13.
           Note that D was "inadmissible."
       b. EMV(A) > EMV(B) > EMV(C) > EMV(D) when a > 816,667

21.20 a. EMV(check) = 18,600
           EMV(not check) = 18,400
           Therefore, the optimal action: Check the process.
       b. Decision tree:

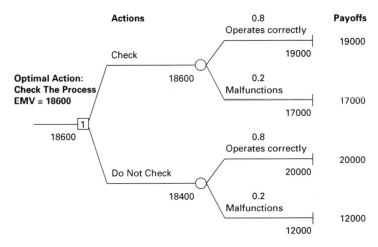

       c. EMV(check) = 19,000p + 17,000(1 − p) > 20,000p + 12,000(1 − p) when p < 5/6

21.22 a.

Extra Ordering	6	7	8	9	10
0	0	−10	−20	−30	−40
1	−20	20	10	0	−10
2	40	0	40	30	20
3	−60	−20	20	60	50
4	−80	−40	0	40	80

       b. Per the EMV criterion, the optimal action is to order 2 extra cars:

Extra Orders	6	7	8	9	10	EMV
0	0(.1)	−10(.3)	−20(.3)	−30(.2)	−40(.1)	−19
1	−20(.1)	20(.3)	10(.3)	0(.2)	−10(.1)	6
2	−40(.1)	0(.3)	40(.3)	30(.2)	20(.1)	16
3	−60(.1)	−20(.3)	20(.3)	60(.2)	50(.1)	11
4	−80(.1)	−40(.3)	0(.3)	40(.2)	80(.1)	−4

21.24 a. Action A1 is taken if $M_{11}p + M_{12}(1 − p) > M_{21}p + (1 − p)M_{22}$ or $p(M_{11} − M_{21}) > (1 − p)(M_{22} − M_{12})$
       b. Action A1 inadmissible implies that A1 will be chosen only if p > 1. In short, for part a. to be true, both payoffs of A1 cannot be less than the corresponding payoffs of A2.

21.26 a. Optimal action per the EMV criterion is action A.
  b. $P(L|P) = .5$
     $P(M|P) = .4$
     $P(H|P) = .1$
  c. $EMV(A) = 280,000$
     $EMV(B) = 305,000$
     $EMV(C) = 345,000$
     Therefore, the optimal action: C
  d. $P(L|F) = .2903$
     $P(M|F) = .5161$
     $P(H|F) = .1935$
  e. $EMV(A) = 383,815$, $EMV(B) = 385,435$, $EMV(C) = 395,115$
     Therefore, the optimal action: C
  f. $P(L|G) = .1538$
     $P(M|G) = .3077$
     $P(H|G) = .5385$
  g. $EMV(A) = 607,692$, $EMV(B) = 523,077$, $EMV(C) = 484,615$
     Therefore, the optimal action: A

21.28 a. $P(E|P) = .9231$, $P(\text{not } E|P) = .0769$
  b. $EMV(S) = 50,000$, $EMV(R) = 114,615$. Therefore, optimal action: retain
  c. $P(E|N) = .25$, $P(\text{not } E|N) = .75$
  d. $EMV(S) = 50,000$
     $EMV(R) = 23,750$
     Therefore, optimal action: sell

21.30 a. $P(2|10\%) = .01$, $P(1|10\%) = .18$, $P(0|10\%) = .81$
  b. $P(2|30\%) = .09$, $P(1|30\%) = .42$, $P(0|30\%) = .49$
  c. Probability of the states of 10% defective and 30% defective given:

	# Defective	10% Defect	30% Defect
i	2 defective	.308	.692
ii	1 defective	.632	.368
iii	0 defective	.869	.131

EMV of Actions	Check	Do Not Check
2 defective	17,616*	14,464
1 defective	18,264*	17,056
0 defective	18,737	18,952*

*optimal action given the circumstance

21.32 a. Perfect information is defined as the case where the decision maker is able to gain information to tell with certainty which state will occur.
  b. The optimal action: Low risk stock fund (see Problem 21.12)
     $EVPI = .2(6600 - 4300) + .5(0) + .3(1200 - (-600)) = 1000$

21.34 Given that the optimal action is: New center
     $EVPI = 24,000$

21.36 The expected value of sample information is $\sum_{i=1}^{M} P(A_i)V_i$ where $P(A_i) = \sum_{j=1}^{H} P(A_i/s_j)$
     For perfect information, $P(A_i|s_j) = 0$ for $i \neq j$ and $P(A_i|s_j) = 1$ for $i = j$, thus $P(A_i) = P(s_i)$

21.38 $EVSI = 23003$

21.40 Given that the optimal action: retain the patent (see Problem 21.28).
     $EVSI = 13,650$

21.42 a. EVSI = 34.1   b. EVSI = 55.87   c. The difference = 21.77
       d. None   e. 24.75

21.44 a.

Payoff	−10000	30000	60000	70000	90000	13000
Utility	0	35	60	70	85	100

b. EU(New) = 64
    EU(Old) = 59
    Therefore, the optimal action: New center

21.46 $94000p - 16000(1-p) = 0$ ➜ $p = 16 / 110$

Payoff	−160000	0	94000
Utility	0	160/110	100

Slope(-16000,0) = .00009
Slope(0,94000) = .00105
Therefore, the contractor has a preference for risk.

21.48 a. P(S1) = .3(.6) = .18, P(S2) = .42, P(S3) = .12, P(S4) = .28
       b. EMV(A1) = 460, EMV(A2) = 330, EMV(A3) = 0, EMV(A4) = 510
           Therefore, the optimal action: A4
       c. Draw the decision tree:

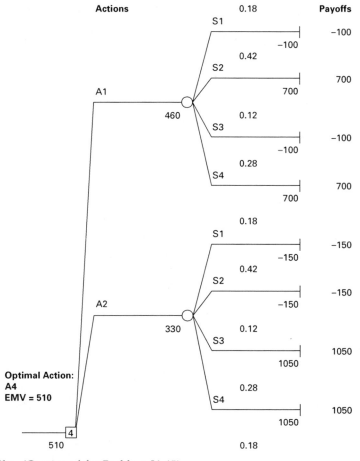

TreePlan (Continued for Problem 21.48):

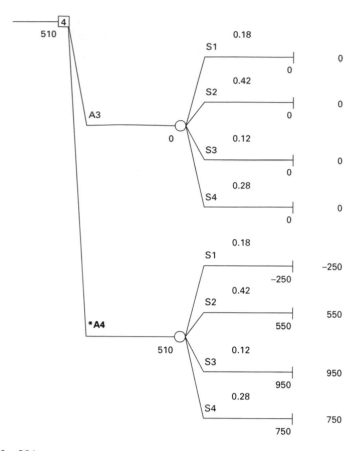

d. EVPI = 204
e. 79

Appendix 5

Answers to Problems from
Barrow

Chapter 9

Problem 9.1 GNP versus GDP; gross or net national product; factor cost or market prices; coverage (UK, GB, England and Wales); current or constant prices are some of the issues.

Problem 9.3 The following are measures of UK and US GDP, both at year 2000 prices. The UK figures are £bn, the US figures are $bn. Your own figures may be slightly different, but should be highly correlated with these numbers.

	1995	1996	1997	1998	1999	2000	2001	2002	2003
UK	821.4	843.6	875.0	897.7	929.7	961.9	979.2	997.5	1 023.2
US	8031.7	8328.9	8703.5	9066.9	9470.3	9817.0	9890.7	10 074.8	10 381.3

Problem 9.5 $n = 1.96^2 \times 400/2^2 = 385$.

Appendix 6

Answers to 'Self-Check
Questions' from Burton

Chapter 11: Calculus and business applications
•••

11.1 (a) 9   (b) $8x$ (c) $9x^2$ (d) $20x^3$

(e) x^2 (f) x^3 (g) $\dfrac{1}{2}x^{-\frac{1}{2}} = \dfrac{1}{2\sqrt{x}}$

(h) $\dfrac{1}{3}x^{-\frac{2}{3}} = \dfrac{1}{3\sqrt[3]{x^2}}$ (i) $\dfrac{2}{3}x^{-\frac{1}{3}} = \dfrac{2}{3\sqrt[3]{x}}$ (j) 0

11.2 (a) (i) 9   (ii) 9   (b) (i) 8 (ii) 16   (c) (i) 9 (ii) 36

(d) (i) 20 (ii) 160   (e) (i) 1 (ii) 4   (f) (i) 1 (ii) 8

(g) (i) $\dfrac{1}{2}$ (ii) 0.354   (h) (i) $\dfrac{1}{3}$ (ii) 0.210

(i) (i) $\dfrac{2}{3}$ (ii) 0.529   (j) both zero

11.3 (a) $\dfrac{dy}{dx} = 2x - 10 = 0$ for turning point

$$2x = 10$$

$$\underline{x = 5}$$

$$\frac{d^2y}{dx^2} = +2$$

So $x = 5$ is a turning point, and this is a minimum since 2nd derivative is positive.

(b) $\frac{dy}{dx} = -6 + 2x = 0$ for turning point

$$2x = 6$$

$$\underline{x = 3}$$

$$\frac{d^2y}{dx^2} = +2$$

So $x = 3$ is a minimum turning point since 2nd derivative is positive.

(c) $\frac{dy}{dx} = 4 - 2x - 0$ for a turning point

$$4 = 2x$$

$$\underline{2 = x}$$

$$\frac{d^2y}{dx^2} = -2$$

So $x = 2$ is a maximum turning point since the second derivative is negative.

(d) $\frac{dy}{dx} = 3x^2 - 27 = 0$ for a turning point

$$3x^2 = 27$$

$$\underline{x = \pm 3}$$

$$\frac{d^2y}{dx^2} = 6x$$

▶ when $x = +3$, 2nd derivative is positive (+18), so minimum turning point.
▶ when $x = -3$, 2nd derivative is negative (−18), so maximum turning point.

(e) $\frac{dy}{dx} = 3x^2 - 6x = 0$ for a turning point

$$x(3x - 6) = 0$$

which solves when $x = 0$ or $+2$

$$\frac{d^2y}{dx^2} = 6x - 6$$

▶ when $x = 0$, 2nd derivative is negative (-6), so maximum turning point.

▶ when $x = +2$, 2nd derivative is positive $(+6)$, so minimum turning point.

(f) $\dfrac{dy}{dx} = x^2 - 7x + 12 = 0$ for a turning point

$$(x - 3)(x - 4) = 0$$

This solves for either $\underline{x = +3 \text{ or } x = +4}$

$$\dfrac{d^2 y}{dx^2} = 2x - 7$$

▶ Second derivative is negative (-1) when $x = +3$, so maximum turning point.

▶ Second derivative is positive $(+1)$ when $x = +4$, so minimum turning point.

11.4 (a) $\dfrac{dy}{dx} = \dfrac{du}{dx} + \dfrac{dv}{dx} = 35x^4 + 6x$

(b) $\dfrac{dy}{dx} = \dfrac{du}{dx} - \dfrac{dv}{dx} = 20x^4 - 12x^2$

(c) $\dfrac{dy}{dx} = u\dfrac{dv}{dx} + v\dfrac{du}{dx}$

$u = 2x + 3, \dfrac{du}{dx} = 2$

$v = 2x^3, \dfrac{dv}{dx} = 6x^2$

$\dfrac{dy}{dx} = (2x + 3) \cdot (6x^2) + (2x^3) \cdot (2)$

$\dfrac{dy}{dx} = 12x^3 + 18x^2 + 4x^3 = 16x^3 + 18x^2$

(d) Using above approach

$\dfrac{dy}{dx} = (3x + 4)(12x^3) + (3x^4) \cdot (3)$

$\dfrac{dy}{dx} = 36x^4 + 48x^3 + 9x^4 = 45x^4 + 48x^3$

(e) $y = \dfrac{u}{v}$, so $\dfrac{dy}{dx} = \dfrac{u\dfrac{dv}{dx} - v\dfrac{du}{dx}}{v^2}$

$\dfrac{dy}{dx} = \dfrac{(2x + 3)(4x) - (2x^2) \cdot (2)}{(2x^2)^2} = \dfrac{8x^2 + 12x - 4x^2}{4x^4}$

$\dfrac{dy}{dx} = \dfrac{4x^2 + 12x}{4x^4} = \dfrac{4x + 12}{4x^3}$

(f) Using above approach

$$\frac{dy}{dx} = \frac{(4x^2 - 2) \cdot (4x) - (2x^2 + 4) \cdot (8x)}{(2x^2 + 4)^2}$$

$$\frac{dy}{dx} = \frac{16x^3 - 8x - 16x^3 - 32x}{4x^4 + 16x^2 + 16}$$

$$\frac{dy}{dx} = \frac{-40x}{4x^4 + 16x^2 + 16}$$

(g) $y = f(u)$ where $u = f(x)$

$$\frac{dy}{dx} = \frac{dy}{du} \cdot \frac{du}{dx}$$

$y = u^2$ where $u = (2x^2 + 3)$

$$\frac{dy}{dx} = 2u \cdot 4x$$

i.e. $\dfrac{dy}{dx} = 2(2x^2 + 3) \cdot 4x = 16x^3 + 24x$

(h) Using above approach

$$\frac{dy}{dx} = 3u^2 \cdot 9x^2$$

$$\frac{dy}{dx} = 3(3x^3 + 4)^2 \cdot 9x^2 = 3(9x^6 + 24x^3 + 16) \cdot 9x^2$$

$$\frac{dy}{dx} = 243x^8 + 648x^5 + 432x^2$$

11.5 (a) (i) TR = AR × output

TR = $[32 - \dfrac{2}{3}x^2]x$

TR $- 32x - \dfrac{2}{3}x^3$

(ii) TC = ATC × output

TC = $[\dfrac{1}{3}x^2 - x + 11] \cdot x$

TC = $\dfrac{1}{3}x^3 - x^2 + 11x$

(iii) TP = TR − TC

TP = $32x - \dfrac{2}{3}x^3 - [\dfrac{1}{3}x^3 - x^2 + 11x]$

TP$(y) = -x^3 + x^2 + 21x$

(b) $\dfrac{dy}{dx} = 0$ for a turning point

$-3x^2 + 2x + 21 = 0$ for a turning point

$(-3x - 7)(x - 3) = 0$

i.e. when $-3x - 7 = 0$ $x = -2\frac{1}{3}$

and when $x - 3 = 0$ $x = 3$

2nd derivative $\dfrac{d^2 y}{dx^2} = -6x + 2$

when $x = +3$, the 2nd derivative $= -16$

when $x = -2\frac{1}{3}$, the 2nd derivative $= +16$

so the turning point $\underline{x = +3 \text{ is the maximum}}$

▶ Producing three units of output will maximise total profit.

▶ At this output total profit $(y) = -(3^3) + 3^2 + 21(3) = £45$.

▶ Price = AR $= 32 - \dfrac{2}{3}(3^2) = £26$.

11.6 (a) TP (y) = TR − TC

$$y = (40x - 8x^2) - (8 + 16x - x^2)$$

$$y = -7x^2 + 24x - 8$$

$$\frac{dy}{dx} = 0 \text{ for a turning point}$$

i.e. $-14x + 24 = 0$ for a turning point

$$24 = 14x$$

$$\frac{24}{14} = x$$

$$\underline{1\frac{5}{7} = x}$$

2nd derivative $\dfrac{d^2 y}{dx^2} = -14$

So turning point $x = 1\frac{5}{7}$ is a maximum

Maximum Total Profit is earned at an output of $1\frac{5}{7}$ (000) units.

Price = AR $= \dfrac{TR}{\text{output}} = \dfrac{TR}{x} = \dfrac{40x - 8x^2}{x} = 40 - 8x$

Price $= 40 - 8\left(1\frac{5}{7}\right)$

$\underline{\text{Price} = £26\frac{2}{7}}$

Total profit $(y) = -7\left(1\frac{5}{7}\right)^2 + 24\left(1\frac{5}{7}\right) - 8$

$$y = \frac{-144}{7} + \frac{288}{7} - 8$$

$$y = 20\frac{4}{7} - 8$$

$$\underline{y = 12\frac{4}{7}}$$

Total profit is £$12\frac{4}{7}$ 000

(b) We now seek to maximise total revenue

TR$(y) = 40x - 8x^2$

$\dfrac{dy}{dx} = 40 - 16x = 0$ for a turning point

$16x = 40$

$\underline{x = 2.5}$

2nd derivative $\dfrac{d^2y}{dx^2} = -16$, so $x = 2.5$ is a maximum

The output which maximises total revenue is 2.5 (000) units, which is greater than the $1\frac{5}{7}$ (000) units which maximises total profit.

The total profit earned would be:

(TP) $y = -7(2.5)^2 + 24(2.5) - 8$

$y = -43.75 + 60 - 8$

$\underline{y = 8.25}$

Total profit is £8,250

This is less than the total profit (£$12\frac{4}{7}$, 000) earned by the profit maximising firm, as we should expect.

11.7 ATC$(y) = \dfrac{x^2}{3} - x + 11$

$\dfrac{dy}{dx} - \dfrac{2}{3}x - 1 = 0$ for t.p.

$x = \dfrac{3}{2}$ for t.p. Since 2nd derivative positive $(+\frac{2}{3})$ then ATC is minimum at 1,500 units of output.

11.8 (a) Marginal revenue (MR) $= \dfrac{dy}{dx} = 20 - 4x$

(b) MR should be negatively sloped and intersect the horizontal axis at $x = 5$. At this output total revenue (TR) should be at its maximum value of 50.

11.9 (a) MC $= \dfrac{dy}{dx} = x^2 - 6x + 9$

(b) Total cost is entirely variable here, so the total cost curve goes through the origin. The marginal cost curve reaches a minimum at $x = 3$

11.10 (a) (i) Lead time is approximately two weeks.

(ii) Minimum stock level is 100 units.

(iii) Re-order quantity is 300 units.

(iv) Stock-out occurs at the beginning of August.

(b) (i) Stock have gone below the safety limit presumably because the new supplier was unable to respond to the increased usage rate and to deliver the goods on time. Opting for a cheaper supplier does not necessarily mean a better service or more reliable deliveries.

(ii) The lack of a component will cause a stock-out if delivery is not immediate at the start of August. This in turn will result in production delays, machine downtime and possible delays in completing orders for customers. An inability to meet delivery deadlines could lead to a permanent loss of customers to rival firms.

(c) $EOQ = \sqrt{\dfrac{2CoD}{Cc}}$

$EOQ = \sqrt{\dfrac{2 \cdot (200) \cdot (5,000)}{2}}$

$\underline{EOQ = 1,000 \text{ components}}$

11.11 (a) $3x^2 + C$

(b) $\dfrac{1}{2}x^6 + C$

(c) $\dfrac{4}{7}x^7 + C$

(d) $x^4 + \dfrac{5}{3} \cdot x^3 - \dfrac{3}{2}x^2 + 4x + C$

(e) $\dfrac{2}{5}x^5 - x^4 + \dfrac{7}{2}x^2 + C$

11.12 $y = \int (2 - 4x^2)dx$

$y = \int 2dx - \int 4x^2 dx + C$

$y = 2x - \dfrac{4}{3}x^3 + C$

when $x = 1$, $y = 1$

so $1 = 2(1) - \dfrac{4}{3}(1)^3 + C$

$1 - 2 + \dfrac{4}{3} = C$

$\underline{\dfrac{1}{3} = C}$

The equation of the curve is $y = 2x - \dfrac{4}{3}x^3 + \dfrac{1}{3}$

11.13 $\int_{1}^{2}(3x + 2x^2 + x^3)\,dx = \left| \frac{3}{2}x^2 + \frac{2}{3}x^3 + \frac{1}{4}x^4 \right|_{1}^{2}$

$$= \left(6 + 5\frac{1}{3} + 4\right) - \left(\frac{3}{2} + \frac{2}{3} + \frac{1}{4}\right)$$

$$= 15\frac{4}{12} - 2\frac{5}{12}$$

$$= 12\frac{11}{12} \text{ units}^2$$

Chapter 12: Basic mathematics

12.1 (a) −6   (b) −2   (c) +8
      (d) 2   (e) 96   (f) 9

12.2 (a) 2.64   (b) 1.34   (c) 17.6
      (d) 7.5   (e) 20.0   (f) 0.006

12.3 (a) 20.8%   (b) 12.5   (c) 25%   (d) 13.3%

12.4 (a) £1.30 : £1.95   (b) £4,200 : £3,000 : £1,800

12.5 (a) t^7 (b) m^3 (c) $6x^7$
      (d) $15p^5$ (e) $28m^4$ (f) $12w^3$

12.6 (a) x^4 (b) p^2 (c) $4d^2$

      (d) $2m$ (e) 2   (f) $1\frac{1}{2}m$

12.7 (a) 27   (b) 4   (c) 10
      (d) 1,000,000   (e) 7   (f) 19

12.8 (a) $\frac{1}{49}$ (b) $\frac{1}{512}$ (c) $\frac{1}{x^4}$ (d) $\frac{1}{m}$

      (e) $\frac{4}{g^2}$ (f) $\frac{5}{m^2}$ (g) $\frac{1}{8t^3}$ (h) $\frac{1}{2t^4}$

12.9 (a) $\frac{2}{m}$ (b) $\frac{4}{3t^3}$ (c) $\frac{3}{2x}$ (d) $\frac{c}{d^2}$

      (e) a   (f) $\frac{3a}{b}$ (g) $\frac{9}{5q}$ (h) $\frac{2m}{p}$

      (i) $\frac{3}{4}$ (j) 5   (k) $\frac{4t^3}{3}$ (l) $\frac{5}{2}$

12.10 (a) $3^{\frac{1}{2}}$ (b) 4^1 (c) $7^{-\frac{1}{2}}$

(d) 5^{-1} (e) $3^{\frac{2}{3}}$ (f) $5^{\frac{3}{4}}$

12.11 (a) $y = \dfrac{x+2}{2}$ (b) $y = \dfrac{x}{b+7}$ (c) $y = \dfrac{t}{5} - \dfrac{p}{35}$

12.12 (a) $8x^2 - 12x + 2x - 3 = 8x^2 - 10x - 3$ (b) $3x^2 - 4x - 15$

(c) $2pm + pt - 3tm + pt = 2pm + 2pt - 3tm$

12.13 (a) $t(3 + 7t)$ (b) $2m^2(m - 3)$ (c) $3mp(2p + 3mt)$

(d) $(x - 4)(x - 3)$ (e) $(x + 5)(x - 5)$ (f) $(2x + 5)(x - 3)$

12.14 (a) $x = 7$ (b) $x = -1$ (c) $x = \dfrac{19}{8}$

12.15 (a) $(x + 4)(x + 3) = 0$, so $x = -4$ and -3

(b) Use formula method, with $a = 5$, $b = 6$, $c = -2$

$$x = \frac{-6 \pm \sqrt{36 - 4(5)(-2)}}{10}$$

$$x = \frac{-6 \pm \sqrt{76}}{10} = \frac{-6 \pm 8.7}{10}$$

$$x = \frac{-14.7}{10} \text{ or } \frac{+2.87}{10} = -1.47 \text{ or } +0.29$$

(c) Use formula method, with $a = 1$, $b = 4$, $c = -117$

$$x = \frac{-4 \pm \sqrt{16 - 4(1)(-117)}}{2}$$

$$x = \frac{-4 \pm \sqrt{484}}{2} = \frac{-4 \pm 22}{2}$$

$$x = \frac{-26}{2} \text{ or } +\frac{18}{2} = -13 \text{ or } +9$$

12.16 (a)

$$5x + y = 0 \quad \ldots (1)$$
$$3x - 2y = 13 \ldots (2)$$
$(1) \times 2 \quad \underline{10x + 2y = 0} \quad \ldots (3)$
$(2) + (3) \qquad 13x = 13$
$$\underline{x = 1}$$
substitute $\quad x = 1$ in equation (1)
$$5(1) + y = 0$$
$$y = -5$$
Solutions are $x = 1$ and $y = -5$

(b) $7x + 3y = 18 \ldots (1)$

              $x + y = 4 \ldots (2)$

$(2) \times 3$ $3x + 3y = 12 \ldots (3)$

$(1) - (3)$ $4x = 6$

              $x = 1.5$

Substitute $x = 1.5$ in equation (2)

              $1.5 + y = 4$

              $y = 2.5$

Solutions are $x = 1.5$ and $y = 2.5$

12.17 (a) $x > \dfrac{32}{5}$ (b) $t < \dfrac{5t}{4} - 2$ (c) $-6 < x < 6$

(d) Treat each side separately

$-2 \leq 5x + 3$ $5x + 3 < 4$

$-2 - 3 \leq 5x$ $5x < 4 - 3$

$-\dfrac{5}{5} \leq x$ $5x < 1$

$-1 \leq x$ $x < \dfrac{1}{5}$

Hence $-1 \leq x < \dfrac{1}{5}$

12.18

x	-4	-3	-2	-1	0	1	2	3
x^2	16	9	4	1	0	1	4	9
$+x$	-4	-3	-2	-1	0	1	2	3
-6	-6	-6	-6	-6	-6	-6	-6	-6
y	6	0	-4	-6	-6	-4	0	6

(a) Your graph should look similar to Figure 12.6(b) (p. 304).

(b) Solutions are $x = -3$ and $x = +2$

12.19 Gradient $= \dfrac{(y_2 - y_1)}{(x_2 - x_1)} = \dfrac{9 - -3}{4 - -2} = \dfrac{12}{6} = +2$

12.20 Note (a) and (b) use arithmetic progression formula

(a) $S_8 = \dfrac{8}{2}[84 + 7(4)] = 448$

(b) $S_8 = \dfrac{8}{2}[400 + 7(-5)] = 1{,}460$

Note (c) and (d) use geometric progression formula

(d) $S_8 = \dfrac{4(1 - 1.5^8)}{(1 - 1.5)} = \dfrac{4(1 - 25.63)}{-0.5} = \dfrac{4(-24.63)}{-0.5} = 197.04$

(e) $S_8 = \dfrac{1{,}000(1 - 0.5^8)}{(1 - 0.5)} = \dfrac{1{,}000(1 - 0.0039)}{0.5} = \dfrac{1{,}000(0.9961)}{0.5} = 1{,}992.2$

Appendix 7

Responses to 'Pause for Thought'
from Burton

Chapter 11: Calculus and business applications

Pause for thought 11.1

Many possibilities here. All of the following suggest zero as the *limit* to which something tends, though it never actually gets there:

▶ Zero is the limit of $\left(\dfrac{1}{2}\right)^n$ as n rises to infinity.

▶ Zero is the limit to which the slope of a unit elastic demand curve tends as output rises to infinity.

▶ Zero is the limit to which the slope of an average fixed cost curve tends as output rises to infinity, etc.

Pause for thought 11.2

The rate of change of the curves identified give us:

(a) Marginal cost
(b) Marginal revenue
(c) Marginal profit.

Pause for thought 11.3

By finding the turning point for the equation relating total revenue to output, they can find where total revenue is a maximum, should they be interested in a sales revenue maximising output. Also total profit = total revenue − total cost, so this equation can be worked out, and the turning point calculated for which total profit is a maximum. In these ways the levels of output which achieve maximum revenue, maximum profit, etc. can be estimated.

Pause for thought 11.4

Just-in-time manufacturing is a production system, which is designed to minimise stock-holding costs by carefully planning the flow of resources through the production process. It requires a highly efficient ordering system and reliable delivery, often directly to the production line. This type of system is highly sensitive to customer demand. In some cases production only begins when an order is placed. The system originated in Japan in the 1950s but is now universally applied, especially in firms using flow production such as car assembly, electronics and bottling plants.

Benefits to Mondeo from its introduction include the following:

▶ Improved cash flow since money is no longer tied up in stocks.
▶ Reduced waste from obsolete or damaged stock.
▶ Reduced cost of handling stock (e.g. in terms of space, shelving, security, store personnel).
▶ Less space required for stock holding therefore more available for production.
▶ Relationships with suppliers are improved.
▶ More scope for use of computerised information system to improve integration of departments.
▶ Workforce is given more responsibility and encouraged to work in teams or 'cells'. This should improve motivation.

Appendix 8

Answers to Review Questions from Burton

Chapter 11: Calculus and business applications
....

11.1
$$Q = 80L^2 - 0.1L^4$$

$$\frac{dQ}{dL} = 0 \qquad \text{for a turning point}$$

i.e. $160L - 0.4L^3 = 0$

$$160L = 0.4L^3 \quad \text{divide both sides by } L \text{ gives } 160 = 0.4L^2,$$

$$L^2 = 400 \quad L = \pm 20$$

Obviously labour input cannot be –20 therefore the labour input that maximises or minimises daily Q is 20 units.

Find whether maximum or minimum via sign of second derivative

$$\frac{d^2Q}{dL^2} = 160 - 1.2L^2, = -320 \quad \text{when} \quad L = 20$$

Therefore 20 workers will maximise output per day.

11.2 $\dfrac{dY}{dX} = 0$ for a turning point

$$0 = 0.6 - 0.004X \quad X = 0.6/0.004 = 150$$

The sales output that maximises or minimises profits is 150 units.

Second derivative

$$\frac{d^2Y}{dX^2} = -0.004 \therefore \text{ maximum profit at the sales output of 150 units}$$

11.3 $\dfrac{P}{Q} \cdot \dfrac{dQ}{dP} = PED$ and in order to evaluate $\dfrac{dQ}{dP}$ we need to make Q the subject of the equation or invert the result of $\dfrac{dP}{dQ}$

Either way the result is –20 therefore $PED = \dfrac{P}{Q} \cdot (-20)$

▶ when $P = 6$, $6 = 8 - 0.05Q$ so $Q = 40$ and PED $= (6/40) \times (-20) = -3$ so price elastic

▶ when $P = 2$, $2 = 8 - 0.05Q$ so $Q = 120$ and PED $= (2/120) \times (-20) = -0.33$ so price inelastic

To find the price where the demand curve has unitary elasticity

$-1 = P/Q \times (-20)$ so $-1/-20 = P/Q = 0.05$ and $P = 0.05Q = 0.05(160 - 20P)$

$P = 8 - P$ therefore $P = 4$ is where the demand curve has unitary elasticity.

11.4 $\text{ATC} = \text{TC}/Q = 0.01Q + 5 + 100Q^{-1}$

$$\frac{d\text{ATC}}{dQ} = 0 \text{ for a turning point}$$

$$0 = 0.01 - 100Q^{-2} \quad 100/Q^2 = 0.01$$

Therefore $Q^2 = 100/0.01 = 10,000$ $Q = \pm 100$ for a turning point. Obviously output cannot be -100 therefore the output that minimises or maximises cost per unit is likely to be 100. Check that this is the minimum we required by finding the second derivative

$$\frac{d^2\text{ATC}}{dQ^2} = 200Q^{-3}, = +0.0002$$

Since positive sign for second derivative, $Q = +100$ is the output that minimises ATC.

11.5 (a) $\dfrac{dR}{dX} = 0$ for a turning point

$$0 = 5,000 - 40X, \quad 40X = 5,000 \quad \text{therefore} \quad X = 125$$

The number of machines that maximise revenue is 125. The second derivative (-40) is negative. Therefore maximum revenue at $X = 125$.

(b) Total profit (TP) = revenue – costs $= (5,000X - 20X^2) - 1800X$
$$= 3,200X - 20X^2$$

$$\frac{d\text{TP}}{dX} = 0 \quad \text{for a turning point}$$

$$0 = 3,200 - 40X, \quad 40X = 3,200 \quad \text{therefore} \quad X = 80$$

Check second derivative to find if maximum or minimum turning point. This is -40, so maximum at $X = 80$.
The number of machines that maximise profits = 80

(c) Break even is where revenue = costs, $5,000X - 20X^2 = 1,800X$
$$3,200X = 20X^2, \quad 3,200 = 20X, \quad X = 160$$
The break-even number of machines is 160.

11.6 Let the side of the square $= x$ cm. The sides of the rectangular box will be $10 - 2x$ cm, and $16 - 2x$ cm respectively and its depth will be x cm.

Vol. of box $(V) = (16 - 2x)(10 - 2x)(x) = 160x - 52x^2 + 4x^3$

$\dfrac{dV}{dx} = 0$ for a turning point

$160 - 104x + 12x^2 = 0$; dividing by 4 gives $40 - 26x + 3x^2 = 0$

i.e. $(2 - x)(20 - 3x) = 0$, therefore $x = 2$ or 6.667.

To find which turning point is the maximum we take the second derivative.

$\dfrac{dV^2}{d^2 x} = -104 + 24x$

When $x = 2$ the second derivative $= -56$, when $x = 6.667$ the second derivative $= +56$.

The value of x that maximises the volume of the box is therefore 2 cm.

11.7 (a) $TR = P.Q = -5Q^2 + 3,000Q$. A turning point $\dfrac{dTR}{dQ} = 0$

Therefore $-10Q + 3,000 = 0$, i.e. $Q = 300$. The output level that maximises revenue is 300 units, since the second derivative is -10, indicating a maximum turning point.

(b) Profit $(TP) = TR - TC = (-5Q^2 + 3,000Q) - (50Q + 10,000)$

$TP = -5Q^2 + 2,950Q - 10,000$. At a turning point $\dfrac{dTP}{dQ} = 0$

Therefore $-10Q + 2,950 = 0$, giving $Q = 295$.

The output level that maximises profits is 295 units (since second derivative is -10, indicating a maximum turning point)

Price charged $P = -5Q + 3,000 = -5(295) + 3,000 = £1,525$

(c) Maximum profit $= -5Q^2 + 2,950Q - 10,000 = -5(295)^2 + 2,950(295) - 10,000$

Maximum profit $= £425,125$.

11.8 (a) Profit $(TP) = (-5Q^2 + 3,000Q) - (110Q + 10,000) = -5Q^2 + 2,890Q - 10,000$

At a turning point $\dfrac{dTP}{dQ} = 0$

Therefore $-10Q + 2,890 = 0$ and $Q = 289$.

The output that maximises profit is 289 units (since the second derivative is -10).

Price charged $P = -5Q + 3,000 = -5(289) + 3,000 = £1,555$

(b) New profit $= -5Q^2 + 2,890Q - 10,000 = -5(289)^2 + 2,890(289) - 10,000$

Maximum profit is $£407,605$ (a reduction of $£17,520$)

(c) Price increase to customer = 1,555 − 1,525 = £30. The tax is £60 per unit, therefore 50 per cent or one half of the tax is passed on to the customer.

11.9 The solution to this problem involves the use of *partial differentiation* (see p. 271).

(a) The marginal revenue from the sale of one extra football shirt

$$= \frac{\partial \text{TR}}{\partial x} = -4x + 6 + 10y = -4(4) + 6 + 10(3) = 20$$

(b) The marginal revenue from the sale of one extra cricket jumper

$$= \frac{\partial \text{TR}}{\partial y} = -6y + 6 + 10x = -6(3) + 6 + 10(4) = 28$$

11.10 The solution to this question involves partial differentiation (p. 271).

(a) $Q = -2(5)^2 + 4(4)(50) = 750$

$$\text{PED} = \frac{P}{Q} \times \frac{\partial Q}{\partial P} = \frac{5}{750} \times -4P = \frac{5}{750} \times -4(5) = -0.1333 \text{ (inelastic)}$$

(b) $\text{IED} = \frac{Y}{Q} \times \frac{\partial Q}{\partial Y} = \frac{50}{750} \times 4P_B = \frac{50}{750} \times 4(4) = 1.0667 \text{ (normal good)}$

(c) $\text{CED} = \frac{P_B}{Q} \times \frac{\partial Q}{\partial P_B} = \frac{4}{750} \times 4Y = \frac{4}{750} \times 4(50) = 1.0667$

This is positive and therefore the goods are substitutes.

11.11 The solution to this question involves partial differentiation (see p. 271).

▶ Marginal product of labour (MPL) =

$$\frac{\partial Q}{\partial L} = (0.75)(160)K^{0.25}L^{(0.75-1)} = 120K^{0.25}L^{-0.25}$$

$$= 120\left(\frac{K}{L}\right)^{0.25} = 120\left(\frac{400}{81}\right)^{0.25} = 178.89$$

One extra worker contributes 178.89 extra units of output (given $L = 81$ and $K = 400$)

▶ Marginal product of capital (MPK) =

$$\frac{\partial Q}{\partial K} = (0.25)(160)K^{(0.25-1)}L^{0.75} = 40K^{-0.75}L^{0.75}$$

$$= 40\left(\frac{L}{K}\right)^{0.75} = 40\left(\frac{81}{400}\right)^{0.75} = 12.07$$

One extra machine contributes 12.07 extra units of output (given $L = 81$ and $K = 400$).

11.12 $d\text{TR}/dQ$ is the first derivative of total revenue (TR)

We can therefore use *integration* (p. 273) to find the total revenue function.

$$\text{TR} = \int(100 - 40Q - 6Q^2)dQ = 100Q - 40\frac{Q^2}{2} - 6\frac{Q^3}{3} + C$$

$$\text{TR} = 100Q - 20Q^2 - 2Q^3 + C$$

If $Q = 0$ we can assume that TR = 0 hence C in our equation = 0 and TR is

$$\text{TR} = 100Q - 20Q^2 - 2Q^3$$

To find the demand (AR) equation we use the relationship AR = TR/Q

Therefore demand (AR) = price = $\dfrac{100Q - 20Q^2 - 2Q^3}{Q} = 100 - 20Q - 2Q^2$

11.13 $\text{MC} = \dfrac{d\text{TC}}{dQ}$ in order to find TC we therefore need to *integrate* the MC function

$$\int(2.4Q^2 - 0.8Q + 10)dQ = 2.4\frac{Q^3}{3} - 0.8\frac{Q^2}{2} + 10Q + C$$

$\text{TC} = 0.8Q^3 - 0.4Q^2 + 10Q + C$ where C represents the fixed costs of 500

$\text{TC} = 0.8Q^3 - 0.4Q^2 + 10Q + 500$ and when $Q = 100$

$\text{TC} = 0.8(100)^3 - 0.4(100)^2 + 10(100) + 500 = 797{,}500$

11.14 (a) $\text{MPS} = \dfrac{dS}{dY}$. In order to find the savings equation we need to *integrate* MPS

$$\int(0.4 - 0.3Y^{-0.5})dY = 0.4Y - 0.3\frac{Y^{0.5}}{0.5} + C = 0.4Y - 0.6Y^{0.5} + C$$

We can find the vertical intercept, C by finding the value of savings when $Y = 0$

$0 = 0.4(100) - 0.6(100)^{0.5} + C$ therefore $C = -34$

Savings $S = 0.4Y - 0.6Y^{0.5} - 34$ and when $Y = 400$,

$S = 0.4(400) - 0.6(400)^{0.5} - 34 = 114$

11.15 ▶ Profit from end of year 2 to end of year 8, company A:

$$\int_2^8(30 + 10X - X^2)dx = \left[30X + 5X^2 - \frac{X^3}{3}\right]_2^8$$
$$= (240 + 320 - 170.67) - (60 + 20 - 2.67)$$
$$= 312 \text{ i.e. total net profit for A is £312m}$$

▶ Profit from end of year 2 to end of year 8, company B:

$$\int_{2}^{8}\left(\frac{80}{X^2} + 8X - 10\right)dx = \left[\frac{-80}{X} + 4X^2 - 10X\right]_{2}^{8}$$
$$= (-10 + 256 - 80) - (-40 + 16 - 20)$$
$$= 210, \text{ i.e. total net profit for B is £210 m}$$

11.16 (a) Capital accumulated in the first two years ($t = 0$ to $t = 2$)

$$\int_{0}^{2}\left(-t^2 + 6t + 10\right)dt = \left[\frac{-t^3}{3} + 3t^2 + 10t\right]_{0}^{2}$$
$$= (-2.67 + 12 + 20) - (0) = 29.33 \text{ units of capital}$$

(b) Capital accumulated from $t = 2$ to $t = 5$

$$\int_{2}^{5}\left(-t^2 + 6t + 10\right)dt = \left[\frac{-t^3}{3} + 3t^2 + 10t\right]_{2}^{5}$$
$$= (-41.67 + 75 + 50) - (29.33) = 54 \text{ units of capital}$$

11.17 We need to find:

$$TC(80) - TC(50) = \int_{50}^{80}\frac{dTC}{dQ}dQ = \int_{50}^{80}(0.8Q + 9)dQ$$
$$= \left[0.4Q^2 + 9Q\right]_{50}^{80} = (2,560 + 720) - (1,000 + 450)$$
$$= 1,830$$

If TC is in £s, then the additional cost of increasing daily output is £1,830.

Chapter 12: Basic mathematics

··

12.1 (a) $\frac{1}{3} \times 474 = 158$ companies were concerned

(b) In 1980 $\frac{1}{8} \times 900,000 = 112,500$ school leavers go to university.

In 2001 $\frac{1}{3} \times 900,000 = 300,000$ go to university

12.2 (a) Gary Barlow's wealth as a percentage of David Bowie's

$$= \frac{9.5}{14.5} \times 100 = 65.5\%$$

(b) The percentage increase necessary is $\frac{(550 - 520)}{520} \times 100 = 5.8\%$

12.3 Let index at start of day be x then

$$\left(1 - \frac{7}{100}\right) \times x = 7161.15 \text{ therefore } x = \frac{7161.15}{0.93} = 7700.16$$

12.4 (a) Total cost = fixed costs + variable costs = 20,000 + 5Q

Total revenue = price × quantity = 15Q

Profit = total revenue – total cost = 15Q – (20,000 + 5Q)
= 15Q – 20,000 – 5Q

Therefore profit = 10Q – 20,000

If profit is to equal 8,000 then

8,000 = 10Q – 20,000

28,000 = 10Q   so   Q = 2,800

The level of output required to produce £8,000 profit is 2,800 units

(b) In order to break even (profit = 0)

0 = 10Q – 20,000

20,000 = 10Q therefore Q = 2,000.

Break-even output is 2,000 units.

(c) Increase fixed costs by 20 per cent. New fixed costs = 20,000(1 + 20/100)

▶ new fixed costs = 24,000
▶ new profits = 10Q – 24,000
▶ new break-even output is given by 0 = 10Q – 24,000 and Q = 2,400

Break-even output increases by (400/2,000) × 100% = 20%

A 20 per cent increase in fixed costs causes break-even output to increase by 20 per cent.

(d)

figure R12.1
Break-even graph

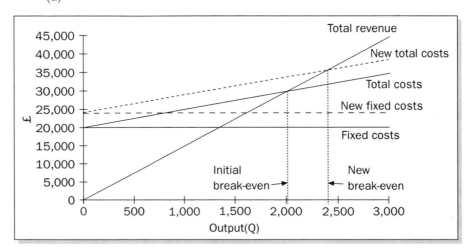

12.5 (a) The general equation of a straight line is $y = mx + c$ where m is the gradient and c and is the intercept. In this specific example the equation is $P = mQ + c$ and the gradient is found from:

$$m = \frac{y_2 - y_1}{x_2 - x_1} \quad \text{or in this case} \quad \frac{P_2 - P_1}{Q_2 - Q_1} = \frac{15 - 13}{5 - 6} = -2$$

The demand equation is therefore $P = -2Q + c$.

To find c substitute one point into this equation.

$15 = -2(5) + c$ therefore $c = 25$.

The demand equation is: $P = -2Q + 25$

(b) The equilibrium price and quantity is where the two lines intersect

▶ $P = 3Q + 5$ Supply equation
▶ $P = -2Q + 25$ Demand equation

These can be solved simultaneously by subtracting demand from supply.

$0 = 3Q - (-2Q) + 5 - 25$

$0 = 5Q - 20$

Therefore $Q = 4$.

Substituting 4 for Q in the demand equation gives the equilibrium price

$P = -2(4) + 25 = 17$

12.6 (a) Break-even output is where TR = TC

$-2Q^2 + 26Q = Q^2 + 23$ To solve for Q we need to rearrange:

$$0 = 3Q^2 - 26Q + 23.$$

This quadratic will not factorise easily, so use the formula method

$$Q = \frac{-b \pm \sqrt{b^2 - 4ac}}{2a} \quad \text{where } a = 3, b = -26 \text{ and } c = 23$$

$$Q = \frac{-(-26) \pm \sqrt{(-26)^2 - 4(3)(23)}}{2(3)} = \frac{26 \pm \sqrt{400}}{6} = \frac{26 \pm 20}{6}$$

$Q = 6/6 = 1$ and $46/6 = 7.67$.

Break-even outputs are $Q = 1$ and $Q = 7.67$ (or 8 units).

(b)

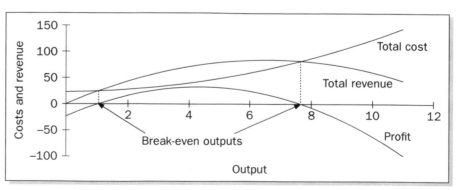

figure R12.2
Break-even output

Appendix 9

Tables

APPENDIX TABLES

Table 1   Cumulative Distribution Function of the Standard Normal Distribution

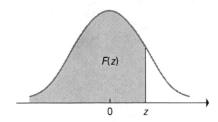

z	F(z)	z	F(z)	z	F(z)	z	F(z)	z	F(z)	z	F(z)
.00	.5000										
.01	.5040	.31	.6217	.61	.7291	.91	.8186	1.21	.8869	1.51	.9345
.02	.5080	.32	.6255	.62	.7324	.92	.8212	1.22	.8888	1.52	.9357
.03	.5120	.33	.6293	.63	.7357	.93	.8238	1.23	.8907	1.53	.9370
.04	.5160	.34	.6331	.64	.7389	.94	.8264	1.24	.8925	1.54	.9382
.05	.5199	.35	.6368	.65	.7422	.95	.8289	1.25	.8944	1.55	.9394
.06	.5239	.36	.6406	.66	.7454	.96	.8315	1.26	.8962	1.56	.9406
.07	.5279	.37	.6443	.67	.7486	.97	.8340	1.27	.8980	1.57	.9418
.08	.5319	.38	.6480	.68	.7517	.98	.8365	1.28	.8997	1.58	.9429
.09	.5359	.39	.6517	.69	.7549	.99	.8389	1.29	.9015	1.59	.9441
.10	.5398	.40	.6554	.70	.7580	1.00	.8413	1.30	.9032	1.60	.9452
.11	.5438	.41	.6591	.71	.7611	1.01	.8438	1.31	.9049	1.61	.9463
.12	.5478	.42	.6628	.72	.7642	1.02	.8461	1.32	.9066	1.62	.9474
.13	.5517	.43	.6664	.73	.7673	1.03	.8485	1.33	.9082	1.63	.9484
.14	.5557	.44	.6700	.74	.7704	1.04	.8508	1.34	.9099	1.64	.9495
.15	.5596	.45	.6736	.75	.7734	1.05	.8531	1.35	.9115	1.65	.9505
.16	.5636	.46	.6772	.76	.7764	1.06	.8554	1.36	.9131	1.66	.9515
.17	.5675	.47	.6803	.77	.7794	1.07	.8577	1.37	.9147	1.67	.9525
.18	.5714	.48	.6844	.78	.7823	1.08	.8599	1.38	.9162	1.68	.9535
.19	.5753	.49	.6879	.79	.7852	1.09	.8621	1.39	.9177	1.69	.9545
.20	.5793	.50	.6915	.80	.7881	1.10	.8643	1.40	.9192	1.70	.9554
.21	.5832	.51	.6950	.81	.7910	1.11	.8665	1.41	.9207	1.71	.9564
.22	.5871	.52	.6985	.82	.7939	1.12	.8686	1.42	.9222	1.72	.9573
.23	.5910	.53	.7019	.83	.7967	1.13	.8708	1.43	.9236	1.73	.9582
.24	.5948	.54	.7054	.84	.7995	1.14	.8729	1.44	.9251	1.74	.9591
.25	.5987	.55	.7088	.85	.8023	1.15	.8749	1.45	.9265	1.75	.9599
.26	.6026	.56	.7123	.86	.8051	1.16	.8770	1.46	.9279	1.76	.9608
.27	.6064	.57	.7157	.87	.8078	1.17	.8790	1.47	.9292	1.77	.9616
.28	.6103	.58	.7190	.88	.8106	1.18	.8810	1.48	.9306	1.78	.9625
.29	.6141	.59	.7224	.89	.8133	1.19	.8830	1.49	.9319	1.79	.9633
.30	.6179	.60	.7257	.90	.8159	1.20	.8849	1.50	.9332	1.80	.9641

Table 1   Cumulative Distribution Function of the Standard Normal Distribution Continued

z	F(z)	z	F(z)	z	F(z)	z	F(z)	z	F(z)	z	F(z)
1.81	.9649	2.21	.9864	2.61	.9955	3.01	.9987	3.41	.9997	3.81	.9999
1.82	.9656	2.22	.9868	2.62	.9956	3.02	.9987	3.42	.9997	3.82	.9999
1.83	.9664	2.23	.9871	2.63	.9957	3.03	.9988	3.43	.9997	3.83	.9999
1.84	.9671	2.24	.9875	2.64	.9959	3.04	.9988	3.44	.9997	3.84	.9999
1.85	.9678	2.25	.9878	2.65	.9960	3.05	.9989	3.45	.9997	3.85	.9999
1.86	.9686	2.26	.9881	2.66	.9961	3.06	.9989	3.46	.9997	3.86	.9999
1.87	.9693	2.27	.9884	2.67	.9962	3.07	.9989	3.47	.9997	3.87	.9999
1.88	.9699	2.28	.9887	2.68	.9963	3.08	.9990	3.48	.9997	3.88	.9999
1.89	.9706	2.29	.9890	2.69	.9964	3.09	.9990	3.49	.9998	3.89	1.0000
1.90	.9713	2.30	.9893	2.70	.9965	3.10	.9990	3.50	.9998	3.90	1.0000
1.91	.9719	2.31	.9896	2.71	.9966	3.11	.9991	3.51	.9998	3.91	1.0000
1.92	.9726	2.32	.9898	2.72	.9967	3.12	.9991	3.52	.9998	3.92	1.0000
1.93	.9732	2.33	.9901	2.73	.9968	3.13	.9991	3.53	.9998	3.93	1.0000
1.94	.9738	2.34	.9904	2.74	.9969	3.14	.9992	3.54	.9998	3.94	1.0000
1.95	.9744	2.35	.9906	2.75	.9970	3.15	.9992	3.55	.9998	3.95	1.0000
1.96	.9750	2.36	.9909	2.76	.9971	3.16	.9992	3.56	.9998	3.96	1.0000
1.97	.9756	2.37	.9911	2.77	.9972	3.17	.9992	3.57	.9998	3.97	1.0000
1.98	.9761	2.38	.9913	2.78	.9973	3.18	.9993	3.58	.9998	3.98	1.0000
1.99	.9767	2.39	.9916	2.79	.9974	3.19	.9993	3.59	.9998	3.99	1.0000
2.00	.9772	2.40	.9918	2.80	.9974	3.20	.9993	3.60	.9998		
2.01	.9778	2.41	.9920	2.81	.9975	3.21	.9993	3.61	.9998		
2.02	.9783	2.42	.9922	2.82	.9976	3.22	.9994	3.62	.9999		
2.03	.9788	2.43	.9925	2.83	.9977	3.23	.9994	3.63	.9999		
2.04	.9793	2.44	.9927	2.84	.9977	3.24	.9994	3.64	.9999		
2.05	.9798	2.45	.9929	2.85	.9978	3.25	.9994	3.65	.9999		
2.06	.9803	2.46	.9931	2.86	.9979	3.26	.9994	3.66	.9999		
2.07	.9808	2.47	.9932	2.87	.9979	3.27	.9995	3.67	.9999		
2.08	.9812	2.48	.9934	2.88	.9980	3.28	.9995	3.68	.9999		
2.09	.9817	2.49	.9936	2.89	.9981	3.29	.9995	3.69	.9999		
2.10	.9821	2.50	.9938	2.90	.9981	3.30	.9995	3.70	.9999		
2.11	.9826	2.51	.9940	2.91	.9982	3.31	.9995	3.71	.9999		
2.12	.9830	2.52	.9941	2.92	.9982	3.32	.9996	3.72	.9999		
2.13	.9834	2.53	.9943	2.93	.9983	3.33	.9996	3.73	.9999		
2.14	.9838	2.54	.9945	2.94	.9984	3.34	.9996	3.74	.9999		
2.15	.9842	2.55	.9946	2.95	.9984	3.35	.9996	3.75	.9999		
2.16	.9846	2.56	.9948	2.96	.9985	3.36	.9996	3.76	.9999		
2.17	.9850	2.57	.9949	2.97	.9985	3.37	.9996	3.77	.9999		
2.18	.9854	2.58	.9951	2.98	.9986	3.38	.9996	3.78	.9999		
2.19	.9857	2.59	.9952	2.99	.9986	3.39	.9997	3.79	.9999		
2.20	.9861	2.60	.9953	3.00	.9986	3.40	.9997	3.80	.9999		

Reproduced with permission of the trustees of Biometrika, from *Biometrika Tables for Statisticians*, vol. 1 (1966).

Table 2   Probability Function of the Binomial Distribution

The table shows the probability of x successes in n independent trials, each with probability of success P. For example, the probability of four successes in eight independent trials, each with probability of success .35, is .1875.

n	x	.05	.10	.15	.20	.25	.30	.35	.40	.45	.50
							P				
1	0	.9500	.9000	.8500	.8000	.7500	.7000	.6500	.6000	.5500	.5000
	1	.0500	.1000	.1500	.2000	.2500	.3000	.3500	.4000	.4500	.5000
2	0	.9025	.8100	.7225	.6400	.5625	.4900	.4225	.3600	.3025	.2500
	1	.0950	.1800	.2550	.3200	.3750	.4200	.4550	.4800	.4950	.5000
	2	.0025	.0100	.0225	.0400	.0625	.0900	.1225	.1600	.2025	.2500
3	0	.8574	.7290	.6141	.5120	.4219	.3430	.2746	.2160	.1664	.1250
	1	.1354	.2430	.3251	.3840	.4219	.4410	.4436	.4320	.4084	.3750
	2	.0071	.0270	.0574	.0960	.1406	.1890	.2389	.2880	.3341	.3750
	3	.0001	.0010	.0034	.0080	.0156	.0270	.0429	.0640	.0911	.1250
4	0	.8145	.6561	.5220	.4096	.3164	.2401	.1785	.1296	.0915	.0625
	1	.1715	.2916	.3685	.4096	.4219	.4116	.3845	.3456	.2995	.2500
	2	.0135	.0486	.0975	.1536	.2109	.2646	.3105	.3456	.3675	.3750
	3	.0005	.0036	.0115	.0256	.0469	.0756	.1115	.1536	.2005	.2500
	4	.0000	.0001	.0005	.0016	.0039	.0081	.0150	.0256	.0410	.0625
5	0	.7738	.5905	.4437	.3277	.2373	.1681	.1160	.0778	.0503	.0312
	1	.2036	.3280	.3915	.4096	.3955	.3602	.3124	.2592	.2059	.1562
	2	.0214	.0729	.1382	.2048	.2637	.3087	.3364	.3456	.3369	.3125
	3	.0011	.0081	.0244	.0512	.0879	.1323	.1811	.2304	.2757	.3125
	4	.0000	.0004	.0022	.0064	.0146	.0284	.0488	.0768	.1128	.1562
	5	.0000	.0000	.0001	.0003	.0010	.0024	.0053	.0102	.0185	.0312
6	0	.7351	.5314	.3771	.2621	.1780	.1176	.0754	.0467	.0277	.0156
	1	.2321	.3543	.3993	.3932	.3560	.3025	.2437	.1866	.1359	.0938
	2	.0305	.0984	.1762	.2458	.2966	.3241	.3280	.3110	.2780	.2344
	3	.0021	.0146	.0415	.0819	.1318	.1852	.2355	.2765	.3032	.3125
	4	.0001	.0012	.0055	.0154	.0330	.0595	.0951	.1382	.1861	.2344
	5	.0000	.0001	.0004	.0015	.0044	.0102	.0205	.0369	.0609	.0938
	6	.0000	.0000	.0000	.0001	.0002	.0007	.0018	.0041	.0083	.0156
7	0	.6983	.4783	.3206	.2097	.1335	.0824	.0490	.0280	.0152	.0078
	1	.2573	.3720	.3960	.3670	.3115	.2471	.1848	.1306	.0872	.0547
	2	.0406	.1240	.2097	.2753	.3115	.3177	.2985	.2613	.2140	.1641
	3	.0036	.0230	.0617	.1147	.1730	.2269	.2679	.2903	.2918	.2734
	4	.0002	.0026	.0109	.0287	.0577	.0972	.1442	.1935	.2388	.2734
	5	.0000	.0002	.0012	.0043	.0115	.0250	.0466	.0774	.1172	.1641
	6	.0000	.0000	.0001	.0004	.0013	.0036	.0084	.0172	.0320	.0547
	7	.0000	.0000	.0000	.0000	.0001	.0002	.0006	.0016	.0037	.0078
8	0	.6634	.4305	.2725	.1678	.1001	.0576	.0319	.0168	.0084	.0039
	1	.2793	.3826	.3847	.3355	.2670	.1977	.1373	.0896	.0548	.0312
	2	.0515	.1488	.2376	.2936	.3115	.2965	.2587	.2090	.1569	.1094
	3	.0054	.0331	.0839	.1468	.2076	.2541	.2786	.2787	.2568	.2188
	4	.0004	.0046	.0185	.0459	.0865	.1361	.1875	.2322	.2627	.2734
	5	.0000	.0004	.0026	.0092	.0231	.0467	.0808	.1239	.1719	.2188
	6	.0000	.0000	.0002	.0011	.0038	.0100	.0217	.0413	.0703	.1094
	7	.0000	.0000	.0000	.0001	.0004	.0012	.0033	.0079	.0164	.0312
	8	.0000	.0000	.0000	.0000	.0000	.0001	.0002	.0007	.0017	.0039
9	0	.6302	.3874	.2316	.1342	.0751	.0404	.0207	.0101	.0046	.0020
	1	.2985	.3874	.3679	.3020	.2253	.1556	.1004	.0605	.0339	.0176
	2	.0629	.1722	.2597	.3020	.3003	.2668	.2162	.1612	.1110	.0703
	3	.0077	.0446	.1069	.1762	.2336	.2668	.2716	.2508	.2119	.1641
	4	.0006	.0074	.0283	.0661	.1168	.1715	.2194	.2508	.2600	.2461
	5	.0000	.0008	.0050	.0165	.0389	.0735	.1181	.1672	.2128	.2461
	6	.0000	.0001	.0006	.0028	.0087	.0210	.0424	.0743	.1160	.1641
	7	.0000	.0000	.0000	.0003	.0012	.0039	.0098	.0212	.0407	.0703

Table 2 Probability Function of the Binomial Distribution Continued

n	x	.05	.10	.15	.20	.25	.30	.35	.40	.45	.50
	8	.0000	.0000	.0000	.0000	.0001	.0004	.0013	.0035	.0083	.0176
	9	.0000	.0000	.0000	.0000	.0000	.0000	.0001	.0003	.0008	.0020
10	0	.5987	.3487	.1969	.1074	.0563	.0282	.0135	.0060	.0025	.0010
	1	.3151	.3874	.3474	.2684	.1877	.1211	.0725	.0403	.0207	.0098
	2	.0746	.1937	.2759	.3020	.2816	.2335	.1757	.1209	.0763	.0439
	3	.0105	.0574	.1298	.2013	.2503	.2668	.2522	.2150	.1665	.1172
	4	.0010	.0112	.0401	.0881	.1460	.2001	.2377	.2508	.2384	.2051
	5	.0001	.0015	.0085	.0264	.0584	.1029	.1536	.2007	.2340	.2461
	6	.0000	.0001	.0012	.0055	.0162	.0368	.0689	.1115	.1596	.2051
	7	.0000	.0000	.0001	.0008	.0031	.0090	.0212	.0425	.0746	.1172
	8	.0000	.0000	.0000	.0001	.0004	.0014	.0043	.0106	.0226	.0439
	9	.0000	.0000	.0000	.0000	.0000	.0001	.0004	.0016	.0042	.0098
	10	.0000	.0000	.0000	.0000	.0000	.0000	.0000	.0001	.0003	.0010
11	0	.5688	.3138	.1673	.0859	.0422	.0198	.0088	.0036	.0014	.0005
	1	.3293	.3835	.3248	.2362	.1549	.0932	.0518	.0266	.0125	.0054
	2	.0867	.2131	.2866	.2953	.2581	.1998	.1395	.0887	.0513	.0269
	3	.0137	.0710	.1517	.2215	.2581	.2568	.2254	.1774	.1259	.0806
	4	.0014	.0158	.0536	.1107	.1721	.2201	.2428	.2365	.2060	.1611
	5	.0001	.0025	.0132	.0388	.0803	.1321	.1830	.2207	.2360	.2256
	6	.0000	.0003	.0023	.0097	.0268	.0566	.0985	.1471	.1931	.2256
	7	.0000	.0000	.0003	.0017	.0064	.0173	.0379	.0701	.1128	.1611
	8	.0000	.0000	.0000	.0002	.0011	.0037	.0102	.0234	.0462	.0806
	9	.0000	.0000	.0000	.0000	.0001	.0005	.0018	.0052	.0126	.0269
	10	.0000	.0000	.0000	.0000	.0000	.0000	.0002	.0007	.0021	.0054
	11	.0000	.0000	.0000	.0000	.0000	.0000	.0000	.0000	.0002	.0005
12	0	.5404	.2824	.1422	.0687	.0317	.0138	.0057	.0022	.0008	.0002
	1	.3413	.3766	.3012	.2062	.1267	.0712	.0368	.0174	.0075	.0029
	2	.0988	.2301	.2924	.2835	.2323	.1678	.1088	.0639	.0339	.0161
	3	.0173	.0852	.1720	.2362	.2581	.2397	.1954	.1419	.0923	.0537
	4	.0021	.0213	.0683	.1329	.1936	.2311	.2367	.2128	.1700	.1208
	5	.0002	.0038	.0193	.0532	.1032	.1585	.2039	.2270	.2225	.1934
	6	.0000	.0005	.0040	.0155	.0401	.0792	.1281	.1766	.2124	.2256
	7	.0000	.0000	.0006	.0033	.0015	.0291	.0591	.1009	.1489	.1934
	8	.0000	.0000	.0001	.0005	.0024	.0078	.0199	.0420	.0762	.1208
	9	.0000	.0000	.0000	.0001	.0004	.0015	.0048	.0125	.0277	.0537
	10	.0000	.0000	.0000	.0000	.0000	.0002	.0008	.0025	.0068	.0161
	11	.0000	.0000	.0000	.0000	.0000	.0000	.0001	.0003	.0010	.0029
	12	.0000	.0000	.0000	.0000	.0000	.0000	.0000	.0000	.0001	.0002
13	0	.5133	.2542	.1209	.0550	.0238	.0097	.0037	.0013	.0004	.0001
	1	.3512	.3672	.2774	.1787	.1029	.0540	.0259	.0113	.0045	.0016
	2	.1109	.2448	.2937	.2680	.2059	.1388	.0836	.0453	.0220	.0095
	3	.0214	.0997	.1900	.2457	.2517	.2181	.1651	.1107	.0660	.0349
	4	.0028	.0277	.0838	.1535	.2097	.2337	.2222	.1845	.1350	.0873
	5	.0003	.0055	.0266	.0691	.1258	.1803	.2154	.2214	.1989	.1571
	6	.0000	.0008	.0063	.0230	.0559	.1030	.1546	.1968	.2169	.2095
	7	.0000	.0001	.0011	.0058	.0186	.0442	.0833	.1312	.1775	.2095
	8	.0000	.0000	.0001	.0011	.0047	.0142	.0336	.0656	.1089	.1571
	9	.0000	.0000	.0000	.0001	.0009	.0034	.0101	.0243	.0495	.0873
	10	.0000	.0000	.0000	.0000	.0001	.0006	.0022	.0065	.0162	.0349
	11	.0000	.0000	.0000	.0000	.0000	.0001	.0003	.0012	.0036	.0095
	12	.0000	.0000	.0000	.0000	.0000	.0000	.0000	.0001	.0005	.0016
	13	.0000	.0000	.0000	.0000	.0000	.0000	.0000	.0000	.0000	.0001
14	0	.4877	.2288	.1028	.0440	.0178	.0068	.0024	.0008	.0002	.0001
	1	.3593	.3559	.2539	.1539	.0832	.0407	.0181	.0073	.0027	.0009
	2	.1229	.2570	.2912	.2501	.1802	.1134	.0634	.0317	.0141	.0056

Table 2 Probability Function of the Binomial Distribution Continued

n	x	.05	.10	.15	.20	.25	.30	.35	.40	.45	.50
	3	.0259	.1142	.2056	.2501	.2402	.1943	.1366	.0845	.0462	.0222
	4	.0037	.0348	.0998	.1720	.2202	.2290	.2022	.1549	.1040	.0611
	5	.0004	.0078	.0352	.0860	.1468	.1963	.2178	.2066	.1701	.1222
	6	.0000	.0013	.0093	.0322	.0734	.1262	.1759	.2066	.2088	.1833
	7	.0000	.0002	.0019	.0092	.0280	.0618	.1082	.1574	.1952	.2095
	8	.0000	.0000	.0003	.0020	.0082	.0232	.0510	.0918	.1398	.1833
	9	.0000	.0000	.0000	.0003	.0018	.0066	.0183	.0408	.0762	.1222
	10	.0000	.0000	.0000	.0000	.0003	.0014	.0049	.0136	.0312	.0611
	11	.0000	.0000	.0000	.0000	.0000	.0002	.0010	.0033	.0093	.0222
	12	.0000	.0000	.0000	.0000	.0000	.0000	.0001	.0005	.0019	.0056
	13	.0000	.0000	.0000	.0000	.0000	.0000	.0000	.0001	.0002	.0009
	14	.0000	.0000	.0000	.0000	.0000	.0000	.0000	.0000	.0000	.0001
15	0	.4633	.2059	.0874	.0352	.0134	.0047	.0016	.0005	.0001	.0000
	1	.3658	.3432	.2312	.1319	.0668	.0305	.0126	.0047	.0016	.0005
	2	.1348	.2669	.2856	.2309	.1559	.0916	.0476	.0219	.0090	.0032
	3	.0307	.1285	.2184	.2501	.2252	.1700	.1110	.0634	.0318	.0139
	4	.0049	.0428	.1156	.1876	.2252	.2186	.1792	.1268	.0780	.0417
	5	.0006	.0105	.0449	.1032	.1651	.2061	.2123	.1859	.1404	.0916
	6	.0000	.0019	.0132	.0430	.0917	.1472	.1906	.2066	.1914	.1527
	7	.0000	.0003	.0030	.0138	.0393	.0811	.1319	.1771	.2013	.1964
	8	.0000	.0000	.0005	.0035	.0131	.0348	.0710	.1181	.1647	.1964
	9	.0000	.0000	.0001	.0007	.0034	.0116	.0298	.0612	.1048	.1527
	10	.0000	.0000	.0000	.0001	.0007	.0030	.0096	.0245	.0515	.0916
	11	.0000	.0000	.0000	.0000	.0001	.0006	.0024	.0074	.0191	.0417
	12	.0000	.0000	.0000	.0000	.0000	.0001	.0004	.0016	.0052	.0139
	13	.0000	.0000	.0000	.0000	.0000	.0000	.0001	.0003	.0010	.0032
	14	.0000	.0000	.0000	.0000	.0000	.0000	.0000	.0000	.0001	.0005
	15	.0000	.0000	.0000	.0000	.0000	.0000	.0000	.0000	.0000	.0000
16	0	.4401	.1853	.0743	.0281	.0100	.0033	.0010	.0003	.0001	.0000
	1	.3706	.3294	.2097	.1126	.0535	.0228	.0087	.0030	.0009	.0002
	2	.1463	.2745	.2775	.2111	.1336	.0732	.0353	.0150	.0056	.0018
	3	.0359	.1423	.2285	.2463	.2079	.1465	.0888	.0468	.0215	.0085
	4	.0061	.0514	.1311	.2001	.2552	.2040	.1553	.1014	.0572	.0278
	5	.0008	.0137	.0555	.1201	.1802	.2099	.2008	.1623	.1123	.0667
	6	.0001	.0028	.0180	.0550	.1101	.1649	.1982	.1983	.1684	.1222
	7	.0000	.0004	.0045	.0197	.0524	.1010	.1524	.1889	.1969	.1746
	8	.0000	.0001	.0009	.0055	.0197	.0487	.0923	.1417	.1812	.1964
	9	.0000	.0000	.0001	.0012	.0058	.0185	.0442	.0840	.1318	.1746
	10	.0000	.0000	.0000	.0002	.0014	.0056	.0167	.0392	.0755	.1222
	11	.0000	.0000	.0000	.0000	.0002	.0013	.0049	.0142	.0337	.0667
	12	.0000	.0000	.0000	.0000	.0000	.0002	.0011	.0040	.0115	.0278
	13	.0000	.0000	.0000	.0000	.0000	.0000	.0002	.0008	.0029	.0085
	14	.0000	.0000	.0000	.0000	.0000	.0000	.0000	.0001	.0005	.0018
	15	.0000	.0000	.0000	.0000	.0000	.0000	.0000	.0000	.0001	.0002
	16	.0000	.0000	.0000	.0000	.0000	.0000	.0000	.0000	.0000	.0000
17	0	.4181	.1668	.0631	.0225	.0075	.0023	.0007	.0002	.0000	.0000
	1	.3741	.3150	.1893	.0957	.0426	.0169	.0060	.0019	.0005	.0001
	2	.1575	.2800	.2673	.1914	.1136	.0581	.0260	.0102	.0035	.0010
	3	.0415	.1556	.2359	.2393	.1893	.1245	.0701	.0341	.0144	.0052
	4	.0076	.0605	.1457	.2093	.2209	.1868	.1320	.0796	.0411	.0182
	5	.0010	.0175	.0668	.1361	.1914	.2081	.1849	.1379	.0875	.0472
	6	.0001	.0039	.0236	.0680	.1276	.1784	.1991	.1839	.1432	.0944
	7	.0000	.0007	.0065	.0267	.0668	.1201	.1685	.1927	.1841	.1484
	8	.0000	.0001	.0014	.0084	.0279	.0644	.1134	.1606	.1883	.1855
	9	.0000	.0000	.0003	.0021	.0093	.0276	.0611	.1070	.1540	.1855

Table 2 Probability Function of the Binomial Distribution Continued

n	x	.05	.10	.15	.20	.25	.30	.35	.40	.45	.50
	10	.0000	.0000	.0000	.0004	.0025	.0095	.0263	.0571	.1008	.1484
	11	.0000	.0000	.0000	.0001	.0005	.0026	.0090	.0242	.0525	.0944
	12	.0000	.0000	.0000	.0000	.0001	.0006	.0024	.0081	.0215	.0472
	13	.0000	.0000	.0000	.0000	.0000	.0001	.0005	.0021	.0068	.0182
	14	.0000	.0000	.0000	.0000	.0000	.0000	.0001	.0004	.0016	.0052
	15	.0000	.0000	.0000	.0000	.0000	.0000	.0000	.0001	.0003	.0010
	16	.0000	.0000	.0000	.0000	.0000	.0000	.0000	.0000	.0000	.0001
	17	.0000	.0000	.0000	.0000	.0000	.0000	.0000	.0000	.0000	.0000
18	0	.3972	.1501	.0536	.0180	.0056	.0016	.0004	.0001	.0000	.0000
	1	.3763	.3002	.1704	.0811	.0338	.0126	.0042	.0012	.0003	.0001
	2	.1683	.2835	.2556	.1723	.0958	.0458	.0190	.0069	.0022	.0006
	3	.0473	.1680	.2406	.2297	.1704	.1046	.0547	.0246	.0095	.0031
	4	.0093	.0700	.1592	.2153	.2130	.1681	.1104	.0614	.0291	.0117
	5	.0014	.0218	.0787	.1507	.1988	.2017	.1664	.1146	.0666	.0327
	6	.0002	.0052	.0301	.0816	.1436	.1873	.1941	.1655	.1181	.0708
	7	.0000	.0010	.0091	.0350	.0820	.1376	.1792	.1892	.1657	.1214
	8	.0000	.0002	.0022	.0120	.0376	.0811	.1327	.1734	.1864	.1669
	9	.0000	.0000	.0004	.0033	.0139	.0386	.0794	.1284	.1694	.1855
	10	.0000	.0000	.0001	.0008	.0042	.0149	.0385	.0771	.1248	.1669
	11	.0000	.0000	.0000	.0001	.0010	.0046	.0151	.0374	.0742	.1214
	12	.0000	.0000	.0000	.0000	.0002	.0012	.0047	.0145	.0354	.0708
	13	.0000	.0000	.0000	.0000	.0000	.0002	.0012	.0044	.0134	.0327
	14	.0000	.0000	.0000	.0000	.0000	.0000	.0002	.0011	.0039	.0117
	15	.0000	.0000	.0000	.0000	.0000	.0000	.0000	.0002	.0009	.0031
	16	.0000	.0000	.0000	.0000	.0000	.0000	.0000	.0000	.0001	.0006
	17	.0000	.0000	.0000	.0000	.0000	.0000	.0000	.0000	.0000	.0001
	18	.0000	.0000	.0000	.0000	.0000	.0000	.0000	.0000	.0000	.0000
19	0	.3774	.1351	.0456	.0144	.0042	.0011	.0003	.0001	.0000	.0000
	1	.3774	.2852	.1529	.0685	.0268	.0093	.0029	.0008	.0002	.0000
	2	.1787	.2852	.2428	.1540	.0803	.0358	.0138	.0046	.0013	.0003
	3	.0533	.1796	.2428	.2182	.1517	.0869	.0422	.0175	.0062	.0018
	4	.0112	.0798	.1714	.2182	.2023	.1419	.0909	.0467	.0203	.0074
	5	.0018	.0266	.0907	.1636	.2023	.1916	.1468	.0933	.0497	.0222
	6	.0002	.0069	.0374	.0955	.1574	.1916	.1844	.1451	.0949	.0518
	7	.0000	.0014	.0122	.0443	.0974	.1525	.1844	.1797	.1443	.0961
	8	.0000	.0002	.0032	.0166	.0487	.0981	.1489	.1797	.1771	.1442
	9	.0000	.0000	.0007	.0051	.0198	.0514	.0980	.1464	.1771	.1762
	10	.0000	.0000	.0001	.0013	.0066	.0220	.0528	.0976	.1449	.1762
	11	.0000	.0000	.0000	.0003	.0018	.0077	.0233	.0532	.0970	.1442
	12	.0000	.0000	.0000	.0000	.0004	.0022	.0083	.0237	.0529	.0961
	13	.0000	.0000	.0000	.0000	.0001	.0005	.0024	.0085	.0233	.0518
	14	.0000	.0000	.0000	.0000	.0000	.0001	.0006	.0024	.0082	.0222
	15	.0000	.0000	.0000	.0000	.0000	.0000	.0001	.0005	.0022	.0074
	16	.0000	.0000	.0000	.0000	.0000	.0000	.0000	.0001	.0005	.0018
	17	.0000	.0000	.0000	.0000	.0000	.0000	.0000	.0000	.0001	.0003
	18	.0000	.0000	.0000	.0000	.0000	.0000	.0000	.0000	.0000	.0000
	19	.0000	.0000	.0000	.0000	.0000	.0000	.0000	.0000	.0000	.0000
20	0	.3585	.1216	.0388	.0115	.0032	.0008	.0002	.0000	.0000	.0000
	1	.3774	.2702	.1368	.0576	.0211	.0068	.0020	.0005	.0001	.0000
	2	.1887	.2852	.2293	.1369	.0669	.0278	.0100	.0031	.0008	.0002
	3	.0596	.1901	.2428	.2054	.1339	.0716	.0323	.0123	.0040	.0011
	4	.0133	.0898	.1821	.2182	.1897	.1304	.0738	.0350	.0139	.0046
	5	.0022	.0319	.1028	.1746	.2023	.1789	.1272	.0746	.0365	.0148
	6	.0003	.0089	.0454	.1091	.1686	.1916	.1712	.1244	.0746	.0370
	7	.0000	.0020	.0160	.0545	.1124	.1643	.1844	.1659	.1221	.0739
	8	.0000	.0004	.0046	.0222	.0609	.1144	.1614	.1797	.1623	.1201

Table 2   Probability Function of the Binomial Distribution Continued

n	x	.05	.10	.15	.20	.25	.30	.35	.40	.45	.50
							P				
	9	.0000	.0001	.0011	.0074	.0271	.0654	.1158	.1597	.1771	.1602
	10	.0000	.0000	.0002	.0020	.0099	.0308	.0686	.1171	.1593	.1762
	11	.0000	.0000	.0000	.0005	.0030	.0120	.0336	.0710	.1185	.1602
	12	.0000	.0000	.0000	.0001	.0008	.0039	.0136	.0355	.0727	.1201
	13	.0000	.0000	.0000	.0000	.0002	.0010	.0045	.0146	.0366	.0739
	14	.0000	.0000	.0000	.0000	.0000	.0002	.0012	.0049	.0150	.0370
	15	.0000	.0000	.0000	.0000	.0000	.0000	.0003	.0013	.0049	.0148
	16	.0000	.0000	.0000	.0000	.0000	.0000	.0000	.0003	.0013	.0046
	17	.0000	.0000	.0000	.0000	.0000	.0000	.0000	.0000	.0002	.0011
	18	.0000	.0000	.0000	.0000	.0000	.0000	.0000	.0000	.0000	.0002
	19	.0000	.0000	.0000	.0000	.0000	.0000	.0000	.0000	.0000	.0000
	20	.0000	.0000	.0000	.0000	.0000	.0000	.0000	.0000	.0000	.0000

Reproduced with permission from National Bureau of Standards, *Tables of the Binomial Probability Distribution*, United States Department of Commerce (1950).

Table 3 Cumulative Binomial Probabilities

The table shows the probability of x or fewer successes in n independent trials each with probability of success P. For example, the probability of two or less successes in four independent trials, each with probability of success, 0.35 is 0.874.

n	x	.05	.10	.15	.20	.25	.30	.35	.40	.45	.500
2	0	.902	.81	.722	.64	.562	.49	.422	.36	.302	.25
	1	.998	.99	.978	.96	.937	.91	.877	.84	.797	.75
	2	1.00	1.00	1.00	1.00	1.00	1.00	1.00	1.00	1.00	1.00
3	0	.857	.729	.614	.512	.422	.343	.275	.216	.166	.125
	1	.993	.972	.939	.896	.844	.784	.718	.648	.575	.500
	2	1.00	.999	.997	.992	.984	.973	.957	.936	.909	.875
	3	1.00	1.00	1.00	1.00	1.00	1.00	1.00	1.00	1.00	1.000
4	0	.815	.656	.522	.41	.316	.24	.179	.13	.092	.062
	1	.986	.948	.89	.819	.738	.652	.563	.475	.391	.312
	2	1.00	.996	.988	.973	.949	.916	.874	.821	.759	.687
	3	1.00	1.00	.999	.998	.996	.992	.985	.974	.959	.937
	4	1.00	1.00	1.00	1.00	1.00	1.00	1.00	1.00	1.00	1.000
5	0	.774	.59	.444	.328	.237	.168	.116	.078	.05	.031
	1	.977	.919	.835	.737	.633	.528	.428	.337	.256	.187
	2	.999	.991	.973	.942	.896	.837	.765	.683	.593	.500
	3	1.00	1.00	.998	.993	.984	.969	.946	.913	.869	.812
	4	1.00	1.00	1.00	1.00	.999	.998	.995	.99	.982	.969
	5	1.00	1.00	1.00	1.00	1.00	1.00	1.00	1.00	1.00	1.000
6	0	.735	.531	.377	.262	.178	.118	.075	.047	.028	.016
	1	.967	.886	.776	.655	.534	.42	.319	.233	.164	.109
	2	.998	.984	.953	.901	.831	.744	.647	.544	.442	.344
	3	1.00	.999	.994	.983	.962	.93	.883	.821	.745	.656
	4	1.00	1.00	1.00	.998	.995	.989	.978	.959	.931	.891
	5	1.00	1.00	1.00	1.00	1.00	.999	.998	.996	.992	.984
	6	1.00	1.00	1.00	1.00	1.00	1.00	1.00	1.00	1.00	1.000
7	0	.698	.478	.321	.21	.133	.082	.049	.028	.015	.008
	1	.956	.85	.717	.577	.445	.329	.234	.159	.102	.062
	2	.996	.974	.926	.852	.756	.647	.532	.42	.316	.227
	3	1.00	.997	.988	.967	.929	.874	.80	.71	.608	.500
	4	1.00	1.00	.999	.995	.987	.971	.944	.904	.847	.773
	5	1.00	1.00	1.00	1.00	.999	.996	.991	.981	.964	.937
	6	1.00	1.00	1.00	1.00	1.00	1.00	.999	.998	.996	.992
	7	1.00	1.00	1.00	1.00	1.00	1.00	1.00	1.00	1.00	1.000
8	0	.663	.43	.272	.168	.10	.058	.032	.017	.008	.004
	1	.943	.813	.657	.503	.367	.255	.169	.106	.063	.035
	2	.994	.962	.895	.797	.679	.552	.428	.315	.22	.145
	3	1.00	.995	.979	.944	.886	.806	.706	.594	.477	.363
	4	1.00	1.00	.997	.99	.973	.942	.894	.826	.74	.637
	5	1.00	1.00	1.00	.999	.996	.989	.975	.95	.912	.855
	6	1.00	1.00	1.00	1.00	1.00	.999	.996	.991	.982	.965
	7	1.00	1.00	1.00	1.00	1.00	1.00	1.00	.999	.998	.996
	8	1.00	1.00	1.00	1.00	1.00	1.00	1.00	1.00	1.00	1.000
9	0	.63	.387	.232	.134	.075	.04	.021	.01	.005	.002
	1	.929	.775	.599	.436	.30	.196	.121	.071	.039	.020
	2	.992	.947	.859	.738	.601	.463	.337	.232	.15	.090
	3	.999	.992	.966	.914	.834	.73	.609	.483	.361	.254
	4	1.00	.999	.994	.98	.951	.901	.828	.733	.621	.500
	5	1.00	1.00	.999	.997	.99	.975	.946	.901	.834	.746
	6	1.00	1.00	1.00	1.00	.999	.996	.989	.975	.95	.910
	7	1.00	1.00	1.00	1.00	1.00	1.00	.999	.996	.991	.980
	8	1.00	1.00	1.00	1.00	1.00	1.00	1.00	1.00	.999	.998
	9	1.00	1.00	1.00	1.00	1.00	1.00	1.00	1.00	1.00	1.000

Table 3   Cumulative Binomial Probabilities Continued

n	x	.05	.10	.15	.20	.25	.30	.35	.40	.45	.500
						P					
10	0	.599	.349	.197	.107	.056	.028	.013	.006	.003	.001
	1	.914	.736	.544	.376	.244	.149	.086	.046	.023	.011
	2	.988	.93	.82	.678	.526	.383	.262	.167	.10	.055
	3	.999	.987	.95	.879	.776	.65	.514	.382	.266	.172
	4	1.00	.998	.99	.967	.922	.85	.751	.633	.504	.377
	5	1.00	1.00	.999	.994	.98	.953	.905	.834	.738	.623
	6	1.00	1.00	1.00	.999	.996	.989	.974	.945	.898	.828
	7	1.00	1.00	1.00	1.00	1.00	.998	.995	.988	.973	.945
	8	1.00	1.00	1.00	1.00	1.00	1.00	.999	.998	.995	.989
	9	1.00	1.00	1.00	1.00	1.00	1.00	1.00	1.00	1.00	.999
	10	1.00	1.00	1.00	1.00	1.00	1.00	1.00	1.00	1.00	1.000
11	0	.569	.314	.167	.086	.042	.02	.009	.004	.001	.000
	1	.898	.697	.492	.322	.197	.113	.061	.03	.014	.006
	2	.985	.91	.779	.617	.455	.313	.20	.119	.065	.033
	3	.998	.981	.931	.839	.713	.57	.426	.296	.191	.113
	4	1.00	.997	.984	.95	.885	.79	.668	.533	.397	.274
	5	1.00	1.00	.997	.988	.966	.922	.851	.753	.633	.500
	6	1.00	1.00	1.00	.998	.992	.978	.95	.901	.826	.726
	7	1.00	1.00	1.00	1.00	.999	.996	.988	.971	.939	.887
	8	1.00	1.00	1.00	1.00	1.00	.999	.998	.994	.985	.967
	9	1.00	1.00	1.00	1.00	1.00	1.00	1.00	.999	.998	.994
	10	1.00	1.00	1.00	1.00	1.00	1.00	1.00	1.00	1.00	1.000
	11	1.00	1.00	1.00	1.00	1.00	1.00	1.00	1.00	1.00	1.000
12	0	.54	.282	.142	.069	.032	.014	.006	.002	.001	.000
	1	.882	.659	.443	.275	.158	.085	.042	.02	.008	.003
	2	.98	.889	.736	.558	.391	.253	.151	.083	.042	.019
	3	.998	.974	.908	.795	.649	.493	.347	.225	.134	.073
	4	1.00	.996	.976	.927	.842	.724	.583	.438	.304	.194
	5	1.00	.999	.995	.981	.946	.882	.787	.665	.527	.387
	6	1.00	1.00	.999	.996	.986	.961	.915	.842	.739	.613
	7	1.00	1.00	1.00	.999	.997	.991	.974	.943	.888	.806
	8	1.00	1.00	1.00	1.00	1.00	.998	.994	.985	.964	.927
	9	1.00	1.00	1.00	1.00	1.00	1.00	.999	.997	.992	.981
	10	1.00	1.00	1.00	1.00	1.00	1.00	1.00	1.00	.999	.997
	11	1.00	1.00	1.00	1.00	1.00	1.00	1.00	1.00	1.00	1.000
	12	1.00	1.00	1.00	1.00	1.00	1.00	1.00	1.00	1.00	1.000
13	0	.513	.254	.121	.055	.024	.01	.004	.001	.00	.000
	1	.865	.621	.398	.234	.127	.064	.03	.013	.005	.002
	2	.975	.866	.692	.502	.333	.202	.113	.058	.027	.011
	3	.997	.966	.882	.747	.584	.421	.278	.169	.093	.046
	4	1.00	.994	.966	.901	.794	.654	.501	.353	.228	.133
	5	1.00	.999	.992	.97	.92	.835	.716	.574	.427	.291
	6	1.00	1.00	.999	.993	.976	.938	.871	.771	.644	.50
	7	1.00	1.00	1.00	.999	.994	.982	.954	.902	.821	.709
	8	1.00	1.00	1.00	1.00	.999	.996	.987	.968	.93	.867
	9	1.00	1.00	1.00	1.00	1.00	.999	.997	.992	.98	.954
	10	1.00	1.00	1.00	1.00	1.00	1.00	1.00	.999	.996	.989
	11	1.00	1.00	1.00	1.00	1.00	1.00	1.00	1.00	.999	.998
	12	1.00	1.00	1.00	1.00	1.00	1.00	1.00	1.00	1.00	1.000
14	0	.488	.229	.103	.044	.018	.007	.002	.001	.00	.000
	1	.847	.585	.357	.198	.101	.047	.021	.008	.003	.001
	2	.97	.842	.648	.448	.281	.161	.084	.04	.017	.006
	3	.996	.956	.853	.698	.521	.355	.22	.124	.063	.029
	4	1.00	.991	.953	.87	.742	.584	.423	.279	.167	.090
	5	1.00	.999	.988	.956	.888	.781	.641	.486	.337	.212

Table 3   Cumulative Binomial Probabilities Continued

n	x	.05	.10	.15	.20	.25	.30	.35	.40	.45	.500
							P				
	6	1.00	1.00	.998	.988	.962	.907	.816	.692	.546	.395
	7	1.00	1.00	1.00	.998	.99	.969	.925	.85	.741	.605
	8	1.00	1.00	1.00	1.00	.998	.992	.976	.942	.881	.788
	9	1.00	1.00	1.00	1.00	1.00	.998	.994	.982	.957	.910
	10	1.00	1.00	1.00	1.00	1.00	1.00	.999	.996	.989	.971
	11	1.00	1.00	1.00	1.00	1.00	1.00	1.00	.999	.998	.994
	12	1.00	1.00	1.00	1.00	1.00	1.00	1.00	1.00	1.00	.999
	13	1.00	1.00	1.00	1.00	1.00	1.00	1.00	1.00	1.00	1.000
15	0	.463	.206	.087	.035	.013	.005	.002	.00	.00	.000
	1	.829	.549	.319	.167	.08	.035	.014	.005	.002	.000
	2	.964	.816	.604	.398	.236	.127	.062	.027	.011	.004
	3	.995	.944	.823	.648	.461	.297	.173	.091	.042	.018
	4	.999	.987	.938	.836	.686	.515	.352	.217	.12	.059
	5	1.00	.998	.983	.939	.852	.722	.564	.403	.261	.151
	6	1.00	1.00	.996	.982	.943	.869	.755	.61	.452	.304
	7	1.00	1.00	.999	.996	.983	.95	.887	.787	.654	.500
	8	1.00	1.00	1.00	.999	.996	.985	.958	.905	.818	.696
	9	1.00	1.00	1.00	1.00	.999	.996	.988	.966	.923	.849
	10	1.00	1.00	1.00	1.00	1.00	.999	.997	.991	.975	.941
	11	1.00	1.00	1.00	1.00	1.00	1.00	1.00	.998	.994	.982
	12	1.00	1.00	1.00	1.00	1.00	1.00	1.00	1.00	.999	.996
	13	1.00	1.00	1.00	1.00	1.00	1.00	1.00	1.00	1.00	1.000
16	0	.44	.185	.074	.028	.01	.003	.001	.00	.00	.000
	1	.811	.515	.284	.141	.063	.026	.01	.003	.001	.000
	2	.957	.789	.561	.352	.197	.099	.045	.018	.007	.002
	3	.993	.932	.79	.598	.405	.246	.134	.065	.028	.011
	4	.999	.983	.921	.798	.63	.45	.289	.167	.085	.038
	5	1.00	.997	.976	.918	.81	.66	.49	.329	.198	.105
	6	1.00	.999	.994	.973	.92	.825	.688	.527	.366	.227
	7	1.00	1.00	.999	.993	.973	.926	.841	.716	.563	.402
	8	1.00	1.00	1.00	.999	.993	.974	.933	.858	.744	.598
	9	1.00	1.00	1.00	1.00	.998	.993	.977	.942	.876	.773
	10	1.00	1.00	1.00	1.00	1.00	.998	.994	.981	.951	.895
	11	1.00	1.00	1.00	1.00	1.00	1.00	.999	.995	.985	.962
	12	1.00	1.00	1.00	1.00	1.00	1.00	1.00	.999	.997	.989
	13	1.00	1.00	1.00	1.00	1.00	1.00	1.00	1.00	.999	.998
	14	1.00	1.00	1.00	1.00	1.00	1.00	1.00	1.00	1.00	1.000
17	0	.418	.167	.063	.023	.008	.002	.001	.00	.00	.000
	1	.792	.482	.252	.118	.05	.019	.007	.002	.001	.000
	2	.95	.762	.52	.31	.164	.077	.033	.012	.004	.001
	3	.991	.917	.756	.549	.353	.202	.103	.046	.018	.006
	4	.999	.978	.901	.758	.574	.389	.235	.126	.06	.025
	5	1.00	.995	.968	.894	.765	.597	.42	.264	.147	.072
	6	1.00	.999	.992	.962	.893	.775	.619	.448	.29	.166
	7	1.00	1.00	.998	.989	.96	.895	.787	.641	.474	.315
	8	1.00	1.00	1.00	.997	.988	.96	.901	.801	.663	.500
	9	1.00	1.00	1.00	1.00	.997	.987	.962	.908	.817	.685
	10	1.00	1.00	1.00	1.00	.999	.997	.988	.965	.917	.834
	11	1.00	1.00	1.00	1.00	1.00	.999	.997	.989	.97	.928
	12	1.00	1.00	1.00	1.00	1.00	1.00	.999	.997	.991	.975
	13	1.00	1.00	1.00	1.00	1.00	1.00	1.00	1.00	.998	.994
	14	1.00	1.00	1.00	1.00	1.00	1.00	1.00	1.00	1.00	.999
	15	1.00	1.00	1.00	1.00	1.00	1.00	1.00	1.00	1.00	1.00
18	0	.397	.15	.054	.018	.006	.002	.00	.00	.00	.000
	1	.774	.45	.224	.099	.039	.014	.005	.001	.00	.000

Table 3   Cumulative Binomial Probabilities Continued

n	x	.05	.10	.15	.20	.25	.30	.35	.40	.45	.500
							P				
	2	.942	.734	.48	.271	.135	.06	.024	.008	.003	.001
	3	.989	.902	.72	.501	.306	.165	.078	.033	.012	.004
	4	.998	.972	.879	.716	.519	.333	.189	.094	.041	.015
	5	1.00	.994	.958	.867	.717	.534	.355	.209	.108	.048
	6	1.00	.999	.988	.949	.861	.722	.549	.374	.226	.119
	7	1.00	1.00	.997	.984	.943	.859	.728	.563	.391	.240
	8	1.00	1.00	.999	.996	.981	.94	.861	.737	.578	.407
	9	1.00	1.00	1.00	.999	.995	.979	.94	.865	.747	.593
	10	1.00	1.00	1.00	1.00	.999	.994	.979	.942	.872	.760
	11	1.00	1.00	1.00	1.00	1.00	.999	.994	.98	.946	.881
	12	1.00	1.00	1.00	1.00	1.00	1.00	.999	.994	.982	.952
	13	1.00	1.00	1.00	1.00	1.00	1.00	1.00	.999	.995	.985
	14	1.00	1.00	1.00	1.00	1.00	1.00	1.00	1.00	.999	.996
	15	1.00	1.00	1.00	1.00	1.00	1.00	1.00	1.00	1.00	.999
	16	1.00	1.00	1.00	1.00	1.00	1.00	1.00	1.00	1.00	1.000
19	0	.377	.135	.046	.014	.004	.001	.00	.00	.00	.000
	1	.755	.42	.198	.083	.031	.01	.003	.001	.00	.000
	2	.933	.705	.441	.237	.111	.046	.017	.005	.002	.000
	3	.987	.885	.684	.455	.263	.133	.059	.023	.008	.002
	4	.998	.965	.856	.673	.465	.282	.15	.07	.028	.010
	5	1.00	.991	.946	.837	.668	.474	.297	.163	.078	.032
	6	1.00	.998	.984	.932	.825	.666	.481	.308	.173	.084
	7	1.00	1.00	.996	.977	.923	.818	.666	.488	.317	.180
	8	1.00	1.00	.999	.993	.971	.916	.815	.667	.494	.324
	9	1.00	1.00	1.00	.998	.991	.967	.913	.814	.671	.500
	10	1.00	1.00	1.00	1.00	.998	.989	.965	.912	.816	.676
	11	1.00	1.00	1.00	1.00	1.00	.997	.989	.965	.913	.820
	12	1.00	1.00	1.00	1.00	1.00	.999	.997	.988	.966	.916
	13	1.00	1.00	1.00	1.00	1.00	1.00	.999	.997	.989	.968
	14	1.00	1.00	1.00	1.00	1.00	1.00	1.00	.999	.997	.990
	15	1.00	1.00	1.00	1.00	1.00	1.00	1.00	1.00	.999	.998
	16	1.00	1.00	1.00	1.00	1.00	1.00	1.00	1.00	1.00	1.000
20	0	.358	.122	.039	.012	.003	.001	.00	.00	.00	.000
	1	.736	.392	.176	.069	.024	.008	.002	.001	.00	.000
	2	.925	.677	.405	.206	.091	.035	.012	.004	.001	.000
	3	.984	.867	.648	.411	.225	.107	.044	.016	.005	.001
	4	.997	.957	.83	.63	.415	.238	.118	.051	.019	.006
	5	1.00	.989	.933	.804	.617	.416	.245	.126	.055	.021
	6	1.00	.998	.978	.913	.786	.608	.417	.25	.13	.058
	7	1.00	1.00	.994	.968	.898	.772	.601	.416	.252	.132
	8	1.00	1.00	.999	.99	.959	.887	.762	.596	.414	.252
	9	1.00	1.00	1.00	.997	.986	.952	.878	.755	.591	.412
	10	1.00	1.00	1.00	.999	.996	.983	.947	.872	.751	.588
	11	1.00	1.00	1.00	1.00	.999	.995	.98	.943	.869	.748
	12	1.00	1.00	1.00	1.00	1.00	.999	.994	.979	.942	.868
	13	1.00	1.00	1.00	1.00	1.00	1.00	.998	.994	.979	.942
	14	1.00	1.00	1.00	1.00	1.00	1.00	1.00	.998	.994	.979
	15	1.00	1.00	1.00	1.00	1.00	1.00	1.00	1.00	.998	.994
	16	1.00	1.00	1.00	1.00	1.00	1.00	1.00	1.00	1.00	.999
	17	1.00	1.00	1.00	1.00	1.00	1.00	1.00	1.00	1.00	1.000

Table 4   Values of $e^{-\lambda}$

λ	$e^{-\lambda}$	λ	$e^{-\lambda}$	λ	$e^{-\lambda}$	λ	$e^{-\lambda}$
0.00	1.000000	2.60	.074274	5.10	.006097	7.60	.000501
0.10	.904837	2.70	.067206	5.20	.005517	7.70	.000453
0.20	.818731	2.80	.060810	5.30	.004992	7.80	.000410
0.30	.740818	2.90	.055023	5.40	.004517	7.90	.000371
0.40	.670320	3.00	.049787	5.50	.004087	8.00	.000336
0.50	.606531	3.10	.045049	5.60	.003698	8.10	.000304
0.60	.548812	3.20	.040762	5.70	.003346	8.20	.000275
0.70	.496585	3.30	.036883	5.80	.003028	8.30	.000249
0.80	.449329	3.40	.033373	5.90	.002739	8.40	.000225
0.90	.406570	3.50	.030197	6.00	.002479	8.50	.000204
1.00	.367879	3.60	.027324	6.10	.002243	8.60	.000184
1.10	.332871	3.70	.024724	6.20	.002029	8.70	.000167
1.20	.301194	3.80	.022371	6.30	.001836	8.80	.000151
1.30	.272532	3.90	.020242	6.40	.001661	8.90	.000136
1.40	.246597	4.00	.018316	6.50	.001503	9.00	.000123
1.50	.223130	4.10	.016573	6.60	.001360	9.10	.000112
1.60	.201897	4.20	.014996	6.70	.001231	9.20	.000101
1.70	.182684	4.30	.013569	6.80	.001114	9.30	.000091
1.80	.165299	4.40	.012277	6.90	.001008	9.40	.000083
1.90	.149569	4.50	.011109	7.00	.000912	9.50	.000075
2.00	.135335	4.60	.010052	7.10	.000825	9.60	.000068
2.10	.122456	4.70	.009095	7.20	.000747	9.70	.000061
2.20	.110803	4.80	.008230	7.30	.000676	9.80	.000056
2.30	.100259	4.90	.007447	7.40	.000611	9.90	.000050
2.40	.090718	5.00	.006738	7.50	.000553	10.00	.000045
2.50	.082085						

Table 5 Individual Poisson Probabilities

	MEAN ARRIVAL RATE λ									
	0.1	0.2	0.3	0.4	0.5	0.6	0.7	0.8	0.9	1.0
0	.9048	.8187	.7408	.6703	.6065	.5488	.4966	.4493	.4066	.3679
1	.0905	.1637	.2222	.2681	.3033	.3293	.3476	.3595	.3659	.3679
2	.0045	.0164	.0333	.0536	.0758	.0988	.1217	.1438	.1647	.1839
3	.0002	.0011	.0033	.0072	.0126	.0198	.0284	.0383	.0494	.0613
4	.0	.0001	.0003	.0007	.0016	.0030	.0050	.0077	.0111	.0153
5	.0	.0	.0	.0001	.0002	.0004	.0007	.0012	.0020	.0031
6	.0	.0	.0	.0	.0	.0	.0001	.0002	.0003	.0005
7	.0	.0	.0	.0	.0	.0	.0	.0	.0	.0001

	MEAN ARRIVAL RATE λ									
	1.1	1.2	1.3	1.4	1.5	1.6	1.7	1.8	1.9	2.0
0	.3329	.3012	.2725	.2466	.2231	.2019	.1827	.1653	.1496	.1353
1	.3662	.3614	.3543	.3452	.3347	.3230	.3106	.2975	.2842	.2707
2	.2014	.2169	.2303	.2417	.2510	.2584	.2640	.2678	.2700	.2707
3	.0738	.0867	.0998	.1128	.1255	.1378	.1496	.1607	.1710	.1804
4	.0203	.0260	.0324	.0395	.0471	.0551	.0636	.0723	.0812	.0902
5	.0045	.0062	.0084	.0111	.0141	.0176	.0216	.0260	.0309	.0361
6	.0008	.0012	.0018	.0026	.0035	.0047	.0061	.0078	.0098	.0120
7	.0001	.0002	.0003	.0005	.0008	.0011	.0015	.0020	.0027	.0034
8	.0	.0	.0001	.0001	.0001	.0002	.0003	.0005	.0006	.0009
9	.0	.0	.0	.0	.0	.0	.0001	.0001	.0001	.0002

	MEAN ARRIVAL RATE λ									
	2.1	2.2	2.3	2.4	2.5	2.6	2.7	2.8	2.9	3.0
0	.1225	.1108	.1003	.0907	.0821	.0743	.0672	.0608	.0550	.0498
1	.2572	.2438	.2306	.2177	.2052	.1931	.1815	.1703	.1596	.1494
2	.2700	.2681	.2652	.2613	.2565	.2510	.2450	.2384	.2314	.2240
3	.1890	.1966	.2033	.2090	.2138	.2176	.2205	.2225	.2237	.2240
4	.0992	.1082	.1169	.1254	.1336	.1414	.1488	.1557	.1622	.1680
5	.0417	.0476	.0538	.0602	.0668	.0735	.0804	.0872	.0940	.1008
6	.0146	.0174	.0206	.0241	.0278	.0319	.0362	.0407	.0455	.0504
7	.0044	.0055	.0068	.0083	.0099	.0118	.0139	.0163	.0188	.0216
8	.0011	.0015	.0019	.0025	.0031	.0038	.0047	.0057	.0068	.0081
9	.0003	.0004	.0005	.0007	.0009	.0011	.0014	.0018	.0022	.0027
10	.0001	.0001	.0001	.0002	.0002	.0003	.0004	.0005	.0006	.0008
11	.0	.0	.0	.0	.0	.0001	.0001	.0001	.0002	.0002
12	.0	.0	.0	.0	.0	.0	.0	.0	.0	.0001

	MEAN ARRIVAL RATE λ									
	3.1	3.2	3.3	3.4	3.5	3.6	3.7	3.8	3.9	4.0
0	.0450	.0408	.0369	.0334	.0302	.0273	.0247	.0224	.0202	.0183
1	.1397	.1304	.1217	.1135	.1057	.0984	.0915	.0850	.0789	.0733
2	.2165	.2087	.2008	.1929	.1850	.1771	.1692	.1615	.1539	.1465
3	.2237	.2226	.2209	.2186	.2158	.2125	.2087	.2046	.2001	.1954
4	.1733	.1781	.1823	.1858	.1888	.1912	.1931	.1944	.1951	.1954
5	.1075	.1140	.1203	.1264	.1322	.1377	.1429	.1477	.1522	.1563
6	.0555	.0608	.0662	.0716	.0771	.0826	.0881	.0936	.0989	.1042
7	.0246	.0278	.0312	.0348	.0385	.0425	.0466	.0508	.0551	.0595
8	.0095	.0111	.0129	.0148	.0169	.0191	.0215	.0241	.0269	.0298
9	.0033	.0040	.0047	.0056	.0066	.0076	.0089	.0102	.0116	.0132
10	.0010	.0013	.0016	.0019	.0023	.0028	.0033	.0039	.0045	.0053
11	.0003	.0004	.0005	.0006	.0007	.0009	.0011	.0013	.0016	.0019
12	.0001	.0001	.0001	.0002	.0002	.0003	.0003	.0004	.0005	.0006
13	.0	.0	.0	.0	.0001	.0001	.0001	.0001	.0002	.0002
14	.0	.0	.0	.0	.0	.0	.0	.0	.0	.0001

Table 5 Individual Poisson Probabilities Continued

	MEAN ARRIVAL RATE λ									
	4.1	4.2	4.3	4.4	4.5	4.6	4.7	4.8	4.9	5.0
0	.0166	.0150	.0136	.0123	.0111	.0101	.0091	.0082	.0074	.0067
1	.0679	.0630	.0583	.0540	.0500	.0462	.0427	.0395	.0365	.0337
2	.1393	.1323	.1254	.1188	.1125	.1063	.1005	.0948	.0894	.0842
3	.1904	.1852	.1798	.1743	.1687	.1631	.1574	.1517	.1460	.1404
4	.1951	.1944	.1933	.1917	.1898	.1875	.1849	.1820	.1789	.1755
5	.1600	.1633	.1662	.1687	.1708	.1725	.1738	.1747	.1753	.1755
6	.1093	.1143	.1191	.1237	.1281	.1323	.1362	.1398	.1432	.1462
7	.0640	.0686	.0732	.0778	.0824	.0869	.0914	.0959	.1002	.1044
8	.0328	.0360	.0393	.0428	.0463	.0500	.0537	.0575	.0614	.0653
9	.0150	.0168	.0188	.0209	.0232	.0255	.0281	.0307	.0334	.0363
10	.0061	.0071	.0081	.0092	.0104	.0118	.0132	.0147	.0164	.0181
11	.0023	.0027	.0032	.0037	.0043	.0049	.0056	.0064	.0073	.0082
12	.0008	.0009	.0011	.0013	.0016	.0019	.0022	.0026	.0030	.0034
13	.0002	.0003	.0004	.0005	.0006	.0007	.0008	.0009	.0011	.0013
14	.0001	.0001	.0001	.0001	.0002	.0002	.0003	.0003	.0004	.0005

	MEAN ARRIVAL RATE λ									
	5.1	5.2	5.3	5.4	5.5	5.6	5.7	5.8	5.9	6.0
0	.0061	.0055	.0050	.0045	.0041	.0037	.0033	.0030	.0027	.0025
1	.0311	.0287	.0265	.0244	.0225	.0207	.0191	.0176	.0162	.0149
2	.0793	.0746	.0701	.0659	.0618	.0580	.0544	.0509	.0477	.0446
3	.1348	.1293	.1239	.1185	.1133	.1082	.1033	.0985	.0938	.0892
4	.1719	.1681	.1641	.1600	.1558	.1515	.1472	.1428	.1383	.1339
5	.1753	.1748	.1740	.1728	.1714	.1697	.1678	.1656	.1632	.1606
6	.1490	.1515	.1537	.1555	.1571	.1584	.1594	.1601	.1605	.1606
7	.1086	.1125	.1163	.1200	.1234	.1267	.1298	.1326	.1353	.1377
8	.0692	.0731	.0771	.0810	.0849	.0887	.0925	.0962	.0998	.1033
9	.0392	.0423	.0454	.0486	.0519	.0552	.0586	.0620	.0654	.0688
10	.0200	.0220	.0241	.0262	.0285	.0309	.0334	.0359	.0386	.0413
11	.0093	.0104	.0116	.0129	.0143	.0157	.0173	.0190	.0207	.0225
12	.0039	.0045	.0051	.0058	.0065	.0073	.0082	.0092	.0102	.0113
13	.0015	.0018	.0021	.0024	.0028	.0032	.0036	.0041	.0046	.0052
14	.0006	.0007	.0008	.0009	.0011	.0013	.0015	.0017	.0019	.0022

	MEAN ARRIVAL RATE λ									
	6.1	6.2	6.3	6.4	6.5	6.6	6.7	6.8	6.9	7.0
0	.0022	.0020	.0018	.0017	.0015	.0014	.0012	.0011	.0010	.0009
1	.0137	.0126	.0116	.0106	.0098	.0090	.0082	.0076	.0070	.0064
2	.0417	.0390	.0364	.0340	.0318	.0296	.0276	.0258	.0240	.0223
3	.0848	.0806	.0765	.0726	.0688	.0652	.0617	.0584	.0552	.0521
4	.1294	.1249	.1205	.1162	.1118	.1076	.1034	.0992	.0952	.0912
5	.1579	.1549	.1519	.1487	.1454	.1420	.1385	.1349	.1314	.1277
6	.1605	.1601	.1595	.1586	.1575	.1562	.1546	.1529	.1511	.1490
7	.1399	.1418	.1435	.1450	.1462	.1472	.1480	.1486	.1489	.1490
8	.1066	.1099	.1130	.1160	.1188	.1215	.1240	.1263	.1284	.1304
9	.0723	.0757	.0791	.0825	.0858	.0891	.0923	.0954	.0985	.1014
10	.0441	.0469	.0498	.0528	.0558	.0588	.0618	.0649	.0679	.0710
11	.0244	.0265	.0285	.0307	.0330	.0353	.0377	.0401	.0426	.0452
12	.0124	.0137	.0150	.0164	.0179	.0194	.0210	.0227	.0245	.0263
13	.0058	.0065	.0073	.0081	.0089	.0099	.0108	.0119	.0130	.0142
14	.0025	.0029	.0033	.0037	.0041	.0046	.0052	.0058	.0064	.0071

Table 5 Individual Poisson Probabilities Continued

	MEAN ARRIVAL RATE λ									
	7.1	7.2	7.3	7.4	7.5	7.6	7.7	7.8	7.9	8.0
0	.0008	.0007	.0007	.0006	.0006	.0005	.0005	.0004	.0004	.0003
1	.0059	.0054	.0049	.0045	.0041	.0038	.0035	.0032	.0029	.0027
2	.0208	.0194	.0180	.0167	.0156	.0145	.0134	.0125	.0116	.0107
3	.0492	.0464	.0438	.0413	.0389	.0366	.0345	.0324	.0305	.0286
4	.0874	.0836	.0799	.0764	.0729	.0696	.0663	.0632	.0602	.0573
5	.1241	.1204	.1167	.1130	.1094	.1057	.1021	.0986	.0951	.0916
6	.1468	.1445	.1420	.1394	.1367	.1339	.1311	.1282	.1252	.1221
7	.1489	.1486	.1481	.1474	.1465	.1454	.1442	.1428	.1413	.1396
8	.1321	.1337	.1351	.1363	.1373	.1381	.1388	.1392	.1395	.1396
9	.1042	.1070	.1096	.1121	.1144	.1167	.1187	.1207	.1224	.1241
10	.0740	.0770	.08	.0829	.0858	.0887	.0914	.0941	.0967	.0993
11	.0478	.0504	.0531	.0558	.0585	.0613	.0640	.0667	.0695	.0722
12	.0283	.0303	.0323	.0344	.0366	.0388	.0411	.0434	.0457	.0481
13	.0154	.0168	.0181	.0196	.0211	.0227	.0243	.0260	.0278	.0296
14	.0078	.0086	.0095	.0104	.0113	.0123	.0134	.0145	.0157	.0169
15	.0037	.0041	.0046	.0051	.0057	.0062	.0069	.0075	.0083	.0090
16	.0016	.0019	.0021	.0024	.0026	.0030	.0033	.0037	.0041	.0045
17	.0007	.0008	.0009	.0010	.0012	.0013	.0015	.0017	.0019	.0021
18	.0003	.0003	.0004	.0004	.0005	.0006	.0006	.0007	.0008	.0009
19	.0001	.0001	.0001	.0002	.0002	.0002	.0003	.0003	.0003	.0004

	MEAN ARRIVAL RATE λ									
	8.1	8.2	8.3	8.4	8.5	8.6	8.7	8.8	8.9	9.0
0	.0003	.0003	.0002	.0002	.0002	.0002	.0002	.0002	.0001	.0001
1	.0025	.0023	.0021	.0019	.0017	.0016	.0014	.0013	.0012	.0011
2	.01	.0092	.0086	.0079	.0074	.0068	.0063	.0058	.0054	.0050
3	.0269	.0252	.0237	.0222	.0208	.0195	.0183	.0171	.0160	.0150
4	.0544	.0517	.0491	.0466	.0443	.0420	.0398	.0377	.0357	.0337
5	.0882	.0849	.0816	.0784	.0752	.0722	.0692	.0663	.0635	.0607
6	.1191	.1160	.1128	.1097	.1066	.1034	.1003	.0972	.0941	.0911
7	.1378	.1358	.1338	.1317	.1294	.1271	.1247	.1222	.1197	.1171
8	.1395	.1392	.1388	.1382	.1375	.1366	.1356	.1344	.1332	.1318
9	.1256	.1269	.1280	.1290	.1299	.1306	.1311	.1315	.1317	.1318
10	.1017	.1040	.1063	.1084	.1104	.1123	.1140	.1157	.1172	.1186
11	.0749	.0776	.0802	.0828	.0853	.0878	.0902	.0925	.0948	.0970
12	.0505	.0530	.0555	.0579	.0604	.0629	.0654	.0679	.0703	.0728
13	.0315	.0334	.0354	.0374	.0395	.0416	.0438	.0459	.0481	.0504
14	.0182	.0196	.0210	.0225	.0240	.0256	.0272	.0289	.0306	.0324
15	.0098	.0107	.0116	.0126	.0136	.0147	.0158	.0169	.0182	.0194
16	.0050	.0055	.0060	.0066	.0072	.0079	.0086	.0093	.0101	.0109
17	.0024	.0026	.0029	.0033	.0036	.0040	.0044	.0048	.0053	.0058
18	.0011	.0012	.0014	.0015	.0017	.0019	.0021	.0024	.0026	.0029
19	.0005	.0005	.0006	.0007	.0008	.0009	.0010	.0011	.0012	.0014

	MEAN ARRIVAL RATE λ									
	9.1	9.2	9.3	9.4	9.5	9.6	9.7	9.8	9.9	10.0
0	.0001	.0001	.0001	.0001	.0001	.0001	.0001	.0001	.0001	.0000
1	.0010	.0009	.0009	.0008	.0007	.0007	.0006	.0005	.0005	.0005
2	.0046	.0043	.0040	.0037	.0034	.0031	.0029	.0027	.0025	.0023
3	.0140	.0131	.0123	.0115	.0107	.01	.0093	.0087	.0081	.0076
4	.0319	.0302	.0285	.0269	.0254	.0240	.0226	.0213	.0201	.0189
5	.0581	.0555	.0530	.0506	.0483	.0460	.0439	.0418	.0398	.0378
6	.0881	.0851	.0822	.0793	.0764	.0736	.0709	.0682	.0656	.0631
7	.1145	.1118	.1091	.1064	.1037	.1010	.0982	.0955	.0928	.0901
8	.1302	.1286	.1269	.1251	.1232	.1212	.1191	.1170	.1148	.1126

Table 5   Individual Poisson Probabilities Continued

					MEAN ARRIVAL RATE λ					
	9.1	9.2	9.3	9.4	9.5	9.6	9.7	9.8	9.9	10.0
9	.1317	.1315	.1311	.1306	.13	.1293	.1284	.1274	.1263	.1251
10	.1198	.1210	.1219	.1228	.1235	.1241	.1245	.1249	.1250	.1251
11	.0991	.1012	.1031	.1049	.1067	.1083	.1098	.1112	.1125	.1137
12	.0752	.0776	.0799	.0822	.0844	.0866	.0888	.0908	.0928	.0948
13	.0526	.0549	.0572	.0594	.0617	.0640	.0662	.0685	.0707	.0729
14	.0342	.0361	.0380	.0399	.0419	.0439	.0459	.0479	.05	.0521
15	.0208	.0221	.0235	.0250	.0265	.0281	.0297	.0313	.0330	.0347
16	.0118	.0127	.0137	.0147	.0157	.0168	.0180	.0192	.0204	.0217
17	.0063	.0069	.0075	.0081	.0088	.0095	.0103	.0111	.0119	.0128
18	.0032	.0035	.0039	.0042	.0046	.0051	.0055	.0060	.0065	.0071
19	.0015	.0017	.0019	.0021	.0023	.0026	.0028	.0031	.0034	.0037

					MEAN ARRIVAL RATE λ					
	10.1	10.2	10.3	10.4	10.5	10.6	10.7	10.8	10.9	11.0
0	.00	.00	.00	.00	.00	.00	.00	.00	.00	.0000
1	.0004	.0004	.0003	.0003	.0003	.0003	.0002	.0002	.0002	.0002
2	.0021	.0019	.0018	.0016	.0015	.0014	.0013	.0012	.0011	.0010
3	.0071	.0066	.0061	.0057	.0053	.0049	.0046	.0043	.0040	.0037
4	.0178	.0168	.0158	.0148	.0139	.0131	.0123	.0116	.0109	.0102
5	.0360	.0342	.0325	.0309	.0293	.0278	.0264	.0250	.0237	.0224
6	.0606	.0581	.0558	.0535	.0513	.0491	.0470	.0450	.0430	.0411
7	.0874	.0847	.0821	.0795	.0769	.0743	.0718	.0694	.0669	.0646
8	.1103	.1080	.1057	.1033	.1009	.0985	.0961	.0936	.0912	.0888
9	.1238	.1224	.1209	.1194	.1177	.1160	.1142	.1124	.1105	.1085
10	.1250	.1249	.1246	.1241	.1236	.1230	.1222	.1214	.1204	.1194
11	.1148	.1158	.1166	.1174	.1180	.1185	.1189	.1192	.1193	.1194
12	.0966	.0984	.1001	.1017	.1032	.1047	.1060	.1072	.1084	.1094
13	.0751	.0772	.0793	.0814	.0834	.0853	.0872	.0891	.0909	.0926
14	.0542	.0563	.0584	.0604	.0625	.0646	.0667	.0687	.0708	.0728
15	.0365	.0383	.0401	.0419	.0438	.0457	.0476	.0495	.0514	.0534
16	.0230	.0244	.0258	.0272	.0287	.0303	.0318	.0334	.0350	.0367
17	.0137	.0146	.0156	.0167	.0177	.0189	.0200	.0212	.0225	.0237
18	.0077	.0083	.0089	.0096	.0104	.0111	.0119	.0127	.0136	.0145
19	.0041	.0045	.0048	.0053	.0057	.0062	.0067	.0072	.0078	.0084
20	.0021	.0023	.0025	.0027	.0030	.0033	.0036	.0039	.0043	.0046

					MEAN ARRIVAL RATE λ					
	11.1	11.2	11.3	11.4	11.5	11.6	11.7	11.8	11.9	12.0
0	.0000	.0000	.0000	.0000	.0000	.0000	.0000	.0000	.0000	.0000
1	.0002	.0002	.0001	.0001	.0001	.0001	.0001	.0001	.0001	.0001
2	.0009	.0009	.0008	.0007	.0007	.0006	.0006	.0005	.0005	.0004
3	.0034	.0032	.0030	.0028	.0026	.0024	.0022	.0021	.0019	.0018
4	.0096	.0090	.0084	.0079	.0074	.0069	.0065	.0061	.0057	.0053
5	.0212	.0201	.0190	.0180	.0170	.0160	.0152	.0143	.0135	.0127
6	.0393	.0375	.0358	.0341	.0325	.0310	.0295	.0281	.0268	.0255
7	.0623	.0600	.0578	.0556	.0535	.0514	.0494	.0474	.0455	.0437
8	.0864	.0840	.0816	.0792	.0769	.0745	.0722	.0700	.0677	.0655
9	.1065	.1045	.1024	.1003	.0982	.0961	.0939	.0917	.0895	.0874
10	.1182	.1170	.1157	.1144	.1129	.1114	.1099	.1082	.1066	.1048
11	.1193	.1192	.1189	.1185	.1181	.1175	.1169	.1161	.1153	.1144
12	.1104	.1112	.1120	.1126	.1131	.1136	.1139	.1142	.1143	.1144
13	.0942	.0958	.0973	.0987	.1001	.1014	.1025	.1036	.1046	.1056
14	.0747	.0767	.0786	.0804	.0822	.0840	.0857	.0874	.0889	.0905

Table 5 Individual Poisson Probabilities Continued

	MEAN ARRIVAL RATE λ									
	11.1	11.2	11.3	11.4	11.5	11.6	11.7	11.8	11.9	12.0
15	.0553	.0572	.0592	.0611	.0630	.0649	.0668	.0687	.0706	.0724
16	.0384	.0401	.0418	.0435	.0453	.0471	.0489	.0507	.0525	.0543
17	.0250	.0264	.0278	.0292	.0306	.0321	.0336	.0352	.0367	.0383
18	.0154	.0164	.0174	.0185	.0196	.0207	.0219	.0231	.0243	.0255
19	.0090	.0097	.0104	.0111	.0119	.0126	.0135	.0143	.0152	.0161
20	.0050	.0054	.0059	.0063	.0068	.0073	.0079	.0084	.0091	.0097

	MEAN ARRIVAL RATE λ									
	12.1	12.2	12.3	12.4	12.5	12.6	12.7	12.8	12.9	13.0
4	.0050	.0046	.0043	.0041	.0038	.0035	.0033	.0031	.0029	.0027
5	.0120	.0113	.0107	.0101	.0095	.0089	.0084	.0079	.0074	.0070
6	.0242	.0230	.0219	.0208	.0197	.0187	.0178	.0169	.0160	.0152
7	.0419	.0402	.0385	.0368	.0353	.0337	.0323	.0308	.0295	.0281
8	.0634	.0612	.0591	.0571	.0551	.0531	.0512	.0493	.0475	.0457
9	.0852	.0830	.0808	.0787	.0765	.0744	.0723	.0702	.0681	.0661
10	.1031	.1013	.0994	.0975	.0956	.0937	.0918	.0898	.0878	.0859
11	.1134	.1123	.1112	.1100	.1087	.1074	.1060	.1045	.1030	.1015
12	.1143	.1142	.1139	.1136	.1132	.1127	.1121	.1115	.1107	.1099
13	.1064	.1072	.1078	.1084	.1089	.1093	.1096	.1098	.1099	.1099
14	.0920	.0934	.0947	.0960	.0972	.0983	.0994	.1004	.1013	.1021
15	.0742	.0759	.0777	.0794	.0810	.0826	.0841	.0856	.0871	.0885
16	.0561	.0579	.0597	.0615	.0633	.0650	.0668	.0685	.0702	.0719
17	.0399	.0416	.0432	.0449	.0465	.0482	.0499	.0516	.0533	.0550
18	.0268	.0282	.0295	.0309	.0323	.0337	.0352	.0367	.0382	.0397
19	.0171	.0181	.0191	.0202	.0213	.0224	.0235	.0247	.0259	.0272
20	.0103	.0110	.0118	.0125	.0133	.0141	.0149	.0158	.0167	.0177

	MEAN ARRIVAL RATE λ									
	13.1	13.2	13.3	13.4	13.5	13.6	13.7	13.8	13.9	14.0
5	.0066	.0062	.0058	.0055	.0051	.0048	.0045	.0042	.0040	.0037
6	.0144	.0136	.0129	.0122	.0115	.0109	.0103	.0097	.0092	.0087
7	.0269	.0256	.0245	.0233	.0222	.0212	.0202	.0192	.0183	.0174
8	.0440	.0423	.0407	.0391	.0375	.0360	.0345	.0331	.0318	.0304
9	.0640	.0620	.0601	.0582	.0563	.0544	.0526	.0508	.0491	.0473
10	.0839	.0819	.0799	.0779	.0760	.0740	.0720	.0701	.0682	.0663
11	.0999	.0983	.0966	.0949	.0932	.0915	.0897	.0880	.0862	.0844
12	.1091	.1081	.1071	.1060	.1049	.1037	.1024	.1011	.0998	.0984
13	.1099	.1098	.1096	.1093	.1089	.1085	.1080	.1074	.1067	.1060
14	.1028	.1035	.1041	.1046	.1050	.1054	.1056	.1058	.1060	.1060
15	.0898	.0911	.0923	.0934	.0945	.0955	.0965	.0974	.0982	.0989
16	.0735	.0751	.0767	.0783	.0798	.0812	.0826	.0840	.0853	.0866
17	.0567	.0583	.0600	.0617	.0633	.0650	.0666	.0682	.0697	.0713
18	.0412	.0428	.0443	.0459	.0475	.0491	.0507	.0523	.0539	.0554
19	.0284	.0297	.0310	.0324	.0337	.0351	.0365	.0380	.0394	.0409
20	.0186	.0196	.0206	.0217	.0228	.0239	.0250	.0262	.0274	.0286

	MEAN ARRIVAL RATE λ									
	14.1	14.2	14.3	14.4	14.5	14.6	14.7	14.8	14.9	15.0
6	.0082	.0078	.0073	.0069	.0065	.0061	.0058	.0055	.0051	.0048
7	.0165	.0157	.0149	.0142	.0135	.0128	.0122	.0115	.0109	.0104
8	.0292	.0279	.0267	.0256	.0244	.0234	.0223	.0213	.0204	.0194
9	.0457	.0440	.0424	.0409	.0394	.0379	.0365	.0351	.0337	.0324
10	.0644	.0625	.0607	.0589	.0571	.0553	.0536	.0519	.0502	.0486
11	.0825	.0807	.0789	.0771	.0753	.0735	.0716	.0698	.0681	.0663

Table 5 Individual Poisson Probabilities Continued

				MEAN ARRIVAL RATE λ					
	14.1	14.2	14.3	14.4	14.5	14.6	14.7	14.8	14.9	15.0
12	.0970	.0955	.0940	.0925	.0910	.0894	.0878	.0861	.0845	.0829
13	.1052	.1043	.1034	.1025	.1014	.1004	.0992	.0981	.0969	.0956
14	.1060	.1058	.1057	.1054	.1051	.1047	.1042	.1037	.1031	.1024
15	.0996	.1002	.1007	.1012	.1016	.1019	.1021	.1023	.1024	.1024
16	.0878	.0889	.0900	.0911	.0920	.0930	.0938	.0946	.0954	.0960
17	.0728	.0743	.0757	.0771	.0785	.0798	.0811	.0824	.0836	.0847
18	.0570	.0586	.0602	.0617	.0632	.0648	.0663	.0677	.0692	.0706
19	.0423	.0438	.0453	.0468	.0483	.0498	.0513	.0528	.0543	.0557
20	.0298	.0311	.0324	.0337	.0350	.0363	.0377	.0390	.0404	.0418
21	.0200	.0210	.0220	.0231	.0242	.0253	.0264	.0275	.0287	.0299
22	.0128	.0136	.0143	.0151	.0159	.0168	.0176	.0185	.0194	.0204
23	.0079	.0084	.0089	.0095	.0100	.0106	.0113	.0119	.0126	.0133
24	.0046	.0050	.0053	.0057	.0061	.0065	.0069	.0073	.0078	.0083

				MEAN ARRIVAL RATE λ					
	15.1	15.2	15.3	15.4	15.5	15.6	15.7	15.8	15.9	16.0
7	.0098	.0093	.0088	.0084	.0079	.0075	.0071	.0067	.0063	.0060
8	.0186	.0177	.0169	.0161	.0153	.0146	.0139	.0132	.0126	.0120
9	.0311	.0299	.0287	.0275	.0264	.0253	.0243	.0232	.0223	.0213
10	.0470	.0454	.0439	.0424	.0409	.0395	.0381	.0367	.0354	.0341
11	.0645	.0628	.0611	.0594	.0577	.0560	.0544	.0527	.0512	.0496
12	.0812	.0795	.0778	.0762	.0745	.0728	.0711	.0695	.0678	.0661
13	.0943	.0930	.0916	.0902	.0888	.0874	.0859	.0844	.0829	.0814
14	.1017	.1010	.1001	.0993	.0983	.0974	.0963	.0953	.0942	.0930
15	.1024	.1023	.1021	.1019	.1016	.1012	.1008	.1003	.0998	.0992
16	.0966	.0972	.0977	.0981	.0984	.0987	.0989	.0991	.0992	.0992
17	.0858	.0869	.0879	.0888	.0897	.0906	.0914	.0921	.0928	.0934
18	.0720	.0734	.0747	.0760	.0773	.0785	.0797	.0808	.0819	.0830
19	.0572	.0587	.0602	.0616	.0630	.0645	.0659	.0672	.0686	.0699
20	.0432	.0446	.0460	.0474	.0489	.0503	.0517	.0531	.0545	.0559
21	.0311	.0323	.0335	.0348	.0361	.0373	.0386	.0400	.0413	.0426
22	.0213	.0223	.0233	.0244	.0254	.0265	.0276	.0287	.0298	.0310
23	.0140	.0147	.0155	.0163	.0171	.0180	.0188	.0197	.0206	.0216
24	.0088	.0093	.0099	.0105	.0111	.0117	.0123	.0130	.0137	.0144
25	.0053	.0057	.0061	.0064	.0069	.0073	.0077	.0082	.0087	.0092

				MEAN ARRIVAL RATE λ					
	16.1	16.2	16.3	16.4	16.5	16.6	16.7	16.8	16.9	17.0
7	.0057	.0054	.0051	.0048	.0045	.0043	.0040	.0038	.0036	.0034
8	.0114	.0108	.0103	.0098	.0093	.0088	.0084	.0080	.0076	.0072
9	.0204	.0195	.0187	.0178	.0171	.0163	.0156	.0149	.0142	.0135
10	.0328	.0316	.0304	.0293	.0281	.0270	.0260	.0250	.0240	.0230
11	.0481	.0466	.0451	.0436	.0422	.0408	.0394	.0381	.0368	.0355
12	.0645	.0628	.0612	.0596	.0580	.0565	.0549	.0534	.0518	.0504
13	.0799	.0783	.0768	.0752	.0736	.0721	.0705	.0690	.0674	.0658
14	.0918	.0906	.0894	.0881	.0868	.0855	.0841	.0828	.0814	.0800
15	.0986	.0979	.0971	.0963	.0955	.0946	.0937	.0927	.0917	.0906
16	.0992	.0991	.0989	.0987	.0985	.0981	.0978	.0973	.0968	.0963
17	.0939	.0944	.0949	.0952	.0956	.0958	.0960	.0962	.0963	.0963
18	.0840	.0850	.0859	.0868	.0876	.0884	.0891	.0898	.0904	.0909
19	.0712	.0725	.0737	.0749	.0761	.0772	.0783	.0794	.0804	.0814
20	.0573	.0587	.0601	.0614	.0628	.0641	.0654	.0667	.0679	.0692
21	.0439	.0453	.0466	.0480	.0493	.0507	.0520	.0533	.0547	.0560

Table 5 Individual Poisson Probabilities Continued

	16.1	16.2	16.3	16.4	16.5	16.6	16.7	16.8	16.9	17.0
22	.0322	.0333	.0345	.0358	.0370	.0382	.0395	.0407	.0420	.0433
23	.0225	.0235	.0245	.0255	.0265	.0276	.0287	.0297	.0309	.0320
24	.0151	.0159	.0166	.0174	.0182	.0191	.0199	.0208	.0217	.0226
25	.0097	.0103	.0108	.0114	.0120	.0127	.0133	.0140	.0147	.0154

MEAN ARRIVAL RATE λ

	17.1	17.2	17.3	17.4	17.5	17.6	17.7	17.8	17.9	18.0
8	.0068	.0064	.0061	.0058	.0055	.0052	.0049	.0046	.0044	.0042
9	.0129	.0123	.0117	.0112	.0107	.0101	.0097	.0092	.0088	.0083
10	.0221	.0212	.0203	.0195	.0186	.0179	.0171	.0164	.0157	.0150
11	.0343	.0331	.0319	.0308	.0297	.0286	.0275	.0265	.0255	.0245
12	.0489	.0474	.0460	.0446	.0432	.0419	.0406	.0393	.0380	.0368
13	.0643	.0628	.0612	.0597	.0582	.0567	.0553	.0538	.0524	.0509
14	.0785	.0771	.0757	.0742	.0728	.0713	.0699	.0684	.0669	.0655
15	.0895	.0884	.0873	.0861	.0849	.0837	.0824	.0812	.0799	.0786
16	.0957	.0951	.0944	.0936	.0929	.0920	.0912	.0903	.0894	.0884
17	.0963	.0962	.0960	.0958	.0956	.0953	.0949	.0945	.0941	.0936
18	.0914	.0919	.0923	.0926	.0929	.0932	.0934	.0935	.0936	.0936
19	.0823	.0832	.0840	.0848	.0856	.0863	.0870	.0876	.0882	.0887
20	.0704	.0715	.0727	.0738	.0749	.0760	.0770	.0780	.0789	.0798
21	.0573	.0586	.0599	.0612	.0624	.0637	.0649	.0661	.0673	.0684
22	.0445	.0458	.0471	.0484	.0496	.0509	.0522	.0535	.0547	.0560
23	.0331	.0343	.0354	.0366	.0378	.0390	.0402	.0414	.0426	.0438
24	.0236	.0246	.0255	.0265	.0275	.0286	.0296	.0307	.0318	.0328
25	.0161	.0169	.0177	.0185	.0193	.0201	.0210	.0218	.0227	.0237

MEAN ARRIVAL RATE λ

	18.1	18.2	18.3	18.4	18.5	18.6	18.7	18.8	18.9	19.0
9	.0079	.0075	.0072	.0068	.0065	.0061	.0058	.0055	.0053	.0050
10	.0143	.0137	.0131	.0125	.0120	.0114	.0109	.0104	.0099	.0095
11	.0236	.0227	.0218	.0209	.0201	.0193	.0185	.0178	.0171	.0164
12	.0356	.0344	.0332	.0321	.0310	.0299	.0289	.0278	.0269	.0259
13	.0495	.0481	.0468	.0454	.0441	.0428	.0415	.0403	.0390	.0378
14	.0640	.0626	.0611	.0597	.0583	.0569	.0555	.0541	.0527	.0514
15	.0773	.0759	.0746	.0732	.0719	.0705	.0692	.0678	.0664	.0650
16	.0874	.0864	.0853	.0842	.0831	.0820	.0808	.0796	.0785	.0772
17	.0931	.0925	.0918	.0912	.0904	.0897	.0889	.0881	.0872	.0863
18	.0936	.0935	.0934	.0932	.0930	.0927	.0924	.0920	.0916	.0911
19	.0891	.0896	.0899	.0902	.0905	.0907	.0909	.0910	.0911	.0911
20	.0807	.0815	.0823	.0830	.0837	.0844	.0850	.0856	.0861	.0866
21	.0695	.0706	.0717	.0727	.0738	.0747	.0757	.0766	.0775	.0783
22	.0572	.0584	.0596	.0608	.0620	.0632	.0643	.0655	.0666	.0676
23	.0450	.0462	.0475	.0487	.0499	.0511	.0523	.0535	.0547	.0559
24	.0340	.0351	.0362	.0373	.0385	.0396	.0408	.0419	.0431	.0442
25	.0246	.0255	.0265	.0275	.0285	.0295	.0305	.0315	.0326	.0336

MEAN ARRIVAL RATE λ

	19.1	19.2	19.3	19.4	19.5	19.6	19.7	19.8	19.9	20.0
10	.0090	.0086	.0082	.0078	.0074	.0071	.0067	.0064	.0061	.0058
11	.0157	.0150	.0144	.0138	.0132	.0126	.0121	.0116	.0111	.0106
12	.0249	.0240	.0231	.0223	.0214	.0206	.0198	.0191	.0183	.0176
13	.0367	.0355	.0344	.0333	.0322	.0311	.0301	.0291	.0281	.0271
14	.0500	.0487	.0474	.0461	.0448	.0436	.0423	.0411	.0399	.0387
15	.0637	.0623	.0610	.0596	.0582	.0569	.0556	.0543	.0529	.0516
16	.0760	.0748	.0735	.0723	.0710	.0697	.0684	.0671	.0659	.0646

Table 5   Individual Poisson Probabilities Continued

	MEAN ARRIVAL RATE λ									
	19.1	19.2	19.3	19.4	19.5	19.6	19.7	19.8	19.9	20.0
17	.0854	.0844	.0835	.0825	.0814	.0804	.0793	.0782	.0771	.0760
18	.0906	.0901	.0895	.0889	.0882	.0875	.0868	.0860	.0852	.0844
19	.0911	.0910	.0909	.0907	.0905	.0903	.0900	.0896	.0893	.0888
20	.0870	.0874	.0877	.0880	.0883	.0885	.0886	.0887	.0888	.0888
21	.0791	.0799	.0806	.0813	.0820	.0826	.0831	.0837	.0842	.0846
22	.0687	.0697	.0707	.0717	.0727	.0736	.0745	.0753	.0761	.0769
23	.0570	.0582	.0594	.0605	.0616	.0627	.0638	.0648	.0659	.0669
24	.0454	.0466	.0477	.0489	.0500	.0512	.0523	.0535	.0546	.0557
25	.0347	.0358	.0368	.0379	.0390	.0401	.0412	.0424	.0435	.0446

	MEAN ARRIVAL RATE λ									
	20.1	20.2	20.3	20.4	20.5	20.6	20.7	20.8	20.9	21.0
10	.0055	.0053	.0050	.0048	.0045	.0043	.0041	.0039	.0037	.0035
11	.0101	.0097	.0092	.0088	.0084	.0080	.0077	.0073	.0070	.0067
12	.0169	.0163	.0156	.0150	.0144	.0138	.0132	.0127	.0122	.0116
13	.0262	.0253	.0244	.0235	.0227	.0219	.0211	.0203	.0195	.0188
14	.0376	.0365	.0353	.0343	.0332	.0322	.0311	.0301	.0292	.0282
15	.0504	.0491	.0478	.0466	.0454	.0442	.0430	.0418	.0406	.0395
16	.0633	.0620	.0607	.0594	.0581	.0569	.0556	.0543	.0531	.0518
17	.0748	.0736	.0725	.0713	.0701	.0689	.0677	.0665	.0653	.0640
18	.0835	.0826	.0817	.0808	.0798	.0789	.0778	.0768	.0758	.0747
19	.0884	.0879	.0873	.0868	.0861	.0855	.0848	.0841	.0834	.0826
20	.0888	.0887	.0886	.0885	.0883	.0881	.0878	.0875	.0871	.0867
21	.0850	.0854	.0857	.0860	.0862	.0864	.0865	.0866	.0867	.0867
22	.0777	.0784	.0791	.0797	.0803	.0809	.0814	.0819	.0824	.0828
23	.0679	.0688	.0698	.0707	.0716	.0724	.0733	.0741	.0748	.0756
24	.0568	.0579	.0590	.0601	.0611	.0622	.0632	.0642	.0652	.0661
25	.0457	.0468	.0479	.0490	.0501	.0512	.0523	.0534	.0545	.0555

Table 6 Cumulative Poisson Probabilities

	MEAN ARRIVAL RATE λ									
	0.1	0.2	0.3	0.4	0.5	0.6	0.7	0.8	0.9	1.0
0	.9048	.8187	.7408	.6703	.6065	.5488	.4966	.4493	.4066	.3679
1	.9953	.9825	.9631	.9384	.9098	.8781	.8442	.8088	.7725	.7358
2	.9998	.9989	.9964	.9921	.9856	.9769	.9659	.9526	.9371	.9197
3	1.0000	.9999	.9997	.9992	.9982	.9966	.9942	.9909	.9865	.9810
4	1.0000	1.0000	1.0000	.9999	.9998	.9996	.9992	.9986	.9977	.9963
5	1.0000	1.0000	1.0000	1.0000	1.0000	1.0000	.9999	.9998	.9997	.9994
6	1.0000	1.0000	1.0000	1.0000	1.0000	1.0000	1.0000	1.0000	1.0000	.9999
7	1.0000	1.0000	1.0000	1.0000	1.0000	1.0000	1.0000	1.0000	1.0000	1.0000

	MEAN ARRIVAL RATE λ									
	1.1	1.2	1.3	1.4	1.5	1.6	1.7	1.8	1.9	2.0
0	.3329	.3012	.2725	.2466	.2231	.2019	.1827	.1653	.1496	.1353
1	.6990	.6626	.6268	.5918	.5578	.5249	.4932	.4628	.4337	.4060
2	.9004	.8795	.8571	.8335	.8088	.7834	.7572	.7306	.7037	.6767
3	.9743	.9662	.9569	.9463	.9344	.9212	.9068	.8913	.8747	.8571
4	.9946	.9923	.9893	.9857	.9814	.9763	.9704	.9636	.9559	.9473
5	.9990	.9985	.9978	.9968	.9955	.9940	.9920	.9896	.9868	.9834
6	.9999	.9997	.9996	.9994	.9991	.9987	.9981	.9974	.9966	.9955
7	1.0000	1.0000	.9999	.9999	.9998	.9997	.9996	.9994	.9992	.9989
8	1.0000	1.0000	1.0000	1.0000	1.0000	1.0000	.9999	.9999	.9998	.9998
9	1.0000	1.0000	1.0000	1.0000	1.0000	1.0000	1.0000	1.0000	1.0000	1.0000

	MEAN ARRIVAL RATE λ									
	2.1	2.2	2.3	2.4	2.5	2.6	2.7	2.8	2.9	3.0
0	.1225	.1108	.1003	.0907	.0821	.0743	.0672	.0608	.0550	.0498
1	.3796	.3546	.3309	.3084	.2873	.2674	.2487	.2311	.2146	.1991
2	.6496	.6227	.5960	.5697	.5438	.5184	.4936	.4695	.4460	.4232
3	.8386	.8194	.7993	.7787	.7576	.7360	.7141	.6919	.6696	.6472
4	.9379	.9275	.9162	.9041	.8912	.8774	.8629	.8477	.8318	.8153
5	.9796	.9751	.9700	.9643	.9580	.9510	.9433	.9349	.9258	.9161
6	.9941	.9925	.9906	.9884	.9858	.9828	.9794	.9756	.9713	.9665
7	.9985	.9980	.9974	.9967	.9958	.9947	.9934	.9919	.9901	.9881
8	.9997	.9995	.9994	.9991	.9989	.9985	.9981	.9976	.9969	.9962
9	.9999	.9999	.9999	.9998	.9997	.9996	.9995	.9993	.9991	.9989
10	1.0000	1.0000	1.0000	1.0000	.9999	.9999	.9999	.9998	.9998	.9997
11	1.0000	1.0000	1.0000	1.0000	1.0000	1.0000	1.0000	1.0000	.9999	.9999
12	1.0000	1.0000	1.0000	1.0000	1.0000	1.0000	1.0000	1.0000	1.0000	1.0000

	MEAN ARRIVAL RATE λ									
	3.1	3.2	3.3	3.4	3.5	3.6	3.7	3.8	3.9	4.0
0	.0450	.0408	.0369	.0334	.0302	.0273	.0247	.0224	.0202	.0183
1	.1847	.1712	.1586	.1468	.1359	.1257	.1162	.1074	.0992	.0916
2	.4012	.3799	.3594	.3397	.3208	.3027	.2854	.2689	.2531	.2381
3	.6248	.6025	.5803	.5584	.5366	.5152	.4942	.4735	.4532	.4335
4	.7982	.7806	.7626	.7442	.7254	.7064	.6872	.6678	.6484	.6288
5	.9057	.8946	.8829	.8705	.8576	.8441	.8301	.8156	.8006	.7851
6	.9612	.9554	.9490	.9421	.9347	.9267	.9182	.9091	.8995	.8893
7	.9858	.9832	.9802	.9769	.9733	.9692	.9648	.9599	.9546	.9489
8	.9953	.9943	.9931	.9917	.9901	.9883	.9863	.9840	.9815	.9786
9	.9986	.9982	.9978	.9973	.9967	.9960	.9952	.9942	.9931	.9919
10	.9996	.9995	.9994	.9992	.9990	.9987	.9984	.9981	.9977	.9972
11	.9999	.9999	.9998	.9998	.9997	.9996	.9995	.9994	.9993	.9991
12	1.0000	1.0000	1.0000	.9999	.9999	.9999	.9999	.9998	.9998	.9997
13	1.0000	1.0000	1.0000	1.0000	1.0000	1.0000	1.0000	1.0000	.9999	.9999
14	1.0000	1.0000	1.0000	1.0000	1.0000	1.0000	1.0000	1.0000	1.0000	1.0000

Table 6 Cumulative Poisson Probabilities Continued

	MEAN ARRIVAL RATE λ									
	4.1	4.2	4.3	4.4	4.5	4.6	4.7	4.8	4.9	5.0
0	.0166	.0150	.0136	.0123	.0111	.0101	.0091	.0082	.0074	.0067
1	.0845	.0780	.0719	.0663	.0611	.0563	.0518	.0477	.0439	.0404
2	.2238	.2102	.1974	.1851	.1736	.1626	.1523	.1425	.1333	.1247
3	.4142	.3954	.3772	.3594	.3423	.3257	.3097	.2942	.2793	.2650
4	.6093	.5898	.5704	.5512	.5321	.5132	.4946	.4763	.4582	.4405
5	.7693	.7531	.7367	.7199	.7029	.6858	.6684	.6510	.6335	.6160
6	.8786	.8675	.8558	.8436	.8311	.8180	.8046	.7908	.7767	.7622
7	.9427	.9361	.9290	.9214	.9134	.9049	.8960	.8867	.8769	.8666
8	.9755	.9721	.9683	.9642	.9597	.9549	.9497	.9442	.9382	.9319
9	.9905	.9889	.9871	.9851	.9829	.9805	.9778	.9749	.9717	.9682
10	.9966	.9959	.9952	.9943	.9933	.9922	.9910	.9896	.9880	.9863
11	.9989	.9986	.9983	.9980	.9976	.9971	.9966	.9960	.9953	.9945
12	.9997	.9996	.9995	.9993	.9992	.9990	.9988	.9986	.9983	.9980
13	.9999	.9999	.9998	.9998	.9997	.9997	.9996	.9995	.9994	.9993
14	1.0000	1.0000	1.0000	.9999	.9999	.9999	.9999	.9999	.9998	.9998

	MEAN ARRIVAL RATE λ									
	5.1	5.2	5.3	5.4	5.5	5.6	5.7	5.8	5.9	6.0
0	.0061	.0055	.0050	.0045	.0041	.0037	.0033	.0030	.0027	.0025
1	.0372	.0342	.0314	.0289	.0266	.0244	.0224	.0206	.0189	.0174
2	.1165	.1088	.1016	.0948	.0884	.0824	.0768	.0715	.0666	.0620
3	.2513	.2381	.2254	.2133	.2017	.1906	.1800	.1700	.1604	.1512
4	.4231	.4061	.3895	.3733	.3575	.3422	.3272	.3127	.2987	.2851
5	.5984	.5809	.5635	.5461	.5289	.5119	.4950	.4783	.4619	.4457
6	.7474	.7324	.7171	.7017	.6860	.6703	.6544	.6384	.6224	.6063
7	.8560	.8449	.8335	.8217	.8095	.7970	.7841	.7710	.7576	.7440
8	.9252	.9181	.9106	.9027	.8944	.8857	.8766	.8672	.8574	.8472
9	.9644	.9603	.9559	.9512	.9462	.9409	.9352	.9292	.9228	.9161
10	.9844	.9823	.9800	.9775	.9747	.9718	.9686	.9651	.9614	.9574
11	.9937	.9927	.9916	.9904	.9890	.9875	.9859	.9841	.9821	.9799
12	.9976	.9972	.9967	.9962	.9955	.9949	.9941	.9932	.9922	.9912
13	.9992	.9990	.9988	.9986	.9983	.9980	.9977	.9973	.9969	.9964
14	.9997	.9997	.9996	.9995	.9994	.9993	.9991	.9990	.9988	.9986

	MEAN ARRIVAL RATE λ									
	6.1	6.2	6.3	6.4	6.5	6.6	6.7	6.8	6.9	7.0
0	.0022	.0020	.0018	.0017	.0015	.0014	.0012	.0011	.0010	.0009
1	.0159	.0146	.0134	.0123	.0113	.0103	.0095	.0087	.0080	.0073
2	.0577	.0536	.0498	.0463	.0430	.0400	.0371	.0344	.0320	.0296
3	.1425	.1342	.1264	.1189	.1118	.1052	.0988	.0928	.0871	.0818
4	.2719	.2592	.2469	.2351	.2237	.2127	.2022	.1920	.1823	.1730
5	.4298	.4141	.3988	.3837	.3690	.3547	.3406	.3270	.3137	.3007
6	.5902	.5742	.5582	.5423	.5265	.5108	.4953	.4799	.4647	.4497
7	.7301	.7160	.7017	.6873	.6728	.6581	.6433	.6285	.6136	.5987
8	.8367	.8259	.8148	.8033	.7916	.7796	.7673	.7548	.7420	.7291
9	.9090	.9016	.8939	.8858	.8774	.8686	.8596	.8502	.8405	.8305
10	.9531	.9486	.9437	.9386	.9332	.9274	.9214	.9151	.9084	.9015
11	.9776	.9750	.9723	.9693	.9661	.9627	.9591	.9552	.9510	.9467
12	.9900	.9887	.9873	.9857	.9840	.9821	.9801	.9779	.9755	.9730
13	.9958	.9952	.9945	.9937	.9929	.9920	.9909	.9898	.9885	.9872
14	.9984	.9981	.9978	.9974	.9970	.9966	.9961	.9956	.9950	.9943

Table 6 Cumulative Poisson Probabilities Continued

	MEAN ARRIVAL RATE λ									
	7.1	7.2	7.3	7.4	7.5	7.6	7.7	7.8	7.9	8.0
0	.0008	.0007	.0007	.0006	.0006	.0005	.0005	.0004	.0004	.0003
1	.0067	.0061	.0056	.0051	.0047	.0043	.0039	.0036	.0033	.0030
2	.0275	.0255	.0236	.0219	.0203	.0188	.0174	.0161	.0149	.0138
3	.0767	.0719	.0674	.0632	.0591	.0554	.0518	.0485	.0453	.0424
4	.1641	.1555	.1473	.1395	.1321	.1249	.1181	.1117	.1055	.0996
5	.2881	.2759	.2640	.2526	.2414	.2307	.2203	.2103	.2006	.1912
6	.4349	.4204	.4060	.3920	.3782	.3646	.3514	.3384	.3257	.3134
7	.5838	.5689	.5541	.5393	.5246	.5100	.4956	.4812	.4670	.4530
8	.7160	.7027	.6892	.6757	.6620	.6482	.6343	.6204	.6065	.5925
9	.8202	.8096	.7988	.7877	.7764	.7649	.7531	.7411	.7290	.7166
10	.8942	.8867	.8788	.8707	.8622	.8535	.8445	.8352	.8257	.8159
11	.9420	.9371	.9319	.9265	.9208	.9148	.9085	.9020	.8952	.8881
12	.9703	.9673	.9642	.9609	.9573	.9536	.9496	.9454	.9409	.9362
13	.9857	.9841	.9824	.9805	.9784	.9762	.9739	.9714	.9687	.9658
14	.9935	.9927	.9918	.9908	.9897	.9886	.9873	.9859	.9844	.9827
15	.9972	.9969	.9964	.9959	.9954	.9948	.9941	.9934	.9926	.9918
16	.9989	.9987	.9985	.9983	.9980	.9978	.9974	.9971	.9967	.9963
17	.9996	.9995	.9994	.9993	.9992	.9991	.9989	.9988	.9986	.9984
18	.9998	.9998	.9998	.9997	.9997	.9996	.9996	.9995	.9994	.9993
19	.9999	.9999	.9999	.9999	.9999	.9999	.9998	.9998	.9998	.9997
20	1.0000	1.0000	1.0000	1.0000	1.0000	1.0000	.9999	.9999	.9999	.9999

	MEAN ARRIVAL RATE λ									
	8.1	8.2	8.3	8.4	8.5	8.6	8.7	8.8	8.9	9.0
0	.0003	.0003	.0002	.0002	.0002	.0002	.0002	.0002	.0001	.0001
1	.0028	.0025	.0023	.0021	.0019	.0018	.0016	.0015	.0014	.0012
2	.0127	.0118	.0109	.0100	.0093	.0086	.0079	.0073	.0068	.0062
3	.0396	.0370	.0346	.0323	.0301	.0281	.0262	.0244	.0228	.0212
4	.0940	.0887	.0837	.0789	.0744	.0701	.0660	.0621	.0584	.0550
5	.1822	.1736	.1653	.1573	.1496	.1422	.1352	.1284	.1219	.1157
6	.3013	.2896	.2781	.2670	.2562	.2457	.2355	.2256	.2160	.2068
7	.4391	.4254	.4119	.3987	.3856	.3728	.3602	.3478	.3357	.3239
8	.5786	.5647	.5507	.5369	.5231	.5094	.4958	.4823	.4689	.4557
9	.7041	.6915	.6788	.6659	.6530	.6400	.6269	.6137	.6006	.5874
10	.8058	.7955	.7850	.7743	.7634	.7522	.7409	.7294	.7178	.7060
11	.8807	.8731	.8652	.8571	.8487	.8400	.8311	.8220	.8126	.8030
12	.9313	.9261	.9207	.9150	.9091	.9029	.8965	.8898	.8829	.8758
13	.9628	.9595	.9561	.9524	.9486	.9445	.9403	.9358	.9311	.9261
14	.9810	.9791	.9771	.9749	.9726	.9701	.9675	.9647	.9617	.9585
15	.9908	.9898	.9887	.9875	.9862	.9848	.9832	.9816	.9798	.9780
16	.9958	.9953	.9947	.9941	.9934	.9926	.9918	.9909	.9899	.9889
17	.9982	.9979	.9977	.9973	.9970	.9966	.9962	.9957	.9952	.9947
18	.9992	.9991	.9990	.9989	.9987	.9985	.9983	.9981	.9978	.9976
19	.9997	.9997	.9996	.9995	.9995	.9994	.9993	.9992	.9991	.9989
20	.9999	.9999	.9998	.9998	.9998	.9998	.9997	.9997	.9996	.9996

	MEAN ARRIVAL RATE λ									
	9.1	9.2	9.3	9.4	9.5	9.6	9.7	9.8	9.9	10.0
0	.0001	.0001	.0001	.0001	.0001	.0001	.0001	.0001	.0001	.0000
1	.0011	.0010	.0009	.0009	.0008	.0007	.0007	.0006	.0005	.0005
2	.0058	.0053	.0049	.0045	.0042	.0038	.0035	.0033	.0030	.0028
3	.0198	.0184	.0172	.0160	.0149	.0138	.0129	.0120	.0111	.0103
4	.0517	.0486	.0456	.0429	.0403	.0378	.0355	.0333	.0312	.0293
5	.1098	.1041	.0986	.0935	.0885	.0838	.0793	.0750	.0710	.0671
6	.1978	.1892	.1808	.1727	.1649	.1574	.1502	.1433	.1366	.1301

Table 6 Cumulative Poisson Probabilities Continued

	MEAN ARRIVAL RATE λ									
	9.1	9.2	9.3	9.4	9.5	9.6	9.7	9.8	9.9	10.0
7	.3123	.3010	.2900	.2792	.2687	.2584	.2485	.2388	.2294	.2202
8	.4426	.4296	.4168	.4042	.3918	.3796	.3676	.3558	.3442	.3328
9	.5742	.5611	.5479	.5349	.5218	.5089	.4960	.4832	.4705	.4579
10	.6941	.6820	.6699	.6576	.6453	.6329	.6205	.6080	.5955	.5830
11	.7932	.7832	.7730	.7626	.7520	.7412	.7303	.7193	.7081	.6968
12	.8684	.8607	.8529	.8448	.8364	.8279	.8191	.8101	.8009	.7916
13	.9210	.9156	.9100	.9042	.8981	.8919	.8853	.8786	.8716	.8645
14	.9552	.9517	.9480	.9441	.9400	.9357	.9312	.9265	.9216	.9165
15	.9760	.9738	.9715	.9691	.9665	.9638	.9609	.9579	.9546	.9513
16	.9878	.9865	.9852	.9838	.9823	.9806	.9789	.9770	.9751	.9730
17	.9941	.9934	.9927	.9919	.9911	.9902	.9892	.9881	.9870	.9857
18	.9973	.9969	.9966	.9962	.9957	.9952	.9947	.9941	.9935	.9928
19	.9988	.9986	.9985	.9983	.9980	.9978	.9975	.9972	.9969	.9965
20	.9995	.9994	.9993	.9992	.9991	.9990	.9989	.9987	.9986	.9984

	MEAN ARRIVAL RATE λ									
	10.1	10.2	10.3	10.4	10.5	10.6	10.7	10.8	10.9	11.0
0	.0000	.0000	.0000	.0000	.0000	.0000	.0000	.0000	.0000	.0000
1	.0005	.0004	.0004	.0003	.0003	.0003	.0003	.0002	.0002	.0002
2	.0026	.0023	.0022	.0020	.0018	.0017	.0016	.0014	.0013	.0012
3	.0096	.0089	.0083	.0077	.0071	.0066	.0062	.0057	.0053	.0049
4	.0274	.0257	.0241	.0225	.0211	.0197	.0185	.0173	.0162	.0151
5	.0634	.0599	.0566	.0534	.0504	.0475	.0448	.0423	.0398	.0375
6	.1240	.1180	.1123	.1069	.1016	.0966	.0918	.0872	.0828	.0786
7	.2113	.2027	.1944	.1863	.1785	.1710	.1636	.1566	.1498	.1432
8	.3217	.3108	.3001	.2896	.2794	.2694	.2597	.2502	.2410	.2320
9	.4455	.4332	.4210	.4090	.3971	.3854	.3739	.3626	.3515	.3405
10	.5705	.5580	.5456	.5331	.5207	.5084	.4961	.4840	.4719	.4599
11	.6853	.6738	.6622	.6505	.6387	.6269	.6150	.6031	.5912	.5793
12	.7820	.7722	.7623	.7522	.7420	.7316	.7210	.7104	.6996	.6887
13	.8571	.8494	.8416	.8336	.8253	.8169	.8083	.7995	.7905	.7813
14	.9112	.9057	.9	.8940	.8879	.8815	.8750	.8682	.8612	.8540
15	.9477	.9440	.9400	.9359	.9317	.9272	.9225	.9177	.9126	.9074
16	.9707	.9684	.9658	.9632	.9604	.9574	.9543	.9511	.9477	.9441
17	.9844	.9830	.9815	.9799	.9781	.9763	.9744	.9723	.9701	.9678
18	.9921	.9913	.9904	.9895	.9885	.9874	.9863	.9850	.9837	.9823
19	.9962	.9957	.9953	.9948	.9942	.9936	.9930	.9923	.9915	.9907
20	.9982	.9980	.9978	.9975	.9972	.9969	.9966	.9962	.9958	.9953

	MEAN ARRIVAL RATE λ									
	11.1	11.2	11.3	11.4	11.5	11.6	11.7	11.8	11.9	12.0
0	.0000	.0000	.0000	.0000	.0000	.0000	.0000	.0000	.0000	.0000
1	.0002	.0002	.0002	.0001	.0001	.0001	.0001	.0001	.0001	.0001
2	.0011	.0010	.0009	.0009	.0008	.0007	.0007	.0006	.0006	.0005
3	.0046	.0042	.0039	.0036	.0034	.0031	.0029	.0027	.0025	.0023
4	.0141	.0132	.0123	.0115	.0107	.0100	.0094	.0087	.0081	.0076
5	.0353	.0333	.0313	.0295	.0277	.0261	.0245	.0230	.0217	.0203
6	.0746	.0708	.0671	.0636	.0603	.0571	.0541	.0512	.0484	.0458
7	.1369	.1307	.1249	.1192	.1137	.1085	.1035	.0986	.0940	.0895
8	.2232	.2147	.2064	.1984	.1906	.1830	.1757	.1686	.1617	.1550
9	.3298	.3192	.3089	.2987	.2888	.2791	.2696	.2603	.2512	.2424
10	.4480	.4362	.4246	.4131	.4017	.3905	.3794	.3685	.3578	.3472
11	.5673	.5554	.5435	.5316	.5198	.5080	.4963	.4847	.4731	.4616
12	.6777	.6666	.6555	.6442	.6329	.6216	.6102	.5988	.5874	.5760
13	.7719	.7624	.7528	.7430	.7330	.7230	.7128	.7025	.6920	.6815
14	.8467	.8391	.8313	.8234	.8153	.8069	.7985	.7898	.7810	.7720

Table 6   Cumulative Poisson Probabilities Continued

	MEAN ARRIVAL RATE λ									
	11.1	11.2	11.3	11.4	11.5	11.6	11.7	11.8	11.9	12.0
15	.9020	.8963	.8905	.8845	.8783	.8719	.8653	.8585	.8516	.8444
16	.9403	.9364	.9323	.9280	.9236	.9190	.9142	.9092	.9040	.8987
17	.9654	.9628	.9601	.9572	.9542	.9511	.9478	.9444	.9408	.9370
18	.9808	.9792	.9775	.9757	.9738	.9718	.9697	.9674	.9651	.9626
19	.9898	.9889	.9879	.9868	.9857	.9845	.9832	.9818	.9803	.9787
20	.9948	.9943	.9938	.9932	.9925	.9918	.9910	.9902	.9893	.9884

	MEAN ARRIVAL RATE λ									
	12.1	12.2	12.3	12.4	12.5	12.6	12.7	12.8	12.9	13.0
5	.0191	.0179	.0168	.0158	.0148	.0139	.0130	.0122	.0115	.0107
6	.0433	.0410	.0387	.0366	.0346	.0326	.0308	.0291	.0274	.0259
7	.0852	.0811	.0772	.0734	.0698	.0664	.0631	.0599	.0569	.0540
8	.1486	.1424	.1363	.1305	.1249	.1195	.1143	.1093	.1044	.0998
9	.2338	.2254	.2172	.2092	.2014	.1939	.1866	.1794	.1725	.1658
10	.3368	.3266	.3166	.3067	.2971	.2876	.2783	.2693	.2604	.2517
11	.4502	.4389	.4278	.4167	.4058	.3950	.3843	.3738	.3634	.3532
12	.5645	.5531	.5417	.5303	.5190	.5077	.4964	.4853	.4741	.4631
13	.6709	.6603	.6495	.6387	.6278	.6169	.6060	.5950	.5840	.5730
14	.7629	.7536	.7442	.7347	.7250	.7153	.7054	.6954	.6853	.6751
15	.8371	.8296	.8219	.8140	.8060	.7978	.7895	.7810	.7724	.7636
16	.8932	.8875	.8816	.8755	.8693	.8629	.8563	.8495	.8426	.8355
17	.9331	.9290	.9248	.9204	.9158	.9111	.9062	.9011	.8959	.8905
18	.9600	.9572	.9543	.9513	.9481	.9448	.9414	.9378	.9341	.9302
19	.9771	.9753	.9734	.9715	.9694	.9672	.9649	.9625	.9600	.9573
20	.9874	.9863	.9852	.9840	.9827	.9813	.9799	.9783	.9767	.9750
21	.9934	.9927	.9921	.9914	.9906	.9898	.9889	.9880	.9870	.9859
22	.9966	.9963	.9959	.9955	.9951	.9946	.9941	.9936	.9930	.9924
23	.9984	.9982	.9980	.9978	.9975	.9973	.9970	.9967	.9964	.9960

	MEAN ARRIVAL RATE λ									
	13.1	13.2	13.3	13.4	13.5	13.6	13.7	13.8	13.9	14.0
5	.0101	.0094	.0088	.0083	.0077	.0072	.0068	.0063	.0059	.0055
6	.0244	.0230	.0217	.0204	.0193	.0181	.0171	.0161	.0151	.0142
7	.0513	.0487	.0461	.0438	.0415	.0393	.0372	.0353	.0334	.0316
8	.0953	.0910	.0868	.0828	.0790	.0753	.0718	.0684	.0652	.0621
9	.1593	.1530	.1469	.1410	.1353	.1297	.1244	.1192	.1142	.1094
10	.2432	.2349	.2268	.2189	.2112	.2037	.1964	.1893	.1824	.1757
11	.3431	.3332	.3234	.3139	.3045	.2952	.2862	.2773	.2686	.2600
12	.4522	.4413	.4305	.4199	.4093	.3989	.3886	.3784	.3684	.3585
13	.5621	.5511	.5401	.5292	.5182	.5074	.4966	.4858	.4751	.4644
14	.6649	.6546	.6442	.6338	.6233	.6128	.6022	.5916	.5810	.5704
15	.7547	.7456	.7365	.7272	.7178	.7083	.6987	.6890	.6792	.6694
16	.8282	.8208	.8132	.8054	.7975	.7895	.7813	.7730	.7645	.7559
17	.8849	.8791	.8732	.8671	.8609	.8545	.8479	.8411	.8343	.8272
18	.9261	.9219	.9176	.9130	.9084	.9035	.8986	.8934	.8881	.8826
19	.9546	.9516	.9486	.9454	.9421	.9387	.9351	.9314	.9275	.9235
20	.9732	.9713	.9692	.9671	.9649	.9626	.9601	.9576	.9549	.9521
21	.9848	.9836	.9823	.9810	.9796	.9780	.9765	.9748	.9730	.9712
22	.9917	.9910	.9902	.9894	.9885	.9876	.9866	.9856	.9845	.9833
23	.9956	.9952	.9948	.9943	.9938	.9933	.9927	.9921	.9914	.9907

	MEAN ARRIVAL RATE λ									
	14.1	14.2	14.3	14.4	14.5	14.6	14.7	14.8	14.9	15.0
6	.0134	.0126	.0118	.0111	.0105	.0098	.0092	.0087	.0081	.0076
7	.0299	.0283	.0268	.0253	.0239	.0226	.0214	.0202	.0191	.0180
8	.0591	.0562	.0535	.0509	.0484	.0460	.0437	.0415	.0394	.0374

Table 6   Cumulative Poisson Probabilities Continued

	MEAN ARRIVAL RATE λ									
	14.1	14.2	14.3	14.4	14.5	14.6	14.7	14.8	14.9	15.0
9	.1047	.1003	.0959	.0918	.0878	.0839	.0802	.0766	.0732	.0699
10	.1691	.1628	.1566	.1507	.1449	.1392	.1338	.1285	.1234	.1185
11	.2517	.2435	.2355	.2277	.2201	.2127	.2054	.1984	.1915	.1848
12	.3487	.3391	.3296	.3203	.3111	.3021	.2932	.2845	.2760	.2676
13	.4539	.4434	.4330	.4227	.4125	.4024	.3925	.3826	.3728	.3632
14	.5598	.5492	.5387	.5281	.5176	.5071	.4967	.4863	.4759	.4657
15	.6594	.6494	.6394	.6293	.6192	.6090	.5988	.5886	.5783	.5681
16	.7472	.7384	.7294	.7204	.7112	.7020	.6926	.6832	.6737	.6641
17	.8200	.8126	.8051	.7975	.7897	.7818	.7737	.7656	.7573	.7489
18	.8770	.8712	.8653	.8592	.8530	.8466	.8400	.8333	.8265	.8195
19	.9193	.9150	.9106	.9060	.9012	.8963	.8913	.8861	.8807	.8752
20	.9492	.9461	.9430	.9396	.9362	.9326	.9289	.9251	.9211	.9170
21	.9692	.9671	.9650	.9627	.9604	.9579	.9553	.9526	.9498	.9469
22	.9820	.9807	.9793	.9779	.9763	.9747	.9729	.9711	.9692	.9673
23	.9899	.9891	.9882	.9873	.9863	.9853	.9842	.9831	.9818	.9805
24	.9945	.9941	.9935	.9930	.9924	.9918	.9911	.9904	.9896	.9888
25	.9971	.9969	.9966	.9963	.9959	.9956	.9952	.9947	.9943	.9938

	MEAN ARRIVAL RATE λ									
	15.1	15.2	15.3	15.4	15.5	15.6	15.7	15.8	15.9	16.0
7	.0170	.0160	.0151	.0143	.0135	.0127	.0120	.0113	.0106	.0100
8	.0355	.0337	.0320	.0304	.0288	.0273	.0259	.0245	.0232	.0220
9	.0667	.0636	.0607	.0579	.0552	.0526	.0501	.0478	.0455	.0433
10	.1137	.1091	.1046	.1003	.0961	.0921	.0882	.0845	.0809	.0774
11	.1782	.1718	.1657	.1596	.1538	.1481	.1426	.1372	.1320	.1270
12	.2594	.2514	.2435	.2358	.2283	.2209	.2137	.2067	.1998	.1931
13	.3537	.3444	.3351	.3260	.3171	.3083	.2996	.2911	.2827	.2745
14	.4554	.4453	.4353	.4253	.4154	.4056	.3959	.3864	.3769	.3675
15	.5578	.5476	.5374	.5272	.5170	.5069	.4968	.4867	.4767	.4667
16	.6545	.6448	.6351	.6253	.6154	.6056	.5957	.5858	.5759	.5660
17	.7403	.7317	.7230	.7141	.7052	.6962	.6871	.6779	.6687	.6593
18	.8123	.8051	.7977	.7901	.7825	.7747	.7668	.7587	.7506	.7423
19	.8696	.8638	.8578	.8517	.8455	.8391	.8326	.8260	.8192	.8122
20	.9128	.9084	.9039	.8992	.8944	.8894	.8843	.8791	.8737	.8682
21	.9438	.9407	.9374	.9340	.9304	.9268	.9230	.9190	.9150	.9108
22	.9652	.9630	.9607	.9583	.9558	.9532	.9505	.9477	.9448	.9418
23	.9792	.9777	.9762	.9746	.9730	.9712	.9694	.9674	.9654	.9633
24	.9880	.9871	.9861	.9851	.9840	.9829	.9817	.9804	.9791	.9777
25	.9933	.9928	.9922	.9915	.9909	.9902	.9894	.9886	.9878	.9869

	MEAN ARRIVAL RATE λ									
	16.1	16.2	16.3	16.4	16.5	16.6	16.7	16.8	16.9	17.0
8	.0208	.0197	.0186	.0176	.0167	.0158	.0149	.0141	.0133	.0126
9	.0412	.0392	.0373	.0355	.0337	.0321	.0305	.0290	.0275	.0261
10	.0740	.0708	.0677	.0647	.0619	.0591	.0565	.0539	.0515	.0491
11	.1221	.1174	.1128	.1084	.1041	.0999	.0959	.0920	.0883	.0847
12	.1866	.1802	.1740	.1680	.1621	.1564	.1508	.1454	.1401	.1350
13	.2664	.2585	.2508	.2432	.2357	.2285	.2213	.2144	.2075	.2009
14	.3583	.3492	.3402	.3313	.3225	.3139	.3054	.2971	.2889	.2808
15	.4569	.4470	.4373	.4276	.4180	.4085	.3991	.3898	.3806	.3715
16	.5560	.5461	.5362	.5263	.5165	.5067	.4969	.4871	.4774	.4677
17	.6500	.6406	.6311	.6216	.6120	.6025	.5929	.5833	.5737	.5640
18	.7340	.7255	.7170	.7084	.6996	.6908	.6820	.6730	.6640	.6550
19	.8052	.7980	.7907	.7833	.7757	.7681	.7603	.7524	.7444	.7363
20	.8625	.8567	.8508	.8447	.8385	.8321	.8257	.8191	.8123	.8055
21	.9064	.9020	.8974	.8927	.8878	.8828	.8777	.8724	.8670	.8615
22	.9386	.9353	.9319	.9284	.9248	.9210	.9171	.9131	.9090	.9047

Table 6 Cumulative Poisson Probabilities Continued

					MEAN ARRIVAL RATE λ					
	16.1	16.2	16.3	16.4	16.5	16.6	16.7	16.8	16.9	17.0
23	.9611	.9588	.9564	.9539	.9513	.9486	.9458	.9429	.9398	.9367
24	.9762	.9747	.9730	.9713	.9696	.9677	.9657	.9637	.9616	.9594
25	.9859	.9849	.9839	.9828	.9816	.9804	.9791	.9777	.9763	.9748
26	.9920	.9913	.9907	.9900	.9892	.9884	.9876	.9867	.9858	.9848

					MEAN ARRIVAL RATE λ					
	17.1	17.2	17.3	17.4	17.5	17.6	17.7	17.8	17.9	18.0
8	.0119	.0112	.0106	.0100	.0095	.0089	.0084	.0079	.0075	.0071
9	.0248	.0235	.0223	.0212	.0201	.0191	.0181	.0171	.0162	.0154
10	.0469	.0447	.0426	.0406	.0387	.0369	.0352	.0335	.0319	.0304
11	.0812	.0778	.0746	.0714	.0684	.0655	.0627	.0600	.0574	.0549
12	.1301	.1252	.1206	.1160	.1116	.1074	.1033	.0993	.0954	.0917
13	.1944	.1880	.1818	.1758	.1699	.1641	.1585	.1531	.1478	.1426
14	.2729	.2651	.2575	.2500	.2426	.2354	.2284	.2215	.2147	.2081
15	.3624	.3535	.3448	.3361	.3275	.3191	.3108	.3026	.2946	.2867
16	.4581	.4486	.4391	.4297	.4204	.4112	.4020	.3929	.3839	.3751
17	.5544	.5448	.5352	.5256	.5160	.5065	.4969	.4875	.4780	.4686
18	.6458	.6367	.6275	.6182	.6089	.5996	.5903	.5810	.5716	.5622
19	.7281	.7199	.7115	.7031	.6945	.6859	.6773	.6685	.6598	.6509
20	.7985	.7914	.7842	.7769	.7694	.7619	.7542	.7465	.7387	.7307
21	.8558	.8500	.8441	.8380	.8319	.8255	.8191	.8126	.8059	.7991
22	.9003	.8958	.8912	.8864	.8815	.8765	.8713	.8660	.8606	.8551
23	.9334	.9301	.9266	.9230	.9193	.9154	.9115	.9074	.9032	.8989
24	.9570	.9546	.9521	.9495	.9468	.9440	.9411	.9381	.9350	.9317
25	.9732	.9715	.9698	.9680	.9661	.9641	.9621	.9599	.9577	.9554
26	.9838	.9827	.9816	.9804	.9791	.9778	.9764	.9749	.9734	.9718
27	.9905	.9898	.9891	.9883	.9875	.9866	.9857	.9848	.9837	.9827

					MEAN ARRIVAL RATE λ					
	18.1	18.2	18.3	18.4	18.5	18.6	18.7	18.8	18.9	19.0
9	.0146	.0138	.0131	.0124	.0117	.0111	.0105	.0099	.0094	.0089
10	.0289	.0275	.0262	.0249	.0237	.0225	.0214	.0203	.0193	.0183
11	.0525	.0502	.0479	.0458	.0438	.0418	.0399	.0381	.0363	.0347
12	.0881	.0846	.0812	.0779	.0748	.0717	.0688	.0659	.0632	.0606
13	.1376	.1327	.1279	.1233	.1189	.1145	.1103	.1062	.1022	.0984
14	.2016	.1953	.1891	.1830	.1771	.1714	.1658	.1603	.1550	.1497
15	.2789	.2712	.2637	.2563	.2490	.2419	.2349	.2281	.2214	.2148
16	.3663	.3576	.3490	.3405	.3321	.3239	.3157	.3077	.2998	.2920
17	.4593	.4500	.4408	.4317	.4226	.4136	.4047	.3958	.3870	.3784
18	.5529	.5435	.5342	.5249	.5156	.5063	.4970	.4878	.4786	.4695
19	.6420	.6331	.6241	.6151	.6061	.5970	.5879	.5788	.5697	.5606
20	.7227	.7146	.7064	.6981	.6898	.6814	.6729	.6644	.6558	.6472
21	.7922	.7852	.7781	.7709	.7636	.7561	.7486	.7410	.7333	.7255
22	.8494	.8436	.8377	.8317	.8256	.8193	.8129	.8065	.7998	.7931
23	.8944	.8899	.8852	.8804	.8755	.8704	.8652	.8600	.8545	.8490
24	.9284	.9249	.9214	.9177	.9139	.9100	.9060	.9019	.8976	.8933
25	.9530	.9505	.9479	.9452	.9424	.9395	.9365	.9334	.9302	.9269
26	.9701	.9683	.9665	.9646	.9626	.9606	.9584	.9562	.9539	.9514
27	.9816	.9804	.9792	.9779	.9765	.9751	.9736	.9720	.9704	.9687

					MEAN ARRIVAL RATE λ					
	19.1	19.2	19.3	19.4	19.5	19.6	19.7	19.8	19.9	20.0
10	.0174	.0165	.0157	.0149	.0141	.0134	.0127	.0120	.0114	.0108
11	.0331	.0315	.0301	.0287	.0273	.0260	.0248	.0236	.0225	.0214
12	.0580	.0556	.0532	.0509	.0488	.0467	.0446	.0427	.0408	.0390
13	.0947	.0911	.0876	.0842	.0809	.0778	.0747	.0717	.0689	.0661

Table 6 Cumulative Poisson Probabilities Continued

	19.1	19.2	19.3	19.4	19.5	19.6	19.7	19.8	19.9	20.0
14	.1447	.1397	.1349	.1303	.1257	.1213	.1170	.1128	.1088	.1049
15	.2084	.2021	.1959	.1899	.1840	.1782	.1726	.1671	.1617	.1565
16	.2844	.2768	.2694	.2621	.2550	.2479	.2410	.2342	.2276	.2211
17	.3698	.3613	.3529	.3446	.3364	.3283	.3203	.3124	.3047	.2970
18	.4604	.4514	.4424	.4335	.4246	.4158	.4071	.3985	.3899	.3814
19	.5515	.5424	.5333	.5242	.5151	.5061	.4971	.4881	.4792	.4703
20	.6385	.6298	.6210	.6122	.6034	.5946	.5857	.5769	.5680	.5591
21	.7176	.7097	.7016	6935	.6854	.6772	.6689	.6605	.6521	.6437
22	.7863	.7794	.7724	.7653	.7580	.7507	.7433	.7358	.7283	.7206
23	.8434	.8376	.8317	.8257	.8196	.8134	.8071	.8007	.7941	.7875
24	.8888	.8842	.8795	.8746	.8697	.8646	.8594	.8541	.8487	.8432
25	.9235	.9199	.9163	.9126	.9087	.9048	.9007	.8965	.8922	.8878
26	.9489	.9463	.9437	.9409	.9380	.9350	.9319	.9288	.9255	.9221
27	.9670	.9651	.9632	.9612	.9591	.9570	.9547	.9524	.9500	.9475

MEAN ARRIVAL RATE λ

	20.1	20.2	20.3	20.4	20.5	20.6	20.7	20.8	20.9	21.0
10	.0102	.0097	.0092	.0087	.0082	.0078	.0074	.0070	.0066	.0063
11	.0204	.0194	.0184	.0175	.0167	.0158	.0150	.0143	.0136	.0129
12	.0373	.0356	.0340	.0325	.0310	.0296	.0283	.0270	.0257	.0245
13	.0635	.0609	.0584	.0560	.0537	.0515	.0493	.0473	.0453	.0434
14	.1010	.0973	.0938	.0903	.0869	.0836	.0805	.0774	.0744	.0716
15	.1514	.1464	.1416	.1369	.1323	.1278	.1234	.1192	.1151	.1111
16	.2147	.2084	.2023	.1963	.1904	.1847	.1790	.1735	.1682	.1629
17	.2895	.2821	.2748	.2676	.2605	.2536	.2467	.2400	.2334	.2270
18	.3730	.3647	.3565	.3484	.3403	.3324	.3246	.3168	.3092	.3017
19	.4614	.4526	.4438	.4351	.4265	.4179	.4094	.4009	.3926	.3843
20	.5502	.5413	.5325	.5236	.5148	.5059	.4972	.4884	.4797	.4710
21	.6352	.6267	.6181	.6096	.6010	.5923	.5837	.5750	.5664	.5577
22	.7129	.7051	.6972	.6893	.6813	.6732	.6651	.6569	.6487	.6405
23	.7808	.7739	.7670	.7600	.7528	.7456	.7384	.7310	.7235	.7160
24	.8376	.8319	.8260	.8201	.8140	.8078	.8016	.7952	.7887	.7822
25	.8833	.8787	.8739	.8691	.8641	.8591	.8539	.8486	.8432	.8377
26	.9186	.9150	.9114	.9076	.9037	.8997	.8955	.8913	.8870	.8826
27	.9449	.9423	.9395	.9366	.9337	.9306	.9275	.9242	.9209	.9175

MEAN ARRIVAL RATE λ

	21.1	21.2	21.3	21.4	21.5	21.6	21.7	21.8	21.9	22.0
11	.0123	.0116	.0110	.0105	.0099	.0094	.0090	.0085	.0080	.0076
12	.0234	.0223	.0213	.0203	.0193	.0184	.0175	.0167	.0159	.0151
13	.0415	.0397	.0380	.0364	.0348	.0333	.0318	.0304	.0291	.0278
14	.0688	.0661	.0635	.0610	.0586	.0563	.0540	.0518	.0497	.0477
15	.1072	.1034	.0997	.0962	.0927	.0893	.0861	.0829	.0799	.0769
16	.1578	.1528	.1479	.1432	.1385	.1340	.1296	.1253	.1211	.1170
17	.2206	.2144	.2083	.2023	.1965	.1907	.1851	.1796	.1743	.1690
18	.2943	.2870	.2798	.2727	.2657	.2588	.2521	.2454	.2389	.2325
19	.3760	.3679	.3599	.3519	.3440	.3362	.3285	.3209	.3134	.3060
20	.4623	.4537	.4452	.4367	.4282	.4198	.4115	.4032	.3950	.3869
21	.5490	.5403	.5317	.5230	.5144	.5058	.4972	.4887	.4801	.4716
22	.6322	.6238	.6155	.6071	.5987	.5902	.5818	.5733	.5648	.5564
23	.7084	.7008	.6930	.6853	.6774	.6695	.6616	.6536	.6455	.6374
24	.7755	.7687	.7619	.7550	.7480	.7409	.7337	.7264	.7191	.7117
25	.8321	.8264	.8206	.8146	.8086	.8025	.7963	.7900	.7836	.7771
26	.8780	.8734	.8686	.8638	.8588	.8537	.8486	.8433	.8379	.8324
27	.9139	.9103	.9065	.9027	.8988	.8947	.8906	.8863	.8820	.8775

Table 7   Cutoff Points of the Chi-Square Distribution Function

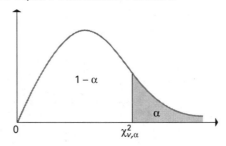

For selected probabilities α, the table shows the values $\chi^2_{v,\alpha}$ such that $P(\chi^2_v > \chi^2_{v,\alpha}) = \alpha$, where χ^2_v is a chi-square random variable with v degrees of freedom. For example, the probability is .100 that a chi-square random variable with 10 degrees of freedom is greater than 15.99.

v	α									
	.995	.990	.975	.950	.900	.100	.050	.025	.010	.005
1	0.0^4393	0.0^3157	0.0^3982	0.0^2393	0.0158	2.71	3.84	5.02	6.63	7.88
2	0.0100	0.0201	0.0506	0.103	0.211	4.61	5.99	7.38	9.21	10.60
3	0.072	0.115	0.216	0.352	0.584	6.25	7.81	9.35	11.34	12.84
4	0.207	0.297	0.484	0.711	1.064	7.78	9.49	11.14	13.28	14.86
5	0.412	0.554	0.831	1.145	1.61	9.24	11.07	12.83	15.09	16.75
6	0.676	0.872	1.24	1.64	2.20	10.64	12.59	14.45	16.81	18.55
7	0.989	1.24	1.69	2.17	2.83	12.02	14.07	16.01	18.48	20.28
8	1.34	1.65	2.18	2.73	3.49	13.36	15.51	17.53	20.09	21.96
9	1.73	2.09	2.70	3.33	4.17	14.68	16.92	19.02	21.67	23.59
10	2.16	2.56	3.25	3.94	4.87	15.99	18.31	20.48	23.21	25.19
11	2.60	3.05	3.82	4.57	5.58	17.28	19.68	21.92	24.73	26.76
12	3.07	3.57	4.40	5.23	6.30	18.55	21.03	23.34	26.22	28.30
13	3.57	4.11	5.01	5.89	7.04	19.81	22.36	24.74	27.69	29.82
14	4.07	4.66	5.63	6.57	7.79	21.06	23.68	26.12	29.14	31.32
15	4.60	5.23	6.26	7.26	8.55	22.31	25.00	27.49	30.58	32.80
16	5.14	5.81	6.91	7.96	9.31	23.54	26.30	28.85	32.00	34.27
17	5.70	6.41	7.56	8.67	10.09	24.77	27.59	30.19	33.41	35.72
18	6.26	7.01	8.23	9.39	10.86	25.99	28.87	31.53	34.81	37.16
19	6.84	7.63	8.91	10.12	11.65	27.20	30.14	32.85	36.19	38.58
20	7.43	8.26	9.59	10.85	12.44	28.41	31.41	34.17	37.57	40.00
21	8.03	8.90	10.28	11.59	13.24	29.62	32.67	35.48	38.93	41.40
22	8.64	9.54	10.98	12.34	14.04	30.81	33.92	36.78	40.29	42.80
23	9.26	10.20	11.69	13.09	14.85	32.01	35.17	38.08	41.64	44.18
24	9.89	10.86	12.40	13.85	15.66	33.20	36.42	39.36	42.98	45.56
25	10.52	11.52	13.12	14.61	16.47	34.38	37.65	40.65	44.31	46.93
26	11.16	12.20	13.84	15.38	17.29	35.56	38.89	41.92	45.64	48.29
27	11.81	12.88	14.57	16.15	18.11	36.74	40.11	43.19	46.96	49.64
28	12.46	13.56	15.31	16.93	18.94	37.92	41.34	44.46	48.28	50.99
29	13.12	14.26	16.05	17.71	19.77	39.09	42.56	45.72	49.59	52.34
30	13.79	14.95	16.79	18.49	20.60	40.26	43.77	46.98	50.89	53.67
40	20.71	22.16	24.43	26.51	29.05	51.81	55.76	59.34	63.69	66.77
50	27.99	29.71	32.36	34.76	37.69	63.17	67.50	71.42	76.15	79.49
60	35.53	37.48	40.48	43.19	46.46	74.40	79.08	83.30	88.38	91.95
70	43.28	45.44	48.76	51.74	55.33	85.53	90.53	95.02	100.4	104.2
80	51.17	53.54	57.15	60.39	64.28	96.58	101.9	106.6	112.3	116.3
90	59.20	61.75	65.65	69.13	73.29	107.6	113.1	118.1	124.1	128.3
100	67.33	70.06	74.22	77.93	82.36	118.5	124.3	129.6	135.8	140.2

Reproduced with permission from C. M. Thompson, "Tables of percentage points of the chi-square distribution," *Biometrika* 32 (1941).

Table 8 Cutoff Points for the Student's *t* Distribution

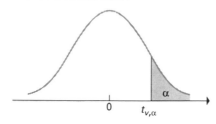

For selected probabilities, α, the table shows the values $t_{v,\alpha}$ such that $P(t_v > t_{v,\alpha}) = \alpha$, where t_v is a Student's *t* random variable with *v* degrees of free-dom. For example, the probability is .10 that a Student's *t* random variable with 10 degrees of freedom exceeds 1.372.

v	α				
	0.100	0.050	0.025	0.010	0.005
1	3.078	6.314	12.706	31.821	63.657
2	1.886	2.920	4.303	6.965	9.925
3	1.638	2.353	3.182	4.541	5.841
4	1.533	2.132	2.776	3.747	4.604
5	1.476	2.015	2.571	3.365	4.032
6	1.440	1.943	2.447	3.143	3.707
7	1.415	1.895	2.365	2.998	3.499
8	1.397	1.860	2.306	2.896	3.355
9	1.383	1.833	2.262	2.821	3.250
10	1.372	1.812	2.228	2.764	3.169
11	1.363	1.796	2.201	2.718	3.106
12	1.356	1.782	2.179	2.681	3.055
13	1.350	1.771	2.160	2.650	3.012
14	1.345	1.761	2.145	2.624	2.977
15	1.341	1.753	2.131	2.602	2.947
16	1.337	1.746	2.120	2.583	2.921
17	1.333	1.740	2.110	2.567	2.898
18	1.330	1.734	2.101	2.552	2.878
19	1.328	1.729	2.093	2.539	2.861
20	1.325	1.725	2.086	2.528	2.845
21	1.323	1.721	2.080	2.518	2.831
22	1.321	1.717	2.074	2.508	2.819
23	1.319	1.714	2.069	2.500	2.807
24	1.318	1.711	2.064	2.492	2.797
25	1.316	1.708	2.060	2.485	2.787
26	1.315	1.706	2.056	2.479	2.779
27	1.314	1.703	2.052	2.473	2.771
28	1.313	1.701	2.048	2.467	2.763
29	1.311	1.699	2.045	2.462	2.756
30	1.310	1.697	2.042	2.457	2.750
40	1.303	1.684	2.021	2.423	2.704
60	1.296	1.671	2.000	2.390	2.660
∞	1.282	1.645	1.960	2.326	2.576

Table 9 Cutoff Points for the *F* Distribution

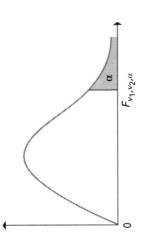

$F_{v_1,v_2,\alpha}$

For probabilities $\alpha = 0.5$ and $\alpha = .01$, the tables show the values $F_{v_1,v_2,\alpha}$ such that $P(F_{v_1,v_2} > F_{v_1,v_2,\alpha}) = \alpha$, where F_{v_1,v_2} is an F random variable, with numerator degrees of freedom v_1 and denominator degrees of freedom v_2. For example, the probability is .05 that an $F_{3,7}$ random variable exceeds 4.35.

$\alpha = .05$

DENOMINATOR v_2	NUMERATOR v_1																		
	1	2	3	4	5	6	7	8	9	10	12	15	20	24	30	40	60	120	∞
1	161.4	199.5	215.7	224.6	230.2	234.0	236.8	238.9	240.5	241.9	243.9	245.9	248.0	249.1	250.1	251.1	252.2	253.3	254.3
2	18.51	19.00	19.16	19.25	19.30	19.33	19.35	19.37	19.38	19.40	19.41	19.43	19.45	19.45	19.46	19.47	19.48	19.49	19.50
3	10.13	9.55	9.28	9.12	9.01	8.94	8.89	8.85	8.81	8.79	8.74	8.70	8.66	8.64	8.62	8.59	8.57	8.55	8.53
4	7.71	6.94	6.59	6.39	6.26	6.16	6.09	6.04	6.00	5.96	5.91	5.86	5.80	5.77	5.75	5.72	5.69	5.66	5.63
5	6.61	5.79	5.41	5.19	5.05	4.95	4.88	4.82	4.77	4.74	4.68	4.62	4.56	4.53	4.50	4.46	4.43	4.40	4.36
6	5.99	5.14	4.76	4.53	4.39	4.28	4.21	4.15	4.10	4.06	4.00	3.94	3.87	3.84	3.81	3.77	3.74	3.70	3.67
7	5.59	4.74	4.35	4.12	3.97	3.87	3.79	3.73	3.68	3.64	3.57	3.51	3.44	3.41	3.38	3.34	3.30	3.27	3.23
8	5.32	4.46	4.07	3.84	3.69	3.58	3.50	3.44	3.39	3.35	3.28	3.22	3.15	3.12	3.08	3.04	3.01	2.97	2.93
9	5.12	4.26	3.86	3.63	3.48	3.37	3.29	3.23	3.18	3.14	3.07	3.01	2.94	2.90	2.86	2.83	2.79	2.75	2.71
10	4.96	4.10	3.71	3.48	3.33	3.22	3.14	3.07	3.02	2.98	2.91	2.85	2.77	2.74	2.70	2.66	2.62	2.58	2.54
11	4.84	3.98	3.59	3.36	3.20	3.09	3.01	2.95	2.90	2.85	2.79	2.72	2.65	2.61	2.57	2.53	2.49	2.45	2.40
12	4.75	3.89	3.49	3.26	3.11	3.00	2.91	2.85	2.80	2.75	2.69	2.62	2.54	2.51	2.47	2.43	2.38	2.34	2.30
13	4.67	3.81	3.41	3.18	3.03	2.92	2.83	2.77	2.71	2.67	2.60	2.53	2.46	2.42	2.38	2.34	2.30	2.25	2.21
14	4.60	3.74	3.34	3.11	2.96	2.85	2.76	2.70	2.65	2.60	2.53	2.46	2.39	2.35	2.31	2.27	2.22	2.18	2.13
15	4.54	3.68	3.29	3.06	2.90	2.79	2.71	2.64	2.59	2.54	2.48	2.40	2.33	2.29	2.25	2.20	2.16	2.11	2.07
16	4.49	3.63	3.24	3.01	2.85	2.74	2.66	2.59	2.54	2.49	2.42	2.35	2.28	2.24	2.19	2.15	2.11	2.06	2.01
17	4.45	3.59	3.20	2.96	2.81	2.70	2.62	2.55	2.49	2.45	2.38	2.31	2.23	2.19	2.15	2.10	2.06	2.01	1.96
18	4.41	3.55	3.16	2.93	2.77	2.66	2.58	2.51	2.46	2.41	2.34	2.27	2.19	2.15	2.11	2.06	2.02	1.97	1.92
19	4.38	3.52	3.13	2.90	2.74	2.63	2.54	2.48	2.42	2.38	2.31	2.23	2.16	2.11	2.07	2.03	1.98	1.93	1.88

Table 9   Cutoff Points for the *F* Distribution Continued

$\alpha = .05$

Denominator v_2	Numerator v_1																		
	1	2	3	4	5	6	7	8	9	10	12	15	20	24	30	40	60	120	∞
20	4.35	3.49	3.10	2.87	2.71	2.60	2.51	2.45	2.39	2.35	2.28	2.20	2.12	2.08	2.04	1.99	1.95	1.90	1.84
21	4.32	3.47	3.07	2.84	2.68	2.57	2.49	2.42	2.37	2.32	2.25	2.18	2.10	2.05	2.01	1.96	1.92	1.87	1.81
22	4.30	3.44	3.05	2.82	2.66	2.55	2.46	2.40	2.34	2.30	2.23	2.15	2.07	2.03	1.98	1.94	1.89	1.84	1.78
23	4.28	3.42	3.03	2.80	2.64	2.53	2.44	2.37	2.32	2.27	2.20	2.13	2.05	2.01	1.96	1.91	1.86	1.81	1.76
24	4.26	3.40	3.01	2.78	2.62	2.51	2.42	2.36	2.30	2.25	2.18	2.11	2.03	1.98	1.94	1.89	1.84	1.79	1.73
25	4.24	3.39	2.99	2.76	2.60	2.49	2.40	2.34	2.28	2.24	2.16	2.09	2.01	1.96	1.92	1.87	1.82	1.77	1.71
26	4.23	3.37	2.98	2.74	2.59	2.47	2.39	2.32	2.27	2.22	2.15	2.07	1.99	1.95	1.90	1.85	1.80	1.75	1.69
27	4.21	3.35	2.96	2.73	2.57	2.46	2.37	2.31	2.25	2.20	2.13	2.06	1.97	1.93	1.88	1.84	1.79	1.73	1.67
28	4.20	3.34	2.95	2.71	2.56	2.45	2.36	2.29	2.24	2.19	2.12	2.04	1.96	1.91	1.87	1.82	1.77	1.71	1.65
29	4.18	3.33	2.93	2.70	2.55	2.43	2.35	2.28	2.22	2.18	2.10	2.03	1.94	1.90	1.85	1.81	1.75	1.70	1.64
30	4.17	3.32	2.92	2.69	2.53	2.42	2.33	2.27	2.21	2.16	2.09	2.01	1.93	1.89	1.84	1.79	1.74	1.68	1.62
40	4.08	3.23	2.84	2.61	2.45	2.34	2.25	2.18	2.12	2.08	2.00	1.92	1.84	1.79	1.74	1.69	1.64	1.58	1.51
60	4.00	3.15	2.76	2.53	2.37	2.25	2.17	2.10	2.04	1.99	1.92	1.84	1.75	1.70	1.65	1.59	1.53	1.47	1.39
120	3.92	3.07	2.68	2.45	2.29	2.17	2.09	2.02	1.96	1.91	1.83	1.75	1.66	1.61	1.55	1.50	1.43	1.35	1.25
∞	3.84	3.00	2.60	2.37	2.21	2.10	2.01	1.94	1.88	1.83	1.75	1.67	1.57	1.52	1.46	1.39	1.32	1.22	1.00

Table 9 Cutoff Points for the F Distribution Continued

α = .01

DENOMINATOR ν_2	NUMERATOR ν_1																		
	1	2	3	4	5	6	7	8	9	10	12	15	20	24	30	40	60	120	∞
1	4052	4999.5	5403	5625	5764	5859	5928	5982	6022	6056	6106	6157	6209	6235	6261	6287	6313	6339	6366
2	98.50	99.00	99.17	99.25	99.30	99.33	99.36	99.37	99.39	99.40	99.42	99.43	99.45	99.46	99.47	99.47	99.48	99.48	99.50
3	34.12	30.82	29.46	28.71	28.24	27.91	27.67	27.49	27.35	27.23	27.05	26.87	26.69	26.60	26.50	26.41	26.32	26.22	26.13
4	21.20	18.00	16.69	15.98	15.52	15.21	14.98	14.80	14.66	14.55	14.37	14.20	14.02	13.93	13.84	13.75	13.65	13.56	13.46
5	16.26	13.27	12.06	11.39	10.97	10.67	10.46	10.29	10.16	10.05	9.89	9.72	9.55	9.47	9.38	9.29	9.20	9.11	9.02
6	13.75	10.92	9.78	9.15	8.75	8.47	8.26	8.10	7.98	7.87	7.72	7.56	7.40	7.31	7.23	7.14	7.06	6.97	6.88
7	12.25	9.55	8.45	7.85	7.46	7.19	6.99	6.84	6.72	6.62	6.47	6.31	6.16	6.07	5.99	5.91	5.82	5.74	5.65
8	11.26	8.65	7.59	7.01	6.63	6.37	6.18	6.03	5.91	5.81	5.67	5.52	5.36	5.28	5.20	5.12	5.03	4.95	4.86
9	10.56	8.02	6.99	6.42	6.06	5.80	5.61	5.47	5.35	5.26	5.11	4.96	4.81	4.73	4.65	4.57	4.48	4.40	4.31
10	10.04	7.56	6.55	5.99	5.64	5.39	5.20	5.06	4.94	4.85	4.71	4.56	4.41	4.33	4.25	4.17	4.08	4.00	3.91
11	9.65	7.21	6.22	5.67	5.32	5.07	4.89	4.74	4.63	4.54	4.40	4.25	4.10	4.02	3.94	3.86	3.78	3.69	3.60
12	9.33	6.93	5.95	5.41	5.06	4.82	4.64	4.50	4.39	4.30	4.16	4.01	3.86	3.78	3.70	3.62	3.54	3.45	3.36
13	9.07	6.70	5.74	5.21	4.86	4.62	4.44	4.30	4.19	4.10	3.96	3.82	3.66	3.59	3.51	3.43	3.34	3.25	3.17
14	8.86	6.51	5.56	5.04	4.69	4.46	4.28	4.14	4.03	3.94	3.80	3.66	3.51	3.43	3.35	3.27	3.18	3.09	3.00
15	8.68	6.36	5.42	4.89	4.56	4.32	4.14	4.00	3.89	3.80	3.67	3.52	3.37	3.29	3.21	3.13	3.05	2.96	2.87
16	8.53	6.23	5.29	4.77	4.44	4.20	4.03	3.89	3.78	3.69	3.55	3.41	3.26	3.18	3.10	3.02	2.93	2.84	2.75
17	8.40	6.11	5.18	4.67	4.34	4.10	3.93	3.79	3.68	3.59	3.46	3.31	3.16	3.08	3.00	2.92	2.83	2.75	2.65
18	8.29	6.01	5.09	4.58	4.25	4.01	3.84	3.71	3.60	3.51	3.37	3.23	3.08	3.00	2.92	2.84	2.75	2.66	2.57
19	8.18	5.93	5.01	4.50	4.17	3.94	3.77	3.63	3.52	3.43	3.30	3.15	3.00	2.92	2.84	2.76	2.67	2.58	2.49
20	8.10	5.85	4.94	4.43	4.10	3.87	3.70	3.56	3.46	3.37	3.23	3.09	2.94	2.86	2.78	2.69	2.61	2.52	2.42
21	8.02	5.78	4.87	4.37	4.04	3.81	3.64	3.51	3.40	3.31	3.17	3.03	2.88	2.80	2.72	2.64	2.55	2.46	2.36
22	7.95	5.72	4.82	4.31	3.99	3.76	3.59	3.45	3.35	3.26	3.12	2.98	2.83	2.75	2.67	2.58	2.50	2.40	2.31
23	7.88	5.66	4.76	4.26	3.94	3.71	3.54	3.41	3.30	3.21	3.07	2.93	2.78	2.70	2.62	2.54	2.45	2.35	2.26
24	7.82	5.61	4.72	4.22	3.90	3.67	3.50	3.36	3.26	3.17	3.03	2.89	2.74	2.66	2.58	2.49	2.40	2.31	2.21
25	7.77	5.57	4.68	4.18	3.85	3.63	3.46	3.32	3.22	3.13	2.99	2.85	2.70	2.62	2.54	2.45	2.36	2.27	2.17
26	7.72	5.53	4.64	4.14	3.82	3.59	3.42	3.29	3.18	3.09	2.96	2.81	2.66	2.58	2.50	2.42	2.33	2.23	2.13
27	7.68	5.49	4.60	4.11	3.78	3.56	3.39	3.26	3.15	3.06	2.93	2.78	2.63	2.55	2.47	2.38	2.29	2.20	2.10
28	7.64	5.45	4.57	4.07	3.75	3.53	3.36	3.23	3.12	3.03	2.90	2.75	2.60	2.52	2.44	2.35	2.26	2.17	2.06
29	7.60	5.42	4.54	4.04	3.73	3.50	3.33	3.20	3.09	3.00	2.87	2.73	2.57	2.49	2.41	2.33	2.23	2.14	2.03
30	7.56	5.39	4.51	4.02	3.70	3.47	3.30	3.17	3.07	2.98	2.84	2.70	2.55	2.47	2.39	2.30	2.21	2.11	2.01
40	7.31	5.18	4.31	3.83	3.51	3.29	3.12	2.99	2.89	2.80	2.66	2.52	2.37	2.29	2.20	2.11	2.02	1.92	1.80
60	7.08	4.98	4.13	3.65	3.34	3.12	2.95	2.82	2.72	2.63	2.50	2.35	2.20	2.12	2.03	1.94	1.84	1.73	1.60
120	6.85	4.79	3.95	3.48	3.17	2.96	2.79	2.66	2.56	2.47	2.34	2.19	2.03	1.95	1.86	1.76	1.66	1.53	1.38
∞	6.63	4.61	3.78	3.32	3.02	2.80	2.64	2.51	2.41	2.32	2.18	2.04	1.88	1.79	1.70	1.59	1.47	1.32	1.00

Table 10 Cutoff Points for the Distribution of the Wilcoxon Test Statistic

For sample size n, the table shows, for selected probabilities α, the numbers T_α such that $P(T \le T_\alpha) = \alpha$, where the distribution of the random variable T is that of the Wilcoxon test statistic under the null hypothesis.

n	α				
	.005	.010	.025	.050	.100
4	0	0	0	0	1
5	0	0	0	1	3
6	0	0	1	3	4
7	0	1	3	4	6
8	1	2	4	6	9
9	2	4	6	9	11
10	4	6	9	11	15
11	6	8	11	14	18
12	8	10	14	18	22
13	10	13	18	22	27
14	13	16	22	26	32
15	16	20	26	31	37
16	20	24	30	36	43
17	24	28	35	42	49
18	28	33	41	48	56
19	33	38	47	54	63
20	38	44	53	61	70

Reproduced with permission from R. L. McCormack, "Extended tables of the Wilcoxon matched pairs signed rank statistics," *Journal of the American Statistical Association* 60 (1965).

Table 11   Cutoff Points for the Distribution
of Spearman Rank Correlation Coefficient

For sample size n, the table shows, for selected probabilities α, the numbers $r_{s,\alpha}$ such that $P(r_s > r_{s,\alpha}) = \alpha$, where the distribution of the random variable r_s is that of Spearman rank correlation coefficient under the null hypothesis of no association.

n	α			
	.050	.025	.010	.005
5	.900	—	—	—
6	.829	.886	.943	—
7	.714	.786	.893	—
8	.643	.738	.833	.881
9	.600	.683	.783	.833
10	.564	.648	.745	.794
11	.523	.623	.736	.818
12	.497	.591	.703	.780
13	.475	.566	.673	.745
14	.457	.545	.646	.716
15	.441	.525	.623	.689
16	.425	.507	.601	.666
17	.412	.490	.582	.645
18	.399	.476	.564	.625
19	.388	.462	.549	.608
20	.377	.450	.534	.591
21	.368	.438	.521	.576
22	.359	.428	.508	.562
23	.351	.418	.496	.549
24	.343	.409	.485	.537
25	.336	.400	.475	.526
26	.329	.392	.465	.515
27	.323	.385	.456	.505
28	.317	.377	.448	.496
29	.311	.370	.440	.487
30	.305	.364	.432	.478

Reproduced with permission from E. G. Olds, "Distribution of sums of squares of rank differences for small samples," *Annals of Mathematical Statistics* 9 (1938).

Table 12 Cutoff Points for the Distribution of the Durbin-Watson Test Statistic

Let d_α be the number such that $P(d < d_\alpha) = \alpha$, where the random variable d has the distribution of the Durbin-Watson statistic under the null hypothesis of no autocorrelation in the regression errors. For probabilities $\alpha = .05$ and $\alpha = .01$, the tables show, for numbers of independent variables, K, values d_L and d_U such that $d_L \leq d_\alpha \leq d_U$, for numbers n of observations.

						$\alpha = .05$					
n						K					
	1		2		3		4		5	
	d_L	d_U	d_L	d_U	d_L	d_U	d_L	d_U	d_L	d_U
15	1.08	1.36	0.95	1.54	0.82	1.75	0.69	1.97	0.56	2.21
16	1.10	1.37	0.98	1.54	0.86	1.73	0.74	1.93	0.62	2.15
17	1.13	1.38	1.02	1.54	0.90	1.71	0.78	1.90	0.67	2.10
18	1.16	1.39	1.05	1.53	0.93	1.69	1.82	1.87	0.71	2.06
19	1.18	1.40	1.08	1.53	0.97	1.68	0.86	1.85	0.75	2.02
20	1.20	1.41	1.10	1.54	1.00	1.68	0.90	1.83	0.79	1.99
21	1.22	1.42	1.13	1.54	1.03	1.67	0.93	1.81	0.83	1.96
22	1.24	1.43	1.15	1.54	1.05	1.66	0.96	1.80	0.86	1.94
23	1.26	1.44	1.17	1.54	1.08	1.66	0.99	1.79	0.90	1.92
24	1.27	1.45	1.19	1.55	1.10	1.66	1.01	1.78	0.93	1.90
25	1.29	1.45	1.21	1.55	1.12	1.66	1.04	1.77	0.95	1.89
26	1.30	1.46	1.22	1.55	1.14	1.65	1.06	1.76	0.98	1.88
27	1.32	1.47	1.24	1.56	1.16	1.65	1.08	1.76	1.01	1.86
28	1.33	1.48	1.26	1.56	1.18	1.65	1.10	1.75	1.03	1.85
29	1.34	1.48	1.27	1.56	1.20	1.65	1.12	1.74	1.05	1.84
30	1.35	1.49	1.28	1.57	1.21	1.65	1.14	1.74	1.07	1.83
31	1.36	1.50	1.30	1.57	1.23	1.65	1.16	1.74	1.09	1.83
32	1.37	1.50	1.31	1.57	1.24	1.65	1.18	1.73	1.11	1.82
33	1.38	1.51	1.32	1.58	1.26	1.65	1.19	1.73	1.13	1.81
34	1.39	1.51	1.33	1.58	1.27	1.65	1.21	1.73	1.15	1.81
35	1.40	1.52	1.34	1.58	1.28	1.65	1.22	1.73	1.16	1.80
36	1.41	1.52	1.35	1.59	1.29	1.65	1.24	1.73	1.18	1.80
37	1.42	1.53	1.36	1.59	1.31	1.66	1.25	1.72	1.19	1.80
38	1.43	1.54	1.37	1.59	1.32	1.66	1.26	1.72	1.21	1.79
39	1.43	1.54	1.38	1.60	1.33	1.66	1.27	1.72	1.22	1.79
40	1.44	1.54	1.39	1.60	1.34	1.66	1.29	1.72	1.23	1.79
45	1.48	1.57	1.43	1.62	1.38	1.67	1.34	1.72	1.29	1.78
50	1.50	1.59	1.46	1.63	1.42	1.67	1.38	1.72	1.34	1.77
55	1.53	1.60	1.49	1.64	1.45	1.68	1.41	1.72	1.38	1.77
60	1.55	1.62	1.51	1.65	1.48	1.69	1.44	1.73	1.41	1.77
65	1.57	1.63	1.54	1.66	1.50	1.70	1.47	1.73	1.44	1.77
70	1.58	1.64	1.55	1.67	1.52	1.70	1.49	1.74	1.46	1.77
75	1.60	1.65	1.57	1.68	1.54	1.71	1.51	1.74	1.49	1.77
80	1.61	1.66	1.59	1.69	1.56	1.72	1.53	1.74	1.51	1.77
85	1.62	1.67	1.60	1.70	1.57	1.72	1.55	1.75	1.52	1.77
90	1.63	1.68	1.61	1.70	1.59	1.73	1.57	1.75	1.54	1.78
95	1.64	1.69	1.62	1.71	1.60	1.73	1.58	1.75	1.56	1.78
100	1.65	1.69	1.63	1.72	1.61	1.74	1.59	1.76	1.57	1.78

Table 12   Cutoff Points for the Distribution of the Durbin-Watson Test Statistic Continued

	$\alpha = .01$									
n					K					
	1		2		3		4		5	
	d_L	d_U	d_L	d_U	d_L	d_U	d_L	d_U	d_L	d_U
15	0.81	1.07	0.70	1.25	0.59	1.46	0.49	1.70	0.39	1.96
16	0.84	1.09	0.74	1.25	0.63	1.44	0.53	1.66	0.44	1.90
17	0.87	1.10	0.77	1.25	0.67	1.43	0.57	1.63	0.48	1.85
18	0.90	1.12	0.80	1.26	0.71	1.42	0.61	1.60	0.52	1.80
19	0.93	1.13	0.83	1.26	0.74	1.41	0.65	1.58	0.56	1.77
20	0.95	1.15	0.86	1.27	0.77	1.41	0.68	1.57	0.60	1.74
21	0.97	1.16	0.89	1.27	0.80	1.41	0.72	1.55	0.63	1.71
22	1.00	1.17	0.91	1.28	0.83	1.40	0.75	1.54	0.66	1.69
23	1.02	1.19	0.94	1.29	0.86	1.40	0.77	1.53	0.70	1.67
24	1.04	1.20	0.96	1.30	0.88	1.41	0.80	1.53	0.72	1.66
25	1.05	1.21	0.98	1.30	0.90	1.41	0.83	1.52	0.75	1.65
26	1.07	1.22	1.00	1.31	0.93	1.41	0.85	1.52	0.78	1.64
27	1.09	1.23	1.02	1.32	0.95	1.41	0.88	1.51	0.81	1.63
28	1.10	1.24	1.04	1.32	0.97	1.41	0.90	1.51	0.83	1.62
29	1.12	1.25	1.05	1.33	0.99	1.42	0.92	1.51	0.85	1.61
30	1.13	1.26	1.07	1.34	1.01	1.42	0.94	1.51	0.88	1.61
31	1.15	1.27	1.08	1.34	1.02	1.42	0.96	1.51	0.90	1.60
32	1.16	1.28	1.10	1.35	1.04	1.43	0.98	1.51	0.92	1.60
33	1.17	1.29	1.11	1.36	1.05	1.43	1.00	1.51	0.94	1.59
34	1.18	1.30	1.13	1.36	1.07	1.43	1.01	1.51	0.95	1.59
35	1.19	1.31	1.14	1.37	1.08	1.44	1.03	1.51	0.97	1.59
36	1.21	1.32	1.15	1.38	1.10	1.44	1.04	1.51	0.99	1.59
37	1.22	1.32	1.16	1.38	1.11	1.45	1.06	1.51	1.00	1.59
38	1.23	1.33	1.18	1.39	1.12	1.45	1.07	1.52	1.02	1.58
39	1.24	1.34	1.19	1.39	1.14	1.45	1.09	1.52	1.03	1.58
40	1.25	1.34	1.20	1.40	1.15	1.46	1.10	1.52	1.05	1.58
45	1.29	1.38	1.24	1.42	1.20	1.48	1.16	1.53	1.11	1.58
50	1.32	1.40	1.28	1.45	1.24	1.49	1.20	1.54	1.16	1.59
55	1.36	1.43	1.32	1.47	1.28	1.51	1.25	1.55	1.21	1.59
60	1.38	1.45	1.35	1.48	1.32	1.52	1.28	1.56	1.25	1.60
65	1.41	1.47	1.38	1.50	1.35	1.53	1.31	1.57	1.28	1.61
70	1.43	1.49	1.40	1.52	1.37	1.55	1.34	1.58	1.31	1.61
75	1.45	1.50	1.42	1.53	1.39	1.56	1.37	1.59	1.34	1.62
80	1.47	1.52	1.44	1.54	1.42	1.57	1.39	1.60	1.36	1.62
85	1.48	1.53	1.46	1.55	1.43	1.58	1.41	1.60	1.39	1.63
90	1.50	1.54	1.47	1.56	1.45	1.59	1.43	1.61	1.41	1.64
95	1.51	1.55	1.49	1.57	1.47	1.60	1.45	1.62	1.42	1.64
100	1.52	1.56	1.50	1.58	1.48	1.60	1.46	1.63	1.44	1.65

Reproduced with permission from J. Durbin and G. S. Watson, "Testing for serial correlation in least squares regression, II," *Biometrika* 38 (1951).

Table 13   Factors for Control Charts

	$\bar{X}$-CHARTS				s-CHARTS				R-CHARTS					
n	A	A_2	A_3	c_4	B_3	B_4	B_5	B_6	d_2	d_3	D_1	D_2	D_3	D_4
2	2.121	1.880	2.659	0.7979	0	3.267	0	2.606	1.128	0.853	0	3.686	0	3.267
3	1.732	1.023	1.954	0.8862	0	2.568	0	2.276	1.693	0.888	0	4.358	0	2.574
4	1.500	0.729	1.628	0.9213	0	2.266	0	2.088	2.059	0.880	0	4.698	0	2.282
5	1.342	0.577	1.427	0.9400	0	2.089	0	1.964	2.326	0.864	0	4.918	0	2.114
6	1.225	0.483	1.287	0.9515	0.030	1.970	0.029	1.874	2.534	0.848	0	5.078	0	2.004
7	1.134	0.419	1.182	0.9594	0.118	1.882	0.113	1.806	2.704	0.833	0.204	5.204	0.076	1.924
8	1.061	0.373	1.099	0.9650	0.185	1.815	0.179	1.751	2.847	0.820	0.388	5.306	0.136	1.864
9	1.000	0.337	1.032	0.969	0.239	1.761	0.232	1.707	2.970	0.808	0.547	5.393	0.184	1.816
10	0.949	0.308	0.975	0.9727	0.284	1.716	0.276	1.669	3.078	0.797	0.687	5.469	0.223	1.777
11	0.905	0.285	0.927	0.9754	0.321	1.679	0.313	1.637	3.173	0.787	0.811	5.535	0.256	1.744
12	0.866	0.266	0.886	0.9776	0.354	1.646	0.346	1.610	3.258	0.778	0.922	5.594	0.283	1.717
13	0.832	0.249	0.850	0.9794	0.382	1.618	0.374	1.585	3.336	0.770	1.025	5.647	0.307	1.693
14	0.802	0.235	0.817	0.9810	0.406	1.594	0.399	1.563	3.407	0.763	1.118	5.696	0.328	1.672
15	0.775	0.223	0.789	0.9823	0.428	1.572	0.421	1.544	3.472	0.756	1.203	5.741	0.347	1.653
16	0.750	0.212	0.763	0.9835	0.448	1.552	0.440	1.526	3.532	0.750	1.282	5.782	0.363	1.637
17	0.728	0.203	0.739	0.9845	0.466	1.534	0.458	1.511	3.588	0.744	1.356	5.820	0.378	1.622
18	0.707	0.194	0.718	0.9854	0.482	1.518	0.475	1.496	3.640	0.739	1.424	5.856	0.391	1.608
19	0.688	0.187	0.698	0.9862	0.497	1.503	0.490	1.483	3.689	0.734	1.487	5.891	0.403	1.597
20	0.671	0.180	0.680	0.9869	0.510	1.490	0.504	1.470	3.735	0.729	1.549	5.921	0.415	1.585
21	0.655	0.173	0.663	0.9876	0.523	1.477	0.516	1.459	3.778	0.724	1.605	5.951	0.425	1.575
22	0.640	0.167	0.647	0.9882	0.534	1.466	0.528	1.448	3.819	0.720	1.659	5.979	0.434	1.566
23	0.626	0.162	0.633	0.9887	0.545	1.455	0.539	1.438	3.858	0.716	1.710	6.006	0.443	1.557
24	0.612	0.157	0.619	0.9892	0.555	1.445	0.549	1.429	3.895	0.712	1.759	6.031	0.451	1.548
25	0.600	0.153	0.606	0.9896	0.565	1.435	0.559	1.420	3.931	0.708	1.806	6.056	0.459	1.541

Source: Adapted from Table 27 of ASTM STP 15D ASTM *Manual on Presentation of Data and Control Chart Analysis.* ©1976 American Society for Testing and Materials, Philadelphia, PA.

Table 14 Cumulative Distribution Function of the Runs Test Statistic

For a given number n of observations, the table shows the probability, for a random time series, that the number of runs will not exceed K.

n	K																		
	2	3	4	5	6	7	8	9	10	11	12	13	14	15	16	17	18	19	20
6	.100	.300	.700	.900	1.000														
8	.029	.114	.371	.629	.886	.971	1.000												
10	.008	.040	.167	.357	.643	.833	.960	.992	1.000										
12	.002	.013	.067	.175	.392	.608	.825	.933	.987	.998	1.000								
14	.001	.004	.025	.078	.209	.383	.617	.791	.922	.975	.996	.999	1.000						
16	.000	.001	.009	.032	.100	.214	.405	.595	.786	.900	.968	.991	.999	1.000	1.000				
18	.000	.000	.003	.012	.044	.109	.238	.399	.601	.762	.891	.956	.988	.997	1.000	1.000	1.000		
20	.000	.000	.001	.004	.019	.051	.128	.242	.414	.586	.758	.872	.949	.981	.996	.999	1.000	1.000	1.000

Reproduced with permission from F. Swed and C. Eisenhart, "Tables for testing randomness of grouping in a sequence of alternatives," *Annals of Mathematical Statistics* 14 (1943).

Index

Tables